Drexel Engineering Core Curriculum

ENGR 100: Introduction to Computer-Aided Design

AutoCAD 2012

&

Pro/ENGINEER Wildfire 5.0

ISBN: 978-1-58503-585-4

SDC
PUBLICATIONS
Schroff Development Corporation
www.SDCpublications.com

Schroff Development Corporation
P.O. Box 1334
Mission, KS 66222
(913) 262-2664
www.SDCpublications.com

Publisher: Stephen Schroff

Table of Contents

PART 1
AutoCAD 2012 Tutorial

Introduction
Getting Started

Introduction	Intro-2
Development of Computer Aided Design	Intro-2
Why use AutoCAD® 2012	Intro-5
Getting Started with AutoCAD® 2012	Intro-7
AutoCAD® 2012 Screen Layout	Intro-8
Application Menu	Intro-9
Workspace Switching	Intro-9
Quick Access Toolbar	Intro-9
AutoCAD Menu Bar	Intro-9
Graphics Window	Intro-10
Graphics Cursor or Crosshairs	Intro-10
Command Prompt Area	Intro-10
Cursor Coordinates	Intro-10
Status Toolbar	Intro-10
Ribbon Tabs and Panels	Intro-10
Draw and Modify Toolbar Panel	Intro-11
Layers Control Toolbar Panel	Intro-11
Annotation Toolbar Panel	Intro-11
Layout/Model Toolbar	Intro-11
Viewing Toolbar	Intro-11
Mouse Buttons	Intro-12
[Esc] - Canceling Commands	Intro-12
On-Line Help	Intro-13
Leaving AutoCAD® 2012	Intro-14
Creating a CAD File Folder	Intro-15

Chapter 1
AutoCAD Fundamentals

Introduction	1-2
Starting Up AutoCAD® 2012	1-2
Drawing Units Display Setup	1-4
Drawing Area Setup	1-5
Using the *InfoCenter* to Get More Information	1-6
Drawing Lines with the *LINE* Command	1-7
Visual Reference	1-9
GRID ON	1-10
SNAP Mode ON	1-11
Using the *ERASER*	1-12
Repeat the Last Command	1-13
The CAD Database and the User Coordinate System	1-14
Changing to the 2D UCS Icon Display	1-15
Cartesian and Polar Coordinate Systems	1-16
Absolute and Relative Coordinates	1-16
Defining Positions	1-17
The *Guide Plate*	1-18
Creating *Circles*	1-22
Save the CAD File	1-24
Close the Current Drawing	1-25
The *Spacer* Design	1-26
Start a New Drawing	1-26
Drawing Units Setup	1-27
Drawing Area Setup	1-28
Using the Line Command	1-30
Using the *ERASE* Command	1-32
Using the Arc Command	1-32
Using the Circle Command	1-34
Saving the CAD Design	1-35
Exit AutoCAD	1-35
Review Questions	1-36
Exercises	1-37

Chapter 2
Basic Object Construction Tools

Introduction	2-2
Starting Up AutoCAD® 2012	2-2
Dynamic Input	2-3

The RockerArm Design   2-6
Activate the Startup Option   2-7
Drawing Units Display Setup   2-8
GRID and SNAP Intervals Setup   2-9
Drawing Area Setup   2-10
Referencing the World Coordinate System   2-11
Creating *Circles*   2-12
Object Snap Toolbar   2-13
Using the *LINE* command   2-14
Creating a *TTR Circles*   2-16
Using the *TRIM* Command   2-18
Using the *Polygon* Command   2-20
Creating a Concentric *Circle*   2-22
Using the QuickCal Calculator to Measure Distance and Angle   2-23
Saving the CAD file   2-27
Exit AutoCAD   2-27
Review Questions   2-28
Exercises   2-29

Chapter 3
Geometric Construction and Editing Tools

Geometric Constructions   3-2
Starting Up AutoCAD® 2012   3-3
Geometric Construction - CAD Method   3-4
• Bisection of a Line or Arc   3-4
• Bisection of an Angle   3-8
• Transfer of an Angle   3-10
• Dividing a Given Line into a Number of Equal Parts   3-14
• Circle through Three Points   3-16
• Line Tangent to a Circle from a Given Point   3-17
• Circle of a Given Radius Tangent to Two Given Lines   3-18
The *Gasket* Design   3-21
Drawing Units Display Setup   3-22
GRID and SNAP Intervals Setup   3-23
Using the *LINE* Command   3-24
Object Snap Toolbar   3-26
Using the *EXTEND* Command   3-29
Using the *TRIM* Command   3-30
Creating a *TTR Circle*   3-31
Using the *FILLET* Command   3-32
Converting Objects into a *Polyline*   3-33
Using the *OFFSET* Command   3-34

Using the Area Inquiry Tool to Measure Area and Perimeter   3-35
Using the *EXPLODE* Command   3-37
Create another *FILLET*   3-37
Saving the CAD file   3-38
Exit AutoCAD   3-38
Review Questions   3-39
Exercises   3-40

Chapter 4
Object Properties and Organization

Introduction   4-2
The *Floor Plan* Design   4-2
Starting Up AutoCAD® 2012   4-3
Using the Setup Wizard   4-3
Drawing Units Setup   4-4
Reference Area Setup   4-4
GRID and *SNAP* Intervals Setup   4-5
Using the *ZOOM Extent* Command   4-6
The AutoCAD *MULTILINE* Command   4-6
Object Snap Toolbar   4-9
Drawing *Multilines*   4-10
Creating Interior Walls   4-13
Joining the Walls using *MULTILINE EDIT*   4-16
Using *Layers* and Object Properties   4-18
Using *ZOOM REALTIME*   4-21
Modeling the Bathroom   4-22
Controlling *Layer Visibility*   4-24
Adding a New Layer   4-24
Moving Objects to a Different Layer   4-25
Matching Layer Properties   4-26
Review Questions   4-28
Exercises   4-29

PART 2
Pro/ENGINEER WILDFIRE 5.0 TUTORIAL

INTRODUCTION to Pro/ENGINEER

A Few Words Before You Dive In... .... Intro - 1
What *IS* Pro/ENGINEER? .... Intro - 2
This sounds like it's pretty complicated!... .... Intro - 5
Overview of the Lessons .... Intro - 6
On-Line Help .... Intro - 9

Lesson 1 : User Interface, View Controls and Model Structure

Synopsis .... 1 - 1
Overview of this Lesson .... 1 - 1
Starting Pro/ENGINEER .... 1 - 3
How commands are entered into Pro/ENGINEER .... 1 - 5
    Pull-Down Menus .... 1 - 5
    Short-cut Buttons .... 1 - 6
    Dialog Windows .... 1 - 6
    Menu Picks .... 1 - 6
    Pop-Up Menus .... 1 - 8
    Command/Message Window .... 1 - 8
    Mouse Functions .... 1 - 9
How this tutorial will represent the command sequence .... 1 - 9
    Table 1-1 Common Pro/E Mouse Functions (3D) .... 1 - 10
How to get On-Line Help .... 1 - 12
Tutorial Files and Working Directory .... 1 - 15
Controlling the Screen: View and Display Commands .... 1 - 17
    Opening a Part File .... 1 - 18
    View Controls using the Mouse .... 1 - 18
    Toolbar View Commands .... 1 - 21
    Using Named Views .... 1 - 21
    Object Display Commands .... 1 - 23
    Other Model Display Commands .... 1 - 23
    Datum Display Commands .... 1 - 24
    Modifying the Environment .... 1 - 25
Anatomy of a Part - Understanding the Model Structure .... 1 - 26
    Preselection Highlighting .... 1 - 26
    Expanding the Model Tree .... 1 - 27
    The Model Player .... 1 - 29

Exploring the Structure of a Part . . . . 1 - 30
Modifying Dimensions . . . . 1 - 33
Parent/Child Relations . . . . 1 - 34
Anatomy of an Assembly . . . . 1 - 36
An Assembly BOM (Bill of Materials) . . . . 1 - 38
Modifying the Assembly . . . . 1 - 38
Exploding an Assembly . . . . 1 - 40
Opening Parts in an Assembly . . . . 1 - 41
Obtaining Hard Copy . . . . 1 - 41
Leaving Pro/ENGINEER . . . . 1 - 43
Questions for Review . . . . 1 - 44
Exercises . . . . 1 - 45

Lesson 2 : Creating a Simple Object (Part I)

Synopsis 2-1
Overview of this Lesson 2-1
Creating a Simple Part 2-2
Creating and Naming the Part 2-2
Create Datum Planes 2-3
Pro/ENGINEER Feature Overview 2-4
Introducing Sketcher 2-6
Table 2-1 Implicit Constraints in Sketcher 2-8
Two Ways to use Sketcher 2-9
Table 2-2 Steps to create a sketched feature 2-9
Creating a Sketched Curve 2-10
Setting Sketch Orientation 2-10
The Sketcher Toolbar 2-14
Table 2-3 Sketcher Toolbar Flyout Buttons 2-15
Table 2-4 Explicit Constraints in Sketcher 2-16
Creating the Sketch 2-16
Weak vs Strong Dimensions 2-18
Sketcher Diagnostic Functions 2-20
Creating a Solid Protrusion 2-21
The Extrude Dashboard 2-22
Saving the Part 2-25
Creating an Extruded Cut 2-26
Using Part Templates 2-31
Questions for Review 2-33
Exercises 2-34

Lesson 3 : Creating a Simple Object (Part II)

Synopsis . . . . 3 - 1
Overview of this Lesson . . . . 3 - 1
Retrieving a Part . . . . 3 - 2
Creating a Hole . . . . 3 - 3

Creating a Chamfer . . . . 3 - 8
Creating a Round . . . . 3 - 9
Exploring the Model . . . . 3 - 12
   Configuring the Model Tree . . . . 3 - 12
   Naming Features . . . . 3 - 14
   Exploring Parent/Child Relations . . . . 3 - 14
Modifying Dimensions . . . . 3 - 17
Creating Feature Relations . . . . 3 - 19
   More about relations: . . . . 3 - 22
Considering Design Intent . . . . 3 - 23
   Design Intent Alternative #1 . . . . 3 - 23
   Design Intent Alternative #2 . . . . 3 - 24
   Design Intent Alternative #3 . . . . 3 - 25
More Sketcher Tools . . . . 3 - 26
   The *Modify* Command . . . . 3 - 26
   Sketcher Relations . . . . 3 - 26
   Sketcher Preferences . . . . 3 - 27
   Using *Undo* . . . . 3 - 28
Pro/E Files Saved Automatically . . . . 3 - 28
Questions for Review . . . . 3 - 30
Exercises . . . . 3 - 31
Project . . . . 3 - 34

Lesson 4 : Revolved Protrusions, Mirror Copies, Rounds, and Chamfers

Synopsis . . . . 4 - 1
Overview of this Lesson . . . . 4 - 1
Creating the Base Feature . . . . 4 - 2
Creating a Revolved Protrusion . . . . 4 - 7
Adding and Mirroring a Cut . . . . 4 - 10
   Creating a Mirror Copy . . . . 4 - 11
Creating Holes . . . . 4 - 13
   Having Problems Mirroring? . . . . 4 - 14
Creating Rounds . . . . 4 - 14
Using Edge Sets with *Chamfer* . . . . 4 - 16
Saving the Part . . . . 4 - 18
Model Analysis Tools . . . . 4 - 19
Exploring the Model, or "What Can Go Wrong?" . . . . 4 - 21
Questions for Review . . . . 4 - 24
Exercises . . . . 4 - 25
Project . . . . 4 - 27

Lesson 5 : Modeling Utilities and the 3 R's

Synopsis . . . . 5 - 1
Overview of this Lesson . . . . 5 - 1
Obtaining Information about the Model . . . . 5 - 2

The Regeneration Sequence . . . . 5 - 3
The Feature List . . . . 5 - 3
The Model Tree . . . . 5 - 4
Parent/Child Relations . . . . 5 - 5
Suppressing and Resuming Features . . . . 5 - 7
Suppressing versus Hiding . . . . 5 - 9
Modifying Feature Definitions . . . . 5 - 9
① Changing the shape of a sketch (*Edit Definition*) . . . . 5 - 11
② Changing a Feature Reference (*Edit References*) . . . . 5 - 12
③ Changing the Sketcher Constraints (*Edit Definition*) . . . . 5 - 14
④ Changing a Feature Reference (*Edit References*) . . . . 5 - 15
⑤ Changing Feature Attributes (*Edit Definition*) . . . . 5 - 15
⑥ Changing the Regeneration Sequence using *Reorder* . . . . 5 - 16
⑦ Changing the Insertion Point . . . . 5 - 17
Conclusion . . . . 5 - 19
Questions for Review . . . . 5 - 20
Exercises . . . . 5 - 21
Project . . . . 5 - 22

Lesson 6 : Datum Planes and Sketcher Tools

Synopsis . . . . 6 - 1
Overview of this Lesson . . . . 6 - 1
Overview of Datum Planes and Axes . . . . 6 - 2
Creating a Datum Plane and Datum Axis . . . . 6 - 4
Creating the *Cutter* Base Feature . . . . 6 - 6
Creating a Coaxial Hole . . . . 6 - 9
First Tooth - Offset Datum . . . . 6 - 10
Second Tooth - Normal and Tangent Datum . . . . 6 - 12
Third Tooth - Using Make Datums . . . . 6 - 14
Exploring the Model . . . . 6 - 17
Considering *Design Intent* . . . . 6 - 18
Questions for Review . . . . 6 - 20
Exercises . . . . 6 - 21
Project . . . . 6 - 22

Lesson 7 : Patterns and Copies

Synopsis . . . . 7 - 1
Overview of this Lesson . . . . 7 - 1
Patterned Features . . . . 7 - 2
Naming Dimension Symbols . . . . 7 - 3
Creating a Uni-directional Pattern . . . . 7 - 4
Creating a Bi-directional Pattern . . . . 7 - 6
Creating a Simple Radial Pattern . . . . 7 - 8
Setting up Pattern Relations . . . . 7 - 10
A Pattern of Grouped Features . . . . 7 - 12

Radial Patterns of Sketched Features . . . . 7 - 13
    Radial Pattern using Make Datum as Sketching Plane . . . . 7 - 14
    Radial Pattern using Make Datum as Reference Plane . . . . 7 - 17
Copying Features with *Paste* and *Paste Special* . . . . 7 - 20
  Copying using *Paste* . . . . 7 - 20
  Copying using *Paste Special* . . . . 7 - 23
    Paste Special Example #1 (default) . . . . 7 - 25
    Paste Special Example #2 (using the Varied Items table) . . . . 7 - 27
    Paste Special Example #3 (Breaking, Restoring, and Removing dependence)
    . . . . 7 - 28
    Paste Special Example #4 (using Advanced Reference Configuration) . 7 - 29
    Paste Special Example #5 (making an independent copy) . . . . 7 - 30
    Paste Special Example #6 (Translated and Rotated copies) . . . . 7 - 30
Design Considerations . . . . 7 - 34
Questions for Review . . . . 7 - 36
Exercises . . . . 7 - 37
Project . . . . 7 - 38

Lesson 8 : Engineering Drawings

Synopsis . . . . 8 - 1
Overview of this Lesson . . . . 8 - 1
The Drawing Environment . . . . 8 - 3
  Drawing Interface . . . . 8 - 3
  Mouse Controls in Drawing Mode . . . . 8 - 5
  Drawing Ribbon and Drawing Tree . . . . 8 - 5
    Layout . . . . 8 - 6
    Table . . . . 8 - 6
    Annotate . . . . 8 - 7
    Sketch . . . . 8 - 7
    Review . . . . 8 - 8
    Publish . . . . 8 - 8
  Shown vs *Created* Dimensions . . . . 8 - 8
  Table 8.1 The Mysteries of Model vs Draft Dimensions . . . . 8 - 9
  Dimension Properties . . . . 8 - 9
  Exploring Associativity . . . . 8 - 11
The L-Bracket . . . . 8 - 12
  Creating the Part . . . . 8 - 12
  Changing Part Units . . . . 8 - 12
  Creating the Drawing of the L-Bracket . . . . 8 - 13
    ① Create the Drawing File . . . . 8 - 13
    ② Adding Views . . . . 8 - 14
    ③ Setting View Display Mode . . . . 8 - 16
    ④ Adding Dimensioning Detail . . . . 8 - 17
    ⑤ Dimension Cosmetics . . . . 8 - 18
    ⑥ Creating a Note . . . . 8 - 21
  Exploring Associativity . . . . 8 - 22

Publishing the Drawing .... 8 - 25
Using Drawing Templates .... 8 - 26
The Pulley .... 8 - 28
Creating the Pulley .... 8 - 28
Creating the Drawing .... 8 - 30
① Selecting a Formatted Sheet .... 8 - 30
② Creating the Primary View .... 8 - 31
③ Add a Full Section View .... 8 - 32
④ Modify the Section View Display .... 8 - 34
⑤ Adding a Detail View .... 8 - 34
⑥ Adding Dimension Details .... 8 - 35
⑦ Improving the Esthetics .... 8 - 36
⑧ Changing Drawing Options .... 8 - 37
⑨ Adding Notes with Parameters .... 8 - 37
⑩ Creating Dimensions .... 8 - 38
Conclusion .... 8 - 39
Questions for Review .... 8 - 40
Exercises .... 8 - 42
Project .... 8 - 43

Lesson 9 : Assembly Fundamentals

Synopsis .... 9 - 1
Overview of this Lesson .... 9 - 1
Creating the Assembly Components .... 9 - 2
The Pulley .... 9 - 2
The Axle .... 9 - 2
The Base Plate .... 9 - 3
The Bolts .... 9 - 4
The Bushings .... 9 - 4
The Washers .... 9 - 5
Assembly Constraints .... 9 - 5
DEFAULT .... 9 - 6
MATE COINCIDENT .... 9 - 6
MATE OFFSET .... 9 - 6
ALIGN COINCIDENT .... 9 - 7
ALIGN OFFSET .... 9 - 7
ALIGN ORIENT .... 9 - 8
INSERT .... 9 - 8
Assembly Design Issues .... 9 - 8
Assembling the Components .... 9 - 10
Creating a Subassembly .... 9 - 10
Creating the Main Assembly .... 9 - 16
Using *Copy* with Components .... 9 - 25
Assigning Appearances to Components .... 9 - 26
Questions for Review .... 9 - 31
Project .... 9 - 32

Lesson 10 : Assembly Operations

Synopsis . . . . 10 - 1
Overview of this Lesson . . . . 10 - 1
Assembly Information . . . . 10 - 2
Assembly Features . . . . 10 - 4
    Creating Assembly Features . . . . 10 - 4
Assembly Display Management . . . . 10 - 5
Assembly and Part Modifications . . . . 10 - 7
    Active Components and Visibility . . . . 10 - 7
    Changing Part Dimensions . . . . 10 - 8
    Adding another Assembly Feature . . . . 10 - 9
    Changing Feature Visibility . . . . 10 - 11
    Changing the Active Component . . . . 10 - 11
Part Creation in Assembly Mode . . . . 10 - 13
Exploding the Assembly . . . . 10 - 15
Component Display Style . . . . 10 - 18
    Modifying Component Display Styles . . . . 10 - 19
    Modifying the Explode State . . . . 10 - 21
Sections . . . . 10 - 22
Assembly Drawings . . . . 10 - 23
Questions for Review . . . . 10 - 27
Project . . . . 10 - 29

Lesson 11 : Sweeps and Blends

Synopsis . . . . 11 - 1
Overview of this Lesson . . . . 11 - 1
Sweeps . . . . 11 - 2
    Closed Section, Open Trajectory - The S-Bracket . . . . 11 - 2
        Alternate Method for Creating Sweep . . . . 11 - 6
        Extending the Trajectory . . . . 11 - 6
    Open Section, Closed Trajectory - The Lawn Sprinkler . . . . 11 - 8
        Creating a Sketched Hole . . . . 11 - 11
Blends . . . . 11 - 13
    Parallel Blend . . . . 11 - 14
        The *Shell* Command . . . . 11 - 18
    Rotational Blend . . . . 11 - 19
Conclusion . . . . 11 - 23
Questions for Review . . . . 11 - 24
Exercises . . . . 11 - 25

Appendix : Interface Customization

Synopsis . . . . A - 1
Overview . . . . A - 1
Configuration Files (*config.pro*) . . . . A - 1

The Configuration File Editor .... A - 3
Adding Settings to *config.pro* .... A - 4
Saving Your *config.pro* Settings .... A - 7
Loading a Configuration File .... A - 7
Deleting Configuration Options .... A - 7
Checking Your Configuration Options .... A - 7
Customizing the Interface .... A - 8
Toolbars .... A - 8
Changing Toolbar Buttons .... A - 9

AutoCAD 2012
Tutorial

Introduction
Getting Started

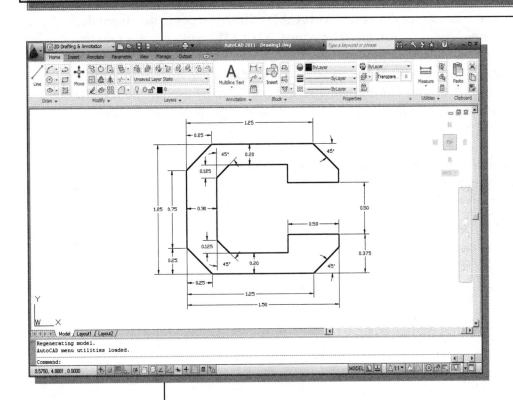

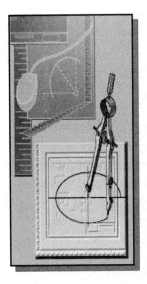

Learning Objectives

♦ **Development of Computer Aided Design**
♦ **Why use AutoCAD 2012?**
♦ **Getting started with AutoCAD 2012**
♦ **The AutoCAD Startup dialog box and Units setup**
♦ **AutoCAD 2012 screen layout**
♦ **Mouse buttons**

Introduction

Computer Aided Design (CAD) is the process of doing designs with the aid of computers. This includes the generation of computer models, analysis of design data, and the creation of the necessary drawings. **AutoCAD® 2012** is a computer aided design software developed by *Autodesk Inc*. The **AutoCAD® 2012** software is a tool that can be used for design and drafting activities. The two-dimensional and three-dimensional models created in **AutoCAD® 2012** can be transferred to other computer programs for further analysis and testing. The computer models can also be used in manufacturing equipment such as machining centers, lathes, mills, or rapid prototyping machines to manufacture the product.

The rapid changes in the field of **computer aided engineering** (CAE) have brought exciting advances in industry. Recent advances have made the long-sought goal of reducing design time, producing prototypes faster, and achieving higher product quality closer to a reality.

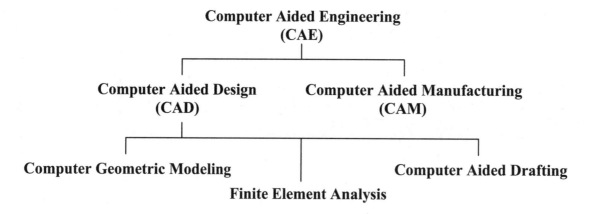

Development of Computer Geometric Modeling

Computer Aided Design is a relatively new technology and its rapid expansion in the last fifty years is truly amazing. Computer modeling technology advanced along with the development of computer hardware. The first generation CAD programs, developed in the 1950s, were mostly non-interactive; CAD users were required to create program codes to generate the desired two-dimensional (2D) geometric shapes. Initially, the development of CAD technology occurred mostly in academic research facilities. The Massachusetts Institute of Technology, Carnegie-Mellon University, and Cambridge University were the lead pioneers at that time. The interest in CAD technology spread quickly and several major industry companies, such as General Motors, Lockheed, McDonnell, IBM, and Ford Motor Co., participated in the development of interactive CAD programs in the 1960s. Usage of CAD systems was primarily in the automotive industry, aerospace industry, and government agencies that developed their own programs for their specific needs. The 1960s also marked the beginning of the development of finite element analysis methods for computer stress analysis and computer aided manufacturing for generating machine tool paths.

The 1970s are generally viewed as the years of the most significant progress in the development of computer hardware, namely the invention and development of **microprocessors**. With the improvement in computing power, new types of 3D CAD programs that were user-friendly and interactive became reality. CAD technology quickly expanded from very simple **computer aided drafting** to very complex **computer aided design**. The use of 2D and 3D wireframe modelers was accepted as the leading edge technology that could increase productivity in industry. The developments of surface modeling and solid modeling technology were taking shape by the late 1970s; but the high cost of computer hardware and programming slowed the development of such technology. During this time period, the available CAD systems all required extremely expensive room-sized mainframe computers.

In the 1980s, improvements in computer hardware brought the power of mainframes to the desktop at less cost and with more accessibility to the general public. By the mid-1980s, CAD technology had become the main focus of a variety of manufacturing industries and was very competitive with traditional design/drafting methods. It was during this period of time that 3D solid modeling technology had major advancements, which boosted the usage of CAE technology in industry.

In the 1990s, CAD programs evolved into powerful design/manufacturing/management tools. CAD technology has come a long way, and during these years of development, modeling schemes progressed from two-dimensional (2D) wireframe to three-dimensional (3D) wireframe, to surface modeling, to solid modeling and, finally, to feature-based parametric solid modeling.

The first generation CAD packages were simply 2D **Computer Aided Drafting** programs, basically the electronic equivalents of the drafting board. For typical models, the use of this type of program would require that several to many views of the objects be created individually as they would be on the drafting board. The 3D designs remained in the designer's mind, not in the computer database. The mental translation of 3D objects to 2D views is required throughout the use of the packages. Although such systems have some advantages over traditional board drafting, they are still tedious and labor intensive. The need for the development of 3D modelers came quite naturally, given the limitations of the 2D drafting packages.

The development of the 3D wireframe modeler was a major leap in the area of computer modeling. The computer database in the 3D wireframe modeler contains the locations of all the points in space coordinates and it is sufficient to create just one model rather than multiple models. This single 3D model can then be viewed from any direction as needed. The 3D wireframe modelers require the least computer power and achieve reasonably good representation of 3D models. But because surface definition is not part of a wireframe model, all wireframe images have the inherent problem of ambiguity.

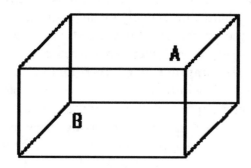

Wireframe Ambiguity: Which corner is in front, A or B?

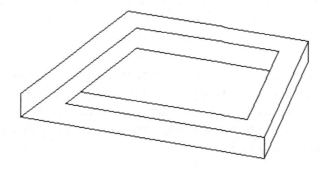

A non-realizable object: Wireframe models contain no surface definitions.

Surface modeling is the logical development in computer geometry modeling to follow the 3D wireframe modeling scheme by organizing and grouping edges that define polygonal surfaces. Surface modeling describes the part's surfaces but not its interiors. Designers are still required to interactively examine surface models to insure that the various surfaces on a model are contiguous throughout. Many of the concepts used in 3D wireframe and surface modelers are incorporated in the solid modeling scheme, but it is solid modeling that offers the most advantages as a design tool.

In the solid modeling presentation scheme, the solid definitions include nodes, edges, and surfaces, and it is a complete and unambiguous mathematical representation of a precisely enclosed and filled volume. Unlike the surface modeling method, solid modelers start with a solid or use topology rules to guarantee that all of the surfaces are stitched together properly. Two predominant methods for representing solid models are **constructive solid geometry** (CSG) representation and **boundary representation** (B-rep).

The CSG representation method can be defined as the combination of 3D solid primitives. What constitutes a "primitive" varies somewhat with the software but typically includes a rectangular prism, a cylinder, a cone, a wedge, and a sphere. Most solid modelers allow the user to define additional primitives, which can be very complex.

In the B-rep representation method, objects are represented in terms of their spatial boundaries. This method defines the points, edges, and surfaces of a volume, and/or issues commands that sweep or rotate a defined face into a third dimension to form a solid. The object is then made up of the unions of these surfaces that completely and precisely enclose a volume.

By the 1990s, a new paradigm called *concurrent engineering* had emerged. With concurrent engineering, designers, design engineers, analysts, manufacturing engineers, and management engineers all work closely right from the initial stages of the design. In this way, all aspects of the design can be evaluated and any potential problems can be identified right from the start and throughout the design process. Using the principles of concurrent engineering, a new type of computer modeling technique appeared. The technique is known as the *feature-based parametric modeling technique*. The key advantage of the *feature-based parametric modeling technique* is its capability to produce very flexible designs. Changes can be made easily and design alternatives can be evaluated with minimum effort. Various software packages offer different approaches to feature-based parametric modeling, yet the end result is a flexible design defined by its design variables and parametric features.

In this text, we will concentrate on creating designs using two-dimensional geometric construction techniques. The fundamental concepts and use of different **AutoCAD® 2012** commands are presented using step-by-step tutorials. We will begin with creating simple geometric entities and then move toward creating detailed working drawings and assembly drawings. The techniques presented in this text will also serve as the foundation for entering the world of three-dimensional solid modeling using packages such as **AutoCAD Mechanical Desktop, AutoCAD Architecture** and **Autodesk Inventor**.

Why use AutoCAD® 2012?

AutoCAD® was first introduced to the public in late 1982, and was one of the first CAD software products that were available for personal computers. Since 1984, **AutoCAD®** has established a reputation for being the most widely used PC-based CAD software around the world. By 2007, it was estimated that there were over 6 million **AutoCAD®** users in more than 150 countries worldwide. **AutoCAD® 2012** is the twenty-fifth release, with many added features and enhancements, of the original **AutoCAD®** software produced by *Autodesk Inc.*

CAD provides us with a wide range of benefits; in most cases, the result of using CAD is increased accuracy and productivity. First of all, the computer offers much higher accuracy than the traditional methods of drafting and design. Traditionally, drafting and detailing are the most expensive cost element in a project and the biggest bottleneck. With CAD systems, such as **AutoCAD® 2012,** the tedious drafting and detailing tasks are simplified through the use of many of the CAD geometric construction tools, such as *grids, snap, trim,* and *auto-dimensioning.* Dimensions and notes are always legible in CAD drawings, and in most cases, CAD systems can produce higher quality prints compared to traditional hand drawings.

CAD also offers much-needed flexibility in design and drafting. A CAD model generated on a computer consists of numeric data that describe the geometry of the object. This allows the designers and clients to see something tangible and to interpret the ramifications of the design. In many cases, it is also possible to simulate operating conditions on the computer and observe the results. Any kind of geometric shape stored in the database can be easily duplicated. For large and complex designs and drawings, particularly those involving similar shapes and repetitive operations, CAD approaches are very efficient and effective. Because computer designs and models can be altered easily, a multitude of design options can be examined and presented to a client before any construction or manufacturing actually takes place. Making changes to a CAD model is generally much faster than making changes to a traditional hand drawing. Only the affected components of the design need to be modified and the drawings can be plotted again. In addition, the greatest benefit is that, once the CAD model is created, it can be used over and over again. The CAD models can also be transferred into manufacturing equipment such as machining centers, lathes, mills, or rapid prototyping machines to manufacture the product directly.

CAD, however, does not replace every design activity. CAD may help, but it does not replace the designer's experience with geometry and graphical conventions and standards for the specific field. CAD is a powerful tool, but the use of this tool does not guarantee correct results; the designer is still responsible for using good design practice and applying good judgment. CAD will supplement these skills to ensure that the best design is obtained.

CAD designs and drawings are stored in binary form, usually as CAD files, to magnetic devices such as diskettes and hard disks. The information stored in CAD files usually requires much less physical space in comparison to traditional hand drawings. However, the information stored inside the computer is not indestructible. On the contrary, the electronic format of information is very fragile and sensitive to the environment. Heat or cold can damage the information stored on magnetic storage devices. A power failure while you are creating a design could wipe out the many hours you spent working in front of the computer monitor. It is a good habit to save your work periodically, just in case something might go wrong while you are working on your design. In general, one should save one's work onto a storage device at an interval of every 15 to 20 minutes. You should also save your work before you make any major modifications to the design. It is also a good habit to periodically make backup copies of your work and put them in a safe place.

Getting started with AutoCAD® 2012

How to start **AutoCAD® 2012** depends on the type of workstation and the particular software configuration you are using. With most *Windows* systems, you may select the **AutoCAD 2012** option on the *Start* menu or select the **AutoCAD 2012** icon on the *Desktop*. Consult with your instructor or technical support personnel if you have difficulty starting the software.

The program takes a while to load, so be patient. Eventually the **AutoCAD® 2012** main *drawing screen* will appear on the screen. The tutorials in this text are based on the assumption that you are using **AutoCAD® 2012**'s default settings. If your system has been customized for other uses, some of the settings may not work with the step-by-step instructions in the tutorials. Contact your instructor and/or technical support personnel to restore the default software configuration.

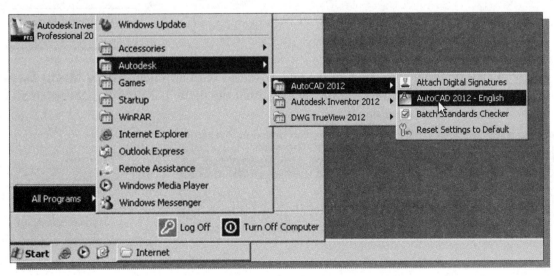

AutoCAD® 2012 Screen Layout

The default **AutoCAD® 2012** *drawing screen* contains the *pull-down* menus, the *Standard* toolbar, the *InfoCenter Help system,* the *scrollbars,* the *command prompt area,* the *Status Bar*, and the *Ribbon Tabs* and *Panels* that contains several *control panels* such as the *Draw and Modify* panel and the *Annotation* panel. You may resize the **AutoCAD® 2012** drawing window by click and drag at the edges of the window, or relocate the window by click and drag at the window title area.

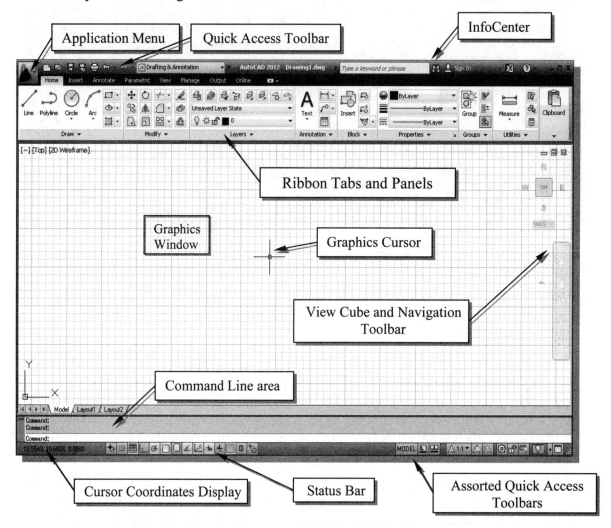

❖ Click on the down-arrow in the *Quick Access* bar and select **Show Menu Bar** to display the **AutoCAD** *Menu* bar. Note that the menu bar provides access to all of the AutoCAD commands.

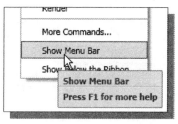

- **Application Menu**

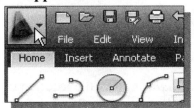

The *Application Menu* at the top of the main window contains commonly used file operations.

- **Workspace Switching**
  The Workspace Switching icon allows us to switch between different system settings.

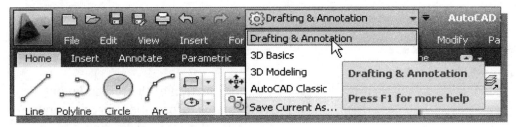

- **Quick Access Toolbar**
  The *Quick Access* toolbar at the top of the *AutoCAD* window allows us quick access to frequently used commands, such as Qnew, Open, Save and also the Undo command. Note that we can customize the quick access toolbar by adding and removing sets of options or individual commands.

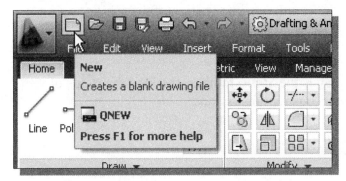

- **AutoCAD Menu Bar**
  The *Menu* bar is the pull-down menu where all operations of AutoCAD can be accessed.

- **Graphics Window**
  The *graphics window* is the area where models and drawings are displayed.

- **Graphics Cursor or Crosshairs**

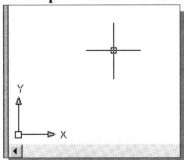

The *graphics cursor*, or *crosshairs*, shows the location of the pointing device in the graphics window. The coordinates of the cursor are displayed at the bottom of the screen layout. The cursor's appearance depends on the selected command or option.

- **Command Prompt Area**

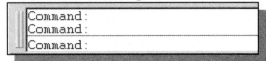

The bottom section of the screen layout provides status information for an operation and it is also the area for data input.

- **Cursor Coordinates**

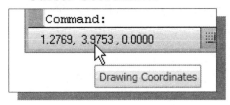

The bottom left section of the screen layout displays the coordinate information of the cursor.

- **Status Toolbar**
  Next to the cursor coordinate display is the *Status* toolbar, showing the status of several commonly used display and construction options.

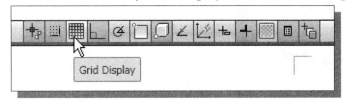

- **Ribbon Tabs and Panels**
  The top section of the screen layout contains customizable icon panels, which contain groups of buttons that allow us to pick commands quickly, without searching through a menu structure. These panels allow us to quickly access the commonly used commands available in AutoCAD.

- **Draw and Modify Toolbar Panels**
  The *Draw* and *Modify* toolbar panels contain icons for basic draw and modify commands.

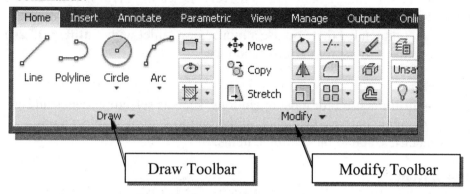

Draw Toolbar   Modify Toolbar

- **Layers Control Toolbar Panel**

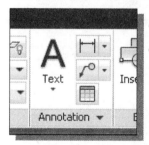

The *Layers Control* toolbar panel contains tools to help manipulate the properties of graphical objects.

- **Annotation Toolbar Panel**

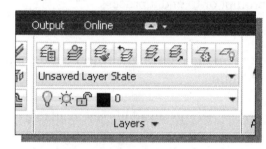

The *Annotation* toolbar panel contains tools for creating and editing dimensions.

- **Layout/Model Toolbar**

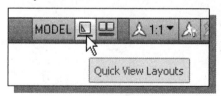

The *Layout/Model* toolbar contains tools for creating and editing layouts.

- **Viewport/View/Display Controls**

The *Viewport/View/Display controls panel* is located at the upper left corner of the graphics area and it can be used to quickly access viewing related commands, such as Viewport and Display style.

Mouse Buttons

AutoCAD® 2012 utilizes the mouse buttons extensively. In learning **AutoCAD® 2012's** interactive environment, it is important to understand the basic functions of the mouse buttons. It is highly recommended that you use a mouse or a tablet with **AutoCAD® 2012** since the package uses the buttons for various functions.

- **Left mouse button**
  The **left-mouse-button** is used for most operations, such as selecting menus and icons, or picking graphic entities. One click of the button is used to select icons, menus and form entries, and to pick graphic items.

- **Right mouse button**
  The **right-mouse-button** is used to bring up additional available options. The software also utilizes the **right-mouse-button** as the same as the **ENTER** key, and is often used to accept the default setting to a prompt or to end a process.

- **Middle mouse button/wheel**
  The middle mouse button/wheel can be used to Pan (hold down the wheel button and drag the mouse) or Zoom (rotate the wheel) realtime.

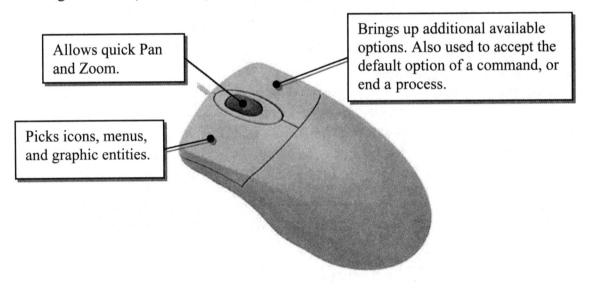

Allows quick Pan and Zoom.

Brings up additional available options. Also used to accept the default option of a command, or end a process.

Picks icons, menus, and graphic entities.

[Esc] – Canceling commands

The [**Esc**] key is used to cancel a command in **AutoCAD® 2012**. The [**Esc**] key is located near the top-left corner of the keyboard. Sometimes, it may be necessary to press the [**Esc**] key twice to cancel a command; it depends on where we are in the command sequence. For some commands, the [**Esc**] key is used to exit the command.

On-Line Help

❖ Several types of on-line help are available at any time during an **AutoCAD® 2012** session. The **AutoCAD® 2012** software provides many on-line help options:

- **Autodesk Exchange**:
  Autodesk Exchange is a new central portal in AutoCAD 2012; AutoCAD Exchange provides a new user interface for Help, learning aids, tips and tricks, videos, and downloadable apps. By default, *Autodesk Exchange* is displayed at **startup**. This allows access to a dynamic selection of tools from the Autodesk community, note that internet connection is required to use this option.

- To use Autodesk Exchange, simply type in a question in the *input box* to search through the Autodesk's Help system as shown in the above figure.

- A list of the search options appears in the Autodesk Exchange window; and we can determine the level and type of searches of the associated information.

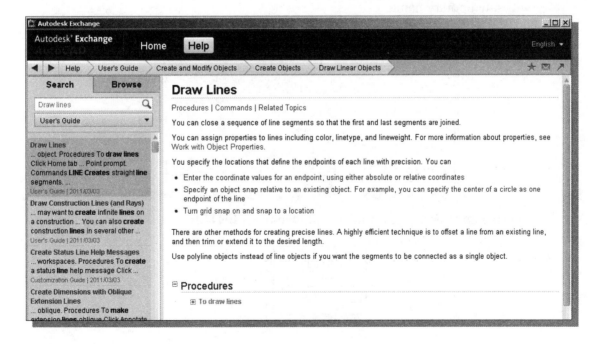

Leaving AutoCAD® 2012

➤ To leave **AutoCAD® 2012**, use the left-mouse-button and click the **Application Menu** button at the top left corner of the **AutoCAD® 2012** screen window, then choose **Exit AutoCAD** from the pull-down menu or type **QUIT** in the command prompt area.

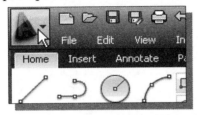 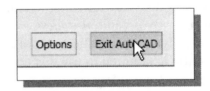

Creating a CAD file folder

❖ It is a good practice to create a separate folder to store your CAD files. You should not save your CAD files in the same folder where the **AutoCAD® 2012** application is located. It is much easier to organize and backup your project files if they are in a separate folder. Making folders within this folder for different types of projects will help you organize your CAD files even further. When creating CAD files in **AutoCAD® 2012**, it is strongly recommended that you *save* your CAD files on the hard drive.

➤ To create a new folder in the Windows environment:

1. In *My Computer*, or start the **Windows Explorer** under the *Start* menu, open the folder in which you want to create a new folder.

2. On the **File** menu, point to **New**, and then click **Folder**. The new folder appears with a temporary name.

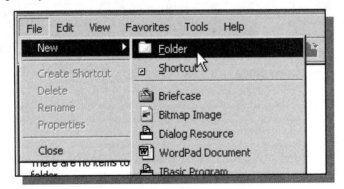

3. Type a name for the new folder, and then press **ENTER**.

Chapter 1
AutoCAD Fundamentals

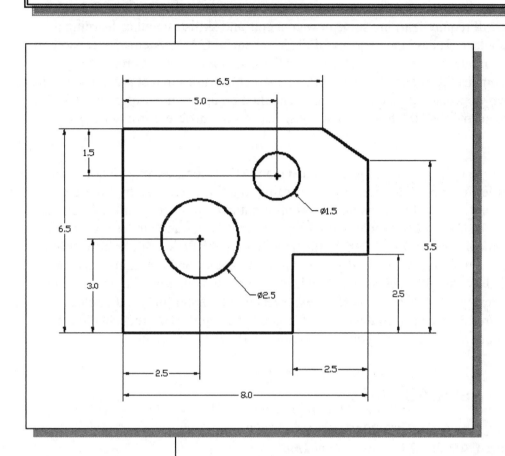

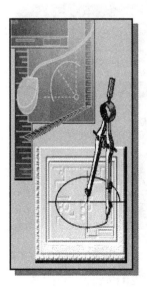

Learning Objectives

♦ **Create and Save AutoCAD drawing files**
♦ **Use the AutoCAD visual reference commands**
♦ **Draw, using the LINE and CIRCLE commands**
♦ **Use the ERASE command**
♦ **Define Positions using the Basic Entry methods**
♦ **Use the AutoCAD Pan Realtime option**

Introduction

Learning to use a CAD system is similar to learning a new language. It is necessary to begin with the basic alphabet and learn how to use it correctly and effectively through practice. This will require learning some new concepts and skills as well as learning a different vocabulary. Today, the majority of the Mechanical CAD systems are capable of creating three-dimensional solid models. Nonetheless, all CAD systems create designs using basic geometric entities and many of the constructions used in technical designs are based upon two-dimensional planar geometry. The method and number of operations that are required to accomplish the basic planar constructions are different from one system to another.

In order to become effective and efficient in using a CAD system, we must learn to create geometric entities quickly and accurately. In learning to use a CAD system, **lines** and **circles** are the first two, and perhaps the most important two, geometric entities that one should master the skills of creating and modifying. Straight lines and circles are used in almost all technical designs. In examining the different types of planar geometric entities, the importance of lines and circles becomes obvious. Triangles and polygons are planar figures bounded by straight lines. Ellipses and splines can be constructed by connecting arcs with different radii. As one gains some experience in creating lines and circles, similar procedures can be applied to create other geometric entities. In this chapter, the different ways of creating lines and circles in **AutoCAD® 2012** are examined.

Starting Up AutoCAD® 2012

1. Select the **AutoCAD 2012** option on the *Program* menu or select the **AutoCAD 2012** icon on the *Desktop*.

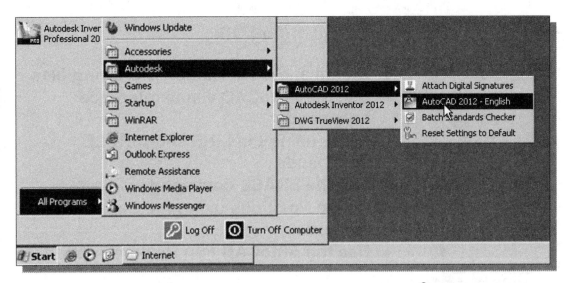

❖ Once the program is loaded into memory, the **AutoCAD® 2012** drawing screen will appear on the screen.

➢ Note that AutoCAD automatically assigns generic name, *Drawing X*, as new drawings are created. In our example, AutoCAD opened the graphics window using the default system units and assigned the drawing name *Drawing1*.

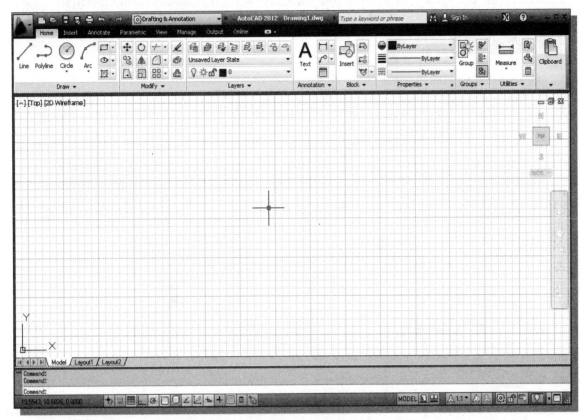

2. If necessary, click on the down-arrow in the *Quick Access* bar and select **Show Menu** to display the **AutoCAD** *Menu Bar*. The *Menu Bar* provides access to all AutoCAD commands.

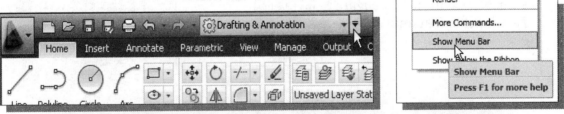

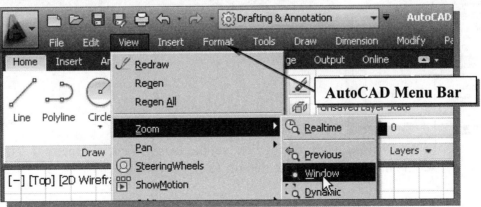

Drawing Units Setup

➢ Every object we construct in a CAD system is measured in **units**. We should determine the system of units within the CAD system before creating the first geometric entities.

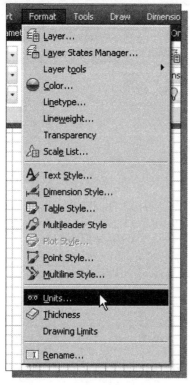

1. In the *Menu Bar* select:
   [Format] → [Units]

- The AutoCAD *Menu Bar* contains multiple pull-down menus, where all of the AutoCAD commands can be accessed. Note that many of the menu items listed in the pull-down menus can also be accessed through the *Quick Access* toolbar and/or *Ribbon* panels.

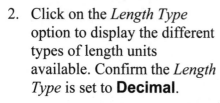

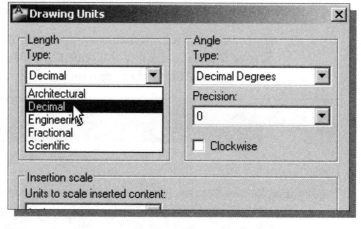

2. Click on the *Length Type* option to display the different types of length units available. Confirm the *Length Type* is set to **Decimal**.

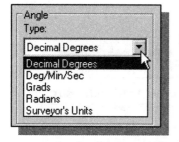

3. On your own, examine the other settings that are available.

4. In the *Drawing Units* dialog box, set the *Length Type* to **Decimal**. This will set the measurement to the default *English* units, inches.

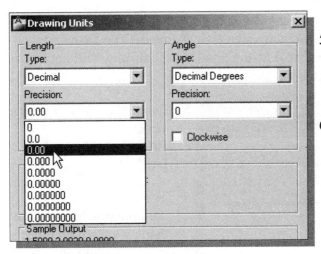

5. Set the *Precision* to **two digits** after the decimal point as shown in the above figure.

6. Pick **OK** to exit the *Drawing Units* dialog box.

Drawing Area Setup

❖ Next, we will set up the **Drawing Limits** by entering a command in the command prompt area. Setting the Drawing Limits controls the extents of the display of the *grid*. It also serves as a visual reference that marks the working area. It can also be used to prevent construction outside the grid limits and as a plot option that defines an area to be plotted/printed. Note that this setting does not limit the region for geometry construction.

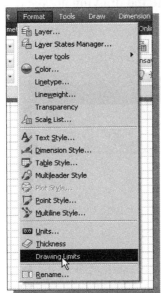

1. In the *Menu Bar* select:
   [Format] → [Drawing Limits]

2. In the command prompt area, the message "*Reset Model Space Limits: Specify lower left corner or [On/Off] <0.00,0.00>:*" is displayed. Press the **ENTER** key once to accept the default coordinates <**0.00,0.00**>.

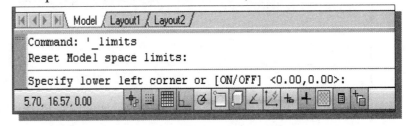

3. In the command prompt area, the message "*Specify upper right corner <12.00,9.00>:*" is displayed. Press the **ENTER** key again to accept the default coordinates <**12.00,9.00**>.

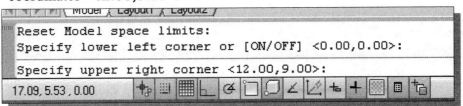

4. On your own, move the graphic cursor near the upper-right corner inside the drawing area and note that the drawing area is unchanged. (The **Drawing Limits** command is used to set the drawing area, but the display will not be adjusted until a display command is used.)

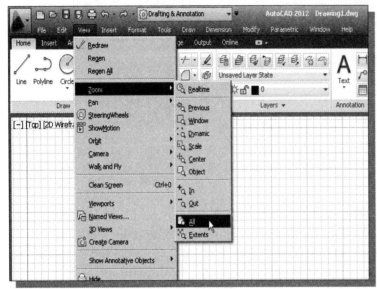

5. Inside the *Menu Bar* area select:
    [View] → [Zoom] → [All]

❖   The **Zoom All** command will adjust the display so that all objects in the drawing are displayed to be as large as possible. If no objects are constructed, the **Drawing Limits** are used to adjust the current viewport.

6. Move the graphic cursor near the upper-right corner inside the drawing area and note that the display area is updated.

7. Hit the function key [**F7**] once to turn **off** the display of the *Grid* lines.

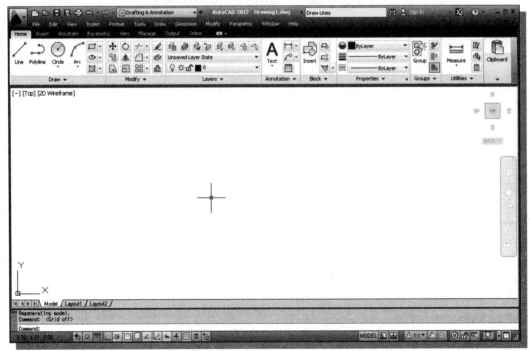

•   Note that function key [F7] is a quick key which can be used to quickly toggle on/off the grid display.

Drawing lines with the *LINE* command

1. Move the graphics cursor to the first icon in the *Draw* panel. This icon is the **Line** icon. Note that a brief description of the Line command appears next to the cursor.

2. Select the icon by clicking once with the **left-mouse-button**, which will activate the Line command.

3. In the command prompt area, near the bottom of the AutoCAD drawing screen, the message "*_line Specify first point:*" is displayed. AutoCAD expects us to identify the starting location of a straight line. Move the graphics cursor inside the graphics window and watch the display of the coordinates of the graphics cursor at the bottom of the AutoCAD drawing screen. The three numbers represent the location of the cursor in the X, Y, and Z directions. We can treat the graphics window as if it was a piece of paper and we are using the graphics cursor as if it were a pencil with which to draw.

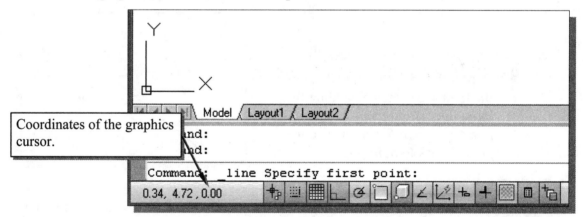

Coordinates of the graphics cursor.

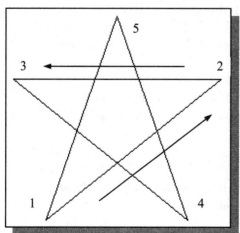

❖ We will create a freehand sketch of a five-point star using the Line command. Do not be overly concerned with the actual size or the accuracy of your freehand sketch. This exercise is to give you a feel for the **AutoCAD® 2012** user interface.

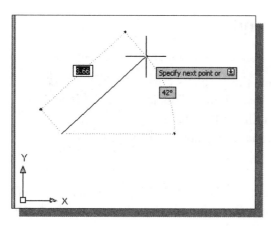

4. We will start at a location about one-third from the bottom of the graphics window. Left-click once to position the starting point of our first line. This will be *point 1* of our sketch. Next move the cursor upward and toward the right side of *point 1*. Notice the rubber-band line that follows the graphics cursor in the graphics window. Left-click again (*point 2*) and we have created the first line of our sketch.

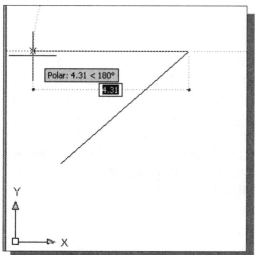

5. Move the cursor to the left of *point 2* and create a horizontal line about the same length as the first line on the screen.

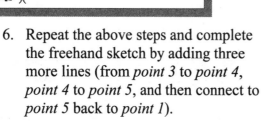

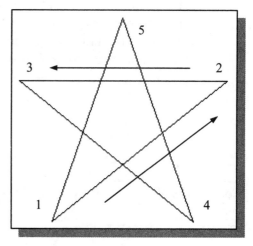

6. Repeat the above steps and complete the freehand sketch by adding three more lines (from *point 3* to *point 4*, *point 4* to *point 5*, and then connect to *point 5* back to *point 1*).

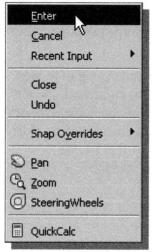

7. Notice that the Line command remains activated even after we connected the last segment of the line to the starting point *(point 1)* of our sketch. Inside the graphics window, **click once** with the **right-mouse-button** and a popup menu appears on the screen.

8. Select **Enter** with the left-mouse-button to end the Line command. (This is equivalent to hitting the [**ENTER**] key on the keyboard.)

9. Move the cursor near *point 2* and *point 3*, and estimate the length of the horizontal line by watching the displayed coordinates for each point.

Visual reference

The method we just used to create the freehand sketch is known as the **interactive method**, where we use the cursor to specify locations on the screen. This method is perhaps the fastest way to specify locations on the screen. However, it is rather difficult to try to create a line of a specific length by watching the displayed coordinates. It would be helpful to know what one inch or one meter looks like on the screen while we are creating entities. **AutoCAD® 2012** provides us with many tools to aid the construction of our designs. For example, the *GRID* and *SNAP MODE* options can be used to get a visual reference as to the size of objects and learn to restrict the movement of the cursor to a set increment on the screen.

The *GRID* and *SNAP MODE* options can be turned *ON* or *OFF* through the *Status Bar*. The *Status Bar* area is located at the bottom left of the AutoCAD drawing screen, next to the cursor coordinates.

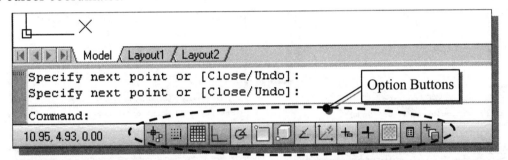

The second button in the *Status Bar* is the *SNAP MODE* option and the third button is the *GRID DISPLAY* option. Note that the buttons in the *Status Bar* area serve two functions: (1) the status of the specific option, and (2) as toggle switches that can be used to turn these special options *ON* and *OFF*. When the corresponding button is *highlighted*, the specific option is turned *ON*. Using the buttons is a quick and easy way to make changes to these *drawing aid* options. Another aspect of the buttons in the *Status Bar* is these options can be switched on and off in the middle of another command.

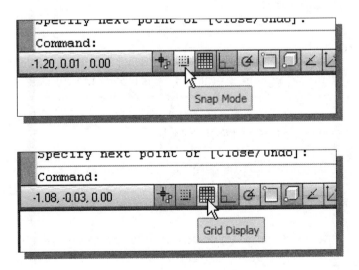

GRID ON

1. Left-click the **GRID** button in the *Status Bar* to turn **ON** the *GRID DISPLAY* option. (Notice in the command prompt area, the message *"<Grid on>"* is also displayed.)

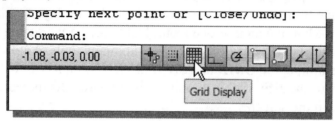

2. Move the cursor inside the graphics window, and estimate the distance in between the grid lines by watching the coordinates display at the bottom of the screen.

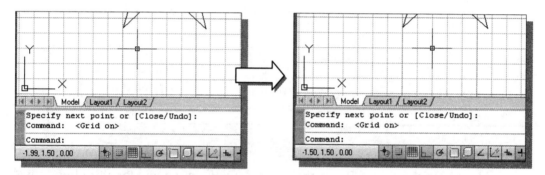

➢ The *GRID* option creates a pattern of lines that extends over an area on the screen. Using the grid is similar to placing a sheet of grid paper under a drawing. The grid helps you align objects and visualize the distance between them. The grid is not displayed in the plotted drawing. The default grid spacing, which means the distance in between two lines on the screen, is 0.5 inches. We can see that the sketched horizontal line in the sketch is about 5 inches long.

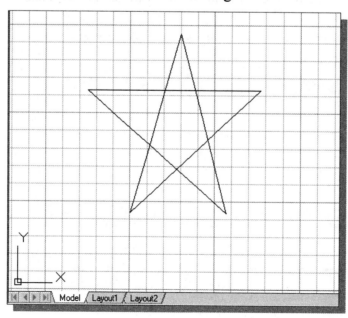

SNAP MODE ON

1. Left-click the **SNAP MODE** button in the *Status Bar* to turn **ON** the *SNAP* option.

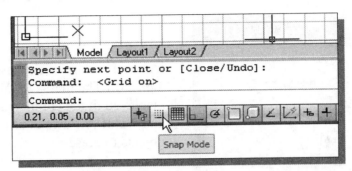

2. Move the cursor inside the graphics window, and move the cursor diagonally on the screen. Observe the movement of the cursor and watch the *coordinates display* at the bottom of the screen.

➢ The *SNAP* option controls an invisible rectangular grid that restricts cursor movement to specified intervals. When *SNAP* mode is on, the screen cursor and all input coordinates are snapped to the nearest point on the grid. The default snap interval is 0.5 inches, and aligned to the grid points on the screen.

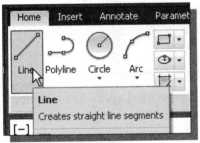

3. Click on the **Line** icon in the *Draw* toolbar. In the command prompt area, the message "*_line Specify first point:*" is displayed.

4. On your own, create another sketch of the five-point star with the *GRID* and *SNAP* options switched *ON*.

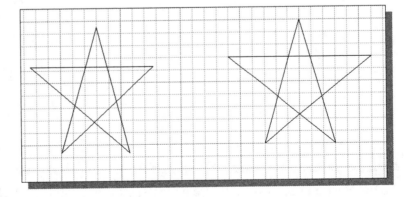

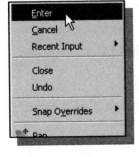

5. Use the **right-mouse-button** and select **Enter** in the popup menu to end the **Line** command if you have not done so.

Using the *ERASE* command

❖ One of the advantages of using a CAD system is the ability to remove entities without leaving any marks. We will erase two of the lines using the **Erase** command.

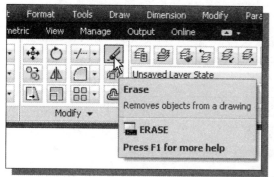

1. Pick **Erase** in the *Modify* toolbar. (The icon is a picture of an eraser at the end of a pencil.) The message "*Select objects*" is displayed in the command prompt area and AutoCAD awaits us to select the objects to erase.

2. Left-click the ***SNAP MODE*** button on the *Status Bar* to turn ***OFF*** the *SNAP MODE* option so that we can more easily move the cursor on top of objects. We can toggle the *Status Bar* options *ON* or *OFF* in the middle of another command.

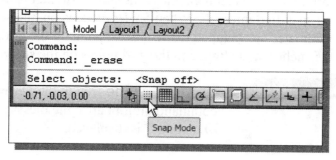

3. Select any two lines on the screen; the selected lines are displayed as dashed lines as shown in the figure below.

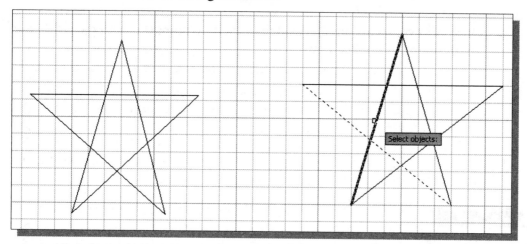

➢ To **deselect** an object from the selection set, hold down the [**SHIFT**] key and select the object again.

4. **Right-mouse-click** once to accept the selections. The selected two lines are erased.

Repeat the last command

1. Inside the graphics window, click once with the right-mouse-button to bring up the popup option menu.

2. Pick **Repeat Erase**, with the left-mouse-button, in the popup menu to repeat the last command. Notice the other options available in the popup menu.

➢ **AutoCAD® 2012** offers many options to accomplish the same task. Throughout this text, we will emphasize the use of the **AutoCAD Heads-up Design™** interface, which means we focus on the screen, not on the keyboard.

3. Move the cursor to a location that is above and toward the left side of the entities on the screen. Left-mouse-click once to start a corner of a rubber-band window.

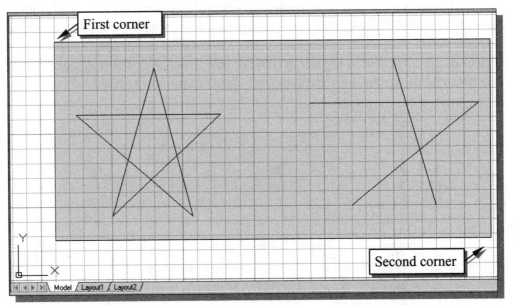

4. Move the cursor toward the right and below the entities, and then left-mouse-click to enclose all the entities inside the **selection window**. Notice all entities that are inside the window are selected.

5. Inside the graphics window, right-mouse-click once to proceed with erasing the selected entities.

➢ On your own, create a free-hand sketch of your choice using the **Line** command. Experiment with using the different commands we have discussed so far. Reset the status buttons so that only the *GRID DISPLAY* option is turned *ON* as shown.

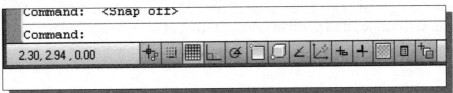

The CAD Database and the User Coordinate System

❖ Designs and drawings created in a CAD system are usually defined and stored using sets of points in what is called **world space**. In most CAD systems, the world space is defined using a three-dimensional *Cartesian coordinate system*. Three mutually perpendicular axes, usually referred to as the X-, Y-, and Z-axes, define this system. The intersection of the three coordinate axes forms a point called the **origin**. Any point in world space can then be defined as the distance from the origin in the X-, Y- and Z-directions. In most CAD systems, the directions of the arrows shown on the axes identify the positive sides of the coordinates.

A CAD file, which is the electronic version of the design, contains data that describes the entities created in the CAD system. Information such as the coordinate values in world space for all endpoints, center points, etc., along with the descriptions of the types of entities are all stored in the file. Knowing that AutoCAD stores designs by keeping coordinate data helps us understand the inputs required to create entities.

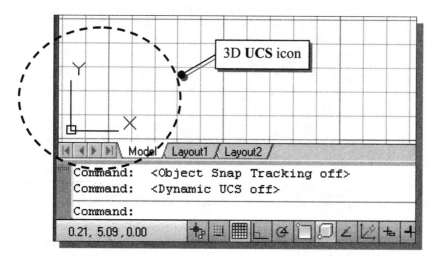

The icon near the bottom left corner of the default AutoCAD graphics window shows the positive X-direction and positive Y-direction of the coordinate system that is active. In AutoCAD, the coordinate system that is used to create entities is called the **user coordinate system** (UCS). By default, the **user coordinate system** is aligned to the **world coordinate system (WCS)**. The **world coordinate system** is a coordinate system used by AutoCAD as the basis for defining all objects and other coordinate systems defined by the users. We can think of the **origin** of the **world coordinate system** as a fixed point being used as a reference for all measurements. The default orientation of the Z-axis can be considered as positive values in front of the monitor and negative values inside the monitor.

Changing to the 2D UCS Icon Display

❖ In **AutoCAD® 2012**, the **UCS** icon is displayed in various ways to help us visualize the orientation of the drawing plane.

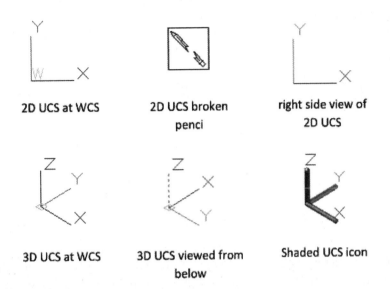

2D UCS at WCS   2D UCS broken   right side view of
                          penci   2D UCS

3D UCS at WCS   3D UCS viewed from   Shaded UCS icon
                          below

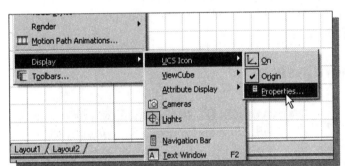

1. Click on the **View** pull-down menu and select

   [Display] → [UCS Icon] → [Properties...]

2. In the *UCS icon style* section, switch to the **2D** option as shown.

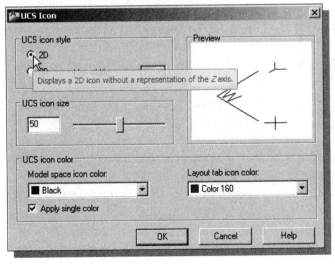

3. Click **OK** to accept the settings.

❖ Note the W symbol in the UCS icon indicates the UCS is aligned to the world coordinate system.

Cartesian and Polar Coordinate Systems

In a two-dimensional space, a point can be represented using different coordinate systems. The point can be located, using a *Cartesian coordinate system*, as X and Y units away from the origin. The same point can also be located using the *polar coordinate system*, as r and θ units away from the origin.

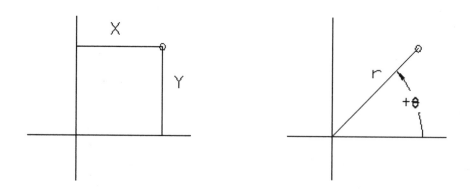

For planar geometry, the polar coordinate system is very useful for certain applications. In the polar coordinate system, points are defined in terms of a radial distance, r, from the origin and an angle θ between the direction of r and the positive X axis. The default system for measuring angles in **AutoCAD® 2012** defines positive angular values as counter-clockwise from the positive X-axis.

Absolute and Relative Coordinates

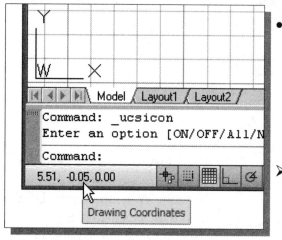

- **AutoCAD® 2012** also allows us to use *absolute* and *relative coordinates* to quickly construct objects. **Absolute coordinate values** are measured from the current coordinate system's origin point. **Relative coordinate values** are specified in relation to previous coordinates.

➢ Note that the *coordinate display area* can also be used as a toggle switch; each left-mouse-click will toggle the coordinate display *on* or *off*.

In **AutoCAD® 2012**, the *absolute* coordinates and the *relative* coordinates can be used in conjunction with the *Cartesian* and *polar* coordinate systems. By default, AutoCAD expects us to enter values in *absolute Cartesian coordinates*, distances measured from the current coordinate system's origin point. We can switch to using the *relative coordinates* by using the @ symbol. The @ symbol is used as the *relative coordinates specifier*, which means that we can specify the position of a point in relation to the previous point.

Defining Positions

In AutoCAD, there are five methods for specifying the locations of points when we create planar geometric entities.

> **Interactive method**: Use the cursor to select on the screen.

> **Absolute coordinates (Format: X,Y)**: Type the X and Y coordinates to locate the point on the current coordinate system relative to the origin.

> **Relative rectangular coordinates (Format: @X,Y)**: Type the X and Y coordinates relative to the last point.

> **Relative polar coordinates (Format: @Distance<angle)**: Type a distance and angle relative to the last point.

> **Direct Distance entry technique**: Specify a second point by first moving the cursor to indicate direction and then entering a distance.

GRID Style Setup

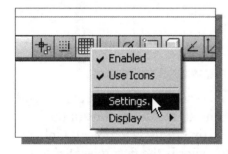

1. In the *Status Bar* area, **right-mouse-click** on *SnapMode* and choose **[Settings]**

2. In the *Drafting Settings* dialog box, select the **Snap and Grid** tab if it is not the page on top.

3. Change *Grid Style* to **Display dotted grid in 2D model Space** as shown in the below figure.

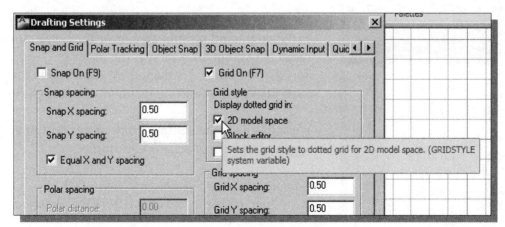

4. Pick **OK** to exit the *Drafting Settings* dialog box.

The *GuidePlate*

We will next create a mechanical design using the different coordinate entry methods.

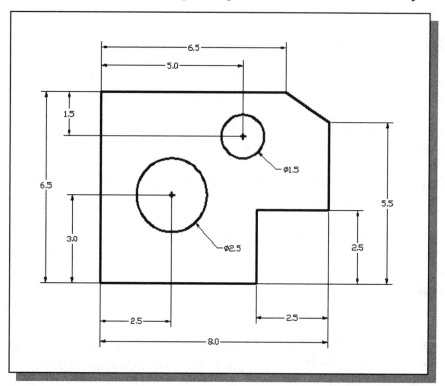

❖ The rule for creating CAD designs and drawings is that they should be created at **full size** using real-world units. The CAD database contains all the definitions of the geometric entities and the design is considered as a virtual, full-sized object. Only when a printer or plotter transfers the CAD design to paper is the design scaled to fit on a sheet. The tedious task of determining a scale factor so that the design will fit on a sheet of paper is taken care of by the CAD system. This allows the designers and CAD operators to concentrate their attention on the more important issues – the design.

1. Select the **Line** command icon in the *Draw* toolbar. In the command prompt area, near the bottom of the AutoCAD graphics window, the message "*_line Specify first point:*" is displayed. AutoCAD expects us to identify the starting location of a straight line.

2. We will locate the starting point of our design at the origin of the *world coordinate system.*

   Command: _line Specify first point: **0,0**
   　　(Type **0,0** and press the [**ENTER**] key once.)

3. We will create a horizontal line by entering the absolute coordinates of the second point.
   Specify next point or [Undo]: **5.5,0 [ENTER]**

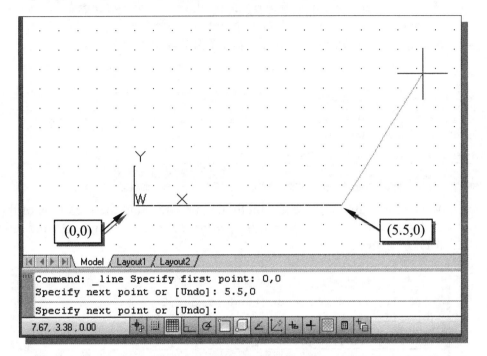

- Note that the line we created is aligned to the bottom edge of the drawing window. Let us adjust the view of the line by using the **Pan Realtime** command.

4. In the *Menu Bar* area select: **[View] → [Pan] → [Realtime]**

❖ The available **Pan** commands enable us to move the view to a different position. The *Pan-Realtime* function acts as if you are using a video camera.

5. Move the cursor, which appears as a hand inside the graphics window, near the center of the drawing window, then push down the left-mouse-button and drag the display toward the right and top side until we can see the sketched line. (Notice the scroll bars can also be used to adjust viewing of the display.)

6. Press the **[Esc]** key to exit the Pan-Realtime command. Notice that AutoCAD goes back to the Line command.

7. We will create a vertical line by using the *relative rectangular coordinates entry method*, relative to the last point we specified:
   Specify next point or [Close/Undo]: **@0,2.5** **[ENTER]**

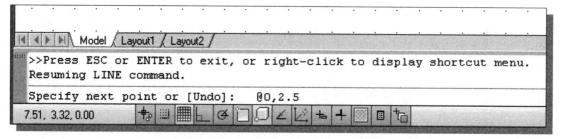

8. We can mix any of the entry methods in positioning the locations of the endpoints. Move the cursor to the *Status Bar* area, and turn **ON** the *SNAP MODE* option.

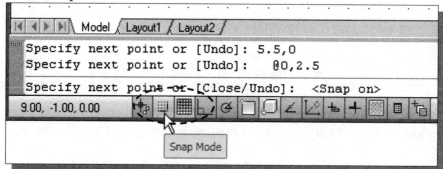

❖ Note that the Line command is resumed as the settings are adjusted.

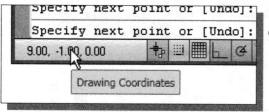

9. Left-click once on the coordinates display area to switch the display options.

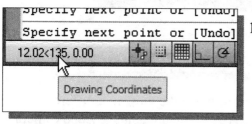

10. Note the coordinates display area has changed to show the length of the new line and its angle. Left-click once on the coordinates display area to switch back to using the world coordinate system.

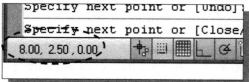

11. Create the next line by picking the location, world coordinates (**8,2.5**), on the screen.

12. We will next use the *relative polar coordinates entry method*, relative to the last point we specified:
Specify next point or [Close/Undo]: **@3<90** [ENTER]
(Distance is **3** inches with an angle of **90** degrees.)

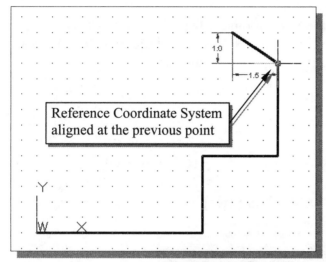

Reference Coordinate System aligned at the previous point

13. Using the *relative rectangular coordinates entry method* to create the next line, we can imagine a *reference coordinate system* aligned at the previous point. Coordinates are measured along the two reference axes.

Specify next point or [Close/Undo]: **@-1.5,1** [ENTER]

(**-1.5** and **1** inches are measured relative to the reference point.)

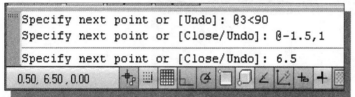

Specify next point or [Undo]: @3<90
Specify next point or [Close/Undo]: @-1.5,1
Specify next point or [Close/Undo]: 6.5
0.50, 6.50, 0.00

14. Move the cursor directly to the left of the last point and use the *direct distance entry technique* by entering **6.5** [ENTER].

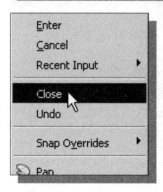

Enter
Cancel
Recent Input
Close
Undo
Snap Overrides
Pan

15. For the last segment of the sketch, we can use the **Close** option to connect back to the starting point. Inside the graphics window, **right-mouse-click** and a *popup menu* appears on the screen.

16. Select **Close** with the left-mouse-button to connect back to the starting point and end the Line command.

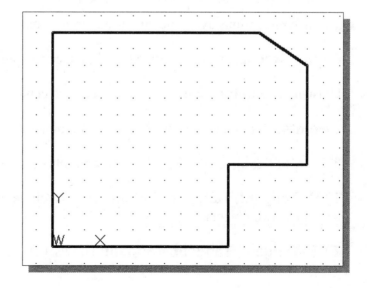

Creating *Circles*

- The menus and toolbars in **AutoCAD® 2012** are designed to allow the CAD operators to quickly activate the desired commands.

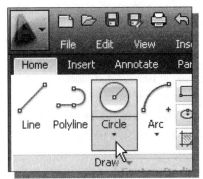

1. In the *Draw* toolbar, click on the little triangle below the circle icon. Note that the little triangle indicates additional options are available.

2. In the option list, select: **[Center, Diameter]**

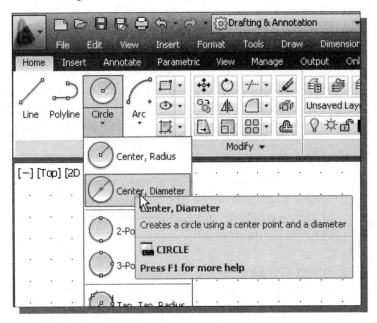

Notice the different options available under the circle submenu:

- **Center, Radius**: Draws a circle based on a center point and a radius.

- **Center, Diameter**: Draws a circle based on a center point and a diameter.

- **2 Points**: Draws a circle based on two endpoints of the diameter.

- **3 Points**: Draws a circle based on three points on the circumference.

- **TTR–Tangent, Tangent**, **Radius**: Draws a circle with a specified radius tangent to two objects.

- **TTT–Tangent, Tangent, Tangent**: Draws a circle tangent to three objects.

3. In the command prompt area, the message "*Specify center point for circle or [3P/2P/Ttr (tan tan radius)]:*" is displayed. AutoCAD expects us to identify the location of a point or enter an option. We can use any of the four coordinate entry methods to identify the desired location. We will enter the **world coordinates (2.5,3)** as the center point for the first circle.

Specify center point for circle or [3P/2P/Ttr (tan tan radius)]: **2.5,3 [ENTER]**

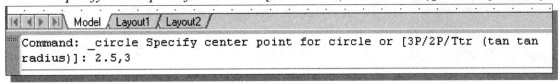

4. In the command prompt area, the message "*Specify diameter of circle:*" is displayed.
    Specify diameter of circle: **2.5 [ENTER]**

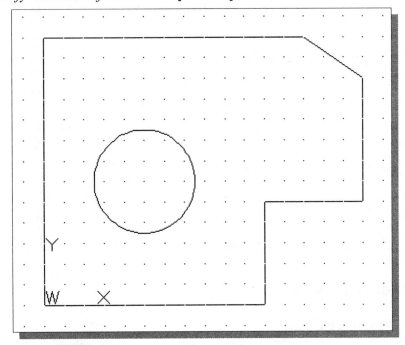

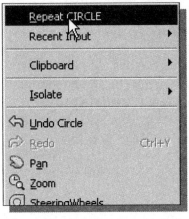

5. Inside the graphics window, right-mouse-click to bring up the popup option menu.

6. Pick **Repeat CIRCLE** with the left-mouse-button in the popup menu to repeat the last command.

7. Using the *relative rectangular coordinates entry method*, relative to the center-point coordinates of the first circle, we specify the location as (**2.5,2**).

Specify center point for circle or [3P/2P/Ttr (tan tan radius)]: **@2.5,2 [ENTER]**

8. In the command prompt area, the message "*Specify Radius of circle: <2.50>*" is displayed. The default option for the Circle command in AutoCAD is to specify the *radius* and the last radius used is also displayed in brackets.

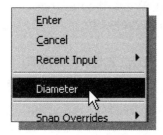

9. Inside the graphics window, **right-mouse-click** to bring up the popup option menu and select **Diameter** as shown.

10. In the command prompt area, enter **1.5** as the diameter.

   Specify Diameter of circle<2.50>: **1.5 [ENTER]**

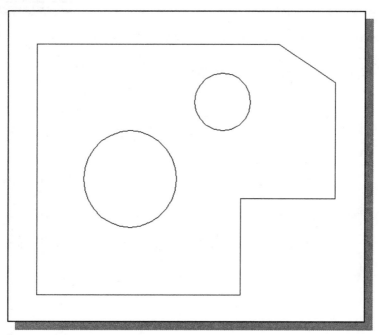

Saving the CAD Design

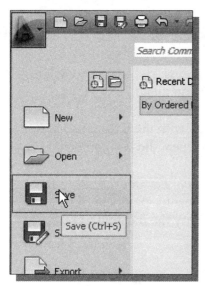

1. In the *Application Menu*, select:

   [Application] → [Save]

   ❖ Note the command can also be activated with quick-key combination of **[Ctrl]+[S]**.

2. In the *Save Drawing As* dialog box, select the folder in which you want to store the CAD file and enter **GuidePlate** in the *File name* box.

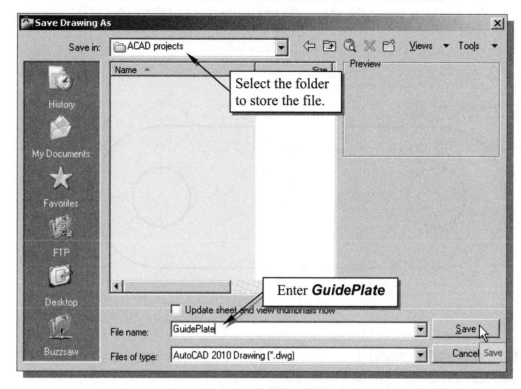

3. Click **Save** in the *Save Drawing As* dialog box to accept the selections and save the file. Note the default file type is DWG, which is the standard AutoCAD drawing format.

Close the Current Drawing

❖ Several options are available to close the current drawing:

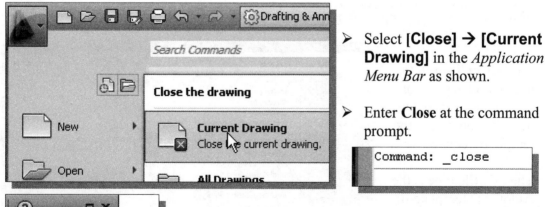

> Select **[Close]** → **[Current Drawing]** in the *Application Menu Bar* as shown.

> Enter **Close** at the command prompt.

```
Command: _close
```

> The third option is to click on the **[Close]** icon, located at the upper-right-hand corner of the drawing window.

The *Spacer* design

❖ We will next create the spacer design using more of the AutoCAD's drawing tools.

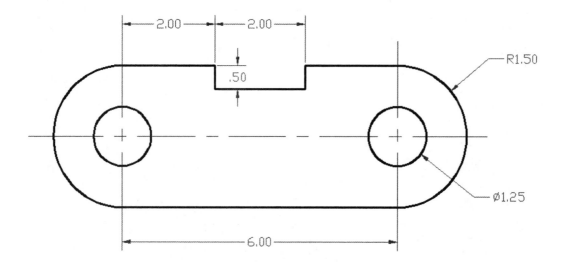

Start a New Drawing

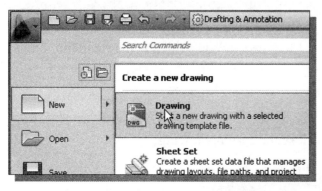

1. In the *Application Menu,* select **[New]** to start a new drawing.

2. The **Select Template** dialog box appears on the screen. Accept the default acad.dwt as the template to open.

➢ The dwt file type is the AutoCAD template file format. An AutoCAD template file contains pre-defined settings to reduce the amount of tedious repetitions.

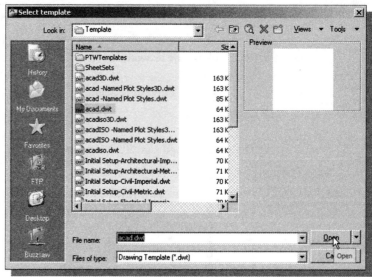

Drawing Units Setup

➢ Every object we construct in a CAD system is measured in **units**. We should determine the system of units within the CAD system before creating the first geometric entities.

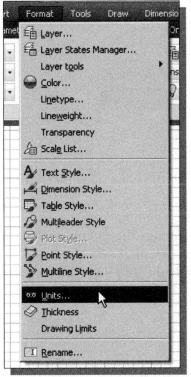

1. In the *Menu Bar* select:
   [Format] → **[Units]**

   • The AutoCAD *Menu Bar* contains multiple pull-down menus, where all of the AutoCAD commands can be accessed. Note that many of the menu items listed in the pull-down menus can also be accessed through the *Quick Access* toolbar and/or *Ribbon* panels.

2. Click on the *Length Type* option to display the different types of length units available. Confirm the *Length Type* is set to **Decimal**.

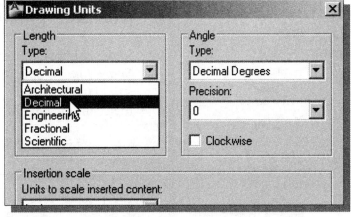

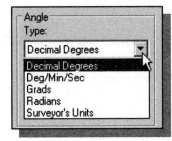

3. On your own, examine the other settings that are available.

4. In the *Drawing Units* dialog box, set the *Length Type* to **Decimal**. This will set the measurement to the default *English* units, inches.

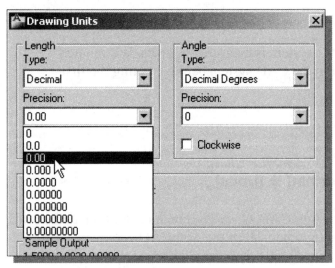

5. Set the *Precision* to **two digits** after the decimal point as shown in the above figure.

6. Pick **OK** to exit the *Drawing Units* dialog box.

Drawing Area Setup

❖ Next, we will set up the **Drawing Limits** by entering a command in the command prompt area. Setting the Drawing Limits controls the extents of the display of the *grid*. It also serves as a visual reference that marks the working area. It can also be used to prevent construction outside the grid limits and as a plot option that defines an area to be plotted/printed. Note that this setting does not limit the region for geometry construction.

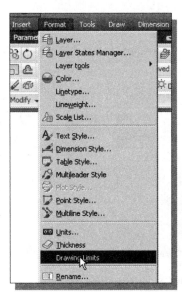

1. In the *Menu Bar* select:
    [Format] → [Drawing Limits]

2. In the command prompt area, the message "*Reset Model Space Limits: Specify lower left corner or [On/Off] <0.00,0.00>:*" is displayed. Press the **ENTER** key once to accept the default coordinates <**0.00,0.00**>.

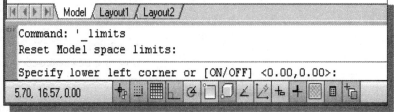

3. In the command prompt area, the message "*Specify upper right corner <12.00,9.00>:*" is displayed. Press the **ENTER** key again to accept the default coordinates <**12.00,9.00**>.

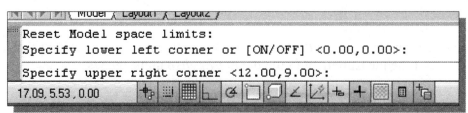

4. On your own, move the graphic cursor near the upper-right corner inside the drawing area and note that the drawing area is unchanged. (The Drawing Limits command is used to set the drawing area, but the display will not be adjusted until a display command is used.)

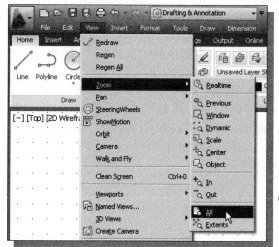

5. Inside the *Menu Bar* area select:
   [View] → [Zoom] → [All]

❖ The **Zoom All** command will adjust the display so that all objects in the drawing are displayed to be as large as possible. If no objects are constructed, the Drawing Limits are used to adjust the current viewport.

6. Move the graphic cursor near the upper-right corner inside the drawing area and note that the display area is updated.

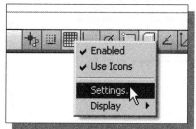

7. In the *Status Bar* area, **right-mouse-click** on *SnapMode* and choose **[Settings]**.

8. In the *Drafting Settings dialog box*, switch **on** the **Snap** and **Grid** options as shown.

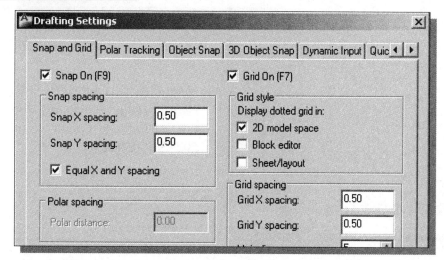

➢ On your own, exit the *Drafting Settings dialog box* and reset the status buttons so that only *GRID DISPLAY* and *SNAP MODE* are turned *ON* as shown.

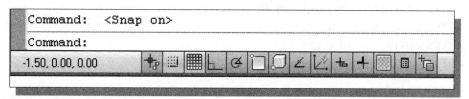

```
Command:   <Snap on>
Command:
-1.50, 0.00, 0.00
```

Using the Line Command

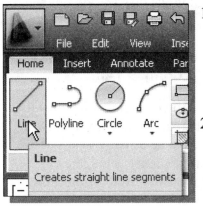

1. Select the **Line** command icon in the *Draw* toolbar. In the command prompt area, near the bottom of the AutoCAD graphics window, the message "*_line Specify first point:*" is displayed. AutoCAD expects us to identify the starting location of a straight line.

2. To further illustrate the usage of the different input methods and tools available in AutoCAD, we will start the line segments at an arbitrary location. Start at a location that is somewhere in the lower left side of the graphics window.

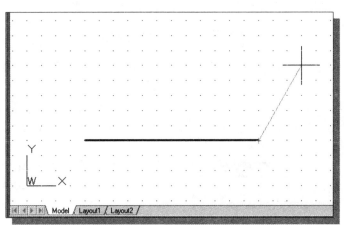

3. We will create a horizontal line by using the *relative rectangular coordinates entry method*, relative to the last point we specified: **@6,0 [ENTER]**

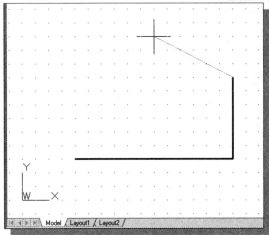

4. Next, create a vertical line by using the *relative polar coordinates entry method*, relative to the last point we specified: **@3<90 [ENTER]**

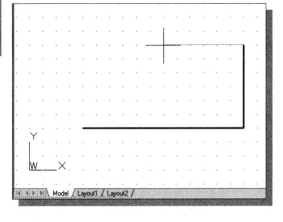

5. Next, we will use the direct input method; first, move the cursor directly to the left of the last endpoint of the line segments.

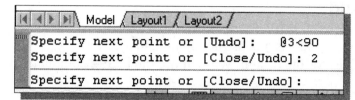

Specify next point or [Undo]:   @3<90
Specify next point or [Close/Undo]: 2

Specify next point or [Close/Undo]:

6. Use the *direct distance entry technique* by entering **2** [**ENTER**].

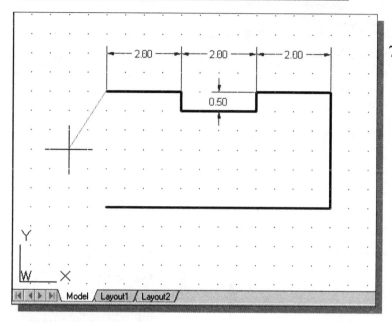

7. On your own, repeat the above steps and create the four additional line segments, using the dimensions as shown.

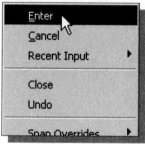

8. To end the line command, we can either hit the [Enter] key on the key board or use the **Enter** option, **right-mouse-click** and a *popup menu* appears on the screen.

9. Select **Enter** with the left-mouse-button to end the Line command.

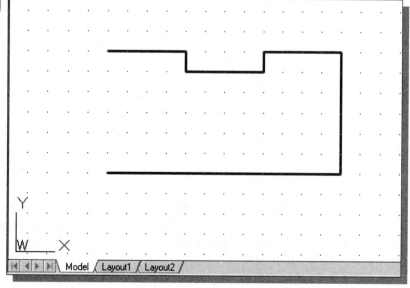

Using the *ERASE* command

❖ The vertical line on the right was created as a construction line, to aide the construction of the rest of the lines for the design. We will use the Erase command to remove it.

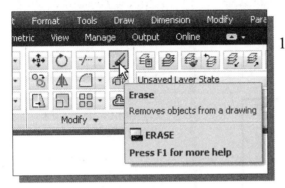

1. Pick **Erase** in the *Modify* toolbar. The message "*Select objects*" is displayed in the command prompt area and AutoCAD awaits us to select the objects to erase.

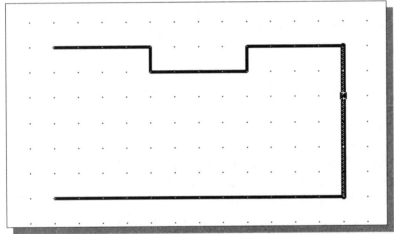

2. Select the vertical line as shown.

3. Click once with the **right-mouse-button** to accept the selection and delete the line.

Using the Arc Command

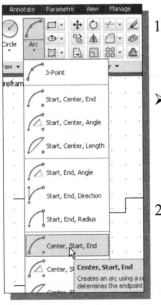

1. Click the down-arrow icon of the **Arc** command in the *Draw* toolbar to display the different Arc construction options.

➢ AutoCAD provides eleven different ways to create arcs. Note that the different options are used based on the geometry conditions of the design. The more commonly used options are the **3-Points** option and the **Center-Start-End** option.

2. Select the **Center-Start-End** option as shown. This option requires the selection of the center point, start point and end point location, in that order, of the arc.

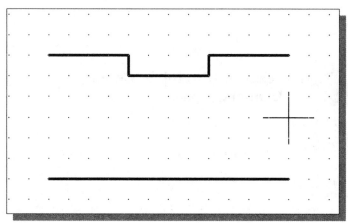

3. Move the cursor to the middle of the two horizontal lines and align the cursor to the two endpoints as shown. Click once with the **right-mouse-button** to select the location as the center point of the new arc.

4. Move the cursor downward and select the right endpoint of the bottom horizontal line as the start point of the arc.

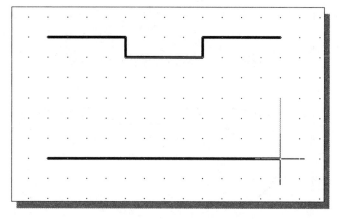

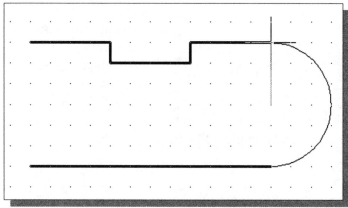

5. Move the cursor to the right endpoint of the top horizontal line as shown. Pick this point as the endpoint of the new arc.

6. On your own, repeat the above steps and create the other arc as shown. Note that in most CAD packages, positive angles are defined as going counterclockwise; therefore the starting point of the second arc is the endpoint on top.

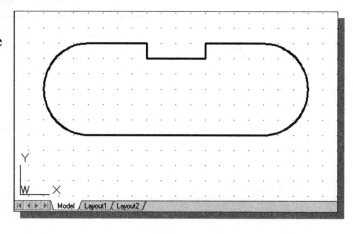

Using the Circle command

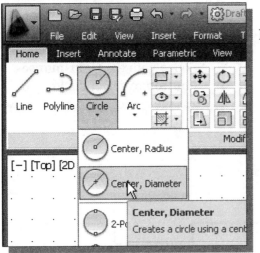

1. Select the **[Circle]** → **[Center, Diameter]** option as shown.

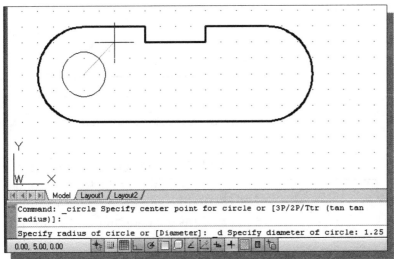

2. Select the same location for the arc center as the center point for the new circle.

3. In the command prompt area, the message "*Specify diameter of circle:*" is displayed. *Specify diameter of circle:* **1.25 [ENTER]**

4. On your own, create the other circle and complete the drawing as shown.

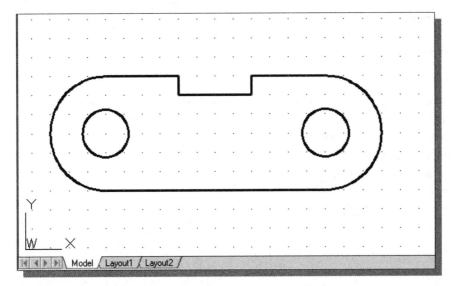

Saving the CAD Design

1. In the *Quick Access Toolbar*, select: **[Save]**

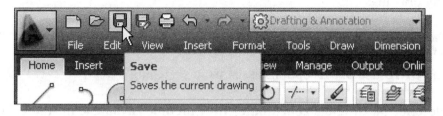

❖ Note the command can also be activated with quick-key combination of **[Ctrl]+[S]**.

2. In the *Save Drawing As* dialog box, select the folder in which you want to store the CAD file and enter **Spacer** in the *File name* box.

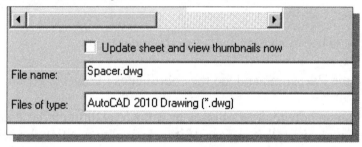

3. Click **Save** in the *Save Drawing As* dialog box to accept the selections and save the file. Note the default file type is DWG, which is the standard AutoCAD drawing format.

Exit AutoCAD 2012

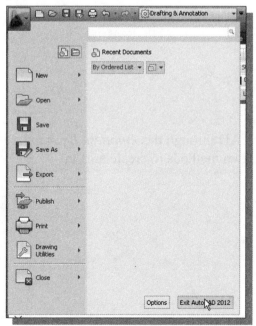

❖ To exit **AutoCAD® 2012**, select **Exit AutoCAD** in the *Menu Bar* or type **QUIT** at the command prompt. Note the command can also be activated with quick-key combination of **[Ctrl]+[Q]**.

Review Questions: (Time: 20 minutes)

1. What are the advantages and disadvantages of using CAD systems to create engineering drawings?

2. What is the default AutoCAD filename extension?

3. How do the **GRID** and **SNAP** options assist us in sketching?

4. List and describe the different **coordinate entry methods** available in AutoCAD?

5. When using the Line command, which option allows us to quickly create a line-segment connecting back to the starting point?

6. List and describe the two types of coordinate systems commonly used for planar geometry.

7. Which key do you use to quickly cancel a command?

8. When you use the Pan command, do the coordinates of objects get changed?

9. Find information on how to draw ellipses in AutoCAD through the *Autodesk Exchange* and create the following arc. If it is desired to position the center of the ellipse to a specific location, which ellipse command is more suitable?

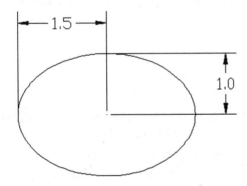

10. Find information on how to draw arcs in AutoCAD through the *Autodesk Exchange* and create the following arc. List and describe two methods to create arcs in AutoCAD.

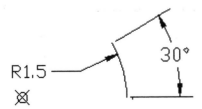

Exercises: (All dimensions are in inches.) (Time: 60 minutes)

1. Angle Spacer

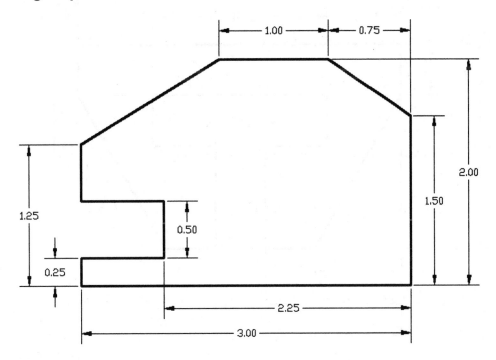

2. Base Plate

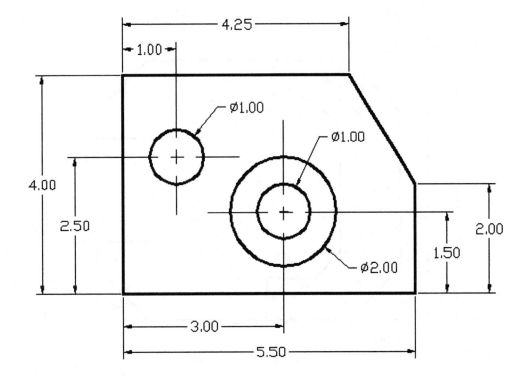

3. T-Clip

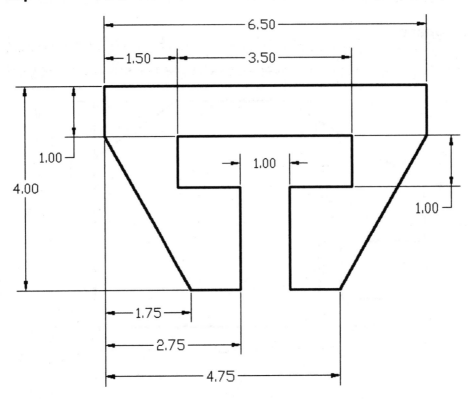

4. Channel Plate

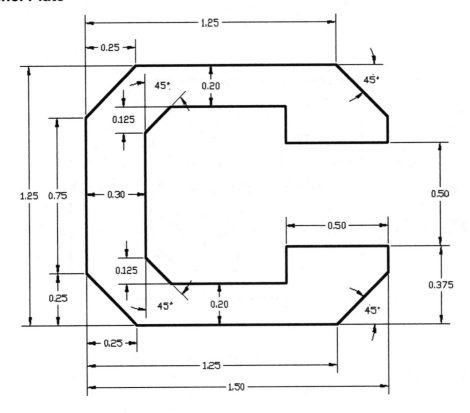

Chapter 2
Basic Object Construction and Dynamic Input

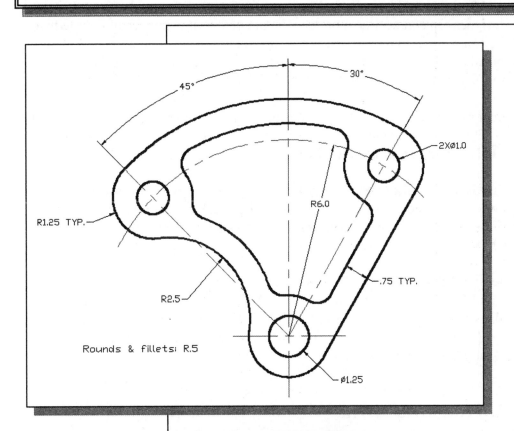

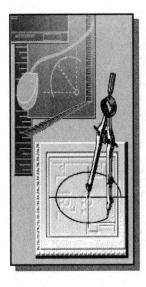

Learning Objectives

♦ **Referencing the WCS**
♦ **Use the Startup dialog box**
♦ **Set up GRID & SNAP intervals**
♦ **Display AutoCAD's toolbars**
♦ **Set up and use OBJECT SNAPS**
♦ **Edit, using the TRIM command**
♦ **Use the POLYGON command**
♦ **Create TTR circles**
♦ **Create Tangent lines**

Introduction

The main characteristic of any CAD system is its ability to create and modify 2D/3D geometric entities quickly and accurately. Most CAD systems provide a variety of object construction and editing tools to relieve the designer of the tedious drudgery of this task, so that the designer can concentrate more on design content. It is important to note that CAD systems can be used to replace traditional drafting with pencil and paper, but the CAD user must have a good understanding of the basic geometric construction techniques to fully utilize the capability of the CAD systems.

One of the major enhancements of AutoCAD® 2006 was the introduction of the *Dynamic Input* feature. This addition, which is also available in AutoCAD® 2012, greatly enhanced the **AutoCAD Heads-up Design™** interface.

The use of the **User Coordinate System (UCS)** and the **World Coordinate System (WCS)** is further discussed in this chapter. In working CAD, one simple approach to creating designs in CAD systems is to create geometry by referencing the **World Coordinate System**. The general procedure of this approach is illustrated in this chapter.

In this chapter, we will examine the *Dynamic Input* options, the basic geometric construction and editing tools provided by **AutoCAD® 2012**. We will first look at the *Dynamic Input* options, also tools such as *UNITS, GRID, SNAP MODE* intervals setup and the *OSNAP* option, followed by construction tools such as circles and polygons; we will also look at the basic Trim command.

Starting Up AutoCAD® 2012

1. Start **AutoCAD® 2012** by selecting the *Autodesk* folder in the **Start** menu as shown. Once the program is loaded into the memory, the **AutoCAD® 2012** drawing screen will appear on the screen.

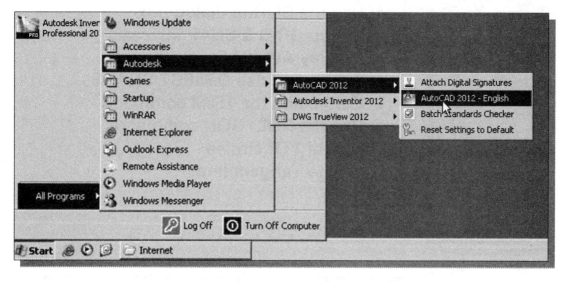

Dynamic Input

In AutoCAD® 2012, the **Dynamic Input** feature provides the user with **visual tooltips** and **entry options** right on the screen.

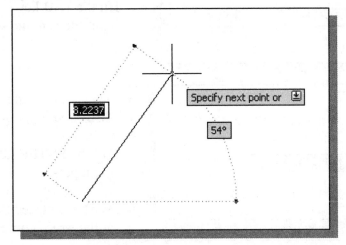

Dynamic Input provides a convenient command interface near the cursor to help the user focus in the graphics area. When *Dynamic Input* is *ON*, tooltips display information near the cursor that is dynamically updated as the cursor moves.

The tooltips also provide a place for user entry when a command is activated. The actions required to complete a command remain the same as those for the command line. Note that **Dynamic Input** is **not** designed to replace the *command line*. The main advantage of using the *Dynamic Input* options is to keep our attention near the cursor.

The *Dynamic Input* features simply enhance the five methods for specifying the locations of points as described in Chapter 1, page 1-18.

1. Switch **ON** only the *Dynamic Input* option by clicking on the button in the *Status Bar* area as shown.

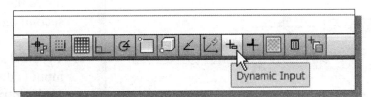

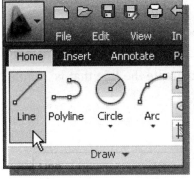

2. Click on the **Line** icon in the *Draw* toolbar. In the command prompt area, the message "*_line Specify first point:*" is displayed.

3. Move the cursor inside the graphics window and notice the displayed tooltip, which shows the coordinates of the cursor position.

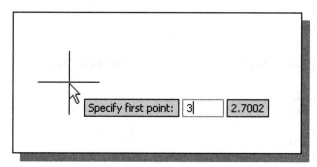

4. Type **3** and notice the input is entered in the first entry box.

5. Hit the **TAB** key once to move the input focus to the second entry box.

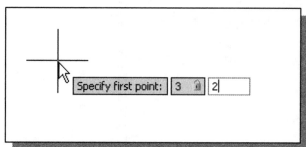

6. Type **2** and notice the input is displayed in the second entry box.

7. Hit the **ENTER** key once to accept the inputs.

❖   We have placed the first endpoint at the world coordinate of 3,2.

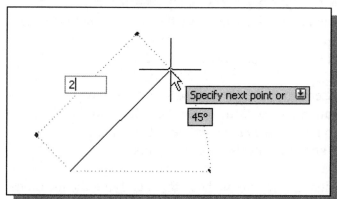

8. Move the cursor upward and toward the right side of the screen. Notice the tooltip is set to use polar coordinates by default.

9. Type **2** and notice the input is displayed in the entry box as shown.

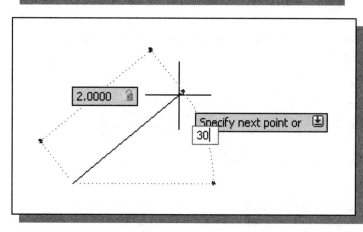

10. Hit the **TAB** key once to move the input focus to the second entry box.

11. Type **30** and notice the input is displayed in the angle entry box.

12. Hit the **ENTER** key once to accept the inputs and create the line that is 2 units long and at an angle of 30 degrees.

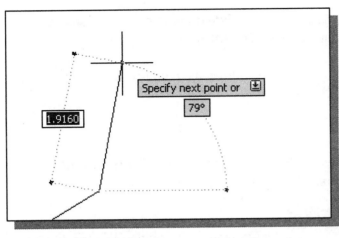

13. Move the cursor upward and toward the right side of the screen. Notice the tooltip is still set to using polar coordinates.

➤ To switch to using the relative Cartesian coordinates input method, use a **comma** as the **specifier** after entering the first number.

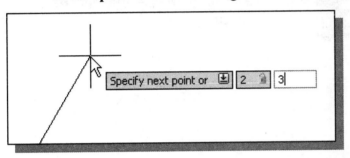

14. Type **2,3** and notice the input option is now set to using relative Cartesian coordinates as shown.

15. Hit the **ENTER** key once to accept the inputs.

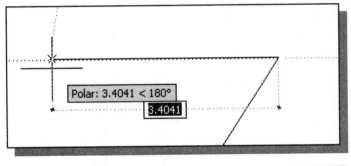

16. Move the cursor toward the right side of the last position until the angle is near 180 degrees as shown.

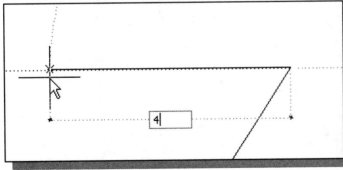

17. Type **4** and notice the input is displayed on the screen.

18. Hit the **ENTER** key once to accept the input and note a horizontal line is created.

➤ In effect, we just created a line using the *Direct Distance* option.

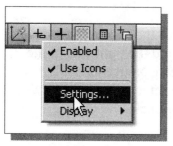

19. In the *Status Bar* area, **right-mouse-click** on *Dynamic Input* and choose **Settings**.

❖ The *Settings* dialog allows us to control what is displayed when *Dynamic Input* is on.

➢ Note that the *Dynamic Input* feature has three components: ***Pointer Input***, ***Dimensional Input***, and ***Dynamic Prompts***.

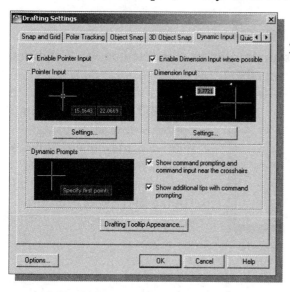

20. On your own, toggle *ON/OFF* the three options and create additional line-segments to see the different effects of the settings.

The *RockerArm* design:

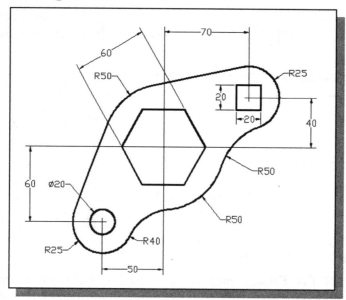

❖ Before continuing to the next page, on your own, make a rough freehand sketch showing the steps that can be used to create the design. Be aware that there are many different approaches to accomplishing the same task.

Activate the Startup option

❖ In **AutoCAD®** **2012**, we can use the *Startup* dialog box to establish different types of drawing settings. The startup dialog box can be activated through the use of the **STARTUP** system variable.

The STARTUP system variable can be set to either 0 or 1:
- 1: displays the *Create New Drawing* dialog box.
- 0: displays the *Select Template* dialog box (default).

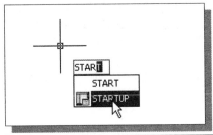

1. In the command prompt area, choose the Startup option from the list or enter the system variable name:
   STARTUP [ENTER]

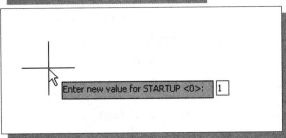

2. Enter **1** as the new value for the *Startup* system variable.

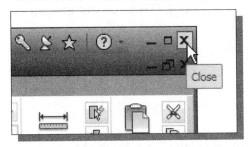

3. To show the effect of the *Startup* option, **exit** AutoCAD by clicking on the **Close** icon as shown.

4. Restart AutoCAD by selecting the **AutoCAD 2012** option through the *Start* menu.

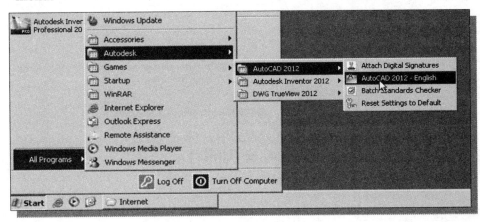

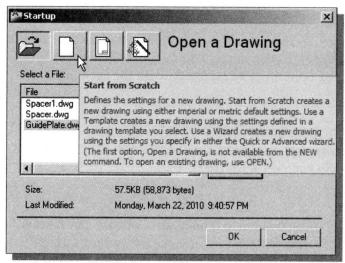

5. The *Startup* dialog box appears on the screen with different options to assist the creation of drawings. Move the cursor on top of the four icons and notice the four options available:
   (1) **Open a drawing**
   (2) **Start from Scratch**
   (3) **Use a Template**
   (4) **Use a Setup Wizard**

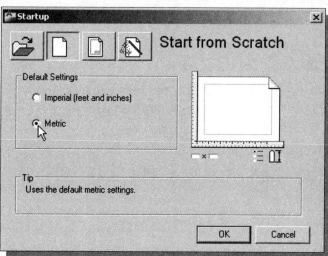

6. In the *Startup* dialog box, select the **Start from Scratch** option as shown in the figure.

7. Choose **Metric** to use the metric settings.

8. Click **OK** to accept the setting.

Drawing Units Display Setup

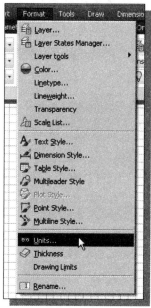

1. On your own, activate the display of the AutoCAD *Menu Bar*. (Refer to page 1-4 for the procedure.)

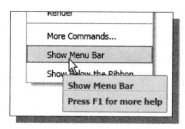

2. Click the *Menu Bar* area, select:
   [Format] → [Units]

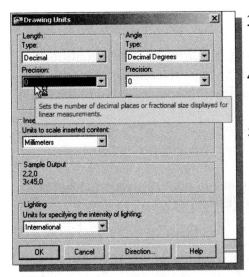

3. Set the *Precision* to **no digits** after the decimal point.

4. Click **OK** to exit the *Drawing Units* dialog box.

5. On your own, adjust the option settings so that only the **Dynamic Input** option is turned *ON* in the *Status Bar* area.

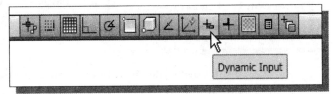

GRID and *SNAP* Intervals Setup

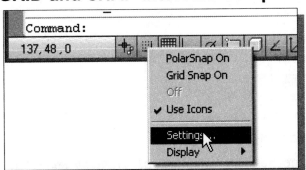

1. In the *Status Bar* area, **right-mouse-click** on *Snap Mode* and choose **[Settings]**

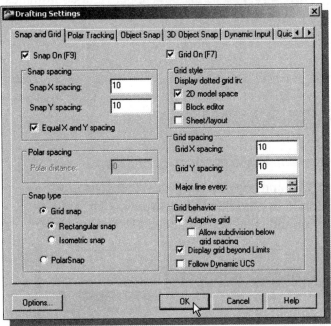

2. In the *Drafting Settings* dialog box, select the **Snap and Grid** tab if it is not the page on top.

3. Change *Grid Spacing* and *Snap Spacing* to **10** for both X and Y directions.

4. Switch *ON* the *Display dotted grid in 2D model Space* option as shown

5. Switch *ON* the *Grid On* and *Snap On* options as shown.

6. Pick **OK** to exit the *Drawing Units* dialog box.

Drawing Area Setup

❖ Next, we will set up the **Drawing Limits**; setting the Drawing Limits controls the extents of the display of the *grid*. It also serves as a visual reference that marks the working area. Note that this setting can also be adjusted through the use of the command prompt area.

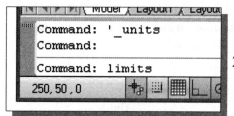

1. Click inside the *command prompt* area.

2. Inside the command prompt area, enter **Limits** and press the **[Enter]** key.

3. In the command prompt area, near the bottom of the AutoCAD drawing screen, the message "*Reset Model Space Limits: Specify lower left corner or [On/Off] <0,0>:*" is displayed. Enter **-200,-150** through the *Dynamic Input* entry boxes.

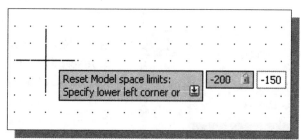

4. In the command prompt area, the message "*Specify upper right corner <420,297>:*" is displayed. Enter **200,150** as the new upper right coordinates as shown.

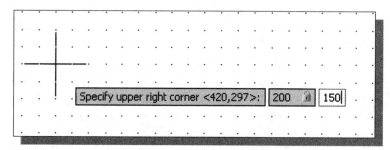

5. On your own, use the *Menu Bar* and confirm the **[View]** → **[Display]** → **[UCS Icon]** → **[Origin]** option is switched **ON** as shown. (The little checked icon next to the option indicates it is switched **ON**.)

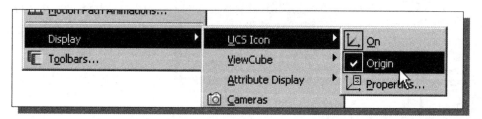

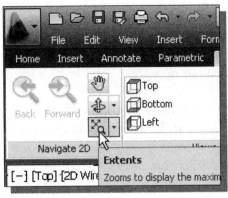

6. On your own, use the **Zoom Extent** command, under the **View** tab, to reset the display.

❖ Notice the *UCS Icon*, which is aligned to the origin, is displayed at the center of the graphics window.

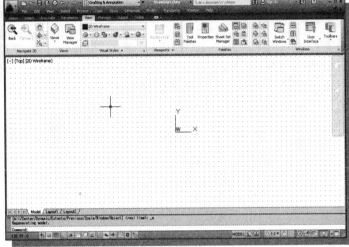

Referencing the World Coordinate System

Design modeling software is becoming more powerful and user friendly, yet the system still does only what the user tells it to do. When using a geometric modeler, we therefore need to have a good understanding of what the inherent limitations are. We should also have a good understanding of what we want to do and what to expect, as the results are based on what is available.

In most geometric modelers, objects are located and defined in what is usually called **world space** or **global space**. Although a number of different coordinate systems can be used to create and manipulate objects in a 3D modeling system, the objects are typically defined and stored using the *world space*. The *world space* is usually a **3D Cartesian coordinate system** that the user cannot change or manipulate.

In most engineering designs, models can be very complex, and it would be tedious and confusing if only one coordinate system were available in CAD systems. Practical CAD systems provide the user with definable **Local Coordinate Systems (LCS)** or **User Coordinate Systems (UCS)**, which are measured relative to the world coordinate system. Once a local coordinate system is defined, we can then create geometry in terms of this more convenient system. For most CAD systems, the default construction coordinate system is initially aligned to the world coordinate system.

In AutoCAD, the default **User Coordinate System (UCS)** is initially aligned to the XY plane of the **World Coordinate System (WCS)**. One simple approach to creating designs in CAD systems is to create geometry by referencing the **World Coordinate System**. The general procedure of this approach is illustrated in the following sections.

Creating *Circles*

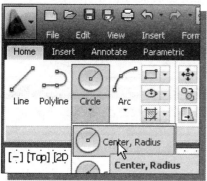

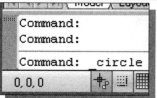

1. Click on and switch back to the **Home** tab in the *Ribbon* tabs and panels area.

2. Select the **Circle – Center, Radius** command icon in the *Draw* toolbar. In the command prompt area, the message "*_circle Specify center point for the circle or [3P/2P/Ttr (tan tan radius)]:*" is displayed.

3. Select the **origin** of the world coordinate system as the center point location.

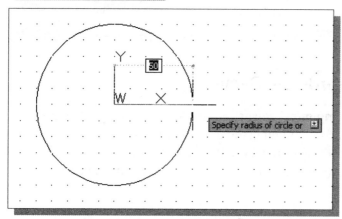

4. In the command prompt area, the message "*Specify radius of circle or [Diameter]:*" is displayed. AutoCAD expects us to identify the radius of the circle. Set the radius to **50** by observing the tooltips as shown.

5. Hit the [**SPACE BAR**] once to repeat the circle command.

6. On your own, select **70,40** as the absolute coordinate values of the center point coordinates of the second circle.

7. Set the value of the radius to **25**.

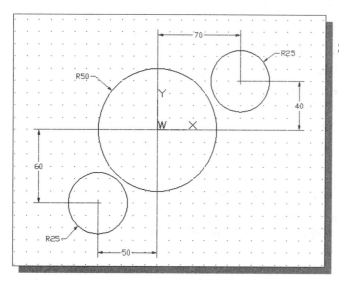

8. On your own, repeat the above procedure and create another circle (radius **25**) at absolute coordinates of **-50,-60** as shown in the figure.

Object Snap Toolbar

1. Move the cursor to the *Menu Bar* area and choose **[Tools] → [Toolbars] → [AutoCAD]**.

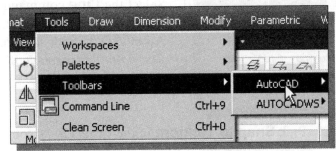

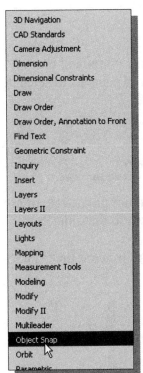

❖ AutoCAD provides 44 predefined toolbars for access to frequently used commands, settings, and modes. A *checkmark* (next to the item) in the list identifies the toolbars that are currently displayed on the screen.

2. Select **Object Snap**, with the left-mouse-button, to display the *Object Snap* toolbar on the screen.

❖ **Object Snap** is an extremely powerful construction tool available on most CAD systems. During an entity's creation operations, we can snap the cursor to points on objects such as endpoints, midpoints, centers, and intersections. For example, we can turn on **Object Snap** and quickly draw a line to the center of a circle, the midpoint of a line segment, or the intersection of two lines.

3. Move the cursor over the icons in the *Object Snap* toolbar and read the description of each icon.

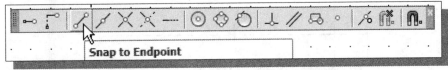

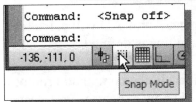

4. We will next turn **OFF** the *GRID SNAP* option by toggling off the **SNAP Mode** button in the *Status Bar* area.

5. On your own, reset the option buttons in the *Status Bar* area, so that only the *GRID DISPLAY* option is switched **ON**.

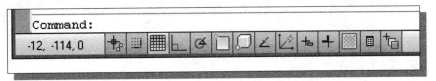

Using the *LINE* command

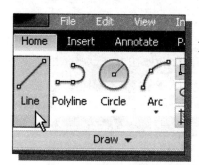

1. Select the **Line** command icon in the *Draw* toolbar. In the command prompt area, near the bottom of the AutoCAD drawing screen, the message "*_line Specify first point:*" is displayed.

2. Pick **Snap to Tangent** in the *Object Snap* toolbar. In the command prompt area, the message "*_tan to*" is displayed. AutoCAD now expects us to select a circle or an arc on the screen.

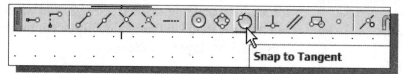

❖ The **Snap to Tangent** option allows us to snap to the point on a circle or arc that, when connected to the last point, forms a line tangent to that object.

3. Pick a location that is near the top left side of the smaller circle on the right; note the tangent symbol is displayed as shown.

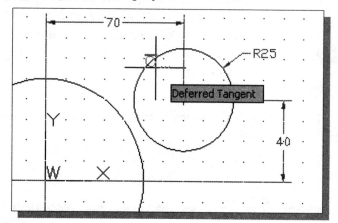

❖ Note that the note "Deferred Tangent" indicates that AutoCAD will calculate the tangent location when the other endpoint of the line is defined.

4. Pick **Snap to Tangent** in the *Object Snap* toolbar. In the command prompt area, the message "*_tan to*" is displayed. AutoCAD now expects us to select a circle or an arc on the screen.

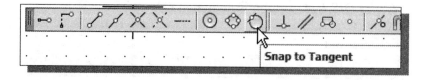

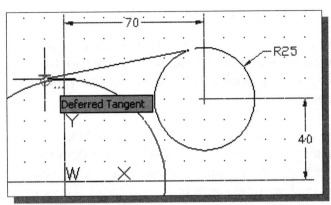

5. Pick a location that is near the top left side of the center circle; note the tangent symbol is displayed as shown.

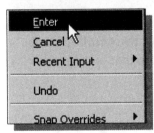

6. Inside the graphics window, **right-mouse-click** to activate the option menu and select **Enter** with the left-mouse-button to end the **Line** command.

❖ A line tangent to both circles is constructed as shown in the figure.

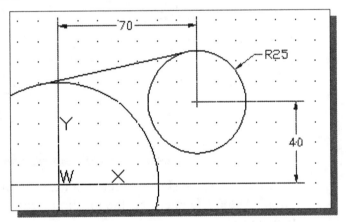

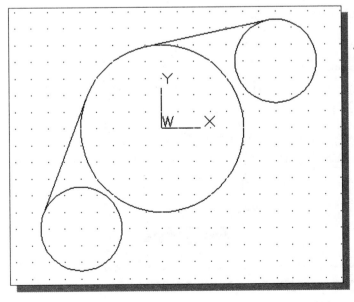

7. On your own, repeat the above steps and create the other tangent line between the center circle and the circle on the left. Your drawing should appear as the figure.

Creating *TTR Circles*

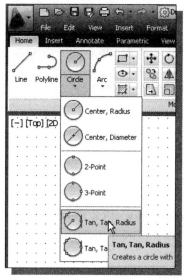

1. Select the **Circle** command icon in the *Draw* toolbar. In the command prompt area, the message "*Specify center point for circle or [3P/2P/Ttr (tan tan radius)]:*" is displayed.

2. Inside the graphics window, right-mouse-click to activate the option menu and select the **Ttr (tan tan radius)** option. This option allows us to create a circle that is tangent to two objects.

3. Pick a location near the **bottom of the smaller circle** on the right. We will create a circle that is tangent to this circle and the center circle.

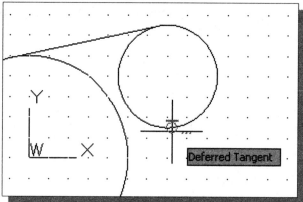

4. Pick the **center circle** by selecting a location that is near the right side of the circle. AutoCAD interprets the locations we selected as being near the tangency.

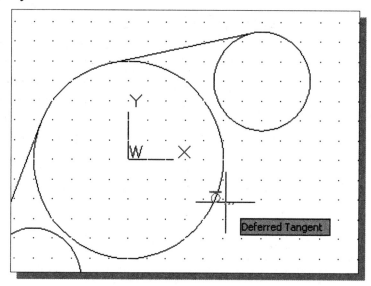

5. In the command prompt area, the message *"Specify radius of circle"* is displayed. Enter **50** as the radius of the circle.

Specify radius of circle: **50 [ENTER]**

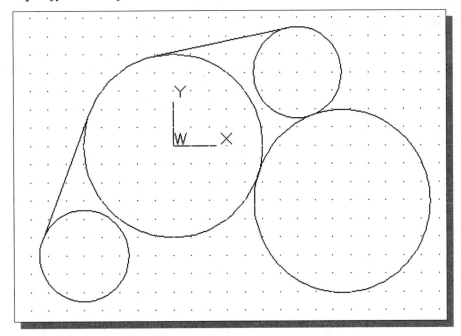

6. On your own, repeat the above steps and create the other TTR circle (radius **40**). Your drawing should appear as the figure below.

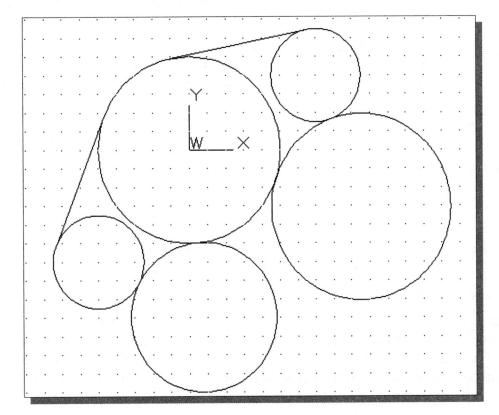

Using the *TRIM* Command

- The **Trim** command shortens an object so that it ends precisely at a selected boundary.

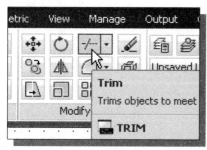

1. Select the **Trim** command icon in the *Modify* toolbar, click on the down-triangle to display additional icons as shown. In the command prompt area, the message "*Select boundary edges... Select objects:*" is displayed.

- First, we will select the objects that define the boundary edges to which we want to trim the object.

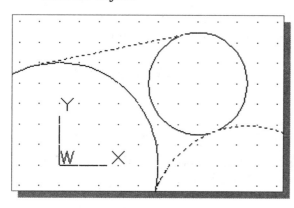

2. Pick the tangent line connecting the center circle and the top right circle.

3. Pick the lower right circle. The two selected entities are highlighted as shown in the figure.

4. Inside the graphics window, **right-mouse-click** once to proceed with the Trim command.

5. The message "*Select object to trim or shift-select object to extend or [Project/Edge/Undo]:*" is displayed in the command prompt area. Pick the **left** section of the upper right circle and note the selected portion is trimmed as shown.

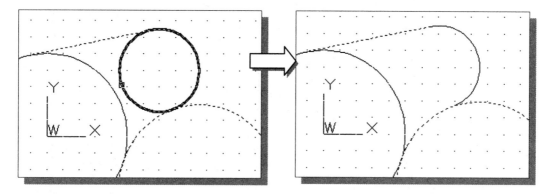

- ❖ In AutoCAD, the Trim command requires first selection of objects that define the cutting edges at which an object is to stop. Valid cutting edge objects include most 2D geometry such as lines, arcs, circles, ellipses, polylines, splines, and text. For 3D objects, a 2D projection method is used where objects are projected onto the XY plane of the current user coordinate system (UCS).

6. Select the upper right side of the center circle to remove the selected portion.

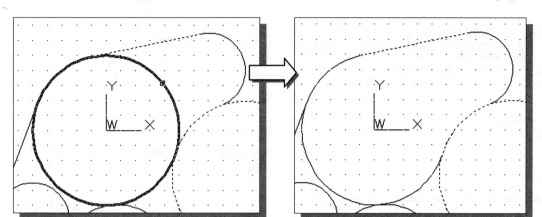

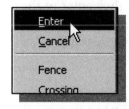

7. Inside the graphics window, **right-mouse-click** to activate the option menu and select **Enter** to end the Trim command.

8. Hit the **[SPACE BAR]** once to repeat the **Trim** command.

9. Select the two arcs that were trimmed as the two cutting edges and trim the lower section of the TTR circle as shown.

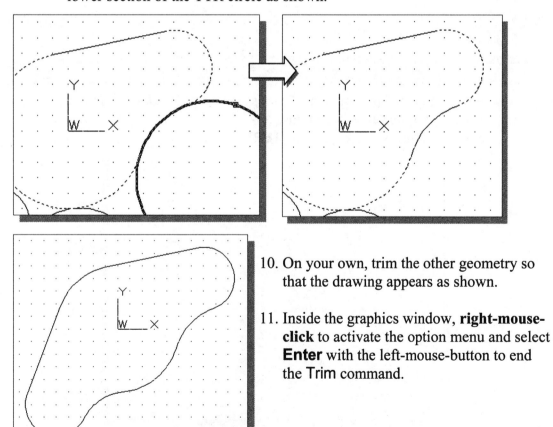

10. On your own, trim the other geometry so that the drawing appears as shown.

11. Inside the graphics window, **right-mouse-click** to activate the option menu and select **Enter** with the left-mouse-button to end the Trim command.

Using the *POLYGON* command

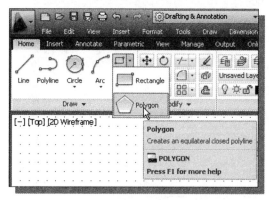

1. Select the **Polygon** command icon in the *Draw* toolbar. Click on the triangle icon next to the rectangle icon to display the additional icon list.

2. Enter **6** to create a six-sided hexagon. *polygon Enter number of sides <4>:* **6** [ENTER]

3. The message "*Specify center of polygon or [Edge]:*" is displayed. Since the center of the large circle is aligned to the origin of the WCS, the center of the polygon can be positioned using several methods. Set the center point to the origin by entering the absolute coordinates. *Specify center of polygon or [Edge]:* **0,0** [ENTER]

4. In the command prompt area, the message "*Enter an option [Inscribed in circle/Circumscribed about circle] <I>:*" is displayed. Enter **c** to select the *Circumscribed about circle* option.

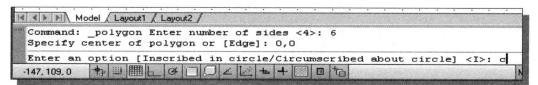

5. In the command prompt area, the message *Specify radius of circle:*" is displayed. Enter **30** as the radius. *Specify radius of circle :* **30** [ENTER]

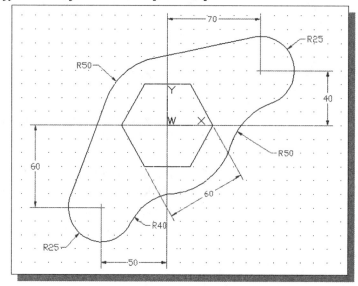

❖ Note that the polygon option [Inscribed in circle/Circumscribed about circle] allows us to create either **flat to flat** or **corner to corner** distance.

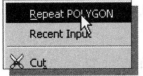

6. Inside the graphics window, **right-mouse-click** to activate the option menu and select **Repeat Polygon**. In the command prompt area, the message "*_polygon Enter number of sides <6>:*" is displayed.

7. Enter **4** to create a four-sided polygon.
   _polygon Enter number of sides <6>: **4 [ENTER]**

8. In the command prompt area, the message "*Specify center of polygon or [Edge]:*" is displayed. Let's use the *Object Snap* options to locate its center location. Pick **Snap to Center** in the *Object Snap* toolbar as shown.

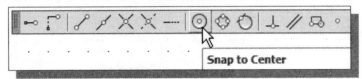

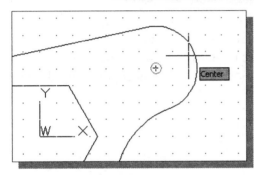

9. Move the cursor on top of the arc on the right and notice the center point is automatically highlighted. Select the arc to accept the highlighted location.

10. Inside the graphics window, **right-mouse-click** to activate the option menu and select **Circumscribed about circle**.

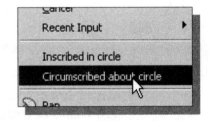

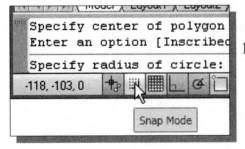

11. Switch *ON* the *GRID SNAP* option in the *Status Bar* as shown.

12. Create a square by selecting one of the adjacent grid points next to the center point as shown. Note that the orientation of the polygon can also be adjusted as the cursor is moved to other locations.

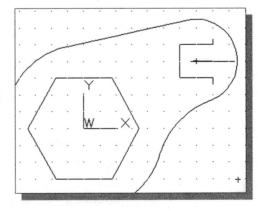

Creating a Concentric *Circle*

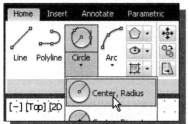

1. Select the **Circle** command icon in the *Draw* toolbar. In the command prompt area, the message "*Specify center point for circle or [3P/2P/Ttr (tan tan radius)]:*" is displayed.

2. Let's use the *Object Snap* options to assure the center location is aligned properly. Pick **Snap to Center** in the *Object Snap* toolbar as shown.

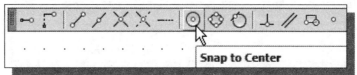

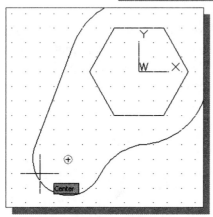

3. Move the cursor on top of the lower arc on the left and notice the center point is automatically highlighted. Select the arc to accept the highlighted location.

4. In the command prompt area, the message "*Specify radius of circle <25>*" is displayed. Enter **10** to complete the Circle command.
   Specify radius of circle <25>: **10** **[ENTER]**

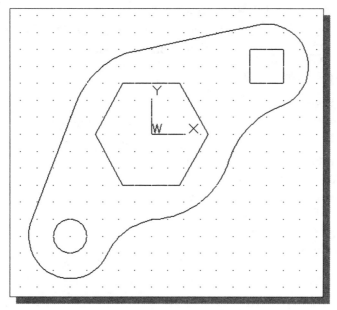

Using the QuickCal calculator to Measure Distance and Angle

- AutoCAD also provides several tools that will allow us to measure distance, area, perimeter, and even mass properties. With the use of the *Object Snap* options, getting measurements of the completed design can be done very quickly.

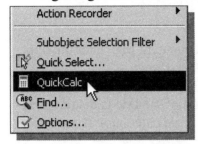

1. Inside the graphics window, **right-mouse-click** once to bring up the option menu.

2. Select **QuickCalc** in the option menu as shown.

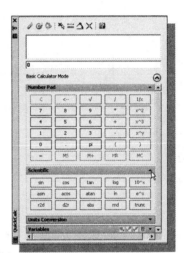

❖ Note that the QuickCalc option brings up the AutoCAD calculator, which can be used to perform a full range of mathematical, scientific, and geometric calculations. We can also use QuickCalc to create and use variables, as well as to convert units of measurement.

3. Click the **Measure Distance** icon, which is located on the top section of the *QuickCalc* calculator pad.

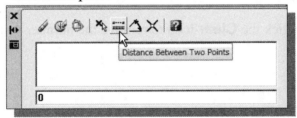

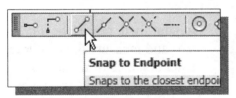

4. Pick **Snap to Endpoint** in the *Object Snap* toolbar.

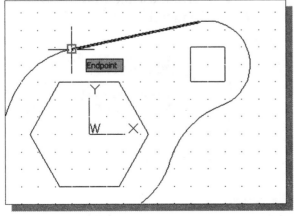

5. Select the tangent line, near the lower endpoint, as shown.

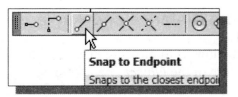

6. Pick **Snap to Endpoint** in the *Object Snap* toolbar.

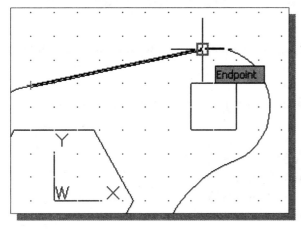

7. Select the tangent line, near the upper endpoint, as shown.

❖ The length of the line is displayed in the *Quickcalc* calculator as shown.

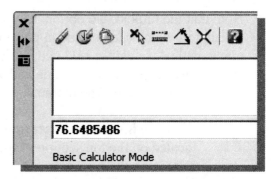

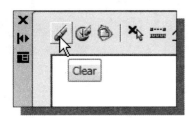

8. Click the **Clear** icon to remove the number displayed.

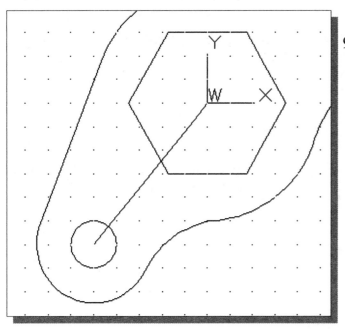

9. On your own, repeat the above steps and measure the center to center distance of the lower region of the design as shown. (Hint: use the **Snap to Center** option.)

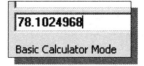

10. Click the **Measure Angle** icon, which is located on the top section of the *QuickCalc* calculator pad.

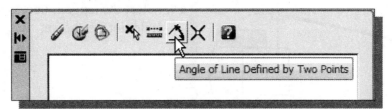

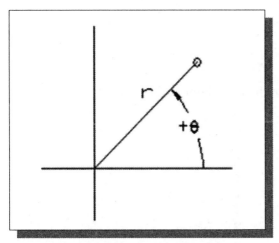

❖ Note that this option allows us to measure the angle between the horizontal axis and the line formed by the selected two points. A positive angle indicates a counterclockwise direction.

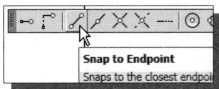

11. Pick **Snap to Endpoint** in the *Object Snap* toolbar.

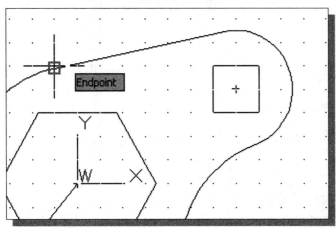

12. Select the tangent line, near the lower endpoint, as shown.

13. Pick **Snap to Endpoint** in the *Object Snap* toolbar.

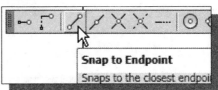

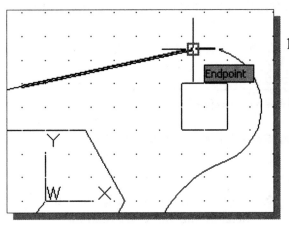

14. Select the tangent line, near the upper endpoint, as shown.

➢ The measured angle is displayed in the calculator pad as shown.

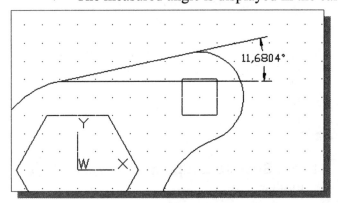

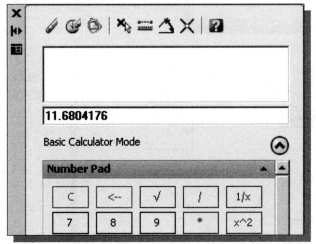

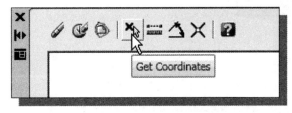

15. On your own, experiment with the available **Get Coordinates** options.

➢ Note also that the QuickCalc calculator can remain active while you are using the other AutoCAD commands.

Saving the CAD file

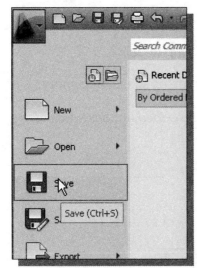

1. In the *Application Menu*, select:

    [Application] → [Save]

    ❖ Note the command can also be activated with quick-key combination of **[Ctrl]+[S]**.

2. In the *Save Drawing As* dialog box, select the folder in which you want to store the CAD file and enter **RockerArm** in the *File name* box.

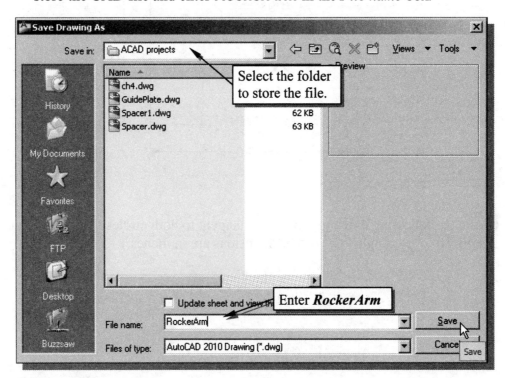

3. Pick **Save** in the *Save Drawing As* dialog box to accept the selections and save the file.

Exit AutoCAD

*   To exit **AutoCAD® 2012**, select **Exit AutoCAD** from the *Application Menu* or type **QUIT** at the command prompt.

Review Questions: (Time: 20 minutes)

1. Describe the procedure to activate the AutoCAD **Startup** option.

2. List and describe three options in the AutoCAD *Object Snap* toolbar.

3. Which AutoCAD command can we use to remove a portion of an existing entity?

4. Describe the difference between the *circumscribed* and *inscribed* options when using the AutoCAD **Polygon** command.

5. Create the following triangle and fill in the blanks: Length = ____, Angle = ____. (Dimensions are in inches.)

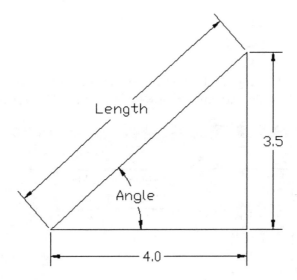

6. Create the following drawing; line **AB** is tangent to both circles. Fill in the blanks: Length = _____, Angle = _____. (Dimensions are in inches.)

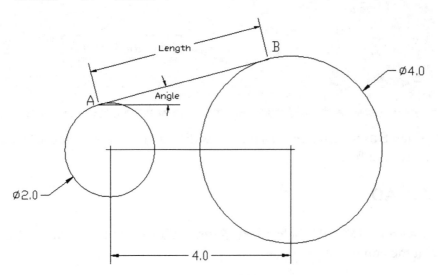

Exercises:

(Unless otherwise specified, dimensions are in inches. Time: 90 minutes.)

1. Adjustable Support

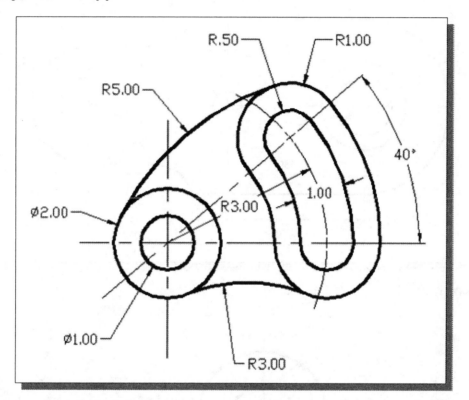

2. V-Slide Plate (The design has two sets of parallel lines with implied tangency.)

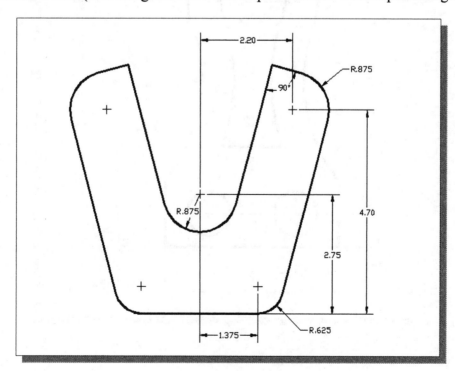

3. Swivel Base (Dimensions are in Millimeters.)

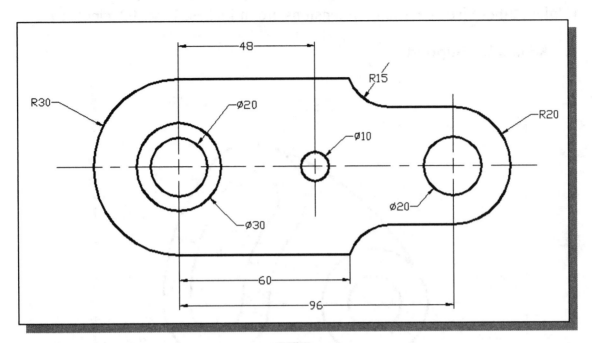

4. Sensor Mount

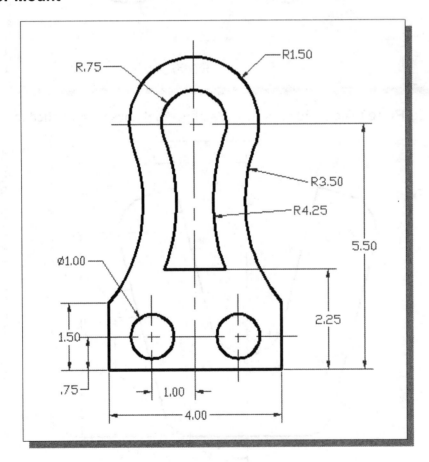

5. Flat Hook (Dimensions are in Millimeters. Thickness: 25 mm.)

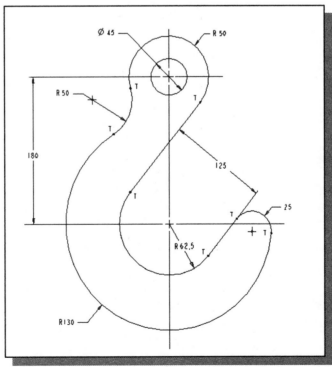

NOTES:

Chapter 3
Geometric Construction and Editing Tools

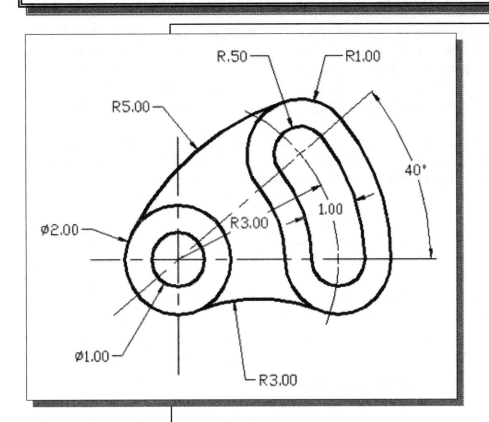

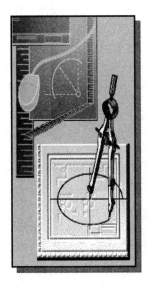

Learning Objectives

- ♦ **Set up the display of Drawing Units**
- ♦ **Display AutoCAD's toolbars**
- ♦ **Set up and use OBJECT SNAPS**
- ♦ **Edit, using EXTEND and TRIM**
- ♦ **Use the FILLET command**
- ♦ **Create parallel geometric entities**
- ♦ **Using the PEDIT command**
- ♦ **Use the EXPLODE command**

Geometric Constructions

The creation of designs usually involves the manipulations of geometric shapes. Traditionally, manual graphical construction uses simple hand tools like a T-square, straightedge, scales, triangles, compass, dividers, pencils, and paper. The manual drafting tools are designed specifically to assist the construction of geometric shapes. For example, the T-square and drafting machine can be used to construct parallel and perpendicular lines very easily and quickly. Today, modern CAD systems provide designers much better control and accuracy in the construction of geometric shapes.

In technical drawings, many of the geometric shapes are constructed with specific geometric properties, such as perpendicularity, parallelism and tangency. For example, in the drawing below, quite a few implied geometric properties are present.

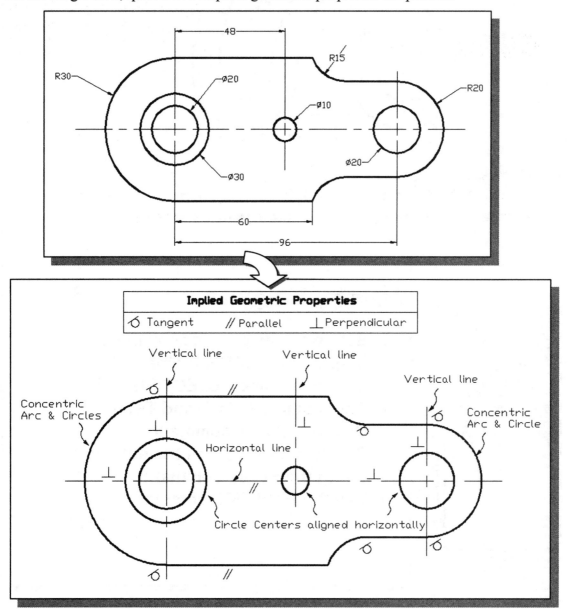

Starting Up AutoCAD® 2012

1. Select the AutoCAD 2012 option on the *Program* menu or select the AutoCAD 2012 icon on the *Desktop*. Once the program is loaded into the memory, the **AutoCAD® 2012** drawing screen will appear on the screen.

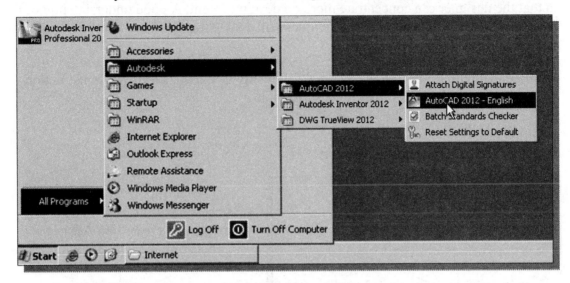

2. In the *Startup* window, select **Start from Scratch**, as shown in the figure below.

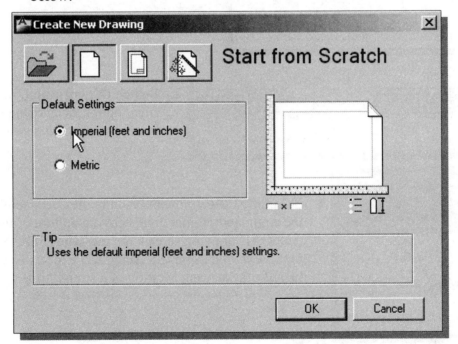

3. In the *Default Settings* section, pick **Imperial (feet and inches)** as the drawing units.

4. Pick **OK** in the *Startup* dialog box to accept the selected settings.

Geometric Construction – CAD Method

The main characteristic of any CAD system is its ability to create and modify 2D/3D geometric entities quickly and accurately. Most CAD systems provide a variety of object construction and editing tools to relieve the designer of the tedious drudgery of this task, so that the designer can concentrate more on design content. A good understanding of the computer geometric construction techniques will enable the CAD users to fully utilize the capability of the CAD systems.

➢ Note that with CAD systems, besides following the classic geometric construction methods; quite a few options are also feasible.

- ### Bisection of a Line or Arc

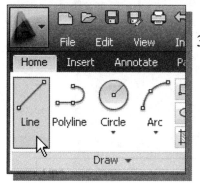

1. Create an arbitrary arc **AB** at any angle, and create line **AB** by connecting the two endpoints of the arc.

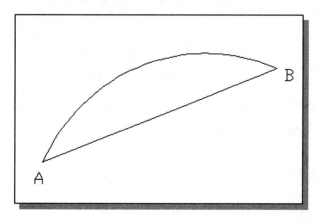

2. Switch **ON** only the *Dynamic Input* option by clicking on the buttons in the *Status Bar* area as shown.

3. Select the **Line** command icon in the *Draw* toolbar. In the command prompt area, near the bottom of the AutoCAD drawing screen, the message "*_line Specify first point:*" is displayed. AutoCAD expects us to identify the starting location of a straight line.

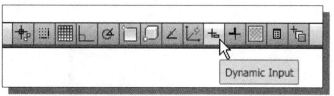

4. Pick **Snap to Perpendicular** in the *Object Snap* toolbar. In the command prompt area, the message "*_per to*" is displayed.

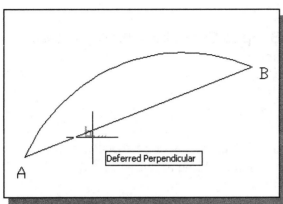

5. Select line **AB** at any position.

❖ Note the tooltip *Deferred Perpendicular* is displayed indicating the construction is deferred until all inputs are completed.

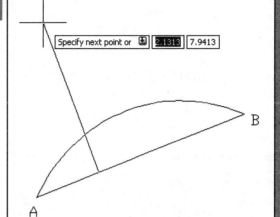

6. Select an arbitrary point above the line as shown.

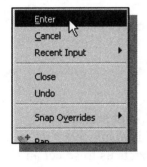

7. Inside the graphics window, **right-mouse-click** to activate the option menu and select **Enter** with the left-mouse-button to end the **Line** command.

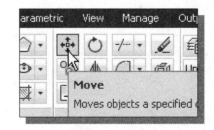

8. Select **Move** in the *Modify* toolbar as shown.

9. Select the perpendicular line we just created.

❖ In the command prompt area, the message: "*Specify the base point or [Displacement]*" is displayed. AutoCAD expects us to select a reference point as the base point for moving the selected object.

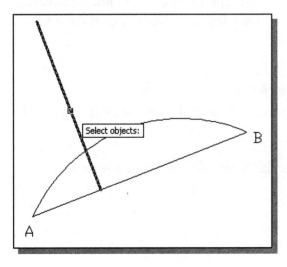

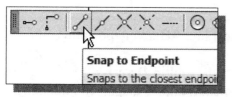

10. Pick **Snap to Endpoint** in the *Object Snap* toolbar.

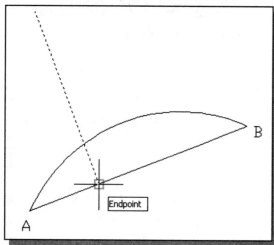

11. Select the lower **Endpoint** of the selected line as shown.

12. Move the cursor inside the graphics window, and notice the line is moved to the new cursor location on the screen,

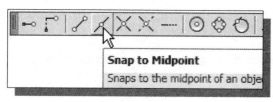

13. Pick **Snap to Midpoint** in the *Object Snap* toolbar.

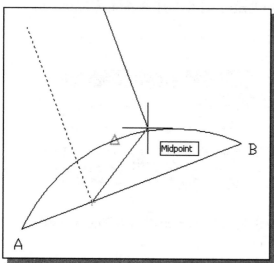

❖ In the command prompt area, the message "*_mid to*" is displayed. AutoCAD now expects us to select an existing arc or line on the screen.

14. Select the arc to move the line to the midpoint of the arc. Note that the midpoint of an arc or a line is displayed when the cursor is on top of the object.

15. On your own, repeat the above process and move the perpendicular line to the midpoint of line **AB**.

➢ The constructed bisecting line is perpendicular to line **AB** and passes through the midpoint of the line or arc **AB**.

- ## Bisection of an Angle

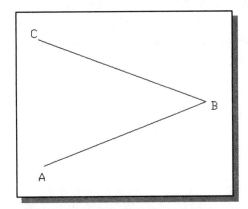

1. Create an arbitrary angle **ABC** as shown in the figure.

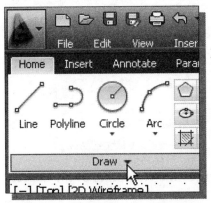

2. Click once with the left-mouse-button on the small triangle in the titlebar of the *Draw* toolbar as shown.

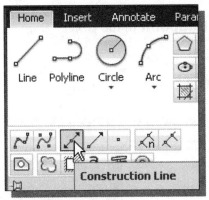

3. Select the **Construction Line** icon in the *Draw* toolbar. In the command prompt area, the message "*_xline Specify a point or [Hor/Ver/Ang/Bisect/ Offset]:*" is displayed.

➤ *Construction lines* are lines that extend to infinity. Construction lines are usually used as references for creating other objects.

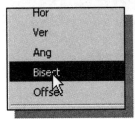

4. Inside the graphics window, **right-mouse-click** once to bring up the option menu.

5. Select **Bisect** from the option list as shown. In the command prompt area, the message "*Specify angle vertex point:*" is displayed.

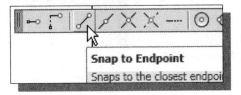

6. Pick **Snap to Endpoint** in the *Object Snap* toolbar.

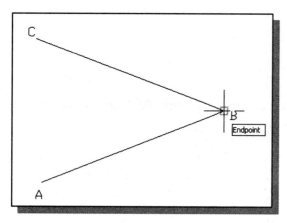

7. Select the vertex point of the angle as shown. In the command prompt area, the message "*Specify angle start point:*" is displayed.

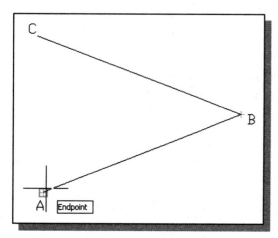

8. Pick **Snap to Endpoint** in the *Object Snap* toolbar.

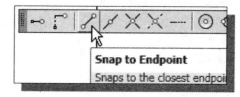

9. Select one of the endpoints of the angle.

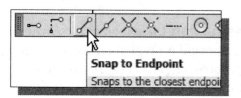

10. Pick **Snap to Endpoint** in the *Object Snap* toolbar.

11. Select the other endpoint of the angle.

➢ Note that the constructed bisection line divides the angle into two equal parts.

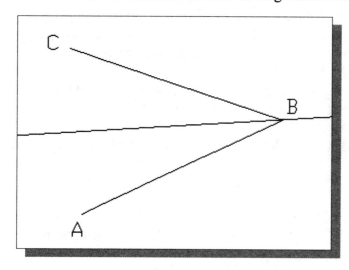

• Transfer of an Angle

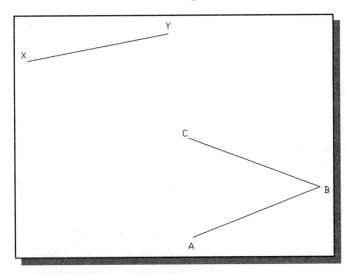

1. Create an arbitrary angle ABC and a separate line **XY** as shown in the figure.

> Besides using the classical transfer method (see page 3-12), CAD systems provide several options to allow the user to accurately measure any constructed objects. In this section, we will use the QuickCalc option to transfer the angle.

2. Select **Copy** in the *Modify* toolbar as shown.

3. Select line **XY** as the object to be copied.

4. **Right-mouse-click** once to proceed with the Copy command.

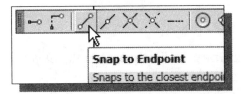

5. Pick **Snap to Endpoint** in the *Object Snap* toolbar.

6. Select point **X** as the base point.

7. Use the **Snap to Endpoint** option and select point **X** again to place another line on top of line **XY**.

8. Hit the **ENTER** key once to end the Copy command.

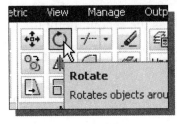

9. Select **Rotate** in the *Draw* toolbar as shown.

10. Select one of the two lines at **XY**.

11. **Right-mouse-click** once to proceed with the Rotate command.

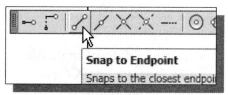

12. Pick **Snap to Endpoint** in the *Object Snap* toolbar.

13. Select point **X** as the base point for the rotation.

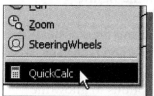

14. Inside the graphics window, **right-mouse-click** once to bring up the option menu.

15. Select **QuickCalc** in the option menu as shown.

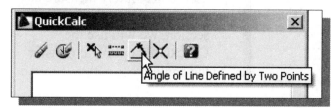

16. Select **Angle of Line Defined by Two Points** as shown.

➢ Note the **Distance** option is also available in the toolbar region.

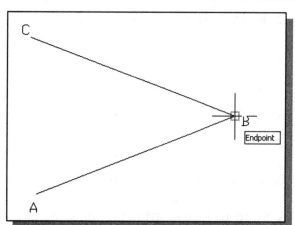

17. Pick **Snap to Endpoint** in the *Object Snap* toolbar.

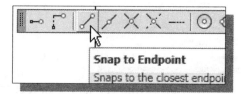

18. Select the vertex, point **B**, of the angle **ABC** as shown.

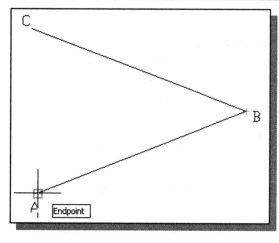

19. Pick **Snap to Endpoint** in the *Object Snap* toolbar.

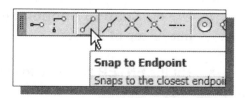

20. Select point **A** as the second point to measure the angle as shown.

➢ The default system for measuring angles in **AutoCAD® 2012** defines positive angular values as counterclockwise from the positive X-axis.

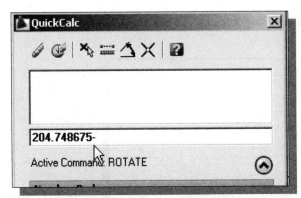

21. Enter a **minus sign** behind the displayed angle in the *QuickCalc* window.

➢ Note the display of Active Command: Rotate in the *QuickCalc* window.

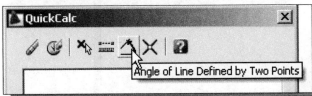

22. Select the **Angle of Line Defined by Two Points** option as shown.

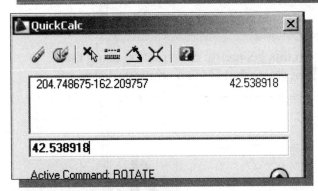

23. Repeat the above process and measure the angle formed by line **BC** and the positive X-axis.

24. Press the **ENTER** key once to calculate the difference between the two values, which is the angle formed by line **AB** and line **BC**.

25. Enter a **minus sign** in front of the calculated value in the *QuickCalc* window as shown.

➢ The minus sign is used to create the new line in the clock-wise direction. (We will rotate the line in a clockwise direction relative to the current **XY** line.)

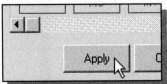

26. Click **Apply** to transfer the calculated value to the command prompt area.

➢ The calculated value is now transferred in the command prompt area.

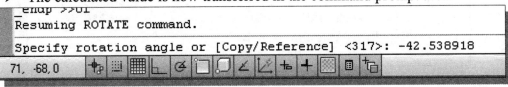

```
_endp >>ot
Resuming ROTATE command.

Specify rotation angle or [Copy/Reference] <317>: -42.538918
```

71, -68,0

27. Press the **ENTER** key once to accept the displayed value and complete the **Rotate** command.

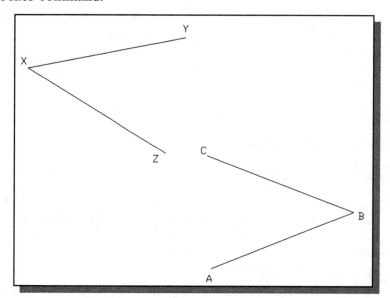

➢ You are also encouraged to perform this geometric construction using the classical method as described below. (Note that R is an arbitrary distance.)

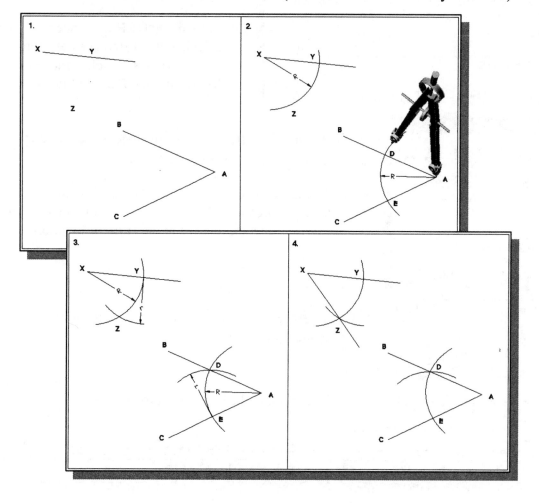

- ## Dividing a Given Line into a Number of Equal Parts

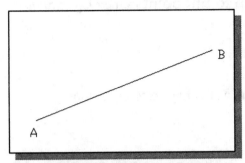

1. Create a line **AB** at an arbitrary angle; the line is to be divided into five equal parts.

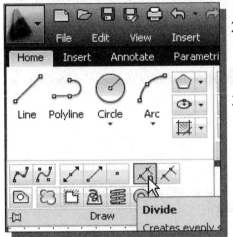

2. From the *Draw* toolbar, select:

   [Divide]

3. Select line **AB**. In the message area, the message "*Enter the number of segments or [Block]:*" is displayed.

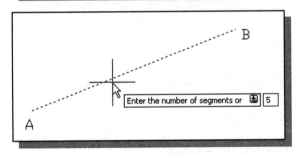

4. Enter **5** as the number of segments needed.

5. On your own, create an arbitrary short line segment at point **A**.

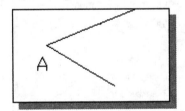

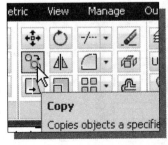

6. Select **Copy** in the *Modify* toolbar as shown.

7. Select the short line as the object to be copied.

8. **Right-mouse-click** once to proceed with the Copy command.

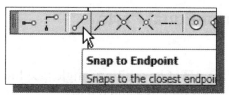

9. Pick **Snap to Endpoint** in the *Object Snap* toolbar.

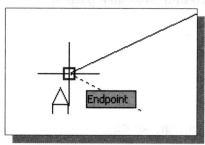

10. **Select** point **A** as the base reference point.

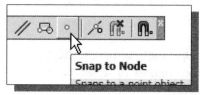

11. Pick **Snap to Node** in the *Object Snap* toolbar.

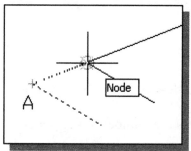

12. Move the cursor along line **AB**, and select the next node point as shown.

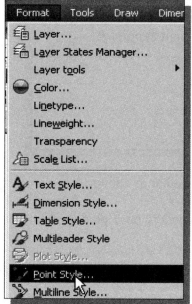

➢ We can also change the display of the created Points.

13. In the *Menu Bar*, select:

   [Format] → [Point Style]

14. In the *Point Style* window, choose the 4th icon in the second row, as shown.

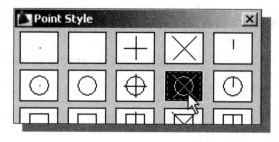

15. Click **OK** to accept the selection and adjust the point style.

- ## Circle through Three Points

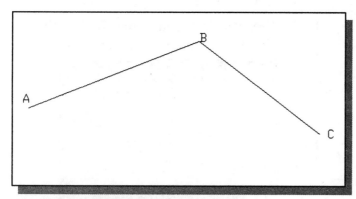

1. Create two arbitrary line segments, **AB** and **BC**, as shown.

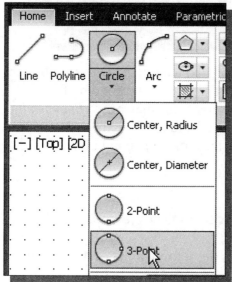

2. Select the **3-Point Circle** command in the *Draw* toolbar as shown.

3. Pick **Snap to Endpoint** in the *Object Snap* toolbar.

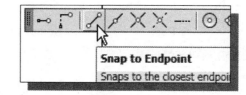

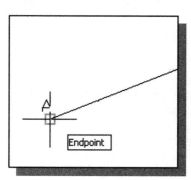

4. Select the first point, point **A**.

5. Repeat the above steps and select points **B** and **C** to create the circle that passes through all three points.

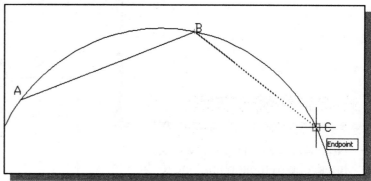

• Line Tangent to a Circle from a Given Point

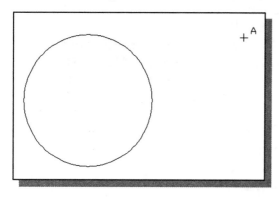

1. Create a circle and a point **A**. (Use the Point command to create point **A**.)

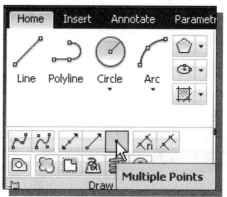

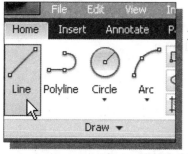

2. Select the **Line** command icon in the *Draw* toolbar. In the command prompt area, near the bottom of the AutoCAD drawing screen, the message "*_line Specify first point:*" is displayed. AutoCAD expects us to identify the starting location of a straight line.

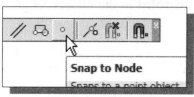

3. Pick **Snap to Node** in the *Object Snap* toolbar.

4. Select point **A** as the starting point of the new line.

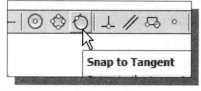

5. Pick **Snap to Tangent** in the *Object Snap* toolbar.

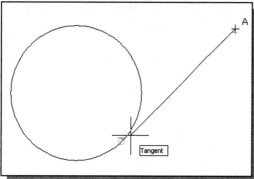

6. Move the cursor on top of the circle and notice the Tangent symbol is displayed.

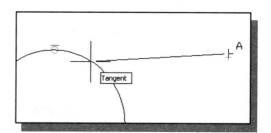

➢ Note that we can create two tangent lines, one to the top and one to the bottom of the circle, from point **A**.

• Circle of a Given Radius Tangent to two Given Lines

Option I: TTR circle

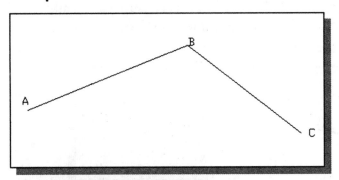

1. Create two arbitrary line segments as shown.

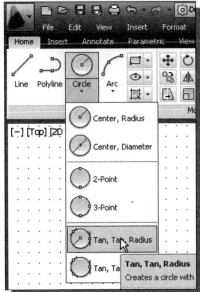

2. Select **TTR Circle** in the *Draw* toolbar as shown.

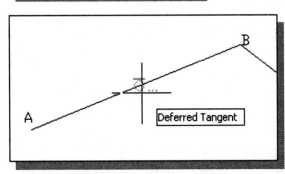

3. Select one of the line segments; note the tangency is deferred until all inputs are completed.

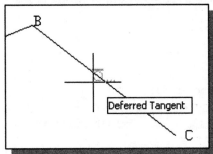

4. Select the other line segment; note the tangency is also deferred until all inputs are completed.

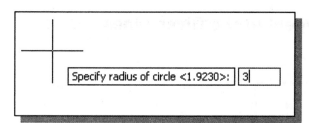

5. Enter **3** as the radius of the circle.

➤ The circle is constructed exactly tangent to both lines.

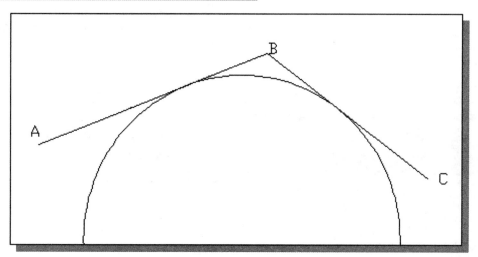

Option II: Fillet command

1. Select the **Undo** icon in the *Standard* toolbar as shown. This will undo the last step, the circle.

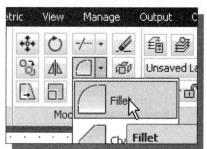

2. Select **Fillet** in the *Modify* toolbar as shown.

3. In the command prompt area, the message "*Select first object or [Undo/Polyline/Radius/Trim/Multiple]*" is displayed. By default *Mode* is set to **Trim** and the current arc *Radius* is set to **0**.

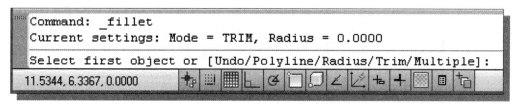

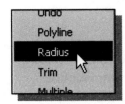

4. Inside the graphics window, **right-mouse-click** once to bring up the option menu.

5. Select **Radius** to adjust the radius of the fillet.

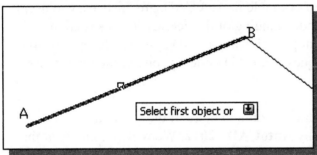

6. Enter **3** as the new radius of the Fillet command.

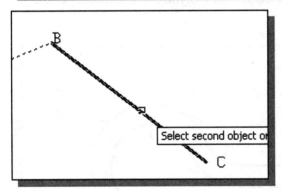

7. Select one of the lines as the first object.

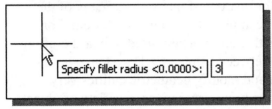

8. Select the other line as the second object.

➢ Note that the default setting of the Fillet command is to trim the edges as shown in the figure below.

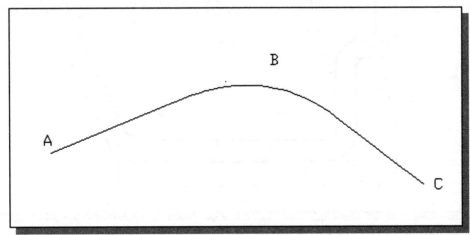

• Note that all of the classical methods for geometric construction, such as the one shown on page 3-14, can also be used in CAD systems.

The *Gasket* design

Exploring the possibilities of a CAD system can be very exciting. For persons who have board drafting experience, the transition from the drafting board to the computer does require some adjusting. But, the essential skills required to work in front of a computer are not that much different from those needed for board drafting. In fact, many of the basic skills acquired in board drafting can also be applied to a computer system. For example, the geometric construction techniques that are typically used in board drafting can be used in AutoCAD. The main difference between using a CAD system over the traditional board drafting is the ability to create and modify geometric entities very quickly and accurately. As it was illustrated in the previous sections, a variety of object construction and editing tools, which are available in AutoCAD, are fairly easy to use. It is important to emphasize that a good understanding of the geometric construction fundamentals remains the most important part of using a CAD system. The application of the basic geometric construction techniques in a CAD system is one of the main tasks in using a CAD system.

In the following sections, we will continue to examine more of the geometric construction and editing tools provided by **AutoCAD® 2012**. We will be looking at the geometric construction tools, such as Trim, Extend, Edit Polyline and Offset that are available in **AutoCAD® 2012**.

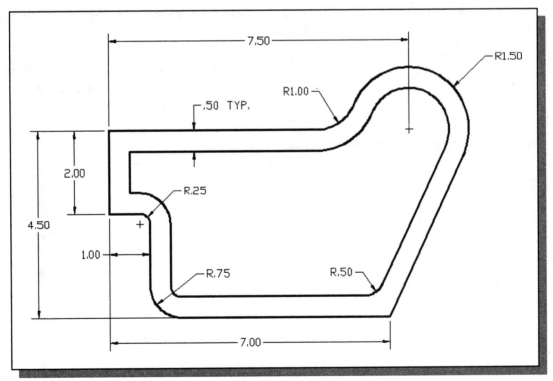

❖ Before continuing to the next page, on your own make a rough sketch showing the steps that can be used to create the design. Be aware that there are many different approaches to accomplishing the same task.

Drawing Units Display Setup

Before creating the first geometric entity, the value of the units within the CAD system should be determined. For example, in one drawing, a unit might equal one millimeter of the real-world object. In another drawing, a unit might equal an inch. The unit type and number of decimal places for object lengths and angles can be set through the **UNITS** command. These *drawing units settings* control how AutoCAD interprets the coordinate and angle entries and how it displays coordinates and units in the *Status Bar* and in the dialog boxes.

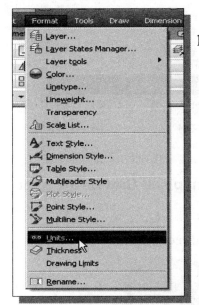

1. In the *Menu Bar* select:

    [Format] → [Units]

2. In the *Drawing Units* dialog box, confirm the *Length Type* to **Decimal**. This is the default measurement to English units, inches.

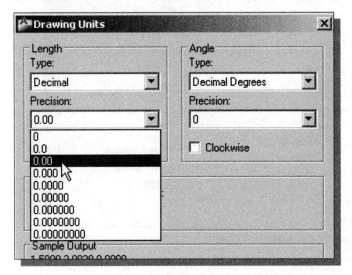

3. Set the *Precision* to **two digits** after the decimal point.

4. Pick **OK** to exit the *Drawing Units* dialog box.

GRID and SNAP Intervals Setup

1. In the *Menu Bar*, select:

   [Tools] → [Drafting Settings]

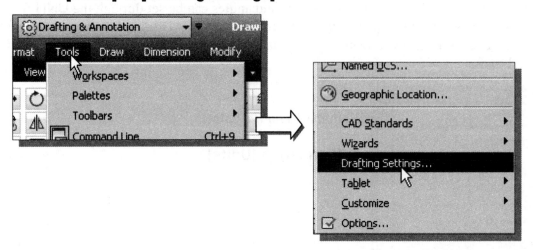

2. In the *Drafting Settings* dialog box, select the **Snap and Grid** tab if it is not the page on top.

3. Change *Grid Spacing* to **1.00** for both X and Y directions.

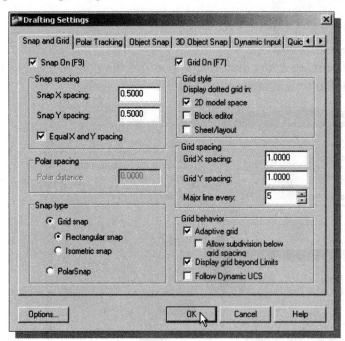

4. Switch **ON** the *Grid On* and *Snap On* options as shown.

5. Pick **OK** to exit the *Drawing Units* dialog box.

6. On your own, use the **Zoom Extent** command, under the **View** tab, to reset the display.

❖ Notice in the *Status Bar* area, the *GRID* and *SNAP* options are pressed down indicating they are switched *ON*. The grid spacing is set to 1 inch and the snap interval is set to 0.5 inch.

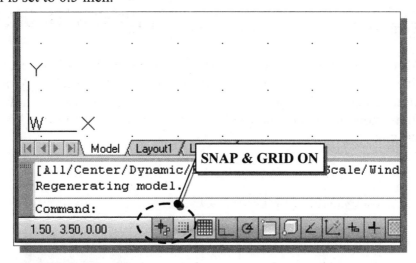

Using the *LINE* command

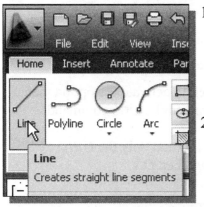

1. Select the **Line** command icon in the *Draw* toolbar. In the command prompt area, near the bottom of the AutoCAD drawing screen, the message "*_line Specify first point:*" is displayed. AutoCAD expects us to identify the starting location of a straight line.

2. In the graphics window, move the cursor to **world coordinates (4,6). Left-click** to position the starting point of the line at that location.

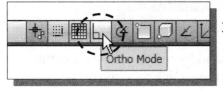

3. We will next turn *ON* the *ORTHO* option by toggling on the **ORTHO** button in the *Status Bar* area.

❖ The *ORTHO* option constrains cursor movement to the horizontal or vertical directions, relative to the current coordinate system. With the Line command, we are now restricted to creating only horizontal or vertical lines with the *ORTHO* option.

4. Move the graphics cursor below the last point we selected on the screen and create a vertical line that is two units long (*Y coordinate: 4.00*).

5. Move the graphics cursor to the right of the last point and create a horizontal line that is one unit long (*X coordinate: 5.00*).

6. Move the graphics cursor below the last point and create a vertical line that is 2.5 units long (*Y coordinate: 1.50*).

7. Turn **OFF** the *SNAP* option in the *Status Bar* area.

8. Move the graphics cursor to the right of the last point and create a horizontal line that is about seven units long (near *X coordinate: 12.00*). As is quite common during the initial design stage, we might not always know all of the dimensions at the beginning.

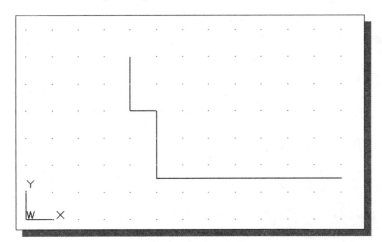

9. Inside the graphics window, **right-mouse-click** to activate the option menu and select **Enter** with the left-mouse-button to end the Line command.

10. In the *Status Bar* area, reset the option buttons so that only the *GRID DISPLAY*, and *ORTHO MODE* options are switched **ON**.

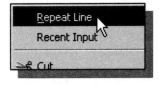

11. Activate the **Line** command by picking the icon in the *Draw* toolbar or **right-mouse-click** to activate the option menu and select **Repeat Line**.

Object Snap Toolbar

❖ **Object Snap** is an extremely powerful construction tool available on most CAD systems. During an entity's creation operations, we can snap the cursor to points on objects such as endpoints, midpoints, centers, and intersections. For example, we can quickly draw a line to the center of a circle, the midpoint of a line segment, or the intersection of two lines.

1. Bring up the *Object Snap* toolbar through the **[Tools]** → **[Toolbars]** menu.

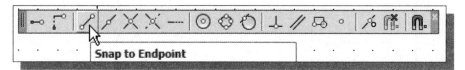

2. In the *Object Snap* toolbar, pick **Snap to Endpoint**. In the command prompt area, the message "*_endp of*" is displayed. AutoCAD now expects us to select a geometric entity on the screen.

❖ The Snap to Endpoint option allows us to snap to the closest endpoint of objects such as lines or arcs. AutoCAD uses the midpoint of the entity to determine which end to snap to.

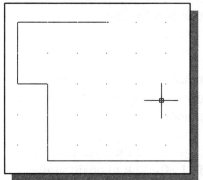

3. Pick the **top left vertical line** by selecting a location above the midpoint of the line. Notice AutoCAD automatically snaps to the top endpoint of the line.

4. Move the graphics cursor to the right of the last point and create a horizontal line that is about three units long (near *X coordinate: 7.00*).

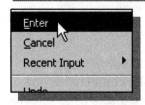

5. Inside the graphics window, **right-mouse-click** to activate the option menu and select **Enter** with the left-mouse-button to end the Line command.

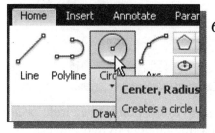

6. Select the **Circle-Radius** command icon in the *Draw* toolbar. In the command prompt area, the message "*Specify center point for circle or [3P/2P/Ttr (tan tan radius)]:*" is displayed.

7. In the *Status Bar* area, switch *ON* the *SNAP* option.

8. In the graphics window, move the cursor to world coordinates (**11.5,6**). **Left-click** to position the center point of the circle at this location.

9. Move the graphics cursor to world coordinates (**13,6**). **Left-click** at this location to create a circle (radius **1.5** inches).

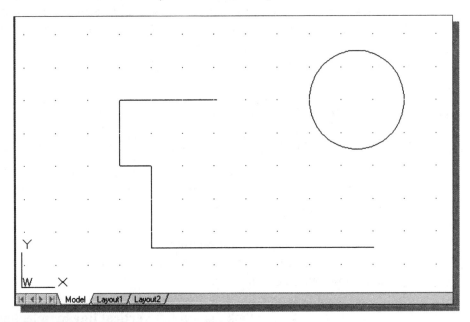

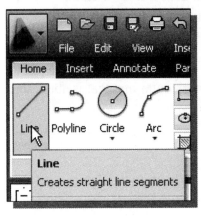

10. Select the **Line** command icon in the *Draw* toolbar. In the command prompt area, the message "*_line Specify first point:*" is displayed.

11. In the graphics window, move the cursor to world coordinates (**11,1.5**). **Left-click** to position the first point of a line at this location.

12. Pick **Snap to Tangent** in the *Object Snap* toolbar. In the command prompt area, the message "*_tan to*" is displayed. AutoCAD now expects us to select a circle or an arc on the screen.

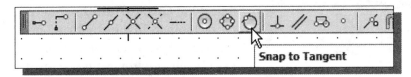

❖ The **Snap to Tangent** option allows us to snap to the point on a circle or arc that, when connected to the last point, forms a line tangent to that object.

13. Pick a location on the right side of the circle and create the line tangent to the circle. Note that the *Object Snap* options take precedence over the *ORTHO* option.

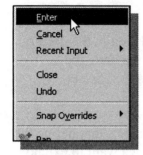

14. Inside the graphics window, **right-mouse-click** to activate the option menu and select **Enter** with the left-mouse-button to end the **Line** command.

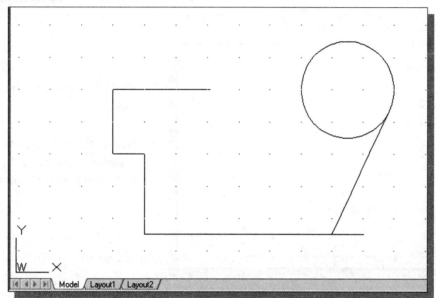

15. In the *Status Bar* area, reset the option buttons so that none of the buttons are switched *ON*.

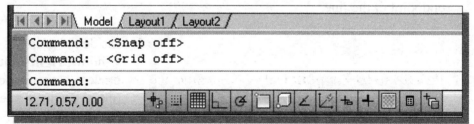

16. Close the *Object Snap* toolbar by **left-clicking** the upper right corner **X** icon.

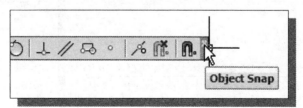

Using the *EXTEND* command

- The Extend command lengthens an object so that it ends precisely at a selected boundary.

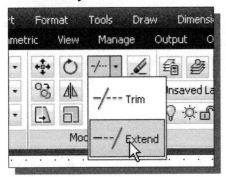

1. Select the **Extend** command icon in the *Modify* toolbar. In the command prompt area, the message "*Select boundary edges... Select objects:*" is displayed.

   ❖ First, we will select the objects that define the boundary edges to which we want to extend the object.

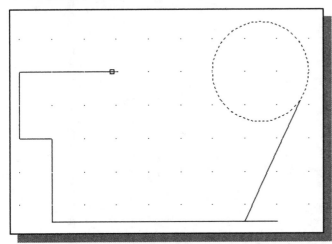

2. Pick the **circle** as the *boundary edge*.

3. Inside the graphics window, **right-mouse-click** to proceed with the Extend command.

4. The message "*Select object to extend or shift-select object to trim or [Project/Edge/Undo]:*" is displayed in the command prompt area. Extend the **horizontal line** that is to the left side of the circle by clicking near the right endpoint of the line.

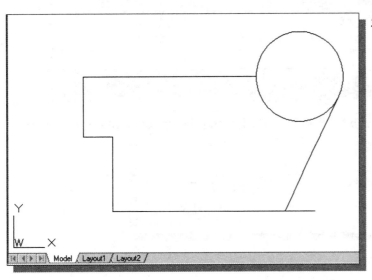

5. Inside the graphics window, **right-mouse-click** to activate the option menu and select **Enter** with the left-mouse-button to end the Extend command.

Using the *TRIM* command

- The Trim command shortens an object so that it ends precisely at a selected boundary.

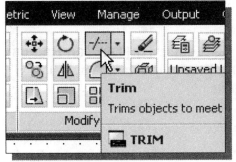

1. Select the **Trim** command icon in the *Modify* toolbar. In the command prompt area, the message "*Select boundary edges... Select objects:*" is displayed.

❖ First, we will select the objects that define the boundary edges to which we want to trim the object.

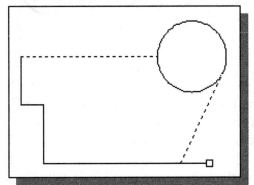

2. Pick the **inclined line** and the **top horizontal line** as the *boundary edges*.

3. Inside the graphics window, **right-mouse-click** to proceed with the Trim command.

4. The message "*Select object to trim or shift-select object to extend or [Fence/Crossing/Project/Edge/eRase/Undo]:*" is displayed in the command prompt area. Pick the **right endpoint** of the bottom horizontal line.

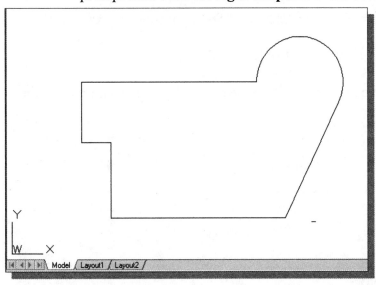

5. Pick the **bottom of the circle** by clicking on the lower portion of the circle.

6. Inside the graphics window, **right-mouse-click** to activate the option menu and select **Enter** with the left-mouse-button to end the Trim command.

- Note that in **AutoCAD® 2012**, we can use the Extend command or the Trim command for trimming or extending an object. For example, when using the **Extend** command, we can select an object to *extend* or hold down **SHIFT** and select an object to *trim*.

Creating a *TTR CIRCLE*

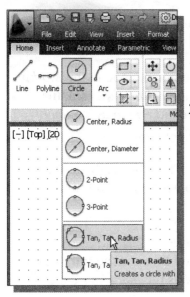

1. In the *Draw* toolbar, click the triangle next to the **Circle** icon to show the additional options.

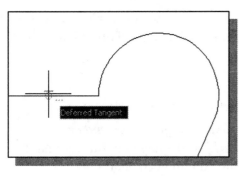

2. In the displayed list, select the **Ttr (Tan Tan Radius)** option. This option allows us to create a circle that is tangent to two objects.

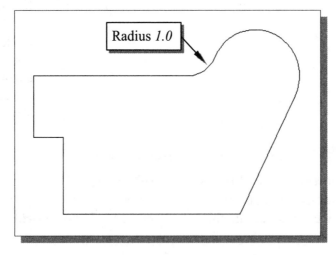

3. Pick the **top horizontal line** that is to the left side of the arc. We will create a circle that is tangent to this line and the circle.

4. Pick the **circle** by selecting a location that is above the right endpoint of the horizontal line. AutoCAD interprets the location we selected as being near the tangency.

5. In the command prompt area, the message "*Specify radius of circle <1.50>*" is displayed.
   Specify radius of circle <1.50>: **1.0** [ENTER]

➢ On your own, use the **Trim** command and trim the circle, the horizontal line, and the arc as shown.

Radius *1.0*

Using the *FILLET* command

- Fillet rounds or fillets the edges of two arcs, circles, elliptical arcs, or lines with an arc of a specified radius.

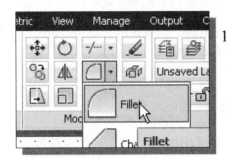

1. Select the **Fillet** command icon in the *Modify* toolbar. In the command prompt area, the message *"Select first object or [Polyline/Radius/Trim]:"* is displayed.

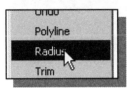

2. Inside the graphics window, right-mouse-click to activate the option menu and select the **Radius** option with the left-mouse-button to specify the radius of the fillet.

3. In the command prompt area, the message *"Specify fillet radius:"* is displayed.

   Specify fillet radius: **0.75** **[ENTER]**

4. Pick the **bottom horizontal line** and the **adjacent vertical line** to create a rounded corner as shown.

➢ On your own, use the Fillet command and create a radius *0.25* fillet at the corner as shown.

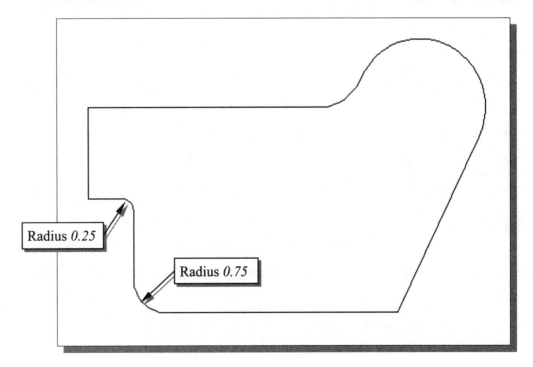

Radius *0.25*

Radius *0.75*

Converting objects into a *Polyline*

- The next task in our project is to use the Offset command and create a scaled copy of the constructed geometry. Prior to using the Offset command, we will simplify the procedure by converting all objects into a **compound object – a *polyline*.**

- ❖ A *polyline* in AutoCAD is a 2D line of adjustable width composed of line and arc segments. A polyline is treated as a single object with definable options.

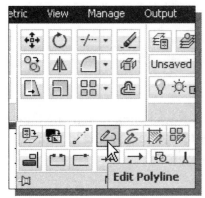

1. In the Ribbon Toolbars, select:

    [Modify] → [Edit Polyline]

2. The message *"Select polyline:"* is displayed in the command prompt area. Select **any** of the objects on the screen.

3. The message *"Object selected is not a polyline, Do you want to turn it into one? <Y>"* is displayed in the command prompt area. **Right-mouse-click** to accept the *Yes* default.

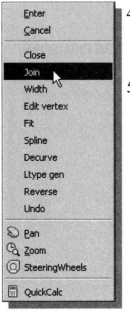

4. Inside the graphics window, **right-mouse-click** to activate the option menu and select the **Join** option with the left-mouse-button to add objects to the polyline.

5. **Pick all objects** by enclosing them inside a *selection window*.

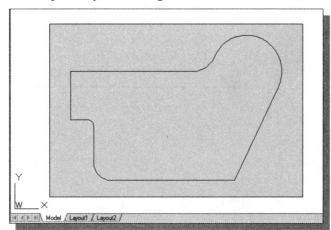

6. Inside the graphics window, **right-mouse-click** to accept the selected objects.

7. Inside the graphics window, right-mouse-click to activate the option menu and select **Enter** to end the Edit Polyline command.

Using the *OFFSET* command

- The Offset command creates a new object at a specified distance from an existing object or through a specified point.

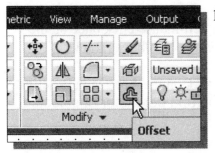

1. Select the **Offset** command icon in the *Modify* toolbar. In the command prompt area, the message "*Specify offset distance or [Through]:*" is displayed.

   Specify offset distance or [Through]:
   0.5 [ENTER]

2. In the command prompt area, the message "*Select object to offset or <exit>:*" is displayed. Select **any segment** of the polyline on the screen.

   ➢ Since all the lines and arcs have been converted into a single object, all segments are now selected.

3. AutoCAD next asks us to identify the direction of the offset. Pick a location that is *inside* the polyline.

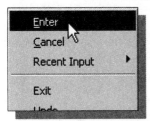

4. Inside the graphics window, **right-mouse-click** and select **Enter** to end the Offset command.

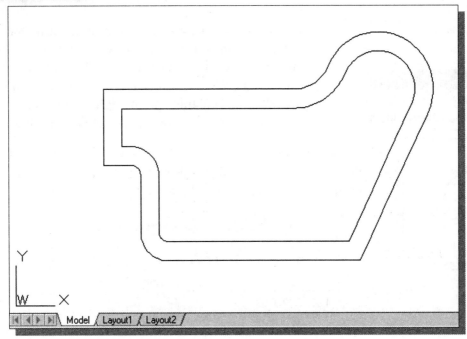

Using the Area Inquiry Tool to Measure Area and Perimeter

- AutoCAD also provides several tools that will allow us to measure distance, area, perimeter, and even mass properties. With the use of polylines, measurements of areas and perimeters can be done very quickly.

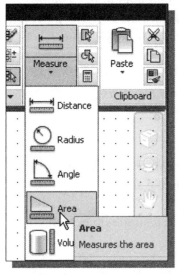

1. In the *Ribbon* tabs area, left-mouse-click once on the **Measure** title in the *Utilities* toolbar as shown.

2. In the *Inquiry* toolbar, click on the **Area** icon to activate the Calculates the area and perimeter of selected objects command.

- Note the different **Measure** options that are available in the list.

3. In the command prompt area, the message "*Specify first corner point or [Object/Add/Subtract]:*" is displayed. By default, AutoCAD expects us to select points that will form a polygon. The area and perimeter of the polygon will then be calculated.

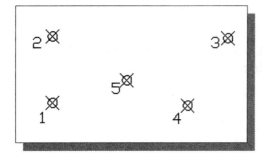
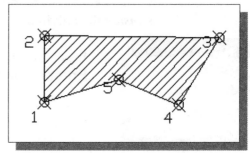

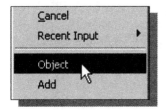

4. AutoCAD can also calculate the area and perimeter of objects that define closed regions. For example, a circle or a rectangle can be selected as both of these objects define closed regions. We can also select a region defined by a *polyline*. To activate this option, **right-mouse-click** once inside the graphics window and select **Object** as shown.

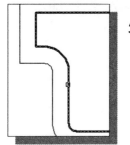

5. In the command prompt area, the message "*Select objects:*" is displayed. Pick the **inside polyline** and the associated area and perimeter information are shown in the prompt area.

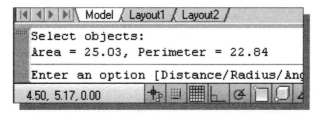

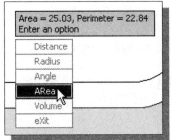

6. Inside the graphics window, select **Repeat AREA** as shown.

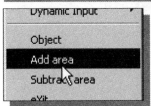

7. We can also select a region defined by multiple *polylines*. To activate this option, **right-mouse-click** once inside the graphics window and select **Add area** as shown.

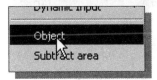

8. To also activate selection of regions *defined* by polylines, **right-mouse-click** once inside the graphics window and select **Object** as shown.

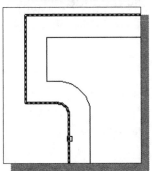

9. In the command prompt area, the message "*[Add Mode] Select objects:*" is displayed. Pick the outside polyline. The associated area and perimeter information are shown in the prompt area.

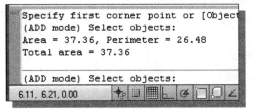

```
Specify first corner point or [Object
(ADD mode) Select objects:
Area = 37.36, Perimeter = 26.48
Total area = 37.36

(ADD mode) Select objects:
6.11, 6.21, 0.00
```

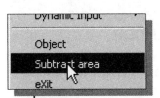

10. Next we will subtract the region defined by the inside polyline. To activate this option, **right-mouse-click** once inside the graphics window and select **Subtract area** as shown.

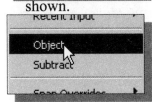

11. To also activate selection of regions defined by polylines, **right-mouse-click** once inside the graphics window and select **Object** as shown.

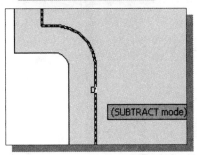

12. In the command prompt area, the message "*Select objects:*" is displayed. Pick the inside polyline and the area between the two polylines is shown in the command prompt area.

```
(SUBTRACT mode) Select objects:
Area = 25.03, Perimeter = 22.84
Total area = 12.33

(SUBTRACT mode) Select objects:
```

Using the *EXPLODE* command

- The Explode command breaks a compound object into its component objects.

    1. Switch back to the **Home** tab and select the **Explode** command icon in the *Modify* toolbar. In the command prompt area, the message "*Select objects:*" is displayed.

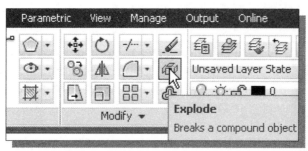

    2. Pick the ***inside polyline*** that we created using the Offset command.

    3. Inside the graphics window, **right-mouse-click** to end the Explode command.

Create another *Fillet*

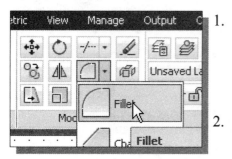

1. Select the **Fillet** command icon in the *Modify* toolbar. In the command prompt area, the message "*Select first object or [Polyline/Radius/Trim]:*" is displayed.

2. On your own, set the *Fillet Radius* to **0.5.** *Specify fillet radius:* **0.5** **[ENTER]**

3. Pick the **horizontal line** and the **adjacent inclined line** to create a rounded corner as shown.

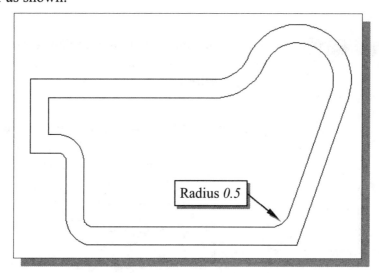

Radius *0.5*

Saving the CAD file

1. In the pull-down menus, select:

   [File] → [Save As]→ [AutoCAD Drawing]

2. In the *Save Drawing As* dialog box, select the folder in which you want to store the CAD file and enter *Gasket* in the *File name* box.

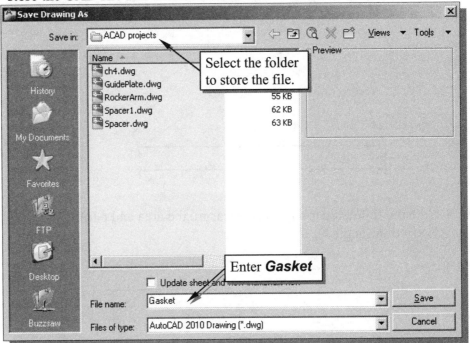

3. Pick **Save** in the *Save Drawing As* dialog box to accept the selections and save the file.

Exit AutoCAD

- To exit **AutoCAD® 2012**, select **Exit AutoCAD** from the *Application Menu* or type *QUIT* at the command prompt.

Review Questions: (Time: 20 minutes)

1. Describe when and why you would use the AutoCAD *ORTHO* option.

2. What is the difference between a *line* and a *polyline* in AutoCAD?

3. Which AutoCAD command can we use to break a compound object, such as a polyline, into its component objects?

4. Which AutoCAD command can we use to quickly calculate the area and perimeter of a closed region defined by a polyline?

5. Describe the procedure to calculate the area and perimeter of a closed region defined by a polyline?

6. What does the **Offset** command allow us to do?

7. Create the following triangle and measure the area and perimeter of the triangle.

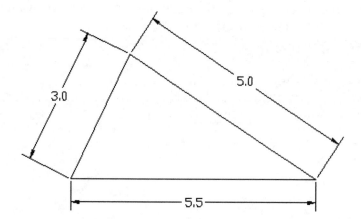

8. Create the following triangle and measure the area and perimeter of the triangle. Also find the angle Θ.

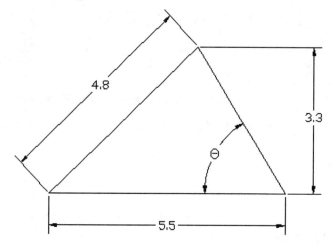

Exercises: (Time: 90 minutes)
(Unless otherwise specified, dimensions are in inches.)

1.   Lines & Squares Pattern

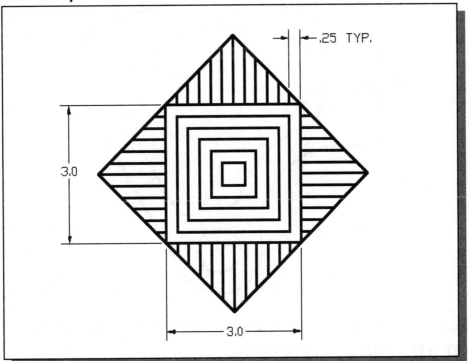

2.   Interlacement Design

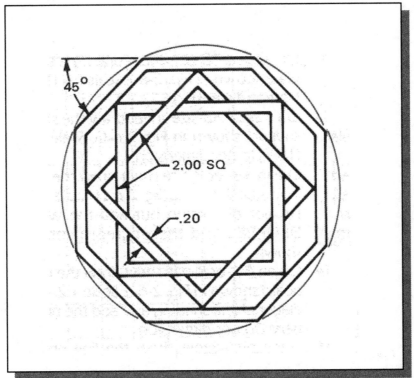

3. Positioning Spacer (Dimensions are in inches.)

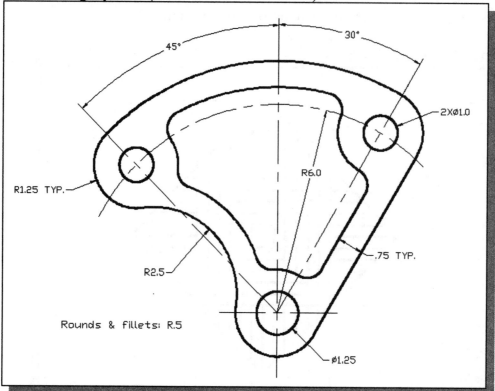

4. Indexing Base (Dimensions are in inches.)

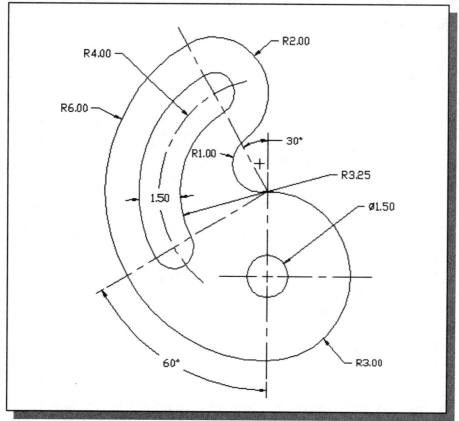

5. Guide Block (Create the front view of the design. Dimensions are in inches.)

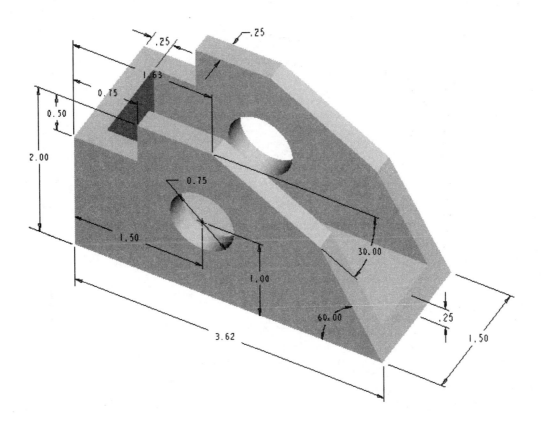

NOTES:

Chapter 4
Object Properties and Organization

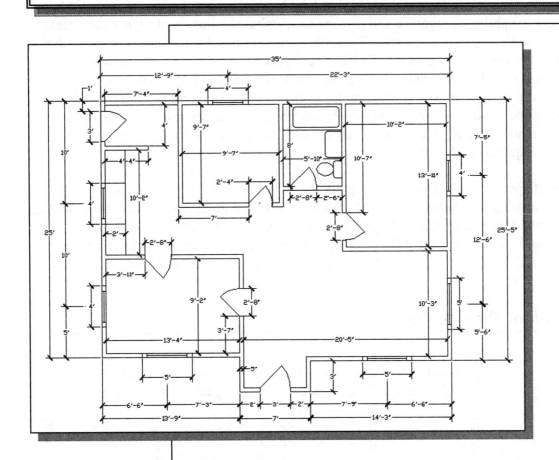

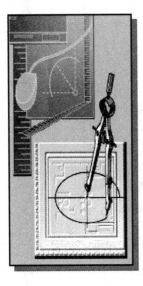

Learning Objectives

- ♦ **Using the AutoCAD Quick Setup Wizard**
- ♦ **Create new Multiline Styles**
- ♦ **Draw, using the MULTILINE command**
- ♦ **Use the Multiline Editing commands**
- ♦ **Create new layers**
- ♦ **Pre-selection of objects**
- ♦ **Controlling Layer Visibility**
- ♦ **Moving objects to a different layer**

Introduction

The CAD database of a design may contain information regarding the hundreds of CAD entities that are used to create the CAD model. One of the advantages of using a CAD system is its ability to organize and manage the database so that the designer can access the information quickly and easily. Typically, CAD entities that are created to describe one feature, function, or process of a design are perceived as related information and therefore are organized into the same group. In AutoCAD, the **Layer** command is used extensively for this purpose. For example, an architectural drawing typically will show walls, doors, windows, and dimensions. Using layers, we can choose to display or hide sub-systems for clarity; we can also change object properties, such as colors and linetypes, quickly and easily.

In this chapter, we will continue to explore the different construction and editing tools that are available in **AutoCAD® 2012**. We will demonstrate the use of the Limits, Mline, Medit, and Layer commands. As you become proficient with the CAD tools and understand the underlying CAD modeling concepts, you are encouraged to experiment with new ideas in using the CAD tools and develop your own style of using the system.

The *Floor Plan* design

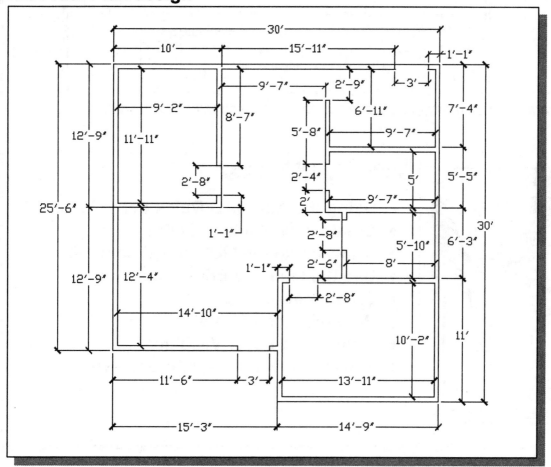

Starting Up AutoCAD® 2012

1. Select the **AutoCAD 2012** option on the *Program* menu or select the **AutoCAD 2012** icon on the *Desktop*. Once the program is loaded into the memory, the **AutoCAD® 2012** drawing screen will appear on the screen.

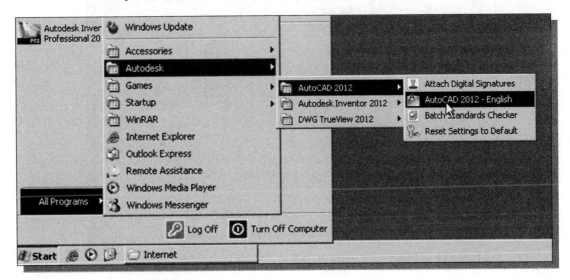

Using the Setup Wizard

1. In the *Startup* dialog box, select the **Use a Wizard** option as shown in the figure below.

2. In the *Select a Wizard* section, pick **Quick Setup**.

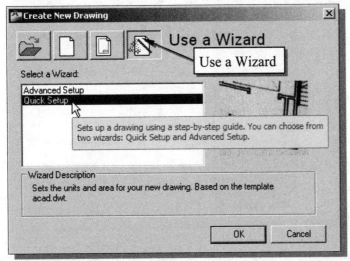

- AutoCAD setup wizards allow us to customize several of the AutoCAD settings depending on the wizard we choose. The *Quick Setup* wizard sets the units and grid display area. Choices for units include *Decimal, Engineering, Architectural, Fractional,* and *Scientific.* We can also specify the width and length of a two-dimensional area to establish the extents of the *grid* displayed, also known as the *limits* of the working area.

Drawing Units Setup

1. In the *Quick Setup Units* option, select **Architectural**.

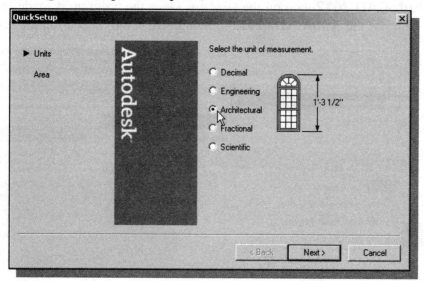

2. Pick **Next** to continue with the *Quick Setup* settings.

Reference Area Setup

1. In the *Quick Setup Area* option, enter **60′** and **40′** for the width and length.

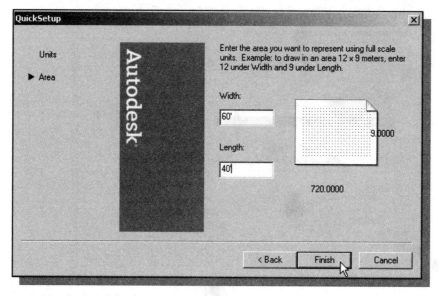

- The two-dimensional area we set up in the *Quick Setup* is the *drawing limits* in AutoCAD.

2. Pick **Finish** to accept the settings and end the *Quick Setup* wizard.

GRID and *SNAP* Intervals Setup

1. In the *Menu Bar*, select:
   [Tools] → [Drafting Settings]

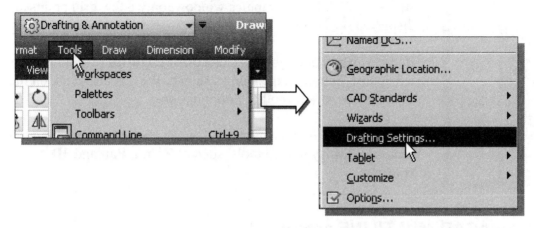

2. In the *Drafting Settings* dialog box, select the **SNAP and GRID** tab if it is not the page on top.

3. Change *Grid Spacing* to **6″** for both X and Y directions.

4. Also adjust the *Snap Spacing* to **6″** for both X and Y directions.

5. Turn *OFF* the **Adaptive Grid** option. (This switch is used to limit the grid display when zooming.)

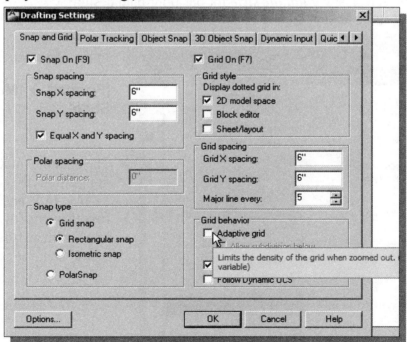

6. Pick **OK** to exit the *Drafting Settings* dialog box.

Using the *ZOOM EXTENTS* command in the Navigation Bar

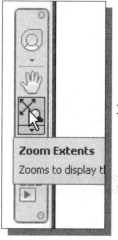

1. Move the cursor inside the graphics window and notice that, although we have set the *limits* to 40′ by 60′, the default display is still 9″ by 12″. In the graphics window, only a few grid points are displayed.

2. In the *Navigation* toolbar, select **Zoom Extents** by clicking the left-mouse-button on the icon as shown. We can also click on the triangle icon to select other Zoom options.

➢ The *navigation bar* is a user interface element that provides quick access to display related tools, such as **Zoom**, **Pan** and **3D rotation.**

The AutoCAD *MULTILINE* command

- The **Multiline** command in **AutoCAD® 2012** is used to create multiple parallel lines. This command is very useful for creating designs that contain multiple parallel lines, such as walls for architectural designs and for highway designs in civil engineering. The Multiline command creates a set of parallel lines (up to 16 lines) and all line segments are grouped together to form a single *multiline object*, which can be modified using Multiline Edit and Explode commands. We will first create a new *multiline style* for our floor plan design.

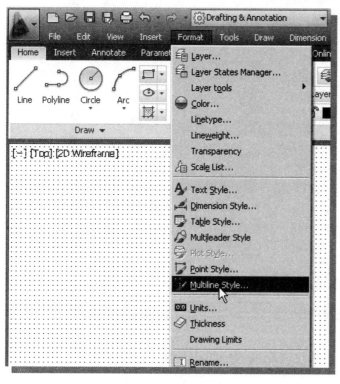

1. In the *Menu Bar*, select:

   [Format] → [Multiline Style]

❖ The default AutoCAD multiline style is called *STANDARD*, and it consists of two elements (two parallel lines) with an offset distance of 1.0 inch.

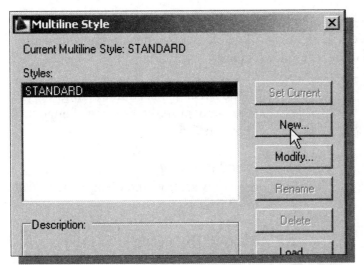

2. In the *Multiline Style* dialog box choose **New** to create a new multiline style.

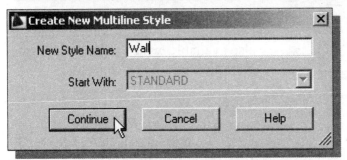

3. In the *New Style Name* box, enter **Wall** as the new *multiline style name*.

4. Click **Continue** to create the new style.

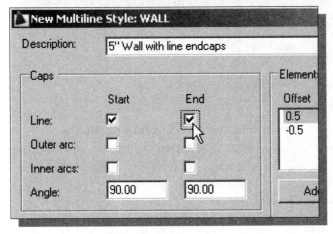

5. Enter **5" Wall with line endcaps** in the *Description* box.

6. In the *Caps* section, switch *ON* the **Start** and **End** boxes to enable *Line* end-caps as shown in the figure.

❖ All line elements in the multiline style are defined by an offset from a reference line, the *multiline origin*.

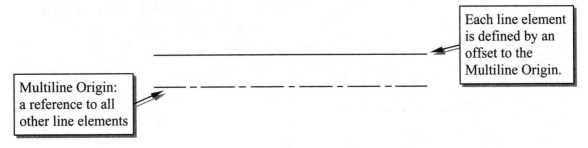

Each line element is defined by an offset to the Multiline Origin.

Multiline Origin: a reference to all other line elements

❖ Note that, in the *Elements* section, all the line elements are listed in descending order with respect to their offsets. We will create two line elements representing a six-inch wall (offsetting on both sides of the reference location).

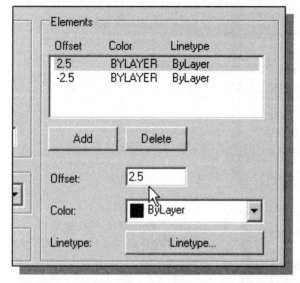

7. In the *Elements* section, highlight the first element in the list, and change the *Offset* to **2.5**.

8. Pick the *second element* in the *Elements* section and change the *Offset* to **-2.5**.

9. Choose **OK** to exit the *Element Properties* dialog box.

❖ Notice the Add and Delete options are also available, which allow us to create or remove additional elements.

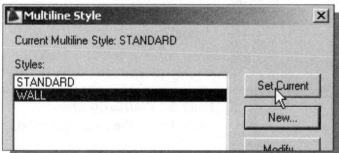

10. With the **Wall** style highlighted, click **Set Current** as shown.

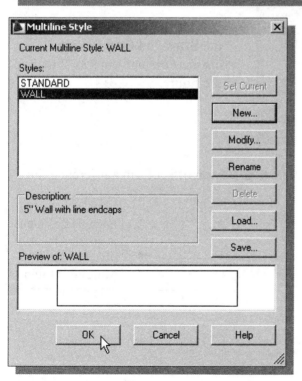

11. Click the **OK** button to end the Multiline Style command. (Note: The *Preview* section shows the current **WALL** style.)

❖ Note that the **Save** button will save a multiline style to the library of multiline styles. By default, AutoCAD saves the multiline styles information to a file called **acad.mln**. The **Load** button allows users to retrieve multiline styles from a library.

Object Snap Toolbar

1. Move the cursor to the *Menu Bar* area and choose **[Tools]** → **[Toolbars]** → **[AutoCAD]**.

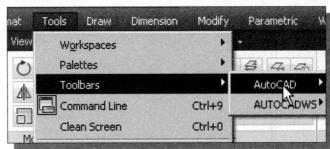

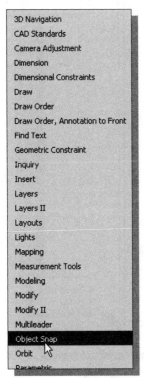

❖ AutoCAD provides 44 predefined toolbars for access to frequently used commands, settings, and modes. A *checkmark* (next to the item) in the list identifies the toolbars that are currently displayed on the screen.

2. Select **Object Snap**, with the left-mouse-button, to display the *Object Snap* toolbar on the screen.

❖ **Object Snap** is an extremely powerful construction tool available on most CAD systems. During an entity's creation operations, we can snap the cursor to points on objects such as endpoints, midpoints, centers, and intersections. For example, we can turn on **Object Snap** and quickly draw a line to the center of a circle, the midpoint of a line segment, or the intersection of two lines.

3. In the previous chapter, we used several of the object snap options to quickly locate positions on existing geometry. In this chapter we will look at the **Snap From** option, which is the second icon in the Object Snap toolbar.

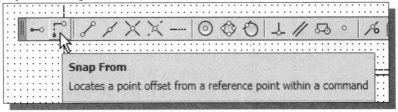

Snap From
Locates a point offset from a reference point within a command

➢ The **Snap From** option allows us to locate a position using a relative coordinate system with respect to a selected position.

4. In the *Status Bar* area, reset the option buttons so that *SNAP MODE, GRID DISPLAY, ORTHO,* and *DYNAMIC INPUT* are switched **ON**.

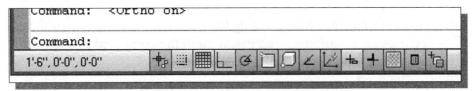

Drawing Multilines

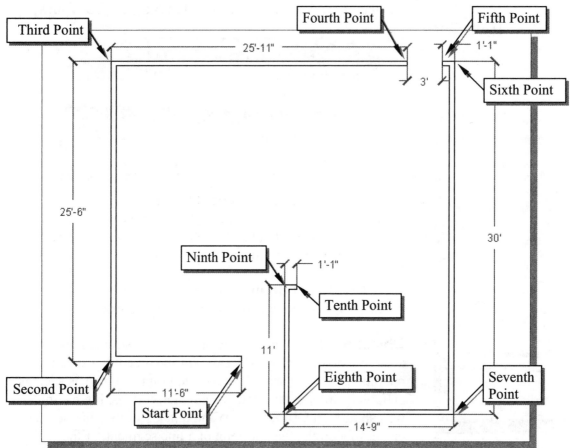

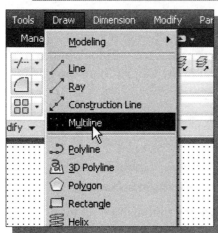

1. Select the **Multiline** command icon in the *Draw* pull-down menu, through the *Menu Bar*, as shown. In the command prompt area, the current settings, such as "*Justification = Top, Scale = 1.00, Style = Wall*" are displayed.

2. On your own, confirm the *Scale* to **1.00** or the *Styles* to **Wall** or the *Justification* to **Top**, by using the **right-mouse-button** to bring up the option list.

3. In the command prompt area, the message "*Specify start point or [Justification/Scale/Style]:*" is displayed. Select a location **near** the bottom center of the graphics window as the **start point** of the multiline.

4. Create a horizontal line by using the *Dynamic Input* option or the *relative rectangular coordinates entry method* in the command prompt area: *Specify next point:* **@-11'6",0** [ENTER]

5. Create a vertical line by using the *Dynamic Input* option or the *relative rectangular coordinates entry method* in the command prompt area:

   Specify next point: **@25'6"<90** [ENTER]

6. Create a horizontal line by using the *Direct Input* option; move the cursor to the right and enter the distance:
   Specify next point: **25'11"** [ENTER]

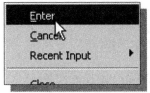

7. Inside the graphics window, **right-mouse-click** and select **Enter** to end the *Multiline* command.

8. Hit the **spacebar** once to repeat the last command, the **Multiline** command. In the command prompt area, the current settings "*Justification = **Top**, Scale = **1.00**, Style = **Wall**"* are displayed.

9. We will use the **Snap from** option to continue creating the exterior walls. In the *Object Snap* toolbar, pick **Snap From**. In the command prompt area, the message "*_from Base point*" is displayed. AutoCAD now expects us to select a geometric entity on the screen.

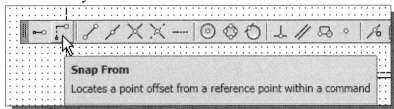

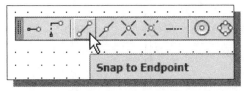

10. We will position the starting point relative to the last position of the previous *multiline*. To assure the selection of the endpoint, choose the **Snap to Endpoint** option as shown.

11. Pick the upper corner of the top horizontal multiline as shown.

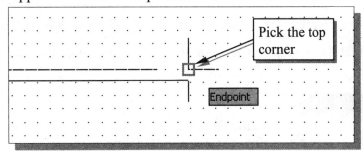

➢ Note that it is feasible to stack snap options for precise positioning of geometry.

12. The position of the starting point of the new *multiline* segments is 3′ to the right of the reference point we just picked. At the command prompt, enter **@3',0"** [ENTER].

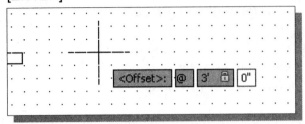

13. Now enter **@1′1″,0**, to define the top corner of the exterior wall.

14. On your own, complete the multiline segments by specifying the rest of the corners using the dimensions as shown in the figure below.

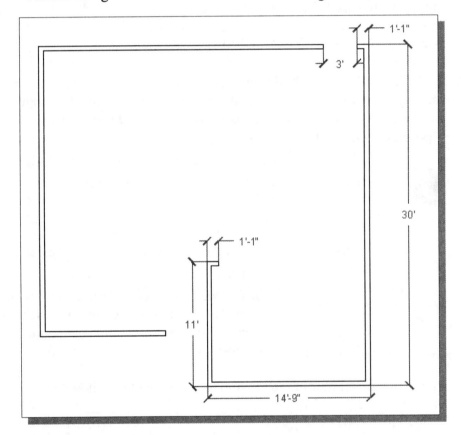

• Note that the points we specified are defining the outside corners of the floor plan design.

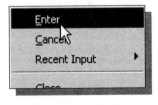

15. Inside the graphics window, right-mouse-click and select **Enter** to end the Multiline command.

Creating interior walls

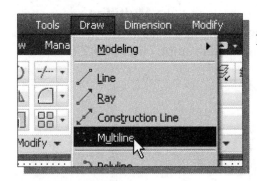

1. Select the **Multiline** command in the *Draw Menu Bar* as shown. In the command prompt area, the current settings "*Justification = Top, Scale = 1.00, Style = Wall*" are displayed. In the command prompt area, the message "*Specify start point or [Justification/ Scale/Style]:*" is displayed.

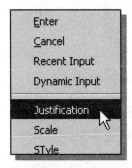

2. Inside the graphics window, **right-mouse-click** to display the option menu.

3. Pick **Justification** in the option menu. In the command prompt area, the message "*Enter justification type [Top/Zero/Bottom] <Top>:*" is displayed.

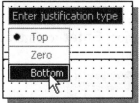

4. Inside the graphics window, right-mouse-click to display the option menu and select **Bottom** so that the points we select will be set as alignments for the bottom element.

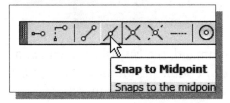

5. In the *Object Snap* toolbar, pick **Snap to Midpoint**. In the command prompt area, the message "*_mid of*" is displayed. AutoCAD now expects us to select a geometric entity on the screen.

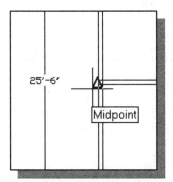

6. Select the outside **left vertical line** as shown.

7. Using the *Dynamic Input* option, create a **10'** inside wall toward the right.

8. Now enter **@0,1'1"**, to define the vertical stub wall.

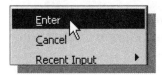

9. Inside the graphics window, right-mouse-click and select **Enter** to end the Multiline command.

- Next, we will create a vertical wall right above the last corner.

10. Hit the **spacebar** once to repeat the last command, the **Multiline** command. Since the last position used is directly below the new location, we will just enter the relative coordinates. At the command prompt, enter **@0,2'8"** [**ENTER**].

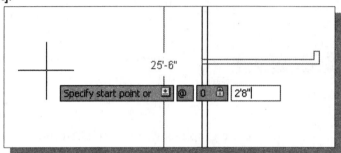

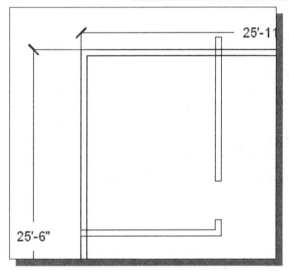

11. Place the other end above the top horizontal line as shown in the figure below. In the next section, we will use the **Multiline Edit** tools to adjust these constructions.

12. Inside the graphics window, right-mouse-click and select **Enter** to end the MultiLine command.

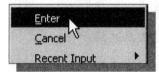

13. Hit the **spacebar** once to repeat the last command, the **Multiline** command. In the text window, the current settings "*Justification = Bottom, Scale = 1.00, Style = Wall*" are displayed. In the command prompt area, the message "*Specify start point or [Justification/Scale/ Style]:*" is displayed.

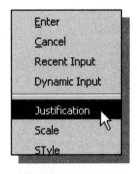

14. Inside the graphics window, **right-mouse-click** to display the option menu.

15. Pick **Justification** in the option menu. In the command prompt area, the message "*Enter justification type [Top/Zero/Bottom] <Bottom>:*" is displayed.

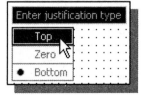

16. Inside the graphics window, right-mouse-click to display the option menu and select **Top** so that the points we select will align to the top element.

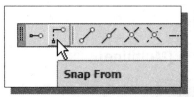

Snap From

17. In the *Object Snap* toolbar, pick **Snap From**. In the command prompt area, the message "*_from Base point*" is displayed. AutoCAD now expects us to select a geometric entity on the screen.

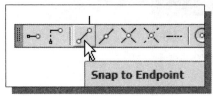

Snap to Endpoint

18. In the *Object Snap* toolbar, pick **Snap to Endpoint**. In the command prompt area, the message "*_endp of*" is displayed.

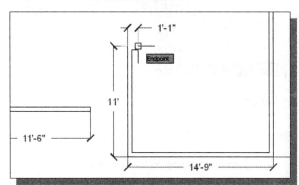

19. We will create another inside wall on the right side. Pick the corner as shown.

20. At the command prompt, enter **@2'8",0 [ENTER]**.

21. Pick a location that it to the right of the right-vertical exterior wall. The drawing should appear as shown in the figure below.

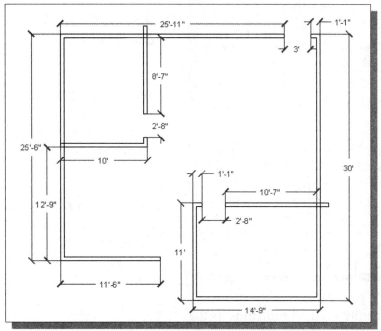

❖ One of the main advantages of using a CAD system to create drawings is the ability to create and/or modify geometric entities quickly, using many of the available tools. Unlike traditional board drafting, where typically only the necessary entities are created, CAD provides a much more flexible environment that requires a slightly different way of thinking, as well as taking a different view of the tasks at hand.

Joining the walls using *MULTILINE EDIT*

1. In the *Menu Bar*, select: **[Modify]** → **[Object]**→ **[Multiline]**

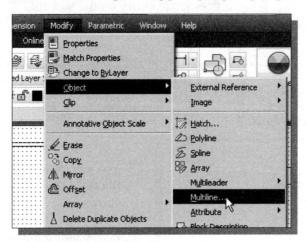

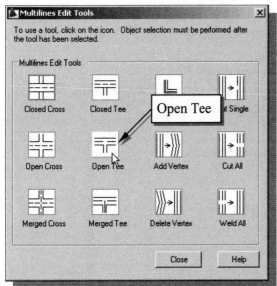

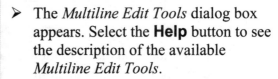

➢ The *Multiline Edit Tools* dialog box appears. Select the **Help** button to see the description of the available *Multiline Edit Tools*.

2. Pick the **Open Tee** option in the dialog box.

➢ We will need to select two multilines for this option: first, select the multiline to trim or extend; and second, select the intersecting multiline.

3. Pick the **horizontal multiline** as the first object, *multiline to trim,* as shown.

4. Pick the **vertical multiline** as the 2nd object, *intersecting multiline.*

➢ The **Open Tee** option automatically trims the lines to form the proper shapes.

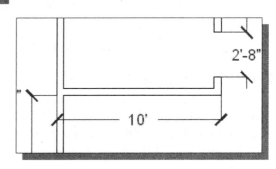

5. Repeat the above steps and modify the connection of the other two inside walls.

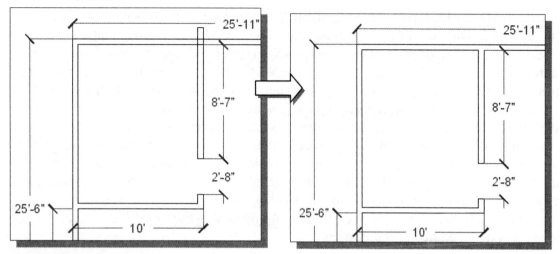

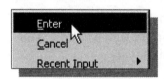

6. Inside the graphics window, right-mouse-click once and select **Enter** to end the Mledit command.

7. Using the *Multiline/MEdit* options, create the additional walls and doorways as shown.

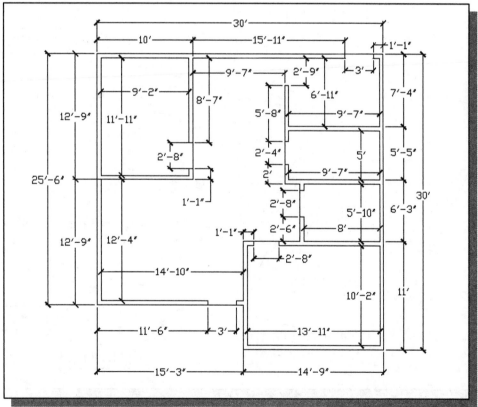

❖ Now is a good time to save the design. Select **[File]** → **[Save As]** in the *Menu Bar* and use **FloorPlan** as the *File name*.

Using *Layers* and Object Properties

In **AutoCAD® 2012**, *layers* can be thought of as transparent overlays on which we organize different kinds of design information. Typically, CAD entities that are created to describe one feature or function of a design are considered as related information and therefore can be organized into the same group. The objects we organized into the same group will usually have common properties such as colors, linetypes, and lineweights. Color helps us visually distinguish similar elements in our designs. Linetype helps us identify easily the different drafting elements, such as centerlines or hidden lines. Lineweight increases the legibility of an object through width. Consider the floor plan we are currently working on. The floor plan can be placed on one layer, electrical layout on another, and plumbing on a third layer. Organizing layers and the objects on layers makes it easier to manage the information in our designs. Layers can be used as a method to control the visibility of objects. We can temporarily switch *ON* or *OFF* any layer to help construction and editing of our designs.

AutoCAD allows us to create an infinite number of layers. In general, twenty to thirty layers are sufficient for most designs. Most companies also require designers and CAD operators to follow the company standards in organizing objects in layers.

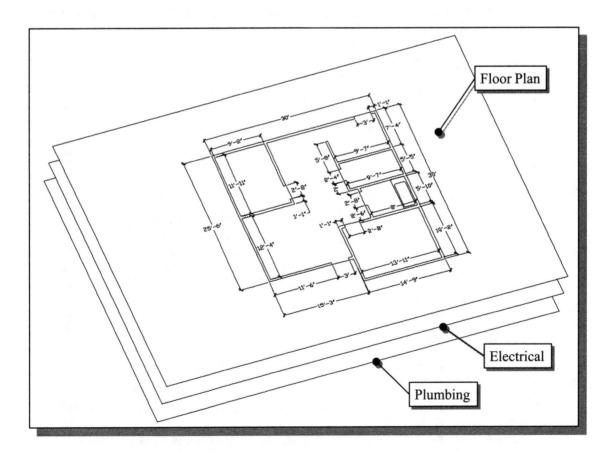

1. Pick **Layers Properties** in the *Layers* toolbar as shown.

❖ The *Layer Properties Manager* dialog box appears. AutoCAD creates a default layer, *layer 0*, which we cannot rename or delete. Note that *Layer 0* has special properties which are used by the system.

❖ In AutoCAD, we always construct entities on a layer. It may be the default layer or a layer that we create. Each layer has associated properties such as the visibility setting, color, linetype, lineweight, and plot style.

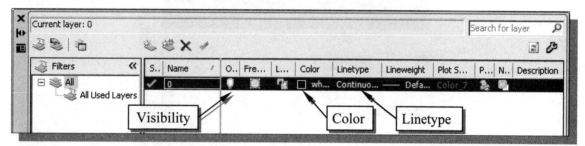

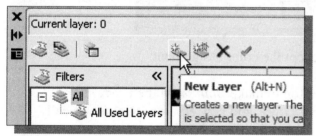

2. Click on the **New Layer** button. Notice a layer is automatically added to the list of layers.

➤ Note that we can create an unlimited number of layers in a drawing.

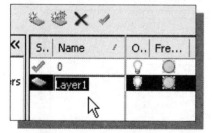

3. AutoCAD will assign a generic name to the new layer (*Layer1*). Enter **BathRoom** as the name of the new layer as shown in the figure below.

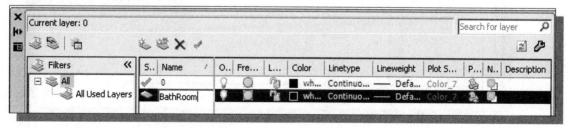

❖ Layer properties can be adjusted by clicking on the icon or name of a property. For example, clicking on the *light-bulb* icon toggles the visibility of the layer *ON* or *OFF*.

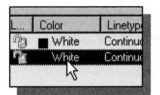

4. Pick the color swatch or the color name (**White**) of the *BathRoom* layer. The *Select Color* dialog box appears.

5. Pick **Cyan** *(Index color: 4)* in the *Standard Colors* section. Notice the current color setting is displayed at the bottom of the dialog box.

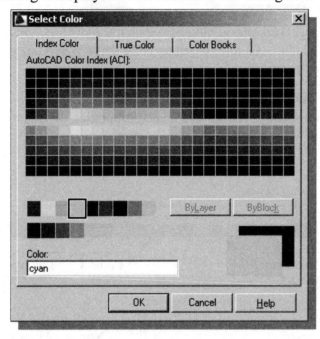

6. Click on the **OK** button to accept the color assignment.

7. Click on the **Set Current** button to make *BathRoom* the *Current Layer*. There can only be one *Current Layer*, and new entities are automatically placed on the layer that is set to be the *Current Layer*.

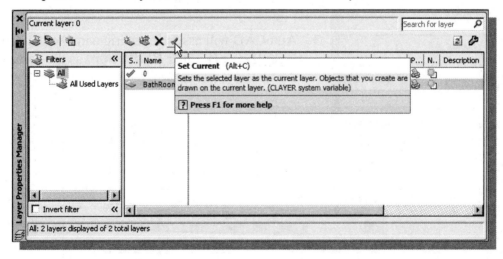

8. Click on the **Close** button, at the upper left corner of the dialog box, to accept the settings and exit the *Layer Properties Manager* dialog box.

❖ The *Layer Control* toolbar in the top of the AutoCAD toolbar panel shows the status of the active layer. The *BathRoom* layer is shown as the current active layer. Note that this *Layer* toolbar can also be used to control the settings of individual layers.

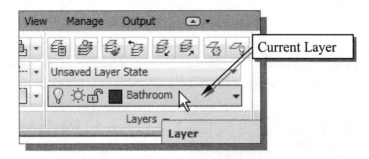

Using *Zoom Realtime*

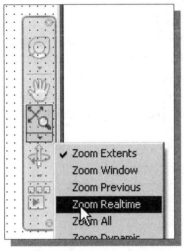

1. Click on the **Zoom Realtime** icon in the *Navigate* toolbar located to the right side of the graphics window.

2. Inside the graphics window, **push and hold down the left-mouse-button**, then move upward to enlarge the current display scale factor. (Press the **[Esc]** key to exit the Zoom command.)

3. Use the **Zoom Realtime** option to reposition the display so that we can work on the bathroom of the floor plan.

➢ Note that the mouse-wheel can also be used to Zoom Realtime; turning the wheel forward will enlarge the current display scale factor.

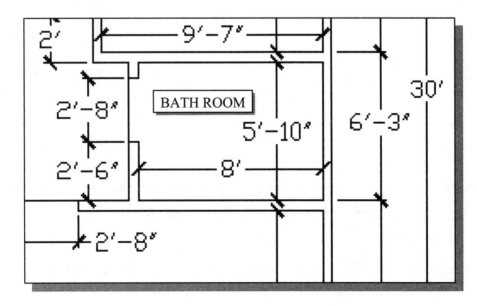

Modeling the bathroom

1. In the *Status Bar* area, reset the option buttons so that all of the buttons are switched *OFF*.

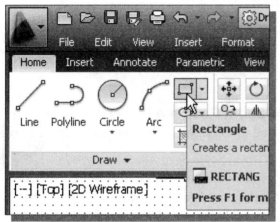

2. Click on the **Rectangle** command icon in the *Draw* toolbar. In the command prompt area, the message "*Specify first corner point:*" is displayed.

3. In the *Object Snap* toolbar, pick **Snap to Endpoint**. In the command prompt area, the message "*_endp of*" is displayed. AutoCAD now expects us to select a geometric entity on the screen.

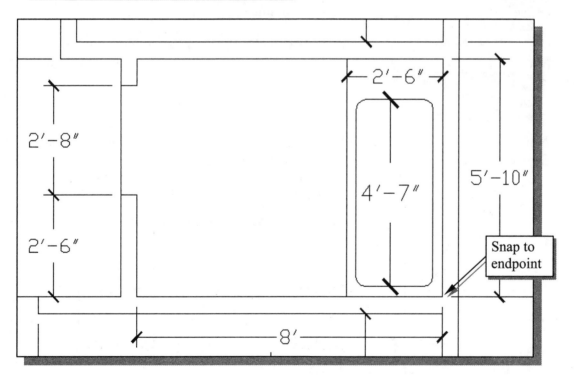

4. Use the *Dynamic Input* options and create the outer rectangle of the tub (**2′-6″ × 5′-10″**).

5. Complete the inner shape by creating a rectangle with a distance of 3″ from the outer rectangle and rounded corners of 3″ radius.

6. Create two rectangles (*10″ × 20″* and *20″ × 30″*) with rounded corners (radius **3″**) and position them as shown.

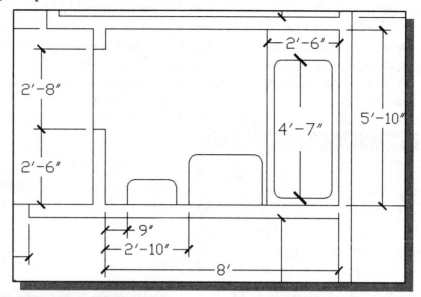

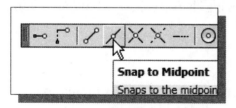

7. Select the **Ellipse → Axis, End** command icon in the *Draw* toolbar. In the command prompt area, the message "*Specify axis endpoint of ellipse or [Arc/Center]:*" is displayed.

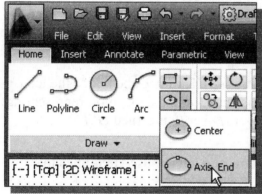

8. In the *Object Snap* toolbar, pick **Snap to Midpoint**. In the command prompt area, the message "*_mid of*" is displayed.

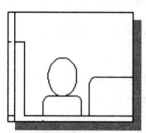

9. Pick the **top horizontal line** of the small rectangle we just created.

10. For the second point location, enter **@0,20″**[ENTER].

11. For the third point, enter **@7.5″,0** [ENTER].

❖ An ellipse has a major axis, the longest distance between two points on the ellipse, and a minor axis, the shorter distance across the ellipse. The three points we specified identify the two axes.

Controlling *Layer Visibility*

AutoCAD does not display or plot the objects that are on invisible layers. To make layers invisible, we can *freeze* or **turn off** those layers. Turning off layers only temporarily removes the objects from the screen; the objects remain active in the CAD database. Freezing layers will make the objects invisible and also disable the objects in the CAD database. Freezing layers will improve object selection performance and reduce regeneration time for complex designs. When we *thaw* a frozen layer, AutoCAD updates the CAD database with the screen coordinates for all objects in the design.

1. On the *Layers* toolbar panel, choose the triangle next to the **Layer Control** box with a click of the left-mouse-button.

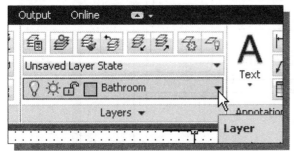

2. Move the cursor over the **light-bulb** icon for *layer 0*. The tool tip *"Turn a layer On or Off"* appears.

3. **Left-mouse-click once** and notice the icon color is changed to a dark color, representing the layer (*Layer 0*) is turned *OFF*.

4. Move the cursor into the graphics window and **left-mouse-click once** to accept the layer control settings.

➤ On your own, practice turning on *Layer 0* and freezing/thawing *Layer 0*. What would happen if we turn off all layers?

Adding a New Layer

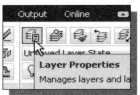

1. Pick **Layer Properties Manager** in the *Layers* toolbar panel. The *Layer Properties Manager* dialog box appears.

2. Create a new layer (layer name: **Walls**) and change the layer color to **Green**.

3. Turn *ON* the *0* layer, turn *OFF* the *BathRoom* layer, and set the **Walls** layer as the *Current Layer*. Click on the **Close** button to exit *Layer Properties*.

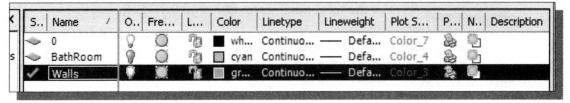

S..	Name	/	O..	Fre...	L...	Color	Linetype	Lineweight	Plot S...	P...	N..	Description
	0					wh...	Continuo...	—— Defa...	Color_7			
s	BathRoom					cyan	Continuo...	—— Defa...	Color_4			
✓	Walls					gr...	Continuo...	—— Defa...	Color_3			

Moving objects to a different layer

❖ **AutoCAD® 2012** provides a flexible graphical user interface that allows users to select graphical entities BEFORE the command is selected (*pre-selection*), or AFTER the command is selected (*post-selection*). The procedure we have used so far is the *post-selection* option. We can pre-select one or more objects by clicking on the objects at the command prompt (**Command:**). To deselect the selected items, press the **[Esc]** key twice.

1. Inside the graphics window, pre-select all objects by enclosing all objects inside a **selection window** as shown.

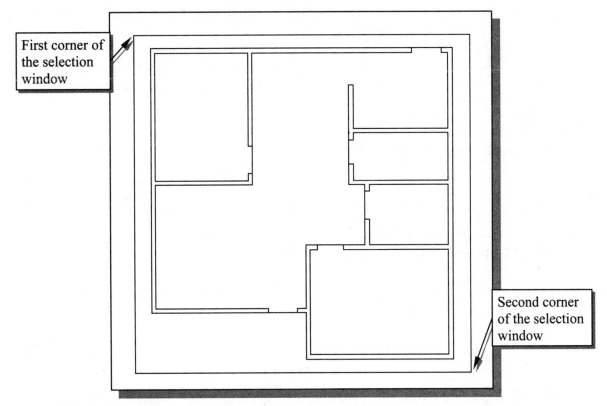

First corner of the selection window

Second corner of the selection window

2. On the *Object Properties* toolbar, choose the **Layer Control** box with the left-mouse-button.

❖ Notice the layer name displayed in the *Layer Control* box is the selected object's assigned layer and layer properties.

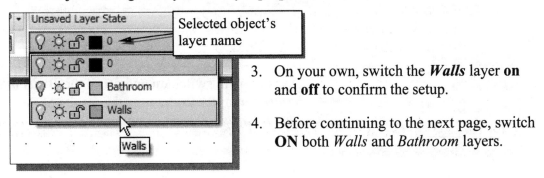

Selected object's layer name

3. On your own, switch the **Walls** layer **on** and **off** to confirm the setup.

4. Before continuing to the next page, switch **ON** both *Walls* and *Bathroom* layers.

Matching Layer Properties

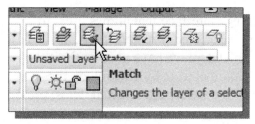

1. Pick **Match** in the *Layer control* toolbar panel. In the command prompt area, the message "*Select objects to be changed:*" is displayed.

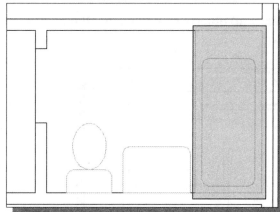

2. Select the **bathtub** using a selection window as shown.

3. Inside the graphics window, **right-mouse-click** once to accept the selection.

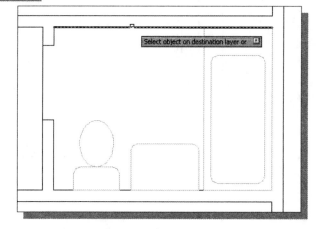

4. Select one of the **Walls** as the object properties to match.

➤ In the command prompt area, notice 13 objects have been moved to the Walls layer.

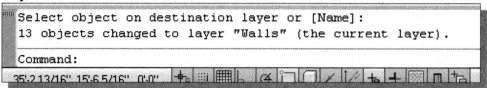

```
Select object on destination layer or [Name]:
13 objects changed to layer "Walls" (the current layer).

Command:
35'-2 13/16" 15'-6 5/16"  0'-0"
```

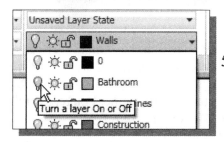

5. On your own, switch **on** and **off** of the *Walls and bathroom* layers to examine the results of the *Match Layer Properties* command.

➢ On your own, complete the floor plan by creating the 4′ and 5′ windows in a new layer *Windows*. The dimensions are as shown in the figure below.

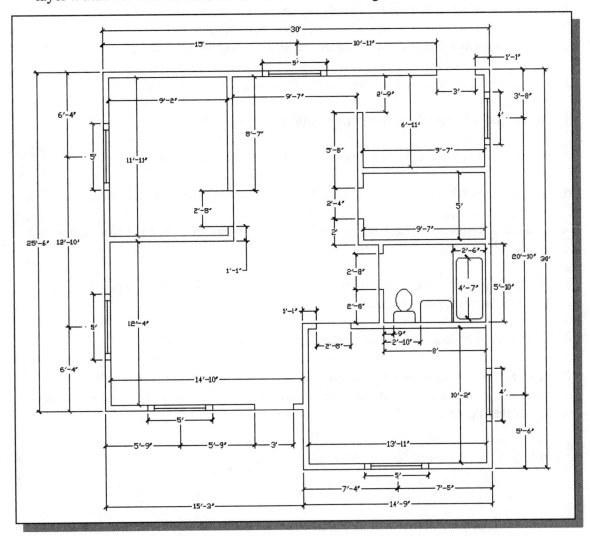

Review Questions: (Time: 25 minutes)

1. List some of the advantages of using *layers*.

2. List two methods to control the *layer visibility* in **AutoCAD® 2012**.

3. Describe the procedure to move objects from one layer to another.

4. When and why should you use the **Multiline** command?

5. Is there a limitation to how many layers we can set up in AutoCAD?

6. List and describe the two options available in AutoCAD to create ellipses.

7. Is there a limitation to how many parallel lines we can set up when using AutoCAD Multiline objects?

8. What is the name of the layer that AutoCAD creates as the default layer (the layer that we cannot rename or delete)?

9. When and why would you use the Match Properties command?

10. A **chamfer** connects two objects with an angled line. A chamfer is usually used to represent a beveled edge on a corner. Construct the following corners by using the **Chamfer** command.

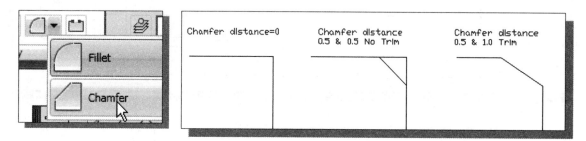

11. List the commands you would use to create the following multilines in a drawing.

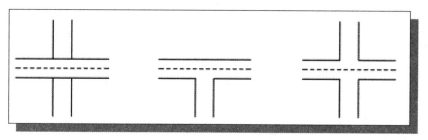

Exercises: (Time: 120 minutes)

1.   Floor Plan A (Wall thickness: 5 inch)

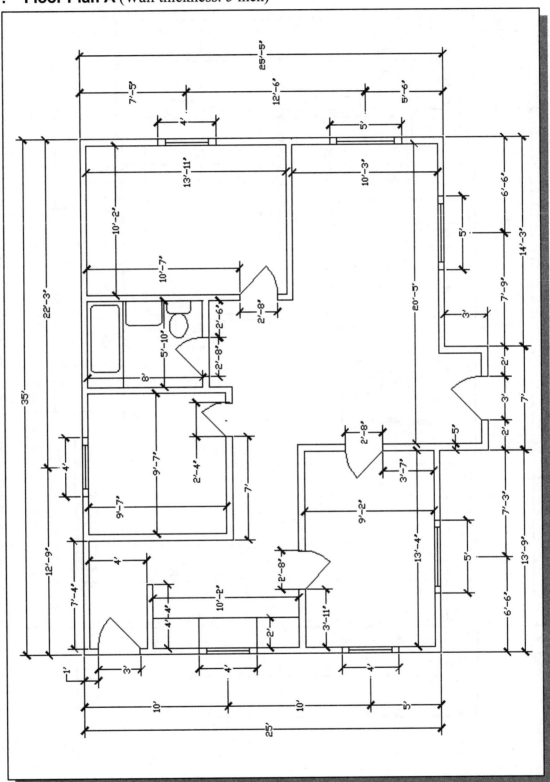

2. Floor Plan B (Wall thickness: 5 inch)

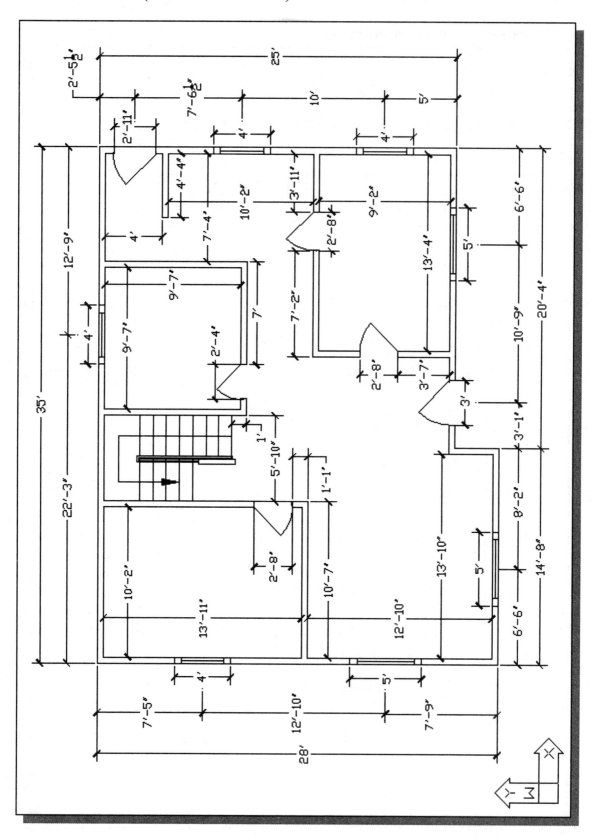

Pro/ENGINEER WILDFIRE 5.0
Tutorial

INTRODUCTION to
Pro | ENGINEER®
W I L D F I R E ™ 5.0

A Few Words Before You Dive In...

This tutorial was written for new users who are getting started with Pro/ENGINEER Wildfire 5.0 (PTC, Needham, MA <**www.ptc.com**>). The lessons in this book will introduce you to the basic functionality of the program and are meant to be used alongside the running Pro/E software. Description of command sequences is accompanied by a discussion of where the commands fit into an overall modeling strategy. In addition to learning *what* each command or function does, it is important to understand *why* it is used. We will sometimes make intentional errors so that we can discover how Wildfire responds. **Therefore, just clicking through the command sequences given here is not enough; you will learn the material best if you take time along the way to read the text carefully and think about what you are doing and observing what happens**. You will also learn considerably more by exploring the program on your own and experimenting with the commands and options.

You are about to learn how to use one of the most sophisticated and powerful solid modeling programs available. It may be the most complex software you will ever use. It's power derives from its extremely rich command set, that understandably requires quite a long time to master. Pro/E's learning curve has the reputation of being very steep although this is diminishing with the arrival of the Wildfire release a number of releases ago. The goal of this tutorial is to help you with this learning as effectively and efficiently as possible. Learning Wildfire is a challenging task, but not impossible. Do not be discouraged, as you will find it well worth the effort.

Please note that this is not a reference manual. Not all the available commands are covered (by a long shot!), nor will a comprehensive discussion of the myriad available options be attempted. The tutorial is meant only to get you started and to give you a solid foundation on which to build further knowledge. Nonetheless, upon completion of these lessons (in about 30 or 40 hours from now), you should:

1.   be able to create models of relatively complex parts and assemblies.
2.   know how to produce the related detailed engineering drawings.
3.   understand the terminology used in the program, and solid modeling in general.
4.   understand the design philosophy and methods embedded in Wildfire.

The last two are important so that you can understand the on-line reference documentation and explore other commands and functions in the software.

In the early lessons and as each new function is introduced, commands are presented in considerable detail to explain what is going on and why. As you progress through the lessons, you will be given fewer details about commands that have been covered previously. For example, in Lesson #2 we find out how to create a two-dimensional sketch, mouse click by mouse click. Later on, you will be asked to "Create the sketch shown in the figure" assuming that you know how to do that. Thus, the tutorials build off each other and are meant to be done in the order presented. It is important for you to go through the lessons in sequence and to have a good understanding of the material before you go on to the next lesson.

You may have to go through each lesson (or some portions) more than once to gain an acceptable level of understanding. Each lesson has some questions and exercises at the end to allow you to check your knowledge of the concepts and commands and to give you a starting point for your own exploration of the program. No answers are given here for these questions - you will learn the material best if you have to dig them out for yourself! And do not worry if you don't get them all right away. Some questions are posed intentionally to encourage your continued and deeper exploration of the program. This sort of "on-the-fly" discovery is a never-ending activity even with experienced Pro/E users because it is such a big program. Finally, each lesson concludes with a project activity that will result in the creation of a simple assembly.

The images presented here should correspond with those obtained in the Pro/E windows, and can be used to check your work as you proceed through the lessons. Figures in this document, however, are only available in black-and-white, whereas color plays an important role in the Pro/E screen. In addition to distinguishing between different parts and making "pretty pictures", color is used to indicate the meaning of lines (edge, axis, datum curve, hidden line, and so on). Where a line interpretation may be ambiguous in the black and white version here, the figures are labeled with the appropriate line color or have been modified to show different thickness or line style. Also, some modifications have been made to the default system font in order to make the figures clearer.

These lessons were developed using the Windows version of the software, however operation under Unix should be practically identical. The version used was preproduction build C000.

What *IS* Pro/ENGINEER?

Actually, Pro/E is a suite of programs that are used in the design, analysis, and manufacturing of a virtually unlimited range of products. Its field of application is generally mechanical design, although recent additions to the program are targeted at ship building and structural steel framework as well[1]. In these lessons, we will be dealing only with the major front-end module, known as Wildfire, used for part and assembly

---

[1] People who work in general architectural or civil engineering design (like highway design) would most likely not use Pro/E, as its design and functions do not lend themselves directly to those activities.

design and model creation, and production of engineering drawings. There are a wide range of additional modules available to handle tasks ranging from sheet metal operations, piping layout, mold design, wiring harness design, NC machining, and other functions. Sensitivity studies and design optimization based purely on geometry are handled by a module called Behavioral Modeling Extension (BMX). Mechanism design, kinematics, and animation is accomplished using the Mechanism Design Extension (MDX). An add-on package, Pro/MECHANICA (also from Parametric Technology)[2], integrates with Wildfire to perform structural analysis (static stress and deformation, buckling and fatigue analysis, vibration), thermal analysis, and dynamic motion analysis of mechanisms. Pro/MECHANICA can also do sensitivity studies and design optimization, based on the model created in Pro/E.

In a nutshell, Pro/E Wildfire is a *parametric, feature-based solid modeling* system.

"Feature-based" means that you create your parts and assemblies by defining high level and physically meaningful features like extrusions, sweeps, cuts, holes, slots, rounds, and so on, instead of specifying low-level geometry like lines, arcs, and circles. This means that you, the designer, can think of your computer model at a very high level, and leave all the low-level geometric detail for Wildfire to figure out. Features are specified by setting values and attributes of elements such as reference planes or surfaces, direction of creation, pattern parameters, shape, dimensions, and others. Features can either add or subtract material from the model, or be simple non-solid geometric entities like references axes and planes.

"Parametric" means that the physical shape of the part or assembly is driven by the values assigned to the attributes (primarily dimensions) of its features. You may define or modify a feature's dimensions or other attributes at any time (within limits!). Any changes will automatically propagate through your model. You can also relate the attributes of one feature to another. For example, if your design intent is such that a hole be centered on a block, you can relate the dimensional location of the hole to the block dimensions using a numeric formula; if the block dimensions change, the centered hole position will be re-computed automatically.

"Solid Modeling" means that the computer model you create contains all the "information" that a real solid object would have. It has volume and therefore, if you provide a value for the density of the material, it has mass and inertia. Unlike a surface model, if you make a hole or cut in a solid model, a new surface is automatically created and the model "knows" which side of this surface is solid

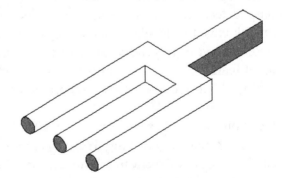

The 3-Pronged Blivot -
A Non-realizable Object
(*NOT* created with Pro/E!)

---

[2] A companion book, *The Pro/MECHANICA Tutorial* is also available from the publisher, Schroff Development Corp.

material. The most useful thing about solid modeling is that it is impossible to create a computer model that is ambiguous or physically non-realizable, such as the "object" shown in the figure above. This figure shows what appears to be a three-pronged tuning fork at the left end, but only has two square prongs coming off the handle at the right end. With solid modeling, you cannot create a "model" such as this that could not physically exist. This type of ambiguity is quite easy to do with just 2D, wireframe, or sometimes even surface modeling.

Although the emphasis in this book is on creation of solid features, Wildfire has a very extensive command set for creating and manipulating surfaces. This advanced surface modeling is becoming more important in, for example, the design of consumer products. Once the surfaces are created, the part model can be "solidified" so that the normal solid features (like standard holes) can be applied.

Whether or not the part could actually be manufactured is another story. Here is a cut-away view of a physically possible part, but don't take this to the machine shop and ask them to machine the cavity inside the part! Pro/E will let you make this model, but concerns of manufacturability are up to you.

Could your machine shop make this?

An important aspect of feature-based modeling in Wildfire is the concept of **parent/child relationships**. Without going in to a lot of detail at this time, a child feature is one that references a previously created (parent) feature. For example, the surface of a block might be used as a reference plane to create a slot. A change to the parent feature will potentially affect the child. For example, deleting a parent feature will delete all its children since one or more references required to create the children would no longer exist. Wildfire has special functions available to manage parent/child relationships. This can get pretty complicated with a complex model (a good reason to try to keep your models simple!), so we will leave the details for later. However, you should keep parent/child relations in mind when you are specifying feature references for a new feature you are creating: If the parent feature is temporary or is likely to change, what effect will this have on the children? Will the references still correctly capture your design intent?

Once your model is created, it is very easy to get Wildfire to produce fully detailed standard format **engineering drawings** almost completely automatically. In this regard, Pro/E also has **bidirectional associativity** - this means you can change a dimension value on the drawing and the shape of the model will automatically change, and vice versa.

Of course, few parts live out their existence in isolation. Thus, a major design function accomplished with Pro/E is the construction of assemblies of parts. Assembly is accomplished by specifying physically-based geometric constraints (insert, mate, align, and so on) between part features. With assemblies you can see how the different parts will fit together or interfere with each other, or see how they move with respect to each other, for example, in a linkage assembly. Assembly models are also associative: in a properly made assembly model, changes can propagate through to other parts in the assembly automatically. To a new user of the program, this is almost magic! And, of course, drawings of assemblies can also be created.

Since the introduction of Wildfire several years ago, PTC has implemented wide-ranging and significant changes in the user interface compared to its predecessor versions. The program is very Windows-like and contains a mode of operation called "Direct Modeling" that makes feature creation very simple. At the same time, for power users, there are a large number of shortcuts (think "right mouse button") which can speed up your work quite a lot. These have made the program easier to use and add a lot of visual excitement to working with the program. Another key aspect of the program is its readiness for collaboration of users over the internet. We will not be delving into these tools here, but instead concentrate on stand-alone usage to create models and assemblies.

If you do not at some point say (or at least think) "WOW!" while learning how to use Wildfire, then you are very hard to impress indeed.

This sounds like it's pretty complicated!...

It is important to realize that you won't be able to master Wildfire overnight, or even after completing these lessons. Its power derives from its flexibility and rich set of commands. It is natural to feel overwhelmed at first! With not too much practice, however, you will soon become comfortable with the basic operation of the program. As you proceed through the lessons, you will begin to get a feel for the operation of the program, and the philosophy behind feature based design. Before you know it, you'll feel like a veteran and will gain a tremendous amount of personal satisfaction from being able to competently use it to assist you in your design tasks. Some work done by students after completing this tutorial is featured in a Project Gallery, available on the Web at the URL **<http://www.mece.ualberta.ca/courses/mec265/vrprojects.htm>**.

You will find that using Wildfire is quite different from previous generation CAD programs. This is a case where not having previous CAD experience might even be an asset since you won't have to unlearn anything! For example, because it is a solid modeling program, all your work is done directly on a 3D model rather than on 2D views of the model. Spatial visualization is very important and, fortunately, the display is very easy to manipulate. Secondly, as with computer programming, with Wildfire you must do a considerable amount of thinking and planning ahead (some fast free-hand sketching ability will come in handy here!) in order to create a clean model of a part or assembly. Don't worry about these issues yet - they will not interfere with your learning the basic operation of the program. As you become more adept with Wildfire, you will naturally want to create more complex models. It is at this time that these high-level issues will assert themselves. In the meantime, have fun and practice, practice, practice.

Overview of the Lessons

A brief synopsis of the lessons in this tutorial is given below. Each lesson should take at least 2 to 3 hours to complete - if you go through the lessons too quickly or thoughtlessly, you may not understand or remember the material. ***Do not confuse recognition with comprehension***. For best results, it is suggested that you scan/browse ahead through each lesson completely before going through it in detail. The CD that is enclosed with the hard copy edition of this book gives a multimedia overview of each lesson and has been created for just this task. You will then have a sense of where the lesson is going, and not be tempted to just follow the commands blindly. You need to have a sense of the whole forest when examining each individual tree!

In order to complete some of the lessons, you will need to install some tutorial files on your hard disk. These are included on the enclosed CD. Further instructions for this are in Lesson #1.

Lesson 1 - User Interface, View Controls and Model Structure

How to start Pro/E; representation of Pro/E command syntax; command flow in Pro/E; special mouse functions; Pro/E windows; controls for managing the view and display of objects; the model tree; how parts and assemblies are structured.

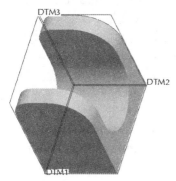

Lesson 2 - Creating a Simple Object (Part I)

Creating a simple part using sketched features; datum curves; Sketcher and Intent Manager are introduced; sketching constraints, alignments, and procedures; feature database functions are introduced; part templates.

Lesson 3 - Creating a Simple Object (Part II)

Placed features (hole, chamfer, round) are added to the block created in Lesson #2; listing and naming features; modifying dimensions; adding relations to control part geometry; more Sketcher tools; implementing *design intent*.

Lesson 4 - More Features for Creating Parts

A new part is modeled using a number of different feature creation commands and options: both sides protrusions, an axisymmetric (revolved) protrusion, a cut, rounds, and chamfer. More Sketcher tools. Edge sets. Mirrored features. Model analysis tools. We will intentionally make some modeling errors to see how Pro/E responds.

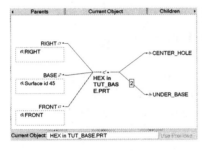

Lesson 5 - Modeling Utilities, Parent/Child Relations, and the 3 R's

These utilities are used to investigate and edit your model: changing references, change feature shapes, changing the order of feature regeneration, changing feature attributes, and so on. Suppressing and resuming features. If your model becomes even moderately complex, you will need to know how to do this!

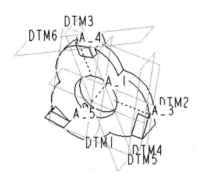

Lesson 6 - Sketcher Tools and Datum Planes

More tools in Sketcher are introduced, including sketching relations. The mysteries of datum planes and make datums are revealed! What are they, how are they created? How are they used to implement design intent?

Lesson 7 - Patterns and Copies

Creating a counterbored hole and hole notes. Patterns (one-dimensional or two-dimensional); radial patterns of placed and sketched features. Pattern groups. Copies using translation, rotation, or mirroring.

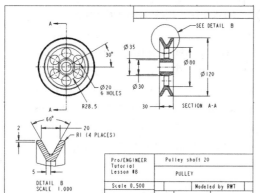

Lesson 8 - Creating an Engineering Drawing

This lesson will introduce you to the process of making dimensioned engineering drawings. Two new parts are created (both parts will also be used in Lesson #9 on assemblies). Much of the work in creating the drawing is done by Pro/E, although a fair amount of manual labor must go into improving the cosmetics of the drawings.

Lesson 9 - Assembly Fundamentals

This lesson will show you how to create an assembly from previously created parts. This involves creating placement constraints that specify how the parts are to fit together. Assigning appearances (colors).

Lesson 10 - Assembly Operations

This lesson will show you how to make modifications to the assembly created in Lesson #9. This includes changing part dimensions, adding assembly features, suppressing and resuming components, creating exploded views, and creating an assembly drawing. Display styles.

Lesson 11 - Sweeps and Blends

These are the most complicated (ie. flexible and powerful) features covered in these lessons. They are both types of solid protrusions, but can also be used to create cuts and slots.

Once again, as you go through these lessons, take the time to explore the options available and experiment with the commands. You will learn the material best when you try to apply it on your own ("flying solo"), perhaps trying to create some of the parts shown in the exercises at the end of each lesson.

On-Line Help

Should you require additional information on any command or function, Pro/E comes with extensive Web-based on-line help. This contains the complete text of *all* reference manuals for the software. There are several ways you can access the on-line help. These are presented in Lesson #1.

To those of you who have read this far: Congratulations! You are probably anxious to get going with Wildfire. Let's get started...

This page left blank.

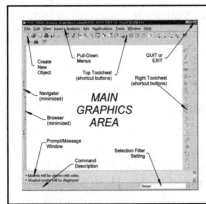

Lesson 1

User Interface, View Controls and Model Structure

Synopsis

Starting Pro/E; command syntax; mouse functions; view and display controls; model structure of parts and assemblies; the model tree; obtaining hard copy; on-line help.

Overview of this Lesson

We are going to cover a lot of introductory ground in this lesson with two main objectives. The first is to introduce you to the Pro/E user interface and locate the commands for controlling the display of parts and assemblies. You need to be very comfortable with these controls so that later on we can concentrate on commands for actually creating new objects or dealing with other issues of running the program.

Our second objective is to explore how models of parts and assemblies are structured[1]: what features are used, how they are ordered, and so on. It is important to keep in mind that creating a Pro/E model involves much more than simply producing geometry or creating pretty pictures. A model can have a number of purposes and end users: engineering analysis and visualization, production of drawings, manufacturing and production planning, marketing, and so on. If the model is centrally involved in design of a new product (which is typically a very iterative process), then we must ensure that it is simple, flexible, and robust to the inevitable modifications that will occur as the design evolves. Plus, there are often several different ways to create the desired geometry. Obviously, if you only know one way of doing something, your options will be limited! If you know several, which one should you use, and why? Furthermore, since a great deal of design these days is done in groups and teams, it is inevitable that you will be passing your models on to someone else. It must be easy for them to figure out how your model was made. *Simple .. flexible .. robust*. These goals are not that much different from those of writing a computer program. In fact, you might think of model creation as

---

[1] An old saying, attributed to Lao Tzu, goes something like: "Give a man a fish and you feed him for a day. Teach him how to fish and you feed him for a lifetime." Perhaps the best way to get started is just to be shown the fish!

"programming" the geometry engine to produce the product you want. As with computer programming, you will be a much more effective Pro/E user if you take some time to plan your model <u>before</u> you sit down at the computer.

The point of these comments is that modeling is not a trivial task. In this tutorial you must try to connect the "what, how, where" of issuing commands with the "when" and "why" in order to improve your modeling skills.

We will go at quite a slow pace at the start[2]. This should leave you sufficient time for experimenting on your own, which you are strongly encouraged to do. Here's what will be covered in this lesson:

1.   Starting Pro/ENGINEER
2.   Layout of the screen and user interface
3.   How commands are entered into Pro/ENGINEER
4.   How this tutorial will represent the command sequence
5.   Files and directories
6.   View and display controls
7.   Exploring the data structure for a part
8.   Exploring the data structure for an assembly
9.   How to get printed hard copy
10. How to get on-line Help

We will spend most of our time on sections 6 through 8. It will be a good idea to browse ahead through each section to get a feel for the direction we are going, before you do the lesson in detail. Even better, use the enclosed CD-ROM[3] for a multi-media overview of the lesson. A few words of caution: Take your time through the lesson. Resist the temptation to skip over the discussion and just execute the commands. There is a lot of material here which will be useful later, and not much that you can ignore without eventually paying for it. It is likely that you won't be able to absorb everything with a single quick pass-through. Good luck and have fun!

Helpful Hint

You may find it helpful to work with a partner on some of these lessons because you can help each other with the "tricky bits." Split the duties so that one person is reading the tutorial out loud while the other is doing the keyboard and mouse stuff, and then switching duties periodically. It will be handy to have two people scanning the menus for the desired commands and watching the screen. Pro/E uses a lot of subtle visual queues to alert you to what the program is doing or requires next. Having two people watching out for this may be helpful.

---

[2] Lao Tzu also said "A journey of a thousand miles begins with a single step."

[3] The CD-ROM, by Jack Zecher at IUPUI, is included with the hard-copy version of this tutorial. For further information, contact the publisher at <**www.schroff.com**>.

Starting Pro/ENGINEER

To start Pro/ENGINEER on a Windows-based machine, there may be an icon right on the desktop or you may have to look in the **Start** menu at the bottom left of the screen on the Windows taskbar. Pro/E launches like any other Windows application. If you are running on a Unix machine (assuming the installation is standard) type ***proewildfire*** at your system prompt and press the **Enter** key[4]. The program takes a while to load so be patient. The startup is complete when your screen looks like Figure 1. The screen shown in the figure is the bare-bones, default Pro/E screen. If your system has been customized[5], the menu bars and window contents of your interface may look slightly different.

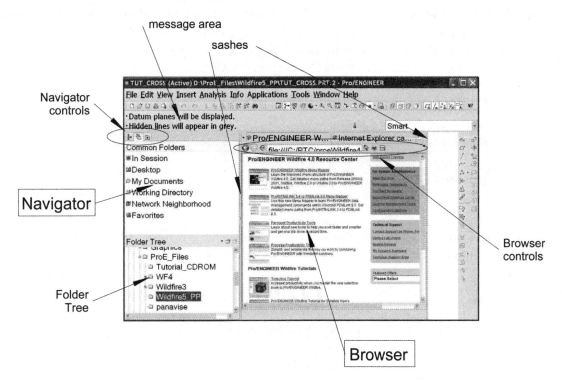

Figure 1 The Pro/ENGINEER Wildfire start-up screen

On the left is a multi-purpose area called the **Navigator**, with some associated controls at the top. In the default start-up, the Navigator shows you the *Common Folder* structure on your machine, among which is your current *working directory*. The working directory is generally where Pro/E will look for and save your files. Other tools in the Navigator allow you to organize folders and web sites into groups of favorites. These are accessed

---

[4] You may have to check this sequence with your local system administrator, as different installations may handle the Pro/E launch differently.

[5] Customizing the operation and interface of Pro/E is discussed in the Appendix to the hard-copy edition of this tutorial. These advanced topics are also discussed in the *Pro/ENGINEER Wildfire Advanced Tutorial* available from Schroff Development Corporation.

using the control tabs at the top. If you place the mouse cursor over these you will see their names (**Model Tree**, **Folder Browser**, **Favorites**) in a pop-up tool-tip. At the bottom of the Navigator pane is the ***Folder Tree*** button which if selected will expand to show the directory structure of your computer. To the right of the Navigator is the **Browser**, which is an integrated web browser. A major focus of Wildfire is connectivity between/among users. To that end, many Internet communication tools are embedded within the program. In addition to communicating with other users, the Browser allows you to launch regular web pages and, for example, download part files from the web directly into Pro/E. The browser functions in the same way as normal web browsers.

The Navigator and Browser areas can be resized by dragging left/right on the vertical sashes. Each area can be minimized by clicking on the thin textured buttons on the sashes - do that now. They will minimize along the left edge of the screen. You are left with the screen shown in Figure 2. Some shortcut buttons will not appear until we load a part.

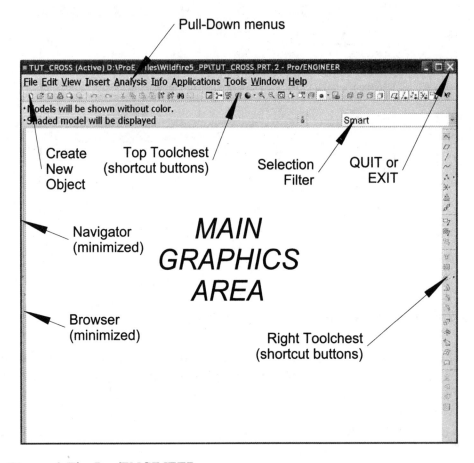

Figure 2 The Pro/ENGINEER screen

> **Helpful Hint**
> Regarding window management, DO NOT maximize the main Pro/E screen, and DO
> NOT resize or move the main or menu windows. Pro/E is pretty good about placing
> these so that they don't collide or overlap. If you start messing with the window size
> and placement, sooner or later you will bury a command menu behind other
> windows, particularly if your computer has a small screen. This will cause you a lot
> of confusion. Let Pro/E do its own window management for now.

In Figure 2, the main graphics area is, of course, where most of the action will take place.
Users familiar with graphical interfaces (like Windows) will be quite at home with the
pull-down menus at the top and the use of the short-cut buttons at the top and right side
of the screen (called the *toolbars*). As you move the mouse (slowly) across the short-cut
buttons at the top or right, a tool tip box will pop up (this may take a couple of seconds).
A number of buttons will be grayed out, meaning they are inactive at this time. The
prompt/message area above the graphics area shows brief system messages (including
errors and warnings) during command execution. Pro/E is usually set up to show only
the last few lines of text in this message area, but you can resize the area by dragging on
its lower horizontal border. When the mouse cursor is in the message area, you can use
the scroll wheel to review the message history.

As you use Pro/E, you will encounter many other windows that will open at appropriate
times. These generally act in very intuitive ways and are very similar in behavior to
other Windows-based programs.

Before we load an object into the program, let's explore the interface a bit. Along the
way we'll discuss how this tutorial will deal with command entry.

How commands are entered into Pro/ENGINEER

There are a number of ways that you will be interacting with the program: menu picks,
shortcut buttons, keyboard entry, and special mouse functions. These are described
below.

Pull-Down Menus

The main pull-down menus are presented across the top of the Pro/E window. Click on
the *File* menu to open it and scan down the list of available commands. Many of these
have direct analogs and similar functions to familiar Windows commands. Commands
unavailable in the current context are always grayed out. The available menu choices
will also change depending on the current operating mode. Move your cursor slowly
across to each pull-down menu in turn (*Edit, View, Insert, . . .*) and have a quick look at
the available commands. Most are grayed out at this time since we have no object loaded
to work on. We will introduce these as they become available and on an "as-needed"

basis as we go through the lessons. Some menu commands will open up a second level menu (these have a filled '>' symbol to their right).

Short-cut Buttons

The buttons in the default toolbar immediately below the pull-down menus are shown in Figure 3. We are going to spend most of this lesson exploring the function(s) of these buttons. There are basically five button groups (plus a *Help* button), as indicated on the figure. Other buttons and button groups may appear on this row as you enter different parts of the program. Buttons not relevant to the current program status are either not shown or grayed out. Move your cursor across the buttons, and a pop-up box will tell you the name of the button. Note that there is another set of buttons on the right side of the graphics window. These are discussed a bit later. You can add your own buttons and toolbars to customize either of these areas[6].

Dialog Windows

Starting several years ago with Wildfire1.0, Pro/E moved away from the cascading menu style of previous releases (a legacy of its Unix heritage), and adopted a more conventional Windows-style interface almost everywhere. Dialog windows play a major role. In these windows you must enter text or numeric data, select options from pull-down lists, set toggles (radio buttons), check options, and so on. These should be very familiar to Windows users. The idea is to set/select data in the dialog window and then select *OK.* Occasionally you will have to select *Apply* in order for the settings to "stick" - if you select *Cancel*, all new dialog settings are ignored. You can usually set the options in any order although sometimes the layout and data entry fields of the dialog window will change when particular options are selected (in which case, obviously, order matters).

Menu Picks

The conversion of the Pro/E interface to eliminate cascading menus is not quite complete. There are a few places in the program where remnants of this old style still exist[7]. In these cases, the text commands (and command options) are initiated using picks on menus that will appear at the time they are needed. These menus will show up to the right of the main window, with commands arranged in a vertical list. As you move the mouse pointer up and down within the list, each command will highlight and a one-line message describing the command under the pointer will appear in the message area.

---

[6] Customization of the interface is discussed in detail in the *Pro/ENGINEER Advanced Tutorial*. Some simple customization methods are shown in the Appendix of this tutorial. HINT: *Right click* the mouse on a blank area of the toolbar.

[7] These sometimes also occur when working with legacy parts, that is, parts created in a previous version of Pro/E. See, for example, the sweep feature (#5) in the part *tut_handle*.

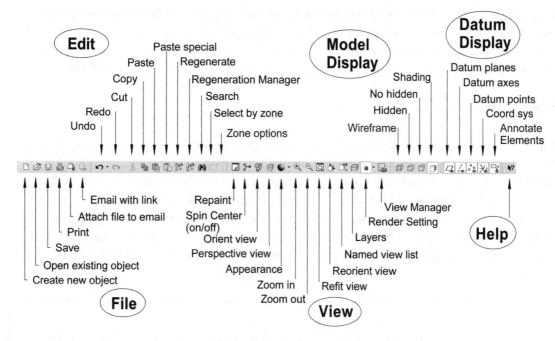

Figure 3 The top toolbar (default) with groups of related shortcut buttons

---

Helpful Hint
Each time you come to a new dialog window or menu get in the habit of quickly
scanning up and down the listed commands and noting the brief message in the
command window. Such exploration builds a familiarity with the location of the
commands.

In the cascading menus, the pre-selected default command in a menu is highlighted. This
default can often be accepted by clicking the middle mouse button (a *middle-click*) with
the mouse positioned anywhere in the graphics window. With the exception of this
default command, you execute a menu command by picking it using the *left* mouse
button. Menu choices that are "grayed-out" are either not available on your system or are
not valid commands at that particular time. Often, when you pick a command, other
menus will pop open below the current one. When these represent options for the current
command, the default option will again be highlighted. You can select another option by
left-clicking on it. There may be several groups of options on a single menu separated by
horizontal lines. Any options not currently valid are grayed out. When all the options in a
menu are set the way you want (by *left-clicking*), click on **Done** at the bottom of the
option menu window (or *middle-click*).

Helpful Hint
Clicking the *middle* mouse button is often synonymous with selecting **Done** or
pressing the **Enter** key on the keyboard.

You can often back out of a command menu by pressing an available ***Done-return*** or ***Quit*** command, or by pressing a command on a higher menu. At some times, you will be given a chance to ***Cancel*** a command. This usually requires an explicit confirmation, so you don't have to worry about an accidental mouse click canceling some of your work.

Pop-Up Menus

Pop-up menus are available in a number of operating modes by holding down the *right* mouse button. This brings up a pop-up menu at the cursor location which contains currently relevant commands. These commands are often available elsewhere in the interface, but having them pop-up at the cursor location means you don't have to keep taking your attention off the pointer location in the graphics window. Often the alternate location for these pop-up commands is several levels deep in the menus on the side so it is much quicker to get to them using the pop-up. This is part of what Pro/E calls the "Direct Modeling" interface.

Helpful Hint

While you are learning the interface, it won't hurt to periodically execute a right-click. This will usually do no harm, and will let you get familiar with the commands available in this way. Remember that the pop-up menus are context sensitive, so they will change depending on what you are doing!

Command/Message Window

There is no command line interface to Pro/E, unlike some other CAD programs. However, you will occasionally enter commands from the keyboard in response to prompts in the command/message window. This is also a remnant of the old interface and due to the continuing development of the Wildfire interface, input to the program in this area has almost vanished.. Note that when Pro/E is expecting input in the command/message window, none of the menu picks will be "live." Generally, you will only use the keyboard to enter alphanumeric data when requested, such as object or file names, numerical values, and so on, into dialog windows that open as required. The keyboard is also used to launch *mapkeys*, which are special keyboard inputs that will launch a pre-programmed sequence of commands (commonly called macros).

Helpful Hint

If your mouse ever seems "dead", that is the menus, toolbars, and so on won't respond to mouse clicks, check the message window; Pro/E is probably waiting for you to type in a response.

You will have to get used to being aware of several areas on the screen: the menu(s) at the top and right, the Navigator window, the graphics window, and the command/message area at the top. At the start, this will get a little hectic at times. Until you become very familiar with the menu picks and command sequence, keep an eye on the one-line message description in the message window. There is often enough information there to help you complete a command sequence. (Also, read the Hint on page 2 about working with another person to start with.)

Mouse Functions

The mouse is by far the most important input device in Pro/E. Wildfire is designed to be used with a 3-button mouse. If it has a middle scroll wheel, all the better. The mouse buttons are sometimes used in combination with keyboard keys. We will assume here that you have the default mouse set-up (with apologies to left handed users who may have re-mapped the mouse buttons). As you will have anticipated, most selections of menu commands, shortcut buttons, and so on, are performed by clicking with the left mouse button (LMB). In this book, whenever you "select", "click", or "pick" a command or entity, this is done with the LMB unless otherwise directed.

The functions controlling the view of the object in the graphics window are all associated with the middle mouse button (MMB) and scroll wheel (if the mouse has one). These are the important Spin, Pan, Zoom functions as shown in Table 1.1 below. Some of these are used in combination with the Shift and Control keys on the keyboard. The action of the mouse is also affected by the selection of a View Mode. All dynamic view operations involve dragging the mouse. The on-line documentation refers to this as 'Direct View Control'. The more comfortable you get with these mouse functions, the quicker you will be able to work. They will become second nature after a while. We will open a part in a few minutes so that you can investigate view control functions.

The dynamic view controls in Table 1-1 on the next page refer to display of 3D objects. When viewing 2D objects such as sketches and drawings, some of the mouse functions change sightly (primarily the spin command). Mouse functions associated with the right mouse button (RMB) will also be introduced a bit later in the lessons. The main function associated with the RMB is to launch context sensitive pop-up menus as described above.

How this tutorial will represent the command sequence

Pro/E generally operates on the assumption that you are an experienced user, so does not blatantly display a lot of prompting and/or unnecessary information that would slow it (or you) down. Prompts and queues that it gives are short, crisp, and sometimes quite subtle (like the color or shape of a small icon on the screen). Not much hand-holding here. And certainly no cute but annoying "wizards!" This is great for power users, but is quite intimidating for new users.

Table 1-1 Common Pro/E Mouse Functions (3D)

Function		Operation	Action
Selection (click left button)		LMB	entity or command under cursor selected
Direct View Control (drag holding middle button down)		MMB	Spin
		Shift + MMB	Pan
		Ctrl + MMB (drag vertical)	Zoom
		Ctrl + MMB (drag horizontal)	Rotate around axis perpendicular to screen
		Roll MMB scroll wheel (if available)	Zoom
Pop-up Menus (click right button)		RMB with cursor over blank graphics window	launch context-sensitive pop-up menus

---

* * *   Caution   * * *

This tutorial tries to present the command sequence as accurately and concisely as possible. This is a difficult task due to the different ways you will be interacting with the program, the many available shortcuts that have been added in Wildfire, and the diverse nature of the presented information (text, graphics, tool icons, line colors, menus, dialogs, etc.). Also, many functions in Wildfire have become highly automated with the use of numerous defaults. In these cases, an inadvertent mouse click on the wrong command can sometimes lead you quite far off the tutorial path. So, in the early lessons, pay very close attention and try not to jump ahead.

We will try to discuss each new command as it is entered (usually by selecting from a toolbar or menu). Eventually, you may be told to enter a long sequence of commands that may span several menus and/or require keyboard input. Fortunately, as Wildfire adopts more and more of the standard Windows interaction methods, it is becoming easier to figure out how to tell Pro/E what you want it to do. You will know that you are beginning to understand the interface when you can enter a part of the program you have not seen before and correctly anticipate the required input.

The following notation will be used to represent command input to the program. Commands are always shown in ***bold italics***. Dialog window titles are shown in **bold**. Otherwise:

♦   If a command is launched using a toolbar button, that will be stated in the text, often with the button shown to help you identify it. For example: ***Regenerate*** .

♦   If you are to select an option from a pull-down list, you will see the name of the option with the desired list member in parentheses as follows:
   Display Style(Shading)

♦   If a setting is a simple toggle, you will see the name of the option with the toggle setting (On or Off, Yes or No) in parentheses as follows:
   Bell (Off)

♦   If you are to enter data through the keyboard and there is the possibility for confusion, you will see the notation using square brackets "*[...]*" as follows:
   [block]
In this case, just enter the characters inside the square brackets.

♦   If you select a command (usually from the pull-down menus) that starts up another menu or window, followed by a selection from the new menu, you will see the notation using the ">" sign as follows:

   menu1_command* > *menu2_command

♦   If a number of picks are to be made from the same menu or window you will see the notation using the "|" sign as follows (these are generally listed in a top-to-bottom order in the menu, but can be chosen in any order in dialog windows):

   option1 | option2 | option3

Be aware that in some dialog windows, the contents, layout, and data entry fields may change substantially if some options are chosen.

Thus you might see a command sequence in a lesson that looks like this:

   Tools > Environment > Colors(On) | Display Style(Shading) | OK

How to get On-Line Help

As you go through these lessons, you might want to consult additional reference material. Some of this might have been listed in the Browser window when you first launched the program. Extensive on-line help is available. The help documentation, consisting of the entire Pro/E user manual set (many thousands of pages), are viewed using a browser. There are several ways to access the help files:

1. Selecting the ***Help > Help Center*** command.
2. Click the ***What's This?*** button ▶?   towards the right end of the top toolbar. Then click on any command or dialog window.
3. Find the location of the help files (its install path[8]) and execute the command ***<ProEHelpInstallPath>/html/proe_help.exe***

As a sampler of the extensive on-line help available, execute the following sequence:

> ***Help > Help Center***
> ***Pro/ENGINEER Functional Areas > Fundamentals***

You should see the window shown below in Figure 4. In the panel on the right side in this window, select the link *Pro/ENGINEER Fundamentals*. If you click the ***Show in Table of Contents*** button at the top right, you will see your current document location in the left panel (see Figure 5). Notice the five tabs in the left pane of Figure 5: ***Table of Contents, Search, Index, Bookmark, Configuration***. You should explore these areas a little to see what is available.

---

[8] You may have to check this with your system administrator.

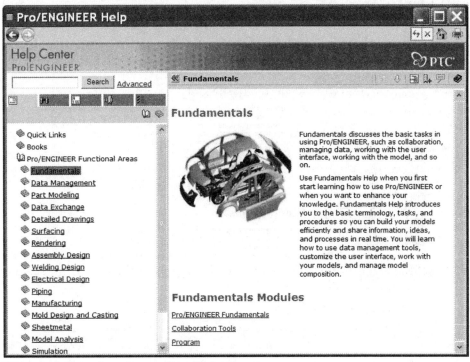

Figure 4 Opening the on-line Help Center

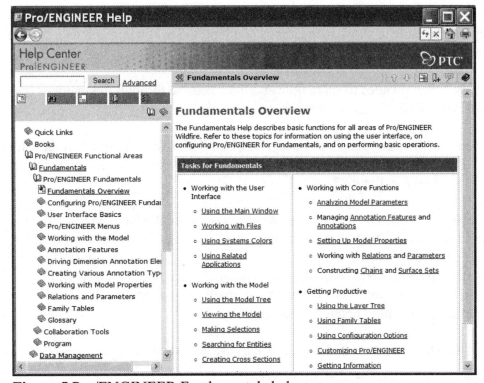

Figure 5 Pro/ENGINEER Fundamentals help area

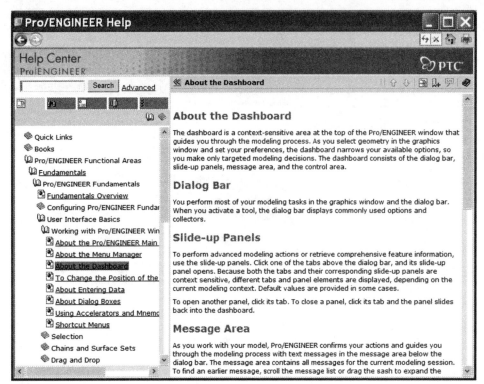

Figure 6 Exploring the Help pages

With the table of contents displayed in the left panel, clicking on the small book icons will expand the table to show subheadings and topics. See if you can locate the topic shown in Figure 6.

If you have a few minutes to spare now and then, browse through the manuals (especially the *Pro/ENGINEER Fundamentals* section).

Enter the term "helical sweep" in the text box beside the **Search** button in the left pane. A number of topics will be listed - pick the "Example" several items down. You should see the contents shown in Figure 7.

In the beginning, it will be a rare event when you explore the Help pages and don't pick up something useful. If you desire and have the local facilities, you can obtain hard copy of these manual pages using the print button at the extreme top right of the help window. Your system may have postscript or pdf versions of these pages - check with your system administrator. Be aware of the cost and time involved in printing off large quantities of documentation (and think about the trees, too!).

Close all the Help windows and proceed on to the next section.

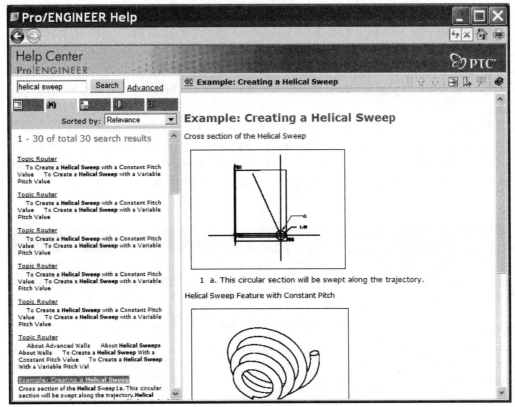

Figure 7 Using the Search function in the Help Center

Tutorial Files and Working Directory

A number of files used in this Tutorial (parts, assemblies, drawings, and support files) are contained on the enclosed CD-ROM. Your instructor may have made local copies of the files available.

These files will have to be stored somewhere on your local hard disk. Note that they must all be in the same directory. This should be your default working directory for Pro/E. To find out where this working directory is, since Pro/E is up and running at this point, all we have to do is try to open a file. Pro/E will automatically look first in the current working directory. Give the following commands (starting in the pull-down menus):

> *File > Open*

or use the toolbar button shown in Figure 3 to open a file. In the left pane of the File Open dialog window, select the ***Working Directory*** folder (symbol ⬜). The full path to the current working directory is shown near the top of the dialog window (see Figure

8) [9]. This uses the Windows Vista style for displaying the path. If the dialog window looks something like Figure 8 (all the files shown in the Figure are listed in the window; you may have to scroll down the list) then proceed on to the next section on view controls. There may, of course, be more files listed in your window, depending on your local situation (other system users, computer lab common directories, and so on).

If your *File Open* dialog window contains the files listed in Figure 8, proceed on to the next section on view and display controls. If it does not contain the files listed in Figure 8, then either they have not been installed or they are in another directory. Select **Cancel**, then depending on your circumstance, pick from either option A or B below.

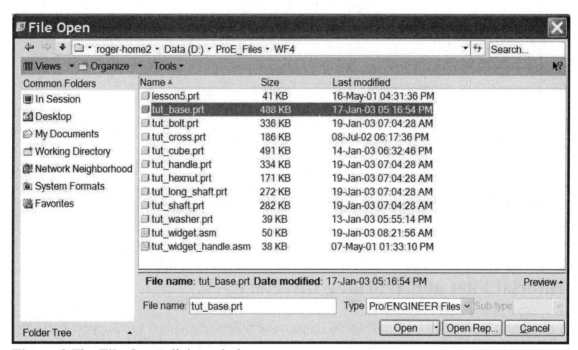

Figure 8 The **File Open** dialog window

Note that an alternative to the *File Open* command we used above, you can directly select the ***Working Directory*** in the Navigator. This will open the directory in the Browser. We will experiment with this alternative a bit later.

OPTION A - Tutorial files not installed

Minimize Pro/E and copy the files to the working directory identified above. If using the Web download, follow the instructions on the download page. Make sure the files are being put in the right directory. You can then restore Pro/E and proceed to the next

---

[9] On Windows systems, the start-up working directory can be set in the shortcut that launches the program. For a desktop shortcut, right click on the icon and select ***Properties > Shortcut*** and enter the path to the desired working directory in the *Start In* field.

section on view controls.

OPTION B - Tutorial files are in another directory (changing the working directory)

One solution here is to copy the files from wherever they are to the current working directory. Presumably, however, they are in the other directory for a reason. So, you have to tell Pro/E to change its working directory by using the commands

File > Set Working Directory

then navigate using the standard Windows operations until the desired directory is shown in the path near the top of the window. Accept the dialog with *OK* (or remember that a middle click is a shortcut for accepting a dialog window) and your working directory is now changed (see the message area). You can also change the working directory by opening the Folder Tree in the Navigator pane, selecting the desired directory, using the RMB pop-up menu to select *Set Working Directory*. The *File > Open* command should now bring up a list of the proper files.

Controlling the Screen: View and Display Commands

In this section, we will examine a number of ways to control how Pro/E displays objects on the screen. You will need the part and assembly files described in the previous section.

Although the difference between the two main types of controls is not critical, we can distinguish between *View* and *Display* controls as follows (refer back to the toolbar groupings in Figure 3):

View Controls - These determine how you will look at the object - its orientation, size, and placement on the screen. This includes commands for zooming in and out, rotating the object, panning across an object, or selecting a pre-defined viewing direction (like TOP, FRONT, etc).

Display Controls - These determine how the object is represented on the screen. Options here include wireframe, hidden line, or shaded displays. All displays can be with or without color turned on. You can also control the display style of some special line types (for example the common edge of two surfaces that are tangent to each other - called tangent edges). There are also separate controls for the display of objects called DATUMS, which we will get to in a little while.

Let's see how these controls work.

Opening a Part File

If they aren't already, close the
Browser and Navigator windows by
clicking on the textured button on
the right sash. Select

File > Open

The dialog box shown in Figure 8
will appear, showing a list of part,
drawing, and assembly files in the
current working directory. These
can be identified by the filename
extensions: **prt**, **drw**, and **asm**,
respectively. Click on the file
tut_base.prt and select *Open*. The
object shown in Figure 9 should
appear, possibly at a slightly
different orientation. The default is

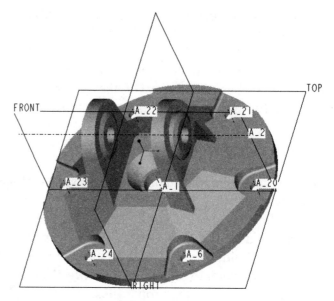

Figure 9 The part tut_base.prt

a color shaded display as shown in the figure. Also shown on the screen are a number of
brown (or black) lines that represent non-solid geometric construction entities called
datums (planes and axes). We will be learning lots more about datums throughout these
lessons. For now, note that all datums have labels, or *tags*, like TOP, FRONT, A_1, A_6,
and so on. You will also discover that datum planes have a positive side (brown) and a
negative side (black). These will be clearly visible when you spin the object.

Many previously grayed out buttons on the top and right toolbars are now active. Scan
these commands and buttons but resist the temptation to select any of them just yet! If
you do, you can usually back out of the command with *Cancel* or *Quit* or selecting the
red ✖ button that might appear at the top right of the screen.

View Controls using the Mouse

The operation of the mouse, as far as controlling the view, depends on two related view
controls: the spin center and the orient mode. We'll deal with the spin center first.

Spin Center On (Default)

The display of the spin center is controlled by a button ⌁ on the top tool bar. Make
sure the spin center icon in the top toolbar is on (pressed in). In the approximate center
of the part you should see a small red-green-blue triad. This is the spin center. Beside the
spin center button in the top toolbar is the *Orient Mode* ⌖ control, which should be off
at this time. We'll deal with it later.

The main mouse functions for view control of 3D objects are shown back in Table 1-1 on page 10. The dynamic view controls for spin, pan, and zoom are all performed by dragging the mouse while holding down the middle mouse button (MMB). Try the following:

SPIN   Hold down the MMB and drag the mouse. The object will spin, with the spin center staying fixed on the screen.

ZOOM   Hold down the Control key (CTRL) and MMB. Drag the mouse towards and away from you. This will cause your view to zoom in and out on the object. Try this with the cursor at different points on the object or screen. The center of the zoom is at the initial location of the mouse cursor.

PAN   Hold down the Shift key and MMB. Dragging the mouse now translates (pans) your view across the object.

ZOOM   If you have a mouse with a scroll wheel, try turning that to zoom in and out on the object. Once again, the zoom is centered on the initial location of the mouse when you start scrolling.

ROTATE   Hold down the CTRL Key and MMB. Drag the mouse left to right. The object will rotate around an axis through the initial location of the mouse cursor and perpendicular to the screen.

Spend some time experimenting with these, especially the spin command which may take some getting use to. Since you will be working in a complex 3D environment, you will be using these more than any other commands in Pro/E, so you should be very comfortable with them.

For added practice with the dynamic view controls, there is a special exercise at the end of this lesson.

See if you can obtain the three part orientations shown in Figure 10 at the right. These are the standard engineering views (top, front, right). These views are so commonly used that there is a shortcut to obtain them that we will see in a minute or two.

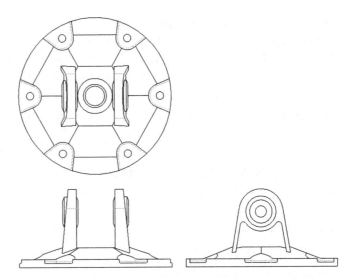

Figure 10 Standard engineering view orientations (top, front, right)

Spin Center Off

Now turn the spin center off using the icon in the top toolbar and see what happens with the mouse controls. The pan and zoom controls work as before. However, using the MMB, the spin occurs around the point on the screen where the cursor is located rather than the spin center. You will find this a useful function when you are zoomed way in on the model and want to spin the part around a specific vertex. If you try this with the spin center turned on, you are liable to spin the object right out of view. So, remember that spin center OFF means that spin occurs around the cursor; spin center ON means spin occurs around the spin center. Leave it off for now as we explore the other view control button.

Orientation Modes

The second control that works with the mouse buttons involves ***Orient Mode*** on the top toolbar. Select that now. Several changes occur on the screen. First, at the location of the spin center, a small round, black circle appears. Second, there is a black diamond with a red center. This is the current center of the dynamic view and can be reset by clicking the MMB. Third, depending on the settings for your installation[10], the datum planes may disappear. Finally, the mouse cursor changes shape from the arrow pointer to the orient mode icon. If you drag the MMB, the model will spin around the red diamond on the screen[11]. Experiment with the operation of the mouse (for example, holding down the CTRL key while spinning with the MMB will cause the model to rotate around a axis normal to the screen). Check the pan and zoom functions - they work the same as before.

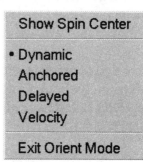

Figure 11 The ***Orient Mode*** pop-up menu

Now, hold down the right mouse button. You will get the pop-up window shown in Figure 11. Try selecting the ***Velocity*** option in this menu. The diamond changes to a circle. Now, drag a short distance with the MMB, and keep it pressed. You will see the object spinning at a constant speed. The speed and direction of the spin is controlled by the mouse position. Drag the mouse and the spin direction and speed will change. Spinning stops when you release the mouse button. When you are in velocity mode, both pan and zoom will occur at a constant velocity until you release the mouse button.

Hold down the RMB and select the ***Delayed*** option. The circle changes to a square. Any view changes are delayed until the mouse button is released. One problem with delayed

---

[10] There is a configuration setting (see the Appendix) that determines whether the datum planes are displayed during some operations. The option is *spin_with_part_entities*. When this is off (default) the datums will disappear whenever you spin the model.

[11] The behavior of Orient Mode has changed slightly from the first release of Wildfire (where it was called View Mode).

mode is it is very easy to make changes that are too large (especially pan) and when the view is updated the object is completely off the screen. If that happens, use the *Refit* button ⟦Q⟧ in the top toolbar (Figure 3). Note that this cancels *Orient Mode*, as does pressing any of the datum display buttons.

Finally, in the RMB pop-up, select *Anchored*. The square changes to a red triangle. Place the cursor on any straight edge, axis, or even a datum plane. Middle click to "grab" the edge. Now hold down the middle mouse button and drag. A portion of the chosen edge will highlight in red, and the model will spin around the highlighted line - it is anchored to it.

As you can see, there are a lot of visual queues to alert you to the current view control state.

The black circle means that *Orient Mode* is on. You can turn it off either using the top toolbar icon or select *Exit Orient Mode* in the pop-up menu (Figure 11).

If the spin center is turned back on, the view mode operations still work as we have just seen. In this case, though, spinning occurs relative to the spin center, as you might expect!

Toolbar View Commands

There are several other buttons on the top toolbar to control the view. The most important of these is probably the *Repaint* button (sometimes called *Redraw*), that looks like ⟦🖉⟧. You can also use *View > Repaint* or simply press *CTRL-R* (hold the Control key while you press R). This command causes a complete refresh of the graphics window, which is sometimes helpful to remove entities no longer required for display (like feature dimensions). Try out the other view buttons in this group ⟦🔍 🔍 Q⟧ (*Zoom In, Zoom Out, Refit*), watching the message area for prompts. The handiest of these is probably the one on the right (*Refit*).

Using Named Views

In addition to the dynamic viewing capabilities available with the mouse, you can go to predefined orientations. To view the object in the default orientation, select the *Named View List* shortcut button ⟦▢ᴬᴮ⟧ in the top toolbar and click on *Default Orientation*. Alternatively, you can select

View > Orientation > Standard Orientation

or press *CTRL-D* (hold the Control key while you press D). Your screen should now look like Figure 9 above. Try the other named orientations (TOP, FRONT, and so on) in the saved view list - these should take you immediately to the view orientations shown in Figure 10. When a drawing is made of a part or assembly, these are exactly the views that most commonly appear. You should bear this in mind when you are creating parts - orientation matters! In the named views (TOP, FRONT, RIGHT) you are looking directly at the brown side of the datum plane of the same name. It appears as a rectangle around the part. This rectangle will stretch or shrink so that it always just encloses the part. The other datums in these views are seen edge-on as pairs of brown and black lines. As mentioned above, the negative side of a datum plane is indicated using black. It is important to get some practice with looking at datum planes and, from their color, figuring out your view orientation. This will be particularly helpful when the model is displayed in wire frame.

Most parts you create will have these standard engineering views already defined, using standard part templates which we will discuss later. If you want to experiment with creating your own named views (handy for documenting the model), select the commands

View > Orientation > Reorient

Figure 12 Dialog for creating saved/named views

(or use the *Reorient View* shortcut button) which brings up the dialog shown in Figure 12. To expand the lower half of the window, click on the blue "Saved Views" region of the window. These named views have already been created in the part. In fact, they will be automatically present in any parts you create using the default template, discussed in the next lesson. If you want to set up your own named views, the general procedure for the *Orient by Reference* type (selected in the pull-down list at the top of the window) is to select two orthogonal surfaces or datum planes and tell Pro/E which way they should face in the desired view. These are called the view references and are specified in the **Options** area of the dialog window. References can be chosen to face the top, front, left, right, front, or back of the screen. For the example shown in Figure 12, the direction of Reference 1 is chosen as **Front**, that is the reference will face the front of the screen (toward you), while Reference 2 has been set to **Top** (the reference will face the top of the screen). In Figure 12, Reference 1 is the RIGHT datum plane; Reference 2 is the TOP datum plane. This combination of planes and directions produces the standard RIGHT engineering view (the saved name in the pane at the bottom). Note that you could obtain the same orientation by picking Reference 2 as the FRONT datum plane facing the left edge of the screen.

Once the view orientation options have been selected, you can enter a new view name at the bottom, then select *Save*. If you select a view in the **Saved Views** list, then *Set*, the model will spin to that orientation, but the options shown at the top of this dialog window are not updated. Data in this dialog window flows top-down only.

As a final note, you might remember that orientation references are not restricted to datum planes, as shown in Figure 12. You can use any planar surface as a reference. It is customary to use datum planes (especially the default planes) since these are less likely to be moved or otherwise changed as the model is created and modified later.

No doubt this all seems terribly confusing since we are using the same words ("top", "front", "right") for three purposes: naming the datum planes, specifying view directions relative to the screen, and giving names to the saved views themselves. Rest assured that this will eventually start to make sense! Close the Orientation window with *OK* (if you have made changes you want to keep) or *Cancel*.

Object Display Commands

These buttons on the top toolbar are fairly self-explanatory. They are (see Figure 3):

Wireframe - all object edges are shown as visible, even those at the back
Hidden line - hidden edges (or portions) are displayed in gray (dark but visible)
No Hidden - hidden edges (or portions) are not shown
Shading - shaded solid model

These display modes persist until changed by selecting a different mode. Try them out now. These buttons do not affect the display of datums. The datums may disappear momentarily when you are changing the view, for example during spinning. Note that the command

View > Shade

produces the same immediate effect as the *Shading* button except that the datums are automatically turned off and the display mode persists until the next *Repaint* regardless of the display toolbar buttons. Of these four modes, you will probably spend most of your time in hidden line mode, since this allows you to see hidden features (although they are dimmed). If you have a slow graphics card, this mode is also quicker than shaded images. Slow graphics cards are especially noticeable during spinning of shaded objects, which can become quite jerky for complicated models (single parts with lots of surfaces, or assemblies of many parts). However, shaded mode is useful to reinforce your mental image of the three dimensional shape, when that is sometimes unclear by looking at only the edges. The display mode is very much a matter of personal preference. Keep trying different modes in different situations to see what works best for you.

Other Model Display Commands

There are three additional model display controls in the top toolbar. Try these out:

Perspective View 🔲 - does as the name suggests. This is not very useful for single or small parts since the model appears distorted (try zooming in close to the model, then spin it - be prepared to get dizzy!).

Appearance Gallery ⬤ - this contains tools to define and apply appearances, which combine color, lighting, texture, transparency, decals, bump mapping, and so on. Appearances can be assigned to parts or individual surfaces. We will explore this at a later time.

Rendering ⬤ - this is a three-way toggle that controls real time rendering. These work with the appearance settings (note that colors must be turned on in the environment) to produce realistic images including shadows, reflections, lighting, background images, and other visual effects. We will not have time to explore these functions here. If you want to experiment, select

>   ***View > Model Setup***

and/or look up the *Rendering* topic in the *Functional Areas* in the Help Center.

Datum Display Commands

The four buttons in the DATUMS group of the top toolbar control the visibility (on or off) of the datums (planes, axes, points, coordinate systems). Try these out now. This model does not contain any datum points or coordinate systems, so you won't notice any effect from those two buttons. Remember that these buttons do not delete these entities from the model, just turn off their display. Also, do not confuse the datum display buttons at the top (each with a little eyeball on them) with the datum creation buttons (without the eyeball) on the right toolbar.

Display
☑ ⬭ Planes
☑ ⬭ Plane Tags
☑ ⁄ Axes
☑ ⁄ Axis Tags
☑ ˣ× Point Symbols
☑ ×ˣ× Point Tags
☑ ⋇ Coordinate Systems
☑ ⋇ Coordinate System Tags
☐ ⌇ Curve Tags
☑ ⌗ Section Tags
☑ }• Spin Center
☑ ⌐ 3D Annotations

Point Symbol
Cross

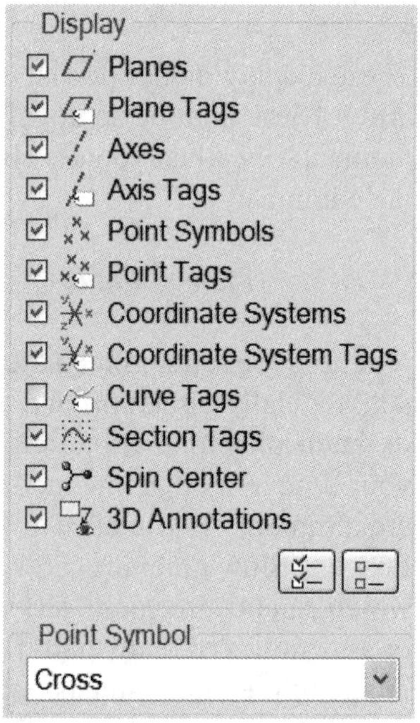

Figure 13 Datum display settings

You can also control the display of the datum labels, or tags. Select

>   ***View > Display Settings***
>   ***Datum Display***

See Figure 13. Turn off all the tag display settings.

Accept the dialog with ***OK***. The labels are gone[12]. Turn them back on again with the same sequence, using the ***Select All*** button below the list.

----

[12] You can easily add shortcut buttons to the top toolbar to control the display of datum tags. See the Appendix section on screen customization.

Modifying the Environment

Try experimenting with the settings in the dialog window obtained using

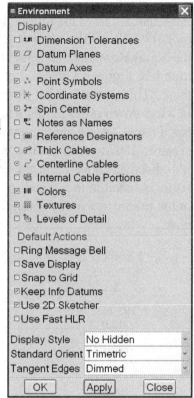

Tools > Environment

See Figure 14 at the right. This single window allows you to set the display of datums, the spin center, colors, as well as the overall display style, orientation, and treatment of tangent edges. Near the bottom of this window, try setting the display style to *No Hidden* and tangent edges to *Dimmed*. Now select *Apply*. Observe the screen carefully to see where the tangent edges have appeared. (You should be aware of tangent edges when you are modeling, since it is good practice to never use them as feature creation references.)

Your new settings will take effect when you select *Apply* or leave the *Environment* menu with *OK*. What happens if you make changes in the settings and then select *Close*? Note that the most common display styles are easily obtained using the short-cut buttons in the top toolbar.

Figure 14 The Environment settings dialog window

Another common setting involves the Colors option. Set the following (in the **Environment** menu):

> *Colors(Off)*
> *Display Style(Shading)*

then select *Apply*. This shows the part in the default neutral gray color. If you set the display style to *Hidden Line*, you will see the visible edges as white lines, hidden edges as gray lines, and tangent edges as dark gray lines.

Your choice of display style is strictly personal preference. However, keep in mind the following:

▸ It is useful to be able to see the entire object at once. *Hidden Line* gives you "x-ray" vision to do just that. *No Hidden* hides too much, and *Wireframe* is sometimes ambiguous.
▸ A lot of information is portrayed using color queues. It is useful, then, to keep your model color neutral so that you won't miss anything.
▸ On the other hand, the 3D shape of the object is most clearly shown in a shaded image. If you have trouble interpreting the line drawing image, go ahead and shade the part. And, color adds interest to what you're doing!

For now, turn *Colors* off, and set the display style to *Shading*.

Anatomy of a Part - Understanding the Model Structure

Now that we have explored most of the viewing and display commands, let's explore the model itself[13]. If the part **tut_base.prt** is not loaded, do that now with *File > Open*. Open the Navigator pane and select the left-most control tab (*Model Tree*). The screen should look like Figure 15 below. Let's examine the information in the model tree in the left pane. This contains a list of the features in the part database. The features were created in a top-down order in this list, called the *regeneration sequence*. Each of these features has a name - some are the default names and others have been specified by the model creator. Beside each feature is a small icon to help you identify the type of feature. We will discover more about these icons in a couple of minutes. As you click on any of the features listed in the model tree, edges of the selected feature are highlighted on the part in the graphics window using red (if colors are on) or white (if colors are off). Try that now.

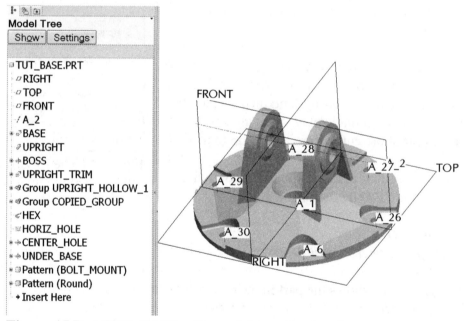

Figure 15 Part TUT_BASE with model tree (top level)

Preselection Highlighting

Preselection highlighting is how Pro/E tells you what will be selected on the model if you pick with the left mouse button. This tool is part of the object/action command structure. Pro/E also allows an action/object style of command. In the object/action structure, you select an object first and then specify the action to be performed on it. For many people, this is a more natural way of doing things. To accommodate this mode, Pro/E allows you

---

[13] It has taken a while, but this is where you finally get to see the fish!

to pick most objects directly in the graphics window by clicking on them[14].   When the display gets very cluttered (or the object you want is behind something else), it may be hard to pick on exactly what you want with the first click of the mouse. Thus, preselection highlighting is a method to make sure you are picking what you want in a complicated model.

To see how preselection highlighting works[15], first make sure that *Smart* is selected in the *Selection* filter list at the top right of the screen, as in Figure 16. Also, turn the color display back on.

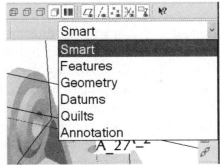

Figure 16 The Selection filter list

Place your cursor on one of the surfaces of the model, but do not click just yet. Some edges of the model will highlight in cyan (or white if you have not turned colors on) and a small box will pop open beside the cursor (there might be a couple of seconds delay). The box and highlighted edges show you which feature is involved with or has created the highlighted surface. As you drag the cursor (slowly!) around on the model, the different features that have created different surfaces are identified by cyan edges and a pop-up box.

If a feature is highlighted and you pick on it with the left button, the highlighted edges will turn red and the feature name will be highlighted in the model tree. If the selected feature is inside a group in the model tree, the group will have to be expanded. The highlighted feature is now selected as the object to be acted upon by the next command. To go deeper into the geometry of that feature, slowly move the cursor over the highlighted (red) surfaces. Now the filter will identify individual surfaces and edges formed by the feature. If you left click on an edge, you can go down to the next level and pick an individual vertex. The entity currently highlighted in red at any time during this selection process is the active entity. As soon as you have the one you want, you can leave selection and proceed on to perform some action on this entity (for example by picking a command from the RMB pop-up menu).

If you set the selection filter to (*Datums*), only datum planes and axes are trapped by the filter. The selection filter (*Geometry*) is the most detailed - it traps surfaces, edges and vertices and shows who they belong to.

Expanding the Model Tree

We would like to set up the model tree to show a bit more information. We will find out

----

[14] A function called *Query Select* has always been available to do this as part of the action/object selection process, and we will investigate it a bit later. The new preselection method is much simpler.

[15] Make sure this is turned on using *Edit > Select > Preferences*, and make sure the option *Preselection Highlighting* is turned on (checked). This is the Pro/E default.

how to do this from scratch in a later lesson. For now, we are going to read in a model tree configuration file that has been created for you. This should be in your working directory, along with all the part files transferred from the CD-ROM or downloaded from the web. To load it, select the **Settings** tab at the top of the model tree. Then pick

Open Settings File

Go to the current working directory and select the file **mod_tree.cfg** and click **Open**. This will add some columns on the right of the model tree (see Figure 17). You may have to drag the right border out a bit to see all the columns. The columns can all be resized by dragging on the vertical separators at the top. The new columns are the feature number, feature type, and feature subtype. The feature number indicates the order of feature creation (*regeneration sequence*). The feature types are datum planes, protrusions, cuts, holes, and so on. The subtypes give further classification

	Feat #	Feat Type	Feat Subtype
TUT_BASE.P			
RIGHT	1	Datum Plane	
TOP	2	Datum Plane	
FRONT	3	Datum Plane	
A_2	4	Datum Axis	
BASE	5	Protrusion	Extrude
UPRIGHT	6	Protrusion	Blend, Parallel, R...
BOSS	7	Protrusion	Revolve
UPRIGHT_	8	Cut	Extrude
Group UPF	9	Group Head	
Group COF	12	Group Head	
HEX	18	Protrusion	Sweep
HORIZ_HC	19	Hole	
CENTER_I	20	Cut	Revolve
UNDER_B	21	Cut	Revolve
Pattern (BC	22	Pattern	PATTERN
Pattern (Rc	53	Pattern	PATTERN
Insert Here			

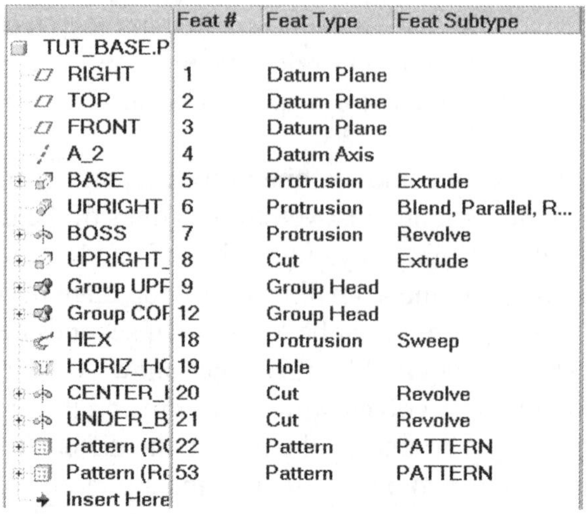

Figure 17 Model tree with added columns

information about each feature. For example, feature #5 is an extruded protrusion, feature #6 is a parallel blend protrusion, feature #7 is a revolved protrusion, etc. We will be spending a lot of time in these tutorials finding out what these features are and how they are created.

Most of the features in this part have been named. This is optional, but a very good idea. Features that have not been named will appear with only the feature type (protrusion, cut, hole, etc.) in the first column of the model tree. In a large model, this becomes very confusing and not very helpful. You should get in the habit of naming at least the key features in your models.

Notice that there seems to be a few features missing (notice the gaps at 9 - 12, 12 - 18, and 22 - 53). Click on the small plus sign beside feature #12 (on the left). This will expand the model tree to the next level for this feature, revealing several features there. Although these have not been named, they are members of a named group. The group was formed by mirroring features 6 through 11 simultaneously through the RIGHT datum plane. The group name indicates the copy operation.

Open the group starting at feature #9. In this group, the icon beside feature #10 (DTM5) is in a gray box. Notice that this datum plane is not visible on the model - it is currently hidden (as indicated by the gray box icon). If you put the cursor on DTM5 in the model tree and hold down the right mouse button, you can select **Unhide**. The datum plane now appears. This plane was used to create the cross sectional sketched shape of the next feature (#11, extruded cut). If you press the + sign beside feature #11, you will see a feature S2D0002. This is the 2D sketch that defines the shape of the cut. Select this in the model tree and hold down the right mouse button. Select **Edit**. The actual sketch now appears in red with yellow dimensions. It is best seen in RIGHT view. Select DTM5 again in the model tree and **Hide** it using the RMB pop-up menu.

Close the groups at features #9 and #12. If there is a bunch of extra stuff on the screen, use **Repaint**. Find out what is in the Pattern starting at feature #22 by expanding the model tree. Technically, this is called a *radial pattern* since all instances of the pattern were created by incrementing an angle around a central axis. The pattern instances are groups of features - these are named in the first group (feature #23). Each group has two hidden datums. See if you can find out what they are for.

The last pattern (starting at feature #53) consists entirely of rounds. These rounded edges were kept separate from the previous group pattern because rounds are normally considered cosmetic features. Rounds often cause problems with downstream design operations such as creating drawings and performing finite element analysis. Adding them last, and keeping the rounds separate means they can be easily selected and temporarily removed from the model (or *suppressed*, see Lesson #5) without disrupting other model geometry.

Compare the feature types and subtypes listed in the model tree with the feature icons on the left. You should be able to easily identify datum planes and axes, and extruded, revolved, and swept features, patterns and groups, and hidden features from their icons.

The Model Player

Just knowing the feature types and creation order doesn't give you a really clear idea of how this model was created. The **Model Player** offers a useful tool if (like now!) you have obtained a model from someone else and want to explore its structure.

Make the model tree pane a bit smaller so that all you can see are the feature names and numbers. Now select

Tools > Model Player

A new dialog window opens (Figure 18). This operates much like a tape player, with buttons at the top to let you move forward and backward through the regeneration sequence. Let's start by picking on the button on the far left to get to the beginning of the sequence. The display shows we are feature 0, with nothing shown on the screen. The model tree shows <none> beside each feature.

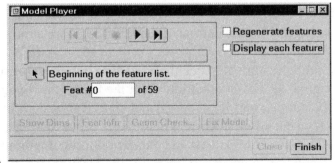

Figure 18 The Model Player window

Exploring the Structure of a Part

We're going to step through the creation of this part using the Model Player. This should give you a feel for how models are created and how the features work together to create the geometry. This very simple part illustrates quite a number of interesting and important ideas about modeling with Pro/E. In the following, feel free to change model orientation and display style whenever you want.

In the Model Player, click on the button (second from right) to step forward a single feature. This brings feature #1 into the model (the RIGHT datum plane). Continue clicking this button until you are at feature #5. This is the first solid feature of the part. It is an *extruded protrusion*, created by sketching a circle on the TOP datum plane and extruding it perpendicular to the sketch. A *protrusion* adds solid material to a model. (A *cut* takes it away.)

Click on the ***Show Dims*** button in the Model Player window. A yellow circle and a couple of dimensions appear on the model (Figure 19). This was the sketch used to define the shape. The circle has a diameter (note the symbol Ø) of 200. The sketch was then extruded a distance 10 to form the solid feature. These are the *parametric dimensions* of the feature.

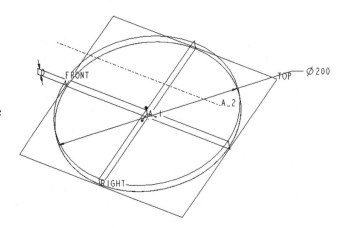

Figure 19 Feature #5 with ***Show Dims***

Move on to feature #6, the UPRIGHT and turn off the datum plane display. Go to the Top view and select ***Show Dims*** in the Model Player. You will see all the dimensions of the sketch used to create this *blend* (containing two rectangles). The blend feature allows you to specify different cross sections along the length of a protrusion. This lets the upright taper towards the top - blending from the large rectangle at the bottom to the small one at the top. We will deal with blends later in these lessons - they are quite an advanced feature and can do much more than demonstrated here.

Still on feature #6, click the ***Feat Info*** button. This opens the Browser pane and presents a great deal of information about the feature: its feature number, an internal ID number, the number and ID of parent and child features, all its attributes and dimensions, and so on. This information will make more sense to you as we proceed through the lessons. The concept of parents and children is quite important. A *parent* feature is one that supplies references necessary for the creation of a subsequent feature, which then becomes a *child* feature of the parent. The circular disk (feat #5, BASE) is a parent for the UPRIGHT (#6), because its upper surface was the sketching plane for the blend. The BOSS (feat #7) is a child of the UPRIGHT since one of the UPRIGHT's surfaces was used as a reference for the BOSS's sketched shape. At the bottom of the browser is a list of all the dimensions used to specify this feature. These are symbolic names of the form "dxx" where "xx" is an automatically created unique integer. *Close* the Browser pane by picking the button on the right sash.

In the Model Player, continue on to feature #7, the BOSS. This is a revolved protrusion, created by sketching a 2D shape on the FRONT datum plane and revolving it around axis A_2. This was the reason for creating this datum axis - an example of planning ahead. Go to the default view, turn on the datum planes, click on *Show Dims* and zoom in on the model to see the sketch.

Move on to feature #8 - this is an extruded cut that trims the top off the upright. *Cut* features always remove material (the opposite of a protrusion). Click on *Show Dims*. The sketch for this feature is on the RIGHT datum plane and has no dimensions! All its geometric information is picked up from previously created features (the sides and top of the upright).

Proceed to feature #11, which is another extruded cut used to hollow out the upright. Click on *Show Dims* and zoom in to see the sketch for this feature. What plane is it sketched on? This is tricky - there was no surface available to define the sketch at the right distance (5 units) from the left vertical surface of the UPRIGHT. So, a special datum plane was used. In previous releases, this would be called a *make datum* (or a *datum-on-the-fly*)[16]. This appears as DTM5 in the model tree, which you can find by opening the group in the model tree. Once the sketch was defined, the make datum disappears from the display (but is listed in the model tree as a hidden feature). Make datums are very powerful tools and we'll find out more about them in lesson 5.

Features #6 through #11 are now mirrored through the RIGHT datum plane to create the other upright. The mirrored features form a group, since they were all mirrored at the same time. Note the group name in the model tree.

Feature #18, HEX, is an interesting one. It could be made with a very shallow blend between two hexagons, in the same way as the UPRIGHT was made. HEX was, however, made in a different way using a *sweep* (observe the icon on the model tree). A swept feature requires a cross section shape that is then moved along a trajectory to sweep out a solid. HEX was created by sweeping a single inclined edge along a hexagonal trajectory. You can see these if you select *Show Dims*. The sweep trajectory is a regular hexagon inscribed in a construction circle of radius 90 (note the "R"). The swept "section" consists of a single inclined line with one end touching the hexagon. A number of special options have been set in creating this feature so that this single line creates solid geometry instead of a surface as it is swept. Sweeps can be used to create cuts or protrusions. They come in many varieties and are among the most complex features to create in Pro/E. We will look at the simpler versions later in this tutorial[17].

---

[16] These are also called *asynchronous datums*. Kind of a mouthful!

[17] An entire lesson in the *Advanced Tutorial* is devoted to more advanced versions: helical sweeps and several kinds of variable section sweeps.

Why, do you suppose, was the feature HEX made *after* the two uprights in this model? This feature creation order is important. (HINT: consider the cut feature UPRIGHT_HOLLOW) Notice that it is quite legal and common to have two or more solid features in the same part that partially overlap each other[18].

The next feature (#19) is the horizontal hole going through the two bosses. This hole is defined on the RIGHT datum plane, is coaxial with A_2, and extends through everything in both directions (technically called a *Thru All, Both Sides* hole). Examine the Feature Element Data list in the browser panel using the **Feat Info** button in the model player. The only dimension required for this hole is its diameter.

Features #20 and #21 are both revolved cuts in the bottom of the part. It would be technically possible to combine both these features into a single revolved cut. This would make the sketched shape considerably more complicated (and hence more difficult to create) and would also give less flexibility to the model. For example, feature #21 (UNDER_BASE) can be easily deleted from the model without affecting feature #20 (the CENTER_HOLE). If these were both parts of the same revolved feature, this would be more difficult.

Helpful Hint

When choosing the features to make up a model, there is always the question of maintaining a balance between a large number of simple features and a smaller number of more complicated ones. When first starting out in Pro/E it is probably better to lean toward the former approach. This is what we'll do in this tutorial, following the "Keep It Simple" principle.

Looking in the model tree, observe that immediately below feature #21 there is an entry for a *pattern*. Expanding this to the next level shows a number of groups. Expanding the first group (#23) shows four features: a hole, a couple of hidden datums, and a cut. Advance the model player to feature #27. Left click on each of the last few features to see them highlighted in the model (in red if color is turned on). The group is then duplicated around the circumference of the base. This is called a *radial pattern* which is produced by incrementing an angular dimension parameter associated with the first group (the pattern leader). There are many other different ways of forming patterns - we will see several of these later in lesson 7.

Advance the model player all the way to the end of this pattern by enter **52** in the **Feat #** text box in the model player. This is the last feature in the last group of the pattern.

This almost concludes the regeneration sequence of the part using the model player. Note that you can step backwards through the sequence, or enter the desired feature number directly in the window. There are some other optional functions that you can

---

[18] However, a solid feature that completely encloses another feature is said to "bury" it. Buried features are often a sign of a poorly thought-out model.

explore on your own.

The last six features in the part are rounds. Rounds are considered to be cosmetic features and are usually added to the model last. Bring them into the model, and leave the model player, by pressing the *Finish* button.

Close up all the levels in the model tree by clicking on the small minus signs, so that only the first level is showing as in Figure 17.

Modifying Dimensions

There is lots more we can do with the information in the model tree. Here are three ways you can modify the dimensions of a feature.

First, select feature #5 (BASE) in the model tree. Hold down the right mouse button with the cursor on the feature name. A pop-up menu appears. Select *Edit*. The feature sketch and dimensions appear in yellow on the screen. Double-click directly on the thickness dimension (currently 10). A small window will appear at the dimension location. Type in *25* and press Enter. Nothing happens on the screen except that the dimension now shows in green (the diameter dimension is still yellow). A green dimension indicates that although the value of the parameter is changed, the geometry has not been updated to reflect the new value. To do this, we must *regenerate* the model. The command to do this is either (starting in the pull-down menu):

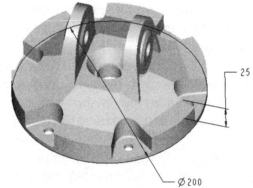

Figure 20 Part with modified base thickness

Edit > Regenerate

or (this is quicker) use the shortcut button ⚏ in the toolbar at the top or (even quicker) press **CTRL-G**. Observe the message window. Eventually, you should be informed that the regeneration was successful. Look at the thickness of the model. See Figure 20.

Let's change the thickness again, but using a different way to launch the command. Make sure the selection filter is set to **Smart**. Move the cursor across the model until the BASE feature is preselected (cyan). Then left click to select it (it highlights in red). Now right click to bring up a pop-up menu in the graphics window. In this menu, select *Edit*.

What happens if we make a mistake here? Change the thickness of the BASE from 25 to *50*. Can you predict what will happen? Once again, you will have to select the **Regenerate** command. A warning window appears that indicates there is a problem. Go ahead and select *OK* to see what happens. Expand the model tree to see that the regeneration has failed on the cut feature #11 (UPRIGHT_HOLLOW) shown in bold red in the model tree. All the features that depend on this one (its children) are also shown in red. There are some tools available to discover exactly why this feature failed[19]. We will be looking at those tools in lesson 5. For now, select

Edit > Undo: Edit Value

(note the shortcut *CTRL-Z*) or use the **Undo** button ↺ . This returns the thickness back to 25. Selecting **Cancel** in the warning window would also have reset the thickness to 25.

A final way to change the value of a dimension is very easy. Just double-click on any surface of the base feature. Make sure you don't accidentally pick a surface of HEX or one of the cuts. If you get the disk, the sketch will appear with dimensions. Change the thickness dimension back to *10* and regenerate the model. Double-clicking on any sketched feature will bring up its sketch and dimension values - no need to go looking for a menu command.

Parent/Child Relations

A parent provides a reference for the creation of a child. To illustrate this, select HEX (either in the model tree or using preselection in the graphics window), right click and select **Info > Reference Viewer**. This brings up the reference information window shown in Figure 21. The pane on the left controls (using Filters) which information to display in the pane on the right. Turn off the **System** reference type so that you will see only direct feature reference types as shown in the Figure. Otherwise, we will accept all the defaults, so you can close the filters pane using the textured buttons on the sash.

The pane on the right shows a graphical display of the relationships between features, with parent features on the left and child features on the right. In an assembly, this display also shows relations between components. The HEX feature is indicated as the current object. Note the icons for each feature that indicate their type (datum plane, extrude, sweep). If necessary, expand this window so that the other feature names are listed, as in Figure 21, and move it so that the model is visible in the graphics area. As you pass the mouse over these features, they will be highlighted on the model (again this is easiest to see if colors are turned on).

---

[19] The change in base thickness has caused the sketch for the UPRIGHT_HOLLOW feature to cross through itself - this is not allowed!

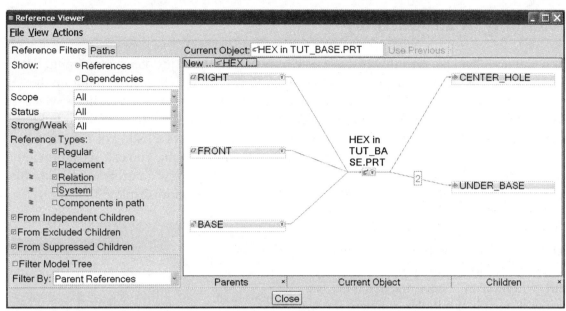

Figure 21 The **Reference Viewer** for exploring parent/child relations

The feature BASE is a parent of HEX. Clicking the small down arrowhead beside BASE shows that a surface of BASE is involved. How? If you hold your mouse on the arrow connecting BASE to HEX, a pop-up message will show that the surface of BASE was the sketching plane for HEX (note the *Used As* item).

What other children does BASE have? If you select BASE and hold down the right mouse button, another pop-up menu appears. In this menu, select *Set as Current*. This changes the current object to BASE. As expected, the child list contains HEX but also numerous other features. Since BASE was the first solid feature in the part, virtually everything else is a child. Some of the reference arrows indicate (using a number on the line) that BASE provides more than one reference for the child. If you click the down arrowhead beside BASE, you will see four entries (an axis, and edge, and two surfaces). As you move your mouse across each entry, they will highlight on the model and the reference arrows to the various child features will highlight in cyan. There is clearly a lot of information available here even for this simple model. We will return to the Reference Viewer in a later lesson.

The relations between parents and children can become very complicated. It is crucial when starting a new model to carefully consider how these are going to be set up - which features should depend (and how) on which others, and which should be independent. Insufficient planning here (or more usually none at all!) will result in a lot of grief later when the model needs to be modified.

This concludes our exploration of the model of a single part. Close the **Reference Viewer** window and the model tree.

Now, of course, very few parts exist in isolation from one another. Most parts are used in assemblies that must perform some function. Let's move on to an assembly and spend some time exploring how it is set up.

Anatomy of an Assembly

We will now load an assembly that uses the base part we have just been examining. Set up the screen as follows: shaded color display with datums off (they just clutter up the view!). You will need to have all the tutorial files installed as discussed earlier. Select the second tab (*Folder Browser*) in the Navigator window to show the Common Folders, then select the *Working Directory*. The Browser window shows a listing of files in the chosen location. If you pick the *Preview* button at the lower right, you can see a preview of the object selected above (Figure 22). The usual dynamic view controls work with this window, plus you can pick on models within the preview window display.

Before we proceed, select the *Views >* *Details* option in the Browser window. Observe the size of the file **tut_widget.asm**. This is the assembly file we will open in a minute. Compare its size to the part file **tut_base.prt** that we have been examining. Although the assembly contains the base part, and many others, the assembly file is quite considerably smaller. Why? The reason is that the assembly file contains only the necessary information for *how* the parts are put together in the assembly. *The assembly file does not contain the parts themselves.* The most common cause of an assembly error is not having the appropriate part files available (where Pro/E can find them). This is a common mistake that many new users make when transferring work from one computer to another, thinking that all they need is the assembly file itself.

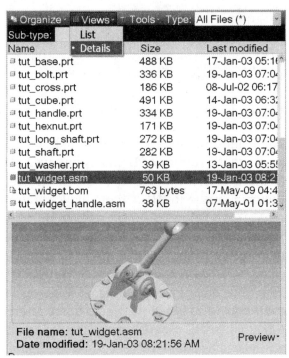

Figure 22 The Browser with preview window and file details turned on

Double-click the file **tut_widget.asm** in the Browser to open the file. Figures 23 and 24 show the assembly model tree and the model itself. Note that the assembly has been created in a new window, and the base part window is still available. If you go to that window by clicking on its border, you will see that the cursor is not its normal shape, and in fact you cannot select anything on the base part. This window is *inactive*. To activate it, in the pull-down menus select *Window > Activate* (or CTRL-A). The same is true if you switch back to the assembly window. The best way to switch windows is via the pull-down Window command - all currently created windows are listed at the bottom of this menu. Selecting one will take you there and activate it at the same time.

If the selection filter is set to *Smart*, moving the cursor back and forth across the assembly will bring up pop-up boxes that list the part names. The parts in Pro/E are called *components*.

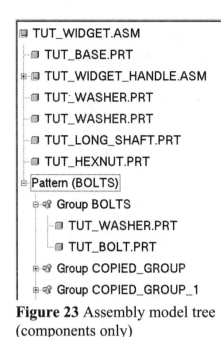

Figure 23 Assembly model tree
(components only)

Figure 24 The assembly
TUT_WIDGET

You can see that the model tree is laid out in the same way as features in a part. Clicking on a component in the model tree will cause it to highlight in red on the model. Note the icons in the model tree. The second component is itself an assembly - usually called a sub-assembly. Opening the model tree of the sub-assembly to the next level shows that it is made up of six other components. Sub-assemblies can be nested like this to as many levels as you want, and are a good way to organize the structure of a complicated assembly. Different groups in a company can even work on different sub-assemblies at the same time, although file management does become an issue for very complex models.

Some parts (like TUT_WASHER) are used several times in the assembly (10 in fact), but only a single washer part file is on the hard disk. This shows that components can be re-used multiple times within an assembly. Common components, like fasteners, can be used in many different assemblies. This can obviously save a lot of file storage space. In fact, many companies will maintain a digital library of commonly used parts. Components like springs can be declared to be flexible, so that only one part file is required but the spring can be used in multiple locations each with a different length, for example.

Notice at the bottom of the model tree is a pattern. The first element in the pattern (the pattern leader) is a group (BOLTS) of two components (TUT_WASHER and TUT_BOLT). Each of the other groups in the pattern contains these components. This is similar to the structure of a pattern of grouped features.

An Assembly BOM (Bill of Materials)

Here is a very useful (and necessary) tool
for assemblies. In the pull-down menus,
select

Info > Bill of Materials

In the BOM window, select **OK**. This opens
the Browser window with a BOM report
for the assembly. This report contains three
tables, the last one is shown in Figure 25.
The buttons in the three right columns in
each table allow you to highlight the part in
the model display, get model info, or open

Summary of parts for assembly TUT_WIDGET:			
Quantity	Type	Name	Actions
1	Part	TUT_BASE	
1	Part	TUT_CROSS	
1	Part	TUT_HANDLE	
10	Part	TUT_WASHER	
1	Part	TUT_SHAFT	
2	Part	TUT_HEXNUT	
1	Part	TUT_LONG_SHAFT	
6	Part	TUT_BOLT	

Figure 25 Bill of Materials summary table

the individual component. If desired, you can use the Browser controls to save or print
this BOM. In any case, the BOM data is automatically saved to a file (in this case,
tut_widget.bom) in the current working directory whenever you run this *Info* command.
Close the Browser with the sash button.

Modifying the Assembly

Returning to the model tree in the Navigator, let's add the extra columns in the model
tree as we did for the single part. Select the tab *Settings,* then *Open Settings File* and
select the file **mod_tree.cfg**. The extra columns are added (Figure 26).

The model tree now also shows
what are called *assembly features*
in the model. For example, the
first three entries on the model tree
of the assembly are datum planes.
Datum features are very common
in assemblies, since they provide
references for placing and
constraining components. To see
an example of this, select feature
#5 **ADTM1** in the assembly model
tree (the datum plane does not have
to be visible on the screen), right

	Feat #	Feat Type	Feat Subtype
TUT_WIDGET.ASM			
ASM_RIGHT	1	Datum Plane	
ASM_TOP	2	Datum Plane	
ASM_FRONT	3	Datum Plane	
TUT_BASE.PRT	4	Component	
ADTM1	5	Datum Plane	
TUT_WIDGET_HAND	6	Component	
TUT_WASHER.PRT	7	Component	
TUT_WASHER.PRT	8	Component	
TUT_LONG_SHAFT.F	9	Component	
TUT_HEXNUT.PRT	10	Component	
Pattern (BOLT_WASH	11	Pattern	PATTERN
Insert Here			

Figure 26 Assembly model tree using *mod_tree.cfg*

click, and select *Edit*. An angular dimension will appear in yellow that gives the rotation
of this datum plane around the horizontal axis **A_2** in the base part. Set the RIGHT view
to see this clearly. Change this angle by double-clicking on the number and typing in a
new value, say *90*, then press Enter. The value will stay green until the model is
regenerated.

Notice there are now two *Regenerate* toolbar icons on the top toolbar. The one on the left
is the same as before (shortcut CTRL-G), and will regenerate the entire model. This can

be time consuming for very large models. If you are sure the regeneration should affect only a limited number of components, try the **Custom Regenerate** button on the right. This won't act much differently in this assembly because the feature we are changing (ADTM1) occurs so early in the assembly sequence. Everything after it is affected if it is modified.

The assembly will regenerate with the subassembly positioned at a new angle (Figure 27). The datum plane **ADTM1** in the top assembly serves as an orientation reference for the subassembly. When the datum plane moves, so does the subassembly. Repeat the **Edit** command to put the subassembly back in its original position (change the 90 back to **30**).

Figure 27 Modified assembly

In the model tree, expand the subassembly TUT_WIDGET_HANDLE. It also contains an assembly datum ADTM1 which controls another angle. Change this to 30° and regenerate the model. Clearly, there is a problem with the model - at least two parts (the handle and the base) are interfering with each other. This interference is quite obvious. Later in these lessons we will find a Pro/E command that will identify interference automatically, often ones that you don't expect. For now, put the datum ADTM1 in the sub-assembly back in the original position (75°) before you continue. (HINT: Use the **Undo** command in the top toolbar.)

In addition to assembly datums, you can create regular features like holes and cuts in the assembly that act on the components. A hole feature would allow you to ensure that holes through several components were aligned perfectly.

Notice that each component listed in the model tree can be expanded to show its individual features: click on the + sign to the left of the component icon on the model tree. For example, Figure 28 shows the expansion of component #10 TUT_HEXNUT. The assembly model tree includes an added **Placement** feature with each component that tells (and gives access to the references) how a component is placed in the assembly. In the case of the hexnut component, these are an alignment of two axes and a mate of two surfaces.

	Feat #	Feat Type	Feat Subtype
TUT_WIDGET.ASM			
ASM_RIGHT	1	Datum Pla...	
ASM_TOP	2	Datum Pla...	
ASM_FRONT	3	Datum Pla...	
TUT_BASE.PRT	4	Component	
ADTM1	5	Datum Pla...	
TUT_WIDGET_HANDLE.	6	Component	
TUT_WASHER.PRT	7	Component	
TUT_WASHER.PRT	8	Component	
TUT_LONG_SHAFT.PRT	9	Component	
TUT_HEXNUT.PRT	10	Component	
Placement	<None>		
Align			
Mate			
RIGHT	1	Datum Pla...	
TOP	2	Datum Pla...	
FRONT	3	Datum Pla...	
Protrusion id 39	4	Protrusion	Revolve
Cut id 99	5	Cut	Extrude
Cut id 154	6	Cut	Revolve
Hole id 2009	7	Hole	
Chamfer id 2122	8	Chamfer	Edge
Cut id 2037	9	Cut	Helical Sweep
Insert Here			
Pattern (BOLTS)	11	Pattern	PATTERN
Insert Here			

Figure 28 Assembly model tree showing features

These will highlight if you select the listed items in the model tree. Selecting part features allows them to be modified the same as before. Try changing the thickness of the base part as we did before. What happens to the bolts and washers?

You can get the same sorts of information about components in the assembly (component info and parent/child relations) as you could for a part. These are usually launched, as before, with a right mouse click in the model tree. In the case of an assembly, the parent/child relations of components involve the datums, surfaces, and edges of components that are used to constrain each component in the assembly. We will look into this in depth in Lesson 8.

Also in a later lesson, we will see how we can create components in the assembly environment. This means that existing components can provide references for the creation of new components. Thus, you can create a new part to fit exactly to a previous part (for example, a shaft in a hole) by using existing geometry rather than manually transferring dimensions from one part to another.

There are just a couple more items we want to cover this lesson. Turn shading and color back on, if they aren't already. Close the Browser and Navigator windows if they are open.

Exploding an Assembly

Exploded views of assemblies are often helpful in showing how they are put together. If you have ever worked on a do-it-yourself project or kit, you have probably seen an exploded view in the plans. Getting this view in Pro/E is a snap. Select

View > Explode
Explode View

The position of each component in the exploded assembly is determined by a default. However, the *explode position* of each component can be easily changed, as has been done here. These positions are stored with the assembly. Note also that while the subassembly is exploded from the main assembly, the components in

Figure 29 The exploded assembly

the sub-assembly (in this case) are not exploded from each other. This indicates that the *explode state* of various components can be individually set. It is also possible to add the explode lines to the view (if you have the appropriately licensed module). We will spend some more time with layout of the exploded view in a later lesson. For now, unexplode the assembly with

View > Explode > Unexplode View

Opening Parts in an Assembly

When an assembly is being worked on, you will frequently want to open up an individual part by itself. This is easy to do. In the graphics window (Selection filter set to *Smart* or *Parts*), left click on the blue handle (part TUT_HANDLE). It will highlight in red. Now hold down the right mouse button and select *Open* from the pop-up menu. The part will open in a new window by itself. Pro/E can have many separate parts and assemblies (and drawings) loaded into memory at once - these are called *in session* (check out the command *Info > Session Info > Object List*) - each in a separate resizable window. To switch to another window, for example, back to the assembly, select (in the pull-down menus at the top)

Window > TUT_WIDGET.ASM

Notice that the TUT_BASE part is also listed there, along with any other windows you may have created in this session.

This concludes our look at the structure and layout of a simple assembly until later in the tutorial. As always, you are encouraged to experiment further with the commands we have covered and see what you can discover on your own.

Obtaining Hard Copy

You may want to produce some hard copy documentation from time to time as you go through these lessons. There are several basic kinds of hard copy:

1.   Plain text containing model, component, or feature information, feature lists, the model tree.
2.   Formatted web documents.
3.   Images of the graphics area of the screen.
4.   Detailed engineering drawings.

For the first type, whenever you query the model for this type of information, Pro/E generally creates a printable text file in the working directory. Look for files with the extension *txt*, *inf*, *lst*, *err*, or *dat*. These can be printed with any simple text editor or word processor.

Web-formatted documents are available for any page viewed in the Browser window (such as the BOM report). Both "Save" and "Print" shortcut buttons are on the Browser toolbar.

Images of the graphics area ("screen shots") can be obtained easily if you have the appropriate printer attached to your system. Generally, this means a Postscript compatible printer. Different printing methods may be required depending on whether the image is shaded or not. Sometimes the Windows Print Manager will take care of this for you. To obtain a screen shot of a line drawing (hidden line or wireframe image), issue the commands

> *File > Print*

or use the ***Print*** shortcut button on the top toolbar. In the **Print** window that opens up, in the Destination field select the appropriate output device. Windows users will usually select MS Print Manager. You might check out the options available by clicking the ***Configure*** button. The default is to print exactly what is shown on the screen (see the **Based on Zoom** option). Then select *OK* (twice). It is not recommended that you do this with shaded images, particularly on some systems with shared printers.

The command

> *File > Quick Print*

allows you to easily produce a drawing (views only - no dimensions or notes) containing your choice of paper size, views, scales, and display style. You must be careful here about scaling the desired views to fit the paper size.

For high quality shaded images, your best bet is to select

> *File > Save a Copy*

and in the **Type** pull-down list, you can find a number of image formats (TIFF, JPG, EPS,...). The image file will be created in your working directory. These images can be very high resolution (up to 600 dpi and 24 bit color), but are also very large (think megabytes). PTC has a special program (Pro/PHOTORENDER) for very high quality rendering of images suitable for glossy marketing purposes. This allows you to have multiple light sources, shadows, reflections, textures, background images, and so on.

A quick and easy way of getting hard copy of a shaded image in Windows is to capture the screen contents to the clipboard. Use ALT-PrtScrn to capture the active window. Then paste the clipboard image (a bitmap) into a graphics utility program or word processor. This image is stuck at the resolution of your screen, however.

If the methods above do not work, your system administrator may have some special instructions that need to be followed.

Obtaining hard copy of engineering drawings will be covered later in these lessons. For these, there are extra considerations of sheet size, drawing scale, pen width, and so on.

Leaving Pro/ENGINEER

When you want to quit Pro/E entirely, you can leave by using the *Exit* command in the **File** menu or the X at the top-right corner. If you accidentally do this, you can cancel the command.

Helpful Hint

Unlike many programs, Pro/E will not automatically save anything for you (like a regular timed backup on some systems). This applies both during operation and when you exit. If you leave the program without saving new work, it is basically gone! Anyone who says they have never lost work this way is probably lying!

Depending on how your system has been set up, Pro/E *may* prompt you to save your work when you exit[20]. This includes any parts, assemblies, drawings, and so on, that are currently *in session* (stored in memory). You will be prompted individually for each object in session. Reply with a *Y* or *N* to save each object in the current working directory. A middle click will accept whatever default is shown. If you are sure you have saved the most recent version of all objects in session, you don't need to do that again so press *Q* (for Quit).

This completes Lesson #1. You will no doubt be relieved to know that it is by far the longest in this series. There was much fundamental material to deal with, however. You are strongly encouraged to experiment with any of the commands that have been presented in this lesson. Explore the other parts in the widget assembly, and experiment with the view controls. Like all sophisticated tools, the only way to become proficient with Pro/E is to use it a lot!

In the next lesson we will create our first part using simple basic features (protrusion, cut, hole) and spend some time learning about the Intent Manager in Sketcher. The important concept of *design intent* will be introduced, with examples.

---

[20] You can include the option *prompt_on_exit* in the configuration file accessible using *Tools* > *Options*. The default for this option is *No*. See the Appendix.

Questions for Review

Here are some questions you should be able to answer at this time, or that may provoke some thought and/or further study:

1. What mouse buttons are used to pan, spin, and resize the object?
2. What is the purpose of the datum planes?
3. What are two ways to get on-line help?
4. How can you get a shaded image of the part?
5. How do you turn the datum plane visibility on and off?
6. How many ways can you think of to modify the value of a dimension?
7. What is the difference between *View > Shade* and the "Shading" shortcut button?
8. Where does your system first look for stored part files? What is this called?
9. What is meant by *preselection*?
10. What is meant by the term *regeneration*?
11. What is the regeneration sequence? How can you determine it for a part?
12. On what menu can you set the datum display, color toggle, and display style simultaneously?
13. How many ways can you get to the default view orientation? What are they?
14. How do you change the working directory?
15. What is the spin center?
16. What is the correct toolbar button to execute the following functions:
    a. toggle display of datum planes
    b. start Orient Mode
    c. regenerate
    d. create a new named view
    e. turn off the spin center
17. What is the function of the following toolbar buttons:

    a)   b)   c)   d)   e)

18. What are the three primary goals in creating models?
19. Describe all the shortcuts and functions associated with the middle mouse button.
20. What is the difference between *view* and *display* controls?
21. Why do datum planes have two colors? What are they?
22. How large is a datum plane?
23. How do you turn off the display of datum tags?
24. What is meant by the *object/action* command style? Give an example. Compare this to the *action/object* style. Give an example of that, too.
25. What is the meaning of the following icons? Where do they appear?

    a)   b) ▊▊   c) ⟆   d) ▱   e) 🖱   f) ⬛

26. Where is the explode command for assemblies?
27. Is it possible to *Hide* a solid feature? Can you *Hide* a component in an assembly?
28. What happens if you preselect a dimension and then right click? This is useful if the

screen gets really crowded.

29.   What does "context sensitive" refer to, and when is this relevant?
30.   A middle-click often means the same as _____?
31.   What is meant by a "buried" feature? Is this good or bad?

Exercises

1.   Try out the model player with the widget assembly.
2.   What are some downstream uses for a Pro/E model? Which are available to you in your local school or installation, and who uses them?
3.   Open the part TUT_CUBE.PRT. Practice manipulating the display of the cube to show each numbered side facing the front of the screen, with the number the right way up. Do this as fast as you can. Hint: turn color and shading on (the cube is translucent, so you can see the numbers on the hidden faces). If your system cannot handle transparency, use hidden line display.
4.   Obtain a printed hard copy of a hidden-line display of the base part.
5.   Obtain a printed hard copy of the model tree for the base part showing the additional columns.
6.   Obtain a hard copy of the Browser window showing the model information for the part TUT_BASE.
7.   Obtain a hard copy of the Browser window showing the feature information for the BASE feature in the part TUT_BASE.
8.   It is possible in the assembly **tut_widget.asm** to position the handle part perpendicular to the base. How can you do that? Obtain a printed hard copy of the assembly (no hidden lines) in this position.
9.   Obtain a printed hard copy of a shaded image of the exploded view of the assembly **tut_widget.asm**. Label this with the part names. Bonus marks if you can figure out how to do this with *Annotations*.
10.   Make an isometric sketch of the three datum planes (TOP, FRONT, RIGHT). Identify two ways to select references for each of the standard engineering drawing views (top, front, right, left, back, bottom).

This page left blank.

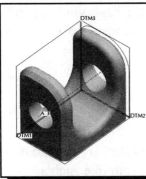

Lesson 2

Creating a Simple Object (Part I)
Introduction to Sketcher

Synopsis

Creating a part; introduction to Sketcher; sketch constraints; creating datum curves, protrusions, cuts; sketch diagnostics; using the dashboard; saving a part; part templates.

Overview of this Lesson

The main objective of this lesson is to introduce you to the general procedures for creating sketched features. We will go at quite a slow pace and the part will be quite simple (see Figure 1 on the next page), but the central ideas need to be elaborated and emphasized so that they are very clearly understood. Some of the material presented here is a repeat of the previous lesson - take this as an indication that it is important! Here's what we are going to cover:

1. Feature Types and Menus
2. Introduction to Sketcher
   - Sketcher menus
   - Intent Manager and Sketcher constraints
   - Sketcher Diagnostics
3. Creating a Datum Curve
4. Creating an Extruded Protrusion
   - Using the Dashboard
5. Creating an Extruded Cut
6. Saving the part
7. Using Part Templates

> It will be a good idea to browse ahead through each section (or use the CD-ROM) to get a feel for the direction we are going, before you do the lesson in detail. There is a lot of material here which you probably won't be able to absorb with a single pass-through.

Start Pro/E as usual. If it is already up, close all windows (except the base window) and erase all objects in session using *File > Erase > Current* and *File > Erase > Not Displayed*. Close the Navigator and Browser windows.

Creating a Simple Part

In this lesson, we will create a simple block with a U-shaped central slot. By the end of the lesson your part should look like Figure 1 below. This doesn't seem like such a difficult part, but we are going to cover a few very important and fundamental concepts in some depth. Try not to go through this too fast, since the material is crucial to your understanding of how Pro/E works. We will be adding some additional features to this part in the next lesson.

We are going to turn off some of the default actions of Pro/E. This will require us to do some things manually instead of letting the program do them automatically. This should give you a better understanding of what the many default actions are. Furthermore, eventually you will come across situations where you don't want the defaults and you'll need to know your way around these options.

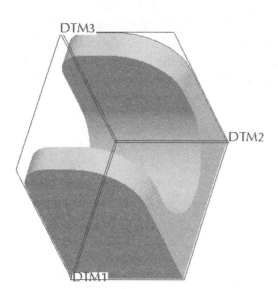

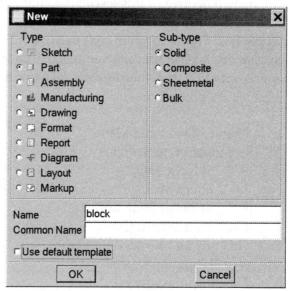

Figure 1 Part at the end of this lesson

Figure 2 Creating a new part

Creating and Naming the Part

Click the *Create New Object* short-cut button, or select *File > New*. A window will open (Figure 2) showing a list of different types and sub-types of objects to create (parts, assemblies, drawings, and so on). In this lesson we are going to make a single solid object called a *part*. Keep the default radio button settings

> *Part | Solid*

IMPORTANT: Turn off (remove the check) the *Use Default Template* option at the bottom. We will discuss templates at the end of this lesson.

Many parts, assemblies, drawings, etc. can be loaded simultaneously (given sufficient computer memory) in the current session. All objects are identified by unique names[1]. A default name for the new part is presented at the bottom of the window, something like **[prt0001]**. It is almost always better to have a more descriptive name. So, double click (left mouse) on this text to highlight it and then type in

> *[block]*

(without the square brackets) as your part name. The *Common Name* of the part is an option for specifying an even more descriptive name. For example, you might have a number of part files named using a part or catalog number such as "TG123_A29". This is not very descriptive, so you could enter a common name such as "small flat rubber washer". We will not use common names in this tutorial, so leave this blank and just press *Enter* or select *OK*.

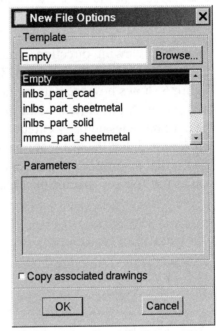

The **New File Options** dialog window opens. Since we elected (in the previous window) to *not* use the default template for this part, Pro/E is presenting a list of alternative templates defined for your system. As mentioned previously, we are going to avoid using defaults this time around. So, for now, as shown in Figure 3 at the right, select

Figure 3 Options for new parts

> *Empty | OK* (or middle click).

At this time, **BLOCK** should appear in the title area at the top of the graphics window. Also, some of the toolbar icons at the right are now "live" (ie. not grayed out).

Create Datum Planes

We will now create the first features of the part: three reference planes to locate it in space. It is not absolutely necessary to have datum planes, but it is a very good practice, particularly if you are going to make a complex part or assembly. Datum planes are created using the "Datum Plane" button on the right toolbar, as shown in Figure 4. Note that these icons look quite similar to the buttons on the top toolbar that control the display of datums. What's the difference?

---

[1] Pro/E can keep track of objects of different types with the same names. A part and a drawing can have the same name since they are different object types.

Select the ***Datum Plane*** button now. Since we currently have no features in the model, Wildfire rightly assumes that we want to create the three standard datum planes.

The datum planes represent three orthogonal planes to be used as references for features that will be created later. You can think of these planes as XY, YZ, XZ planes, although you generally aren't concerned with the X,Y,Z form or notation. Your screen should have the datum planes visible, as shown in Figure 5. (If not, check the datum

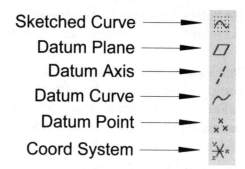

Figure 4 Toolbar buttons for creating DATUMS

display button in the top toolbar.) They will resemble something like a star due to the default 3D viewing direction. Note that each plane has an attached tag that gives its name: **DTM1**, **DTM2**, and **DTM3**. This view may be somewhat hard to visualize, so Figure 6 shows how the datum planes would look if they were solid plates in the same orientation. An important point to note is, while the plates in Figure 6 are finite in size, the datum planes actually extend off to infinity. Finally, before we move on to the next topic, notice that the last feature created (in this case DTM3), is highlighted in red. This is a normal occurrence and means that the last feature created is always preselected for you as the "object" part of the object/action command sequence.

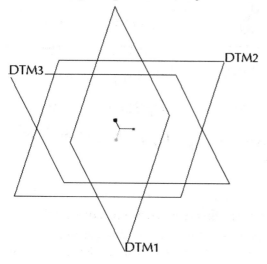

Figure 5 Default datum planes

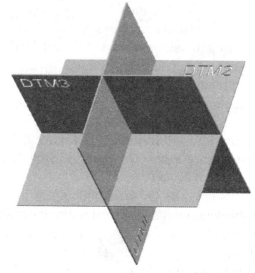

Figure 6 Datum planes as solid plates

Pro/ENGINEER Feature Overview

Below (and/or to the right of) the datum creation buttons in the right toolbar are three other groups of buttons. These are shown in Figures 7, 8, and 9. If you move the cursor over the buttons, the tool tip box will show the button name.

Two of these menus contain buttons for creating features, organized into the following categories:

Placed Features (Figure 7) - (holes, rounds, shells, ...) These are features that are created directly on existing solid geometry. They generally always either add (rib) or remove (hole) material from the solid. Some (round, chamfer, draft) can do either. Examples are placing a hole on an existing surface, or creating a round on an existing edge of a part.

Sketched Features (Figure 8) - (extrusions, revolves, sweeps, blends, ..) These features require the definition of a two-dimensional cross section which is then manipulated into the third dimension. All of these features can either add or remove material from the solid. Although they usually use existing geometry for references, they do not specifically require this. These features will involve the use of an important tool called Sketcher.

The final group of buttons (Figure 9) is used for editing and modifying existing features. We will deal with some of these commands (*Mirror* and *Pattern*) later in the Tutorial.

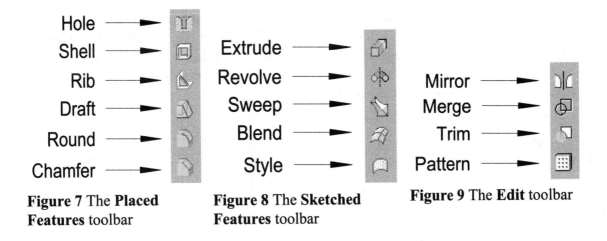

Figure 7 The **Placed Features** toolbar

Figure 8 The **Sketched Features** toolbar

Figure 9 The **Edit** toolbar

In this lesson we will be using the *Extrude* command to create two types of sketched features (a protrusion and a cut). In the next lesson, we will use the *Hole*, *Round*, and *Chamfer* commands to create three placed features. Before we continue, though, we must find out about an important tool - Sketcher.

Introducing Sketcher

Sketcher is the most important tool for creating features in Pro/E. It is therefore critical that you have a good understanding of how it works. We will take a few minutes here to describe its basic operation and will explore the Sketcher tools continually through the next few lessons. It will take you a lot of practice and experience to fully appreciate all that it can do.

Basically, Sketcher is a tool for creating two-dimensional figures. These can be either stand-alone features (*Sketched Curves*) or as embedded elements that define the cross sectional shape of some solid features. The aspects of these figures that must be defined are location, shape, and size, roughly in that order. The sketching plane where we will create the 2D sketch is defined or selected first. Then, within Sketcher the location is further specified by selecting references to existing geometry. You will find the usual drawing tools for lines, arcs, circles, and so on, to create the shape. Finally, you can specify alignments or dimensions to control the size of the sketch and its relation to existing geometry.

Sketcher is really quite smart, that is, it will anticipate what you are going to do (usually correctly!) and do many things automatically. Occasionally, it does make a mistake in guessing what you want. So, learning how to use Sketcher effectively involves understanding exactly what it is doing for you (and why) and discovering ways that you can easily over-ride this when necessary.

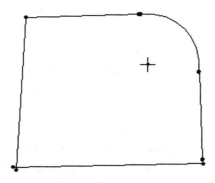

Figure 10 Geometry input by user (Intent Manager rules off). Note misaligned vertices, non-parallel edges, non-tangent curves.

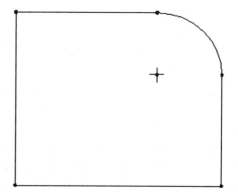

Figure 11 Geometry after processing by Intent Manager. Note aligned vertices, parallel edges, tangent curves.

The brain of Sketcher is called the *Intent Manager*. We will be discussing the notion of *design intent* many times in this tutorial. In Sketcher, design intent is manifest not only in the shape of the sketch but also in how constraints and dimensions are applied to the sketch so that it is both complete and conveys the important design goals for the feature. Completeness of a sketch implies that it contains just enough geometric specification so that it is uniquely determined. Too little information would mean that the sketch is under-specified; too much means that it is over-specified. The function of Intent Manager is to make sure that the sketch always contains just the right amount of information. Moreover, it tries to do this in ways that, most of the time, make sense. Much of the frustration involved in using Sketcher arises from not understanding (or even sometimes not realizing) the nature of the choices it is making for you[2] or knowing how easy it is to override these actions. When you are using Sketcher, Intent Manager must be treated like a partner - the more you understand how it works, the better the two of you will be able to function.

The term *sketch* comes from the fact that you do not have to be particularly exact when you are "drawing" the shape, as shown in Figures 10 and 11. Sketcher (or rather Intent Manager) will interpret what you are drawing within a built-in set of rules. Thus, if you sketch a line that is approximately vertical, Sketcher assumes that you want it vertical. If you sketch two circles or arcs that have approximately the same radius, Sketcher assumes that's what you want. In cases like this, you will see the sketched entity "snap" to a particular orientation or size as Intent Manager fires one of the internal rules (this occurs on-the-fly while you are sketching).

When Sketcher fires one of its internal rules, you will be alerted by a symbol on the sketch that indicates the nature of the assumed condition. If you accept the condition, it becomes a *constraint* on the sketch. These constraint symbols are summarized in Table 2-1. You should become familiar with these rules or constraints, and learn how to use them to your advantage. If you do not want a rule invoked, you must either

      (a) use explicit dimensions or alignments, or

      (b) exaggerate the geometry so that if fired, the rule will fail, or

      (c) tell Sketcher to disable a specific instance of the constraint (Hint: RMB), or

      (d) set up Sketcher to explicitly ignore constraints of a given type.

You will most often use option (a) by specifying your desired alignments and dimensions and letting Sketcher worry about whatever else it needs to solve the sketch. When geometry is driven by an explicit dimension, fewer internal rules will fire. Option (b) is slightly less common. An example is if a line in a sketch must be 2° away from vertical, you would draw it some much larger angle (like 15° or so) and put an explicit dimension on the angle. This prevents the "vertical" rule from firing. Once the sketch has been completed with the exaggerated angle, you can modify the dimension value to the desired 2°. The third option is used while you are sketching to disable a constraint that Intent Manager indicates it wants to place. Finally, there are settings for Sketcher that explicitly turn off the rule checking (for all rules or selected ones only) during sketching. This is very rarely used.

---

[2] Intent Manager is able to "solve" sketches that are much more complicated than mere humans can do. To make sure it doesn't get ahead of you, keep your sketches simple.

Table 2-1 Implicit Constraints in Sketcher

Rule	Symbol	Description
Equal radius and diameter	R	If you sketch two or more arcs or circles with approximately the same radius, the system may assume that the radii are equal
Symmetry	→ ←	Two vertices may be assumed to be symmetric about a centerline
Horizontal or vertical lines	H or V	Lines that are approximately horizontal or vertical may be considered to be exactly so.
Parallel or perpendicular lines	‖ or ⊥	Lines that are sketched approximately parallel or perpendicular may be considered to be exactly so.
Tangency	T	Entities sketched approximately tangent to each other may be assumed to be tangent
Equal segment lengths	L	Lines of approximately the same length may be assumed to have the same length
Point entities lying on other entities or collinear with other entities	 —○—	Point entities that lie near lines, arcs, or circles may be considered to be exactly on them. Points that are near the extension of a line may be assumed to lie on it.
Equal coordinates	▬ ▬	Endpoints and centers of the arcs may be assumed to have the same X- or the same Y-coordinates
Midpoint of line	M	If the midpoint of a line is close to a sketch reference, it will be placed on the reference.

An example of a sketch with the geometric constraints is shown in Figure 12. Note how few dimensions are required to define this sketch. See if you can pick out the following constraints:

- ▸ vertical lines
- ▸ horizontal lines
- ▸ perpendicular lines
- ▸ tangency
- ▸ three sets of equal length lines
- ▸ equal radius
- ▸ vertical alignment (two cases)

How do you suppose Sketcher is able to determine the radius of the rounded corners (fillets) at the top and bottom on the left edge? (Hint: this involves the solution of a system of equations.)

In the following, keep in mind that many functions in Sketcher are available in pop-up menus attached to the RMB. For many sketches, you need never actually pick a shortcut button since everything is available in the graphics window using RMB commands only. Try it!

Sketcher has some very useful tools that make it considerably easier to diagnose errors in sketches (such as duplicated edges) or improper sketches (such as open curves for

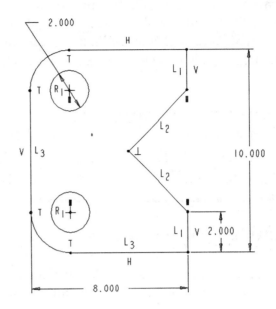

Figure 12 A sketch showing implicit constraints

features that require closed curves). We will investigate these tools by intentionally introducing some errors into our sketches.

Two Ways to use Sketcher

In this lesson, we will use two methods to create a couple of sketched features. The creation of the sketch represents the majority of the work required in creating these features. The two methods will differ in where in the feature creation sequence you will invoke Sketcher. The two methods are shown schematically in Table 2 - 2.

In the first method, we invoke Sketcher first to create the cross sectional shape of the extrusion. This shape is defined in a *sketched curve* which becomes a stand-alone feature in the model. We then launch the extrude command, specifying the curve to define the cross section of the feature. In the second method, we do not create a separate curve but rather invoke Sketcher from inside the extrusion creation sequence.

Table 2-2 Steps to create a sketched feature

	Method 1	Method 2
Step 1	Create shape using Sketcher (sketch becomes stand alone feature)	Launch Extrude tool
Step 2	Launch Extrude tool	Create shape using Sketcher (sketch exists only inside the extrude feature)

In terms of design intent, the first method would be used if the sketched curve was going to be used for additional features, for example an extrude and a revolve. The second method (creating the sketch within the feature) is the traditional mode of operation, and would be the method of choice if the sketched shape was to be used only in a single feature.

Both features we will make here are extrusions: one will be a *protrusion* (which adds material) and the other is a *cut* (which removes material). Either of the two methods shown here can be used to create either protrusions or cuts; for either method, whether you add or remove material is determined by a single mouse click!

Creating a Sketched Curve

When we left the model last, the datum plane DTM3 was highlighted in red. If that is not the case now, use preselection highlighting to select it now.

In the datum toolbar on the right of the screen, pick the ***Sketch Tool*** button. Be careful not to pick the datum curve button below it - that one will create a datum curve using sets of existing datum points, points read from a file, or using equations. If you accidentally pick the wrong button, you can back out with the ***Quit*** command.

Setting Sketch Orientation

The **Sketch** dialog window opens as shown in Figure 13. Since DTM3 was highlighted (in red) prior to the present command, it has been preselected as the Sketch Plane. It is now highlighted in the graphics window in orange. This is the plane on which we will draw the sketch. The view orientation has changed so that you are looking directly at DTM3[3]. Two dashed lines represent sketch references that have been chosen automatically - these are the other datum planes seen on edge. A yellow circle is actually the "tail feathers" of a view direction arrow. Spin the orientation with the middle mouse button to see the arrow. The yellow arrow attached to the edge of DTM3 should be pointing back into the screen. This is the direction of view onto the

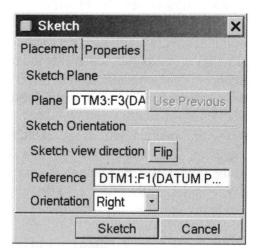

Figure 13 Defining the sketch plane and sketch orientation reference

sketch plane. The direction of view can be reversed by clicking on the yellow arrow or

---

[3] Your system may be customized to let you stay in a 3D orientation when sketching. This is the configuration setting *sketcher_starts_in_2d* set to *No*.

with the **Flip** button in the dialog window (Figure 13). Leave it pointing towards the back. In the dialog window, DTM1 is identified as the Sketch Orientation **Reference**, with the **Orientation** set to **Right**. What is all this about?

The relation between the sketch plane and the sketch orientation reference generally causes a lot of confusion for new users, so pay attention!

The meaning of the sketch plane is pretty obvious - it is the plane on which we will draw the sketch - in this case DTM3. Our view is always perpendicular to the sketch plane[4]. That is not enough by itself to define our view of the sketch since we can be looking at that plane from an infinite number of directions (imagine the sketch plane rotating around an axis perpendicular to the screen). The **Orientation** option list in the dialog window (**Top**, **Bottom**, **Left**, **Right**) refers to directions relative to the computer screen, as in "TOP edge of the screen" or "BOTTOM edge of the screen" and so on. We must combine this direction with a chosen reference plane (*which must be perpendicular to the sketch plane*) so that we get the desired orientation of view onto the sketching plane.

In the present case, when we get into Sketcher we will be looking directly at the brown (positive) side of DTM3. So that the sketch is the right way up, we can choose either DTM2 to face the Top of the screen, or (as was chosen automatically for us) DTM1 can face the Right of the screen. Note that both DTM1 and DTM2 are both perpendicular to the sketch plane, as required. The direction a plane or surface "faces" is determined by its normal vector. The normal vector for a datum plane is perpendicular to the brown side. For a solid surface, the orientation is determined by the outward normal.

Read the last couple of paragraphs again, since new users are quite liable to end up drawing their sketches upside-down!

To illustrate the crucial importance of the reference plane, consider the images shown in Figure 14. These show two cases where the same sketching plane **DTM3** was used, the same sketched shape was drawn, the same reference orientation TOP was chosen, but where different datums were chosen as the sketching reference. On the left, the TOP reference was **DTM2**. On the right, the TOP reference was **DTM1**. The identical sketch, shown in the center, was used for both cases (rounded end of sketch towards the top of the screen). However, notice the difference in the orientation of the part obtained in the final shaded images. Both of these models are displayed in the default orientation (check the datum planes). Clearly, choosing the sketching reference is important, particularly for the base feature.

---

[4]Well, almost always. It is possible to sketch in 3D, in which case you can manipulate your view so that you are not looking perpendicularly at the sketch plane. We will not attempt that here.

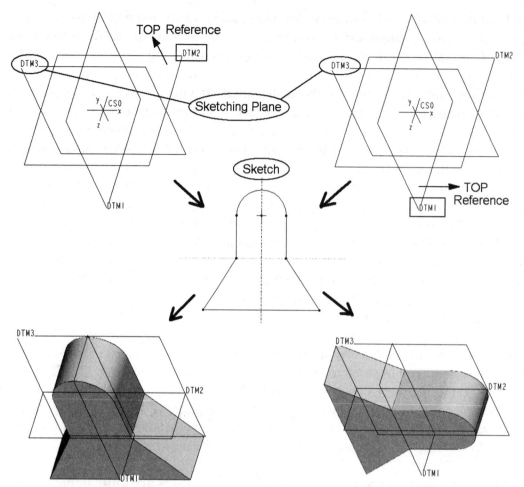

Figure 14 The importance of the sketching reference plane! The shaded images are both in the default orientation. The same sketching plane and sketch was used for both features - the difference in orientation of the solid is because of the choice of the sketching reference plane.

Let's continue on with creating the curve. Make sure the **Sketch** dialog window is completed as in Figure 13. Select the *Sketch* button (or middle click).

To verify the meaning of the dashed orange lines, in the top pull-down menu, select

Sketch > References

(Or select *References* in the RMB pop-up). This opens the **References** dialog window, Figure 15. In this window we can select any existing geometry to help Sketcher locate the new sketch relative to the part. In the present case, there isn't much to choose

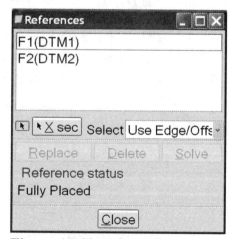

Figure 15 Choosing references in Sketcher

from, and two references have already been chosen for us - DTM1 and DTM2. These references are responsible for the two dashed lines in the graphics window. The number of references you choose is not limited - there may be several listed here. You are also free to delete the ones chosen for you and/or add new ones. However, notice the **Reference Status** at the bottom of this dialog. **Fully Placed** means enough references have been specified to allow Sketcher to locate your sketch in the model. If there are not enough references, the status will be **Unsolved Sketch**. For now, do not proceed beyond this window unless you have a **Fully Placed** status indicated. Once you have that, select *Close* in the References window.

The drawing window is shown in Figure 16. Note that you are looking edge-on to the datums DTM1 and DTM2. The datum DTM1 (actually, its brown side) is facing the right edge of the screen, as specified in the dialog back in Figure 13. Note that we could have obtained the same orientation by selecting DTM2 to face the top of the screen.

Another change is the addition of some new toolbar buttons at the top of the screen[5]. See Figure 17. These are in two groups: a Sketch Display group and a Sketch Diagnosis group.

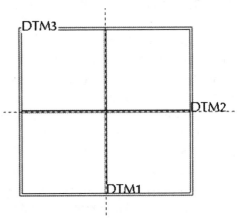

Figure 16 The drawing window

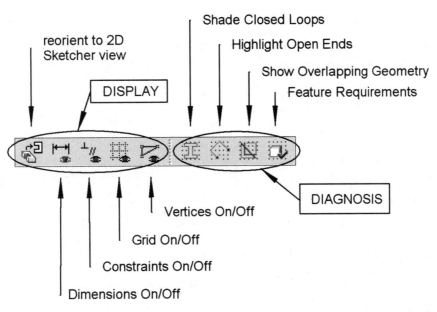

Figure 17 Sketcher top toolbar buttons

---

[5] These commands are, of course, also available in the pull-down menu under *Sketch*.

In the Display group, the four buttons with the eyeballs control display of dimensions, constraints, the grid (default off), and vertices. Leave these buttons in their default position (***Dimensions***, ***Constraints***, ***Vertices***, all turned on). It is seldom (if ever) that you will need to turn on the grid in Sketcher. The button at the far left will return you to the default view of the sketch if you should accidentally (or intentionally) go into 3D view. Buttons in the Diagnosis group will control or launch functions that can help you identify and fix possible problems in the sketch. For our first sketch, turn on the ***Shade Closed Loops*** and ***Highlight Open Ends*** buttons.

The Sketcher Toolbar

The major addition to the screen is the new toolbar on the right of the screen. This contains the Sketcher tools and is shown in Figure 18. Several buttons on this menu have fly-outs, indicated by the ➤ symbol on the right edge. These fly-outs lead to related buttons, and are listed in Tables 2-3 and 2-4 on the next page. Compared to some 2D drawing programs, this doesn't seem like such a large number of drawing commands. Rest assured that there will not be much that you cannot draw with these.

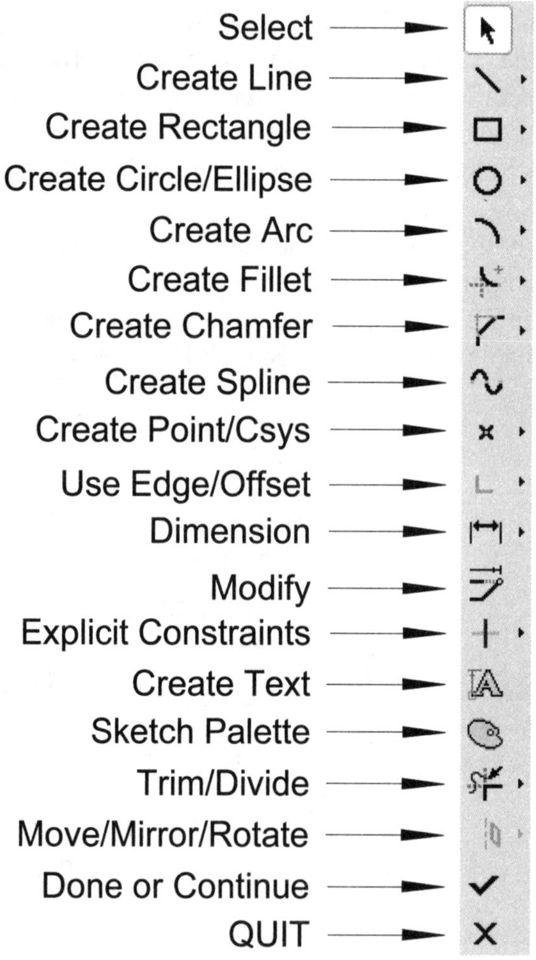

When you are sketching, many of the commands in the right toolbar are instantly available (but context sensitive) by holding down the right mouse button in the graphics window. This will bring up a pop-up window of commands relevant in the current situation.

Finally, a new Sketch pull-down menu is available at the top of the screen. Open this and have a look at the available commands there. Two commands not in the toolbar are ***Data From File*** and ***Options***. The first of these lets you read in a previously created sketch. The second lets you change the default settings used by Sketcher. Have a look at these but don't change anything just yet.

Select ——➤
Create Line ——➤
Create Rectangle ——➤
Create Circle/Ellipse ——➤
Create Arc ——➤
Create Fillet ——➤
Create Chamfer ——➤
Create Spline ——➤
Create Point/Csys ——➤
Use Edge/Offset ——➤
Dimension ——➤
Modify ——➤
Explicit Constraints ——➤
Create Text ——➤
Sketch Palette ——➤
Trim/Divide ——➤
Move/Mirror/Rotate ——➤
Done or Continue ——➤
QUIT ——➤

Figure 18 The Sketcher toolbar

Note that there are two versions of ***Centerline***, ***Point***, and ***Coordinate System*** commands. The "Construction" version will only be visible within the sketch, that is, when you are in Sketcher. The "Geometry" version (indicated by the "G") will create a datum element that is visible outside the sketch (and could be used as reference by another feature). For example, a ***Geom Centerline*** creates a datum axis.

Table 2-3 Sketcher Toolbar Flyout Buttons

Button Flyout Group	Button Commands
	Line ‖ Tan-Tan Line ‖ Const Centerline ‖ Geom Centerline
	Rectangle ‖ Slant Rectangle ‖ Parallelogram
	Circle ‖ Concentric ‖ 3 Point ‖ 3 Tan ‖ Ellipse (ends) ‖ Ellipse (center)
	Tangent End ‖ Concentric ‖ Center ‖ 3 Tan ‖ Conic Arc
	Circular fillet ‖ Conic fillet
	Chamfer corner ‖ Chamfer
	Const Point ‖ Geom Point ‖ Const Coordinate System ‖ Geom Coordinate System
	Use Edge ‖ Offset edge ‖ Thicken
	Dimension ‖ Perimeter ‖ Reference ‖ Baseline
	EXPLICIT Constraints **See Table 2-4**
	Dynamic trim (delete) ‖ Trim(extend) ‖ Divide
	Mirror ‖ Translate/Rotate

Table 2-4 Explicit Constraints in Sketcher

Toolbar Flyout	Constraint		
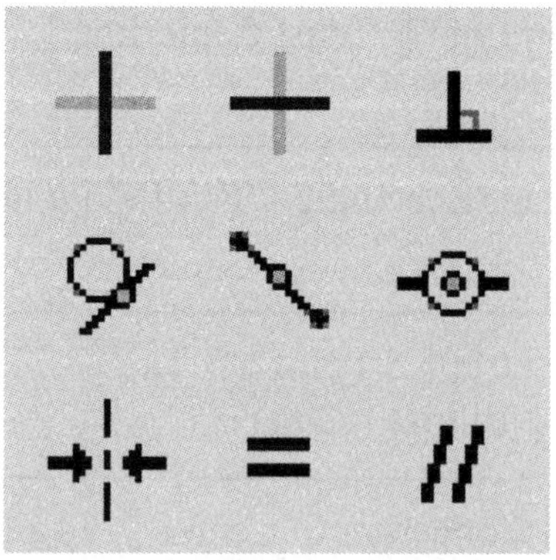	Vertical	Horizontal	Perpendicular
	Tangent	Midpoint	Coincident
	Symmetric	Equal	Parallel

Creating the Sketch

Select the *Line* tool using one of the following three methods:

- using the *Line* toolbar button,

    OR

- in the pull-down menus select *Sketch > Line > Line* ,

    OR (probably the easiest!)

- hold down the right mouse button and select *Line* from the pop-up menu (Figure 19).

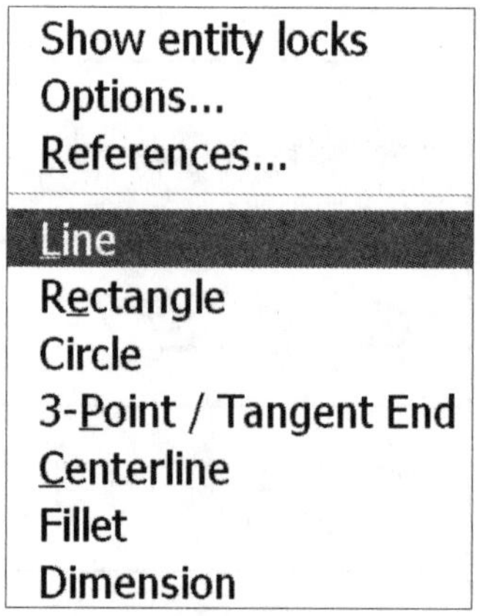

Show entity locks
Options...
References...

Line
Rectangle
Circle
3-Point / Tangent End
Centerline
Fillet
Dimension

Figure 19 RMB pop-up menu in Sketcher

You will now see a small yellow X which will chase the cursor around the screen. Notice that the X will snap to the dashed references when the cursor is brought nearby, but not to the displayed edges of DTM3. While you are creating the sketch, watch for red symbols (V, H, L) that indicate Intent Manager is firing an internal rule to set up a constraint (Vertical, Horizontal, Equal Length). These symbols will come and go while you are sketching. The trick with Sketcher is to get Intent Manager to fire the rule you want, then click the left mouse button to accept the position of the vertex. Click the corners in the order shown in Figure 20. After each click, you will see a straight line rubber-band from the previous position to the cursor position:

1. left-click at the origin (intersection of **DTM1** and **DTM2**)
2. left-click above the origin on **DTM1** (watch for V)
3. left-click horizontally to the right (watch for H and L - we do not want L)
4. left-click straight down on **DTM2** (watch for V)
5. left-click back at the origin (watch for H)
6. middle-click anywhere on the screen to end line creation

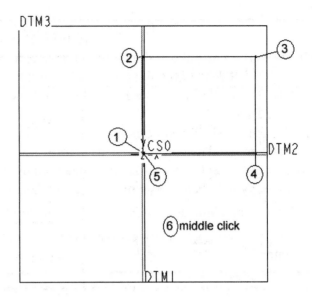

Figure 20 Drawing the Sketch

When you are finished this sequence, you are still in **Line** creation mode (notice the yellow X on screen and the *Line* toolbar button). If you middle click again, you will leave that and return to *Select* mode - the same as if you picked on the *Select* button in the right toolbar, but much faster.

The sketched entities are shown in yellow. Since we have created a closed curve, the interior of the sketch is shaded (see the *Shade Closed Loops* button in the top toolbar). Many features require sketches to contain only closed loops, so this is an easy way to verify that condition. At some point or other, you will create a sketch that you think is closed, but it will not shade. This usually means you have extraneous entities in the sketch (usually duplicated lines or edges). We will see an example of this in a few minutes.

Note that we didn't need to specify any drawing coordinates for the rectangle, nor, for that matter, are any coordinate values displayed anywhere on the screen. This is a significant departure from standard CAD programs. We also didn't need the grid or a grid snap function (although both of these are available if you want them).

You can also sketch beyond the displayed edges of the datum planes - these actually extend off to infinity. The displayed extent of datum planes will (eventually) adjust to the currently displayed object(s).

Helpful Hint

From wherever you are in the Sketcher menu structure, a single **middle** mouse click will often abort the current command and return you to the toolbar with the *Select* command already chosen. Sometimes, you may have to click the middle button twice.

Helpful Hints

If you make a mistake in drawing your shape, here are some ways to delete entities:

1. Pick the *Select* tool in the right toolbar and left click on any entity you want to delete. Then either press the *Delete* key on the keyboard, or hold down the RMB and choose *Delete*.

2. If there are several entities to delete, hold the CTRL key down while you left click on each entity. Then pick *Delete* as before.

3. You can left-click and drag to form a rectangle around a set of entities. Anything completely inside the rectangle is selected. Use *Delete* as before.

4. Notice the *Undo* and *Redo* buttons on the top toolbar ↺ ↻

We will cover more advanced Sketcher commands for deleting and trimming lines a bit later.

After you have finished the sequence above, Sketcher will put two dimensions on the sketch - for the height and width of the rectangle. These will be in dark gray, so may be hard to see unless you pass your cursor over them, but similar to those shown in Figure 21. For the first feature in a part, the numerical values of these dimensions are picked more-or-less at random (although they are in correct proportion to each other)[6]. For later features in the part, Sketcher will know the sketch size more accurately because it will have some existing geometry to set the scale.

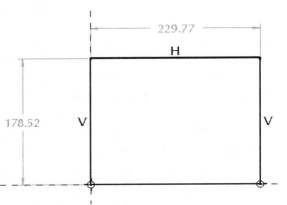

Figure 21 Initial sketch with weak dimensions

Weak vs Strong Dimensions

A dimension created by Sketcher (or actually Intent Manager) is called "weak" and is shown in gray. Strong dimensions, on the other hand, are those that you create. You can make a strong dimension in any of three ways:

    ☞   modify the value of a weak dimension

or   ☞   create a dimension from scratch by identifying entities in the sketch and placing a new dimension on the sketch

or   ☞   select a weak dimension and promote it to strong using the RMB pop-up menu

---

[6] The default datum display with no other features present is actually ±250 units from where they cross.

Strong dimensions will be shown in white (actually a very pale yellow).

The special significance of weak and strong dimensions is as follows. When Intent Manager is "solving" a sketch, it considers the sketch references, any implicit rules that have fired (like H, V, and so on) and any existing dimensions. If there is not enough information to define the drawing (it is *underconstrained*), Sketcher will create the necessary and sufficient missing dimensions. These are the weak dimensions. If Sketcher finds the drawing is *overconstrained* (too many dimensions or constraints) it will first try to solve the sketch by deleting one or more of the weak dimensions (the ones it made itself earlier). It will do this without asking you. This is one way for you to override Intent Manager - if you don't like the dimensioning scheme chosen by Sketcher, just create your own (automatically strong) dimensions. Sketcher will remove whichever of the weak dimensions are no longer needed to define the sketch. Sketcher assumes that any strong dimensions you have created shouldn't be messed with! However, if Sketcher still finds the drawing overconstrained, it will tell you what the redundant information is (which may be dimensions or constraints), and you can choose what you want deleted. Thus, although weak dimensions can be deleted without asking you, Sketcher will never delete a strong dimension without your explicit confirmation.

We want to modify the two weak dimensions on the rectangle in a couple of ways. First, we can make a cosmetic improvement by selecting the dimension text (the number) and performing a drag-and-drop to move it to a better location. Note in passing that preselection highlighting also works with dimensions and constraints. Do that now, so that the dimensions are located as in Figure 22 ("off the sketch").

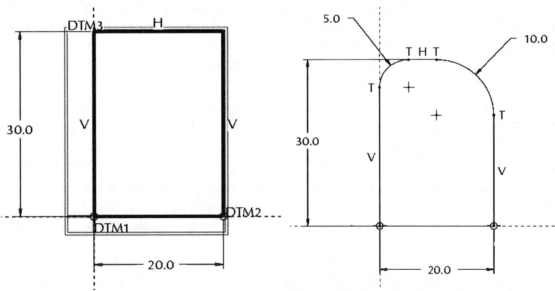

Figure 22 Modified sketch   **Figure 23** Completed sketch

Next we want to change the numeric value of the dimension. Double-click on the horizontal dimension. In the text entry box, enter the value **20**. When you hit Enter, the sketch geometry will be updated with this new dimension. The dimension is now strong. Change the vertical dimension to **30**. It will also now be strong. (Click anywhere on the graphics window to remove the red highlight and update the shading.) See Figure 22.

Notice that the indicated extent of the datum plane DTM3 adjusts to the sketch. You may want to *Refit* the sketch in the graphics window (or use zoom).

Now we'll add a couple of rounded corners, technically known as fillets, on the top corners of the sketch to help us "see" the orientation of the feature in 3D. Select the *Fillet* toolbar button on the right (or from the RMB pop-up menu shown in Figure 19) and pick on the top and right lines in the sketch close to but not at the corner. A circular fillet is created to the pick point closest to the corner. Two tangent constraints (T) are added, along with a weak dimension for the fillet radius. Do the same on the top and left lines. Middle click to return to Select mode. Because our fillet command has removed two vertices on the top of the sketch, Intent Manager has removed our two strong dimensions (which used those vertices) and replaced them with weak ones (see the message window - you may have to scroll back a couple of lines). You can make them strong by selecting them, clicking the RMB, and selecting *Strong* in the pop-up menu. Modify the cosmetics and values of the fillet radius dimensions as shown in Figure 23.

Sketcher Diagnostic Functions

At this point, we have a completed and valid sketch. Select the *Feature Requirements* button in the Sketch tools menu at the top. The window that opens indicates that the sketch is okay (all requirements check out). Let's introduce a common error into the sketch to see what happens. Close the **Feature Requirements** window.

We will create a duplicate line on the sketch - start at vertex 1 (see Figure 20) and end the line part way up the vertical edge towards the top, overlapping the existing line. When you finish the line and return to Select mode, three things will happen. First, the sketch is no longer shaded, indicating that it is no longer a simple closed loop. Second, a big red dot (a "measle") appears where the overlapping line ends. This indicates an open (that is, unconnected) end of the sketch (note the *Highlight Open Ends* button in the top toolbar). Third, a weak dimension will appear for the new line. Although the geometry of the sketch appears visually correct, if we tried to use it to create a solid feature it would fail[7]. Now pick the *Show Overlapping Geometry* button in the top toolbar. All lines touching the offending vertical line will highlight in green. At this point, you would have to do some detective work to figure out where the problem was. Select the short vertical line (note that preselection works here) and delete it. The red measle disappears and the sketch is again shaded.

You should experiment with the Sketch Diagnostic tools periodically as we proceed through the tutorial. Note that these are also available under Sketch in the pull-down menus at the top.

---

[7] This sketch could be used to create an extruded surface feature, but with overlapping surfaces, probably not a good idea. For an extruded solid, the feature would fail with an error message about requiring a closed section only.

This completes the creation of our first sketch. Select the **Done** (or **Continue**) toolbar icon (the check mark). This returns us to the regular graphics window with our new sketched curve shown in red (last feature created). You can spin the model around with the middle mouse button to see this curve from different view points. When you are finished with this, return the model to approximately the default orientation - Figure 24.

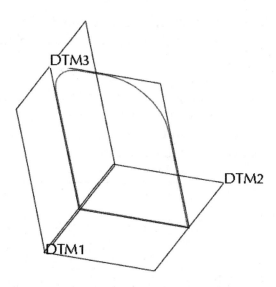

Figure 24 Sketched curve

Creating a Solid Protrusion

Most of the work to create this feature has been done already - creating the sketched curve that defines its shape. This curve should be highlighted in red. If you have been playing around with the model and the sketch is blue, just left click on it to select it again.

There are a number of ways to launch the protrusion creation command. With the sketched curve highlighted, the easiest way is to pick the **Extrude** button in the right toolbar.

What you will see now is a yellow shaded image of the protrusion, Figure 25. On this shape, you will see a yellow arrow that indicates the extrusion direction, which by default comes off the positive side of the sketch. There is also a dashed line ending in a white square. This is a drag handle. Click on this with the mouse and you can drag it to change the length of the extrusion. This length is also shown in a dimension symbol. You can even drag this extrusion out the back of the sketch to extrude in the opposite direction. This direct manipulation of the feature on the screen is called, in Pro/E vernacular, *Direct Modeling*. Bring the protrusion out the front and double click on the numeric dimension, and enter the value **30**.

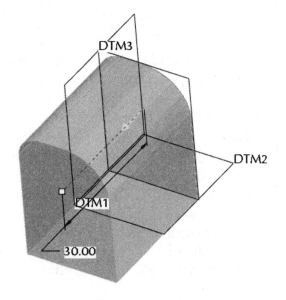

Figure 25 The protrusion preview

Check out what happens if you hold down the RMB with nothing selected. What is in the pop-up menu? What happens if you select the white drag handle? It should turn black. What is in the RMB menu now?

At the top[8] of the graphics window is a new collection of tools. These comprise the *Dashboard*. Many features are constructed with tools arranged using this interface element. It is worth spending some time exploring this one in detail, since you will probably be using it the most.

Helpful Hint
You may accidentally leave the dashboard with an inadvertent click of the middle mouse button. Remember that this is a short cut for *Accept*. If that happens, with the protrusion highlighted in red, hold down the right mouse button and select *Edit Definition*. This will bring you back to the dashboard. The *Undo* command, if executed immediately, will delete the feature.

The Extrude Dashboard

The dashboard collects all of the commands and options for feature creation in an easily navigated interface. Moreover, most optional settings have been set to default values which will work in the majority of cases. You can change options at any time and in any order, often by using a RMB pop-up menu.

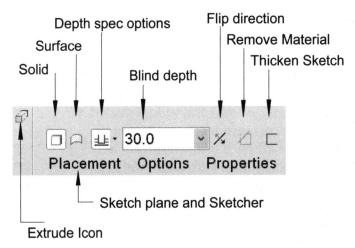

Figure 26 The *Extrude* Dashboard

The dashboard contains two areas. On the left (Figure 26) are commands, settings, and so on for the particular feature under construction. At the top left, the feature is identified with the toolbar icon - extrude in this case. The bottom row contains several pull-down menus which do the following:

Placement - allows you to select, create, or modify the 2D section to be used for the

---

[8] In previous releases of Wildfire the dashboard could be placed either above or below the graphics window, with the default position below. In Wildfire 5.0, the dashboard is above the graphics window and cannot be changed.

feature. Since we preselected the sketched curve, it is now listed on this panel. If we had not preselected the curve, we could have chosen it now, or launched Sketcher from this panel to create a new sketch. This would involve selecting the sketching plane, sketcher reference, and so on. We will go this route in the next feature. If you wanted to change the sketch for the extrude, this is how you access it. The ***Unlink*** button is currently displayed on the **Placement** panel. This button appears if, like now, you have preselected a curve to serve as the sketch for the extrude. Thus, the extrude is linked to the previous curve feature; changes to the geometry or dimensions of the curve would drive changes in the shape of the extrude. The curve itself is a separate entry on the model tree. The purpose of unlinking is to break this (parent/child) connection to the original curve. If you were to select this command (**don't do this now**), a copy of the original curve will be brought into the extrude feature. In that case, a change to the original curve would not affect the extrude. The original curve could be modified, moved, or even deleted, and the extrude would still be able to regenerate. The use of external curves to drive feature geometry is an important aspect of an advanced modeling technique that makes use of *skeleton models*.

Options - information about the depth specification for the feature. We will find out what is meant by "Side 2" in a later lesson. For a simple extrude, the depth specification is easiest to set using one of the icons in the middle dashboard area (see below).

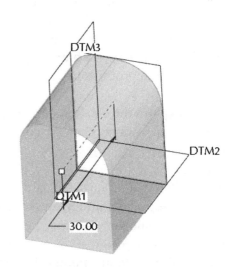

Figure 27 Extruded surface

Properties - specify the name of the feature

The icons on the second row operate as follows:

Solid and ***Surface*** buttons - these are an either/or toggle set. The default button is to create a solid. If you pick the next button, ***Surface***, the sketch will be extruded as an infinitely thin surface (Figure 27). Return this to the ***Solid*** selection.

Depth Spec Options - the next button is a drop-down list of all the possibilities for setting the depth of the extrusion. These are indicated in Figure 28. The default is a ***Blind*** extrusion, which means the extrusion is for a fixed distance. Other options may appear here as more part geometry appears (as in the cut which we will do next).

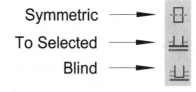

Figure 28 Depth Spec options

Blind Depth - this contains the numeric value of the length of the protrusion. If the depth specification on the button to the left is not Blind, this text input area is grayed out.

Flip - selecting this will reverse the direction of the protrusion (the yellow arrow).

Remove Material - this allows you to change the meaning of the solid feature from a protrusion (which adds solid material) to a cut (which removes solid material). Since there is nothing to remove at this time, this command is grayed out - all we can do is add.

Thicken Sketch - press this to see the solid block replaced by a thin-walled extrusion (formerly called a *Thin Solid*). A new dimension appears in the graphics window and on the dashboard. This is the thickness of the solid wall. Try changing this thickness to something like 1.0. On which side of the sketched curve has this been added? Another *Flip* button has also appeared. Press this a couple of times - it controls which side of the sketch the material is added to. Actually, it is a three way switch since you can also add material equally on both sides of the sketch. Press the *Thicken* button again to return to a full solid protrusion.

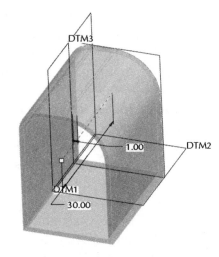

Figure 29 A *Thick* extruded solid

As you explore the creation of new features in Pro/E you should investigate what is in each of these menus. They are context sensitive, so there is a lot of variety in what you will find.

On the right end of the dashboard are several common tools that appear for all features. See Figure 30. These function as follows:

Pause - allow you to temporarily suspend work on this feature so that you can, for example, create a missing reference like a datum plane, measure something in the model, etc. When you are finished with the side trip, press the symbol ▸ that appears here to continue where you left off.

Preview - (default on = checked) this is responsible for the shaded yellow display of the feature under construction. Uncheck this - all you will see is the feature creation direction, drag handle, and depth dimension. Turn this back on.

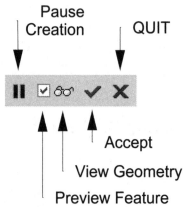

Figure 30 Common dashboard controls

View Geometry (or Verify) - this shows what the geometry will look like when the feature is fully integrated into the part. Not much happens with this first protrusion. Press again to return to preview.

Accept and *Quit* - do just what you expect!

Select *Accept* (or middle click). The block now appears, Figure 31, with its edges highlighted in red (last feature created).

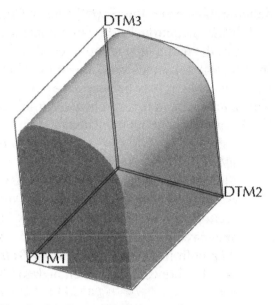

We spent a lot of time discussing the creation of this feature. Let's create it again without all the discussion. Select the *Undo* button at the top - this will delete the protrusion. Now create it again:

- ✓ highlight the sketched curve
- ✓ select the *Extrude* tool
- ✓ change the depth to **30**
- ✓ middle click.

Figure 31 Completed protrusion

You might open the Navigator pane to see the model tree. The three default datum planes are listed. Then comes the sketched curve SKETCH 1 (hidden) and the extrude EXTRUDE 1. Open the listing for the extrude and you will see the internal sketch (also SKETCH 1) that uses the hidden curve and is currently linked to it. If you have used the *Unlink* button in the **Placement** panel, the model tree will appear somewhat differently - the sketch stored inside the extrude is called S2D0001 and is independent of SKETCH 1. Close the Navigator.

We will now add another extruded feature - this time we will create a cut that removes material. Furthermore, instead of creating the sketch first, as we did for the solid protrusion, we will create the sketch within the feature itself. This is actually the more common way to use Sketcher. Before we do that, now is a good time to save the part.

Saving the Part

It is a good idea when you are just getting started to save your model quite frequently, just in case something serious goes wrong. If you have to bail out of the program, you can always reload the most recently saved copy of the part and continue from there.

There are (as usual!) several ways to save the part:

- • in the top toolbar, select the *Save* button, or
- • in the pull-down menus select *File > Save* , or
- • use the keyboard shortcut CTRL-S.

Make sure that the **Save Object** dialog is showing the desired working directory at the top. If not, select it in the Common Folders area in the Navigator. At the bottom of the dialog window, the name of the current active object (remember that you can have more than one object loaded into memory at a time) should already be in view. Accept the default model name **[block.prt]** (this is the *active* part) by pressing the enter key or the middle mouse button. Pro/E will automatically put the part extension (*prt*) on the file. If you save the part a number of times, Pro/E will automatically number each saved version (like block.prt.1, block.prt.2, block.prt.3, and so on). Be aware of how much space you have available. It may be necessary to delete some of the previously saved versions; or you can copy them to an archive location. You can do both of these tasks from within Pro/E - we'll talk about that later.

> **IMPORTANT NOTE:**
> The *Save* command is also available when you are in Sketcher. Executing this command at that time will *not* save the part, but it will save the current sketched section with the file extension *sec*. This may be useful if the sketch is complicated and may be used again on a different part. Rather than recreate the sketch, it can be read in from the saved file (using *Data from File*). In these lessons, none of the sketches are complicated enough to warrant saving them to disk.

Now we will proceed on to the next feature - an extruded cut.

Creating an Extruded Cut

Start by launching the *Extrude* command from the right toolbar. The extrude dashboard at the top of the screen opens. Note the contents of the message area and open the *Placement* slide-up panel (why is it red?) in the dashboard and select *Define*. The **Sketch** dialog window appears. This time, however, nothing has been preselected for us as it was for the previous sketch. We'll have to enter the data ourselves.

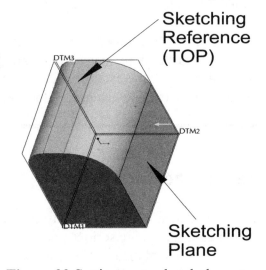

Figure 32 Setting up to sketch the cut

Notice the pale yellow data entry field, called a *collector*. In Pro/E, whenever one or more references can be specified for something, they are placed into a collector. When a collector is active (ready to accept data) it is yellow; otherwise it will be white. If you want to make a collector active, just click it.

First, the dialog is waiting for you to select the sketching plane. Pay attention to preselection here. You will not be able to pick an edge or a curved surface (both of these would be illegal). Pick on the right side surface of the block (see Figure 32). As soon as you pick the sketching plane (it highlights in orange), a yellow arrow will appear showing the default direction of view relative to the surface. The *Flip* button can be used to reverse this direction, but leave it as it is. Pro/E makes a guess at a potential reference plane for you to use. This may depend on the current orientation of your view, and might result in a strange view orientation in sketcher (like sideways or even upside down). We want to be a bit more careful and specific here. The collector for the sketch reference surface is now active (yellow) and showing the default chosen by Pro/E. To override the default for the active collector, pick on the top planar surface (Figure 32), between the two tangent lines of the rounded corners; the surface will highlight in red. In the **Orientation** pull-down list, select **Top** so that the reference will face the top of the screen. We now have our sketch plane and reference set up, so select **Sketch** at the bottom of the dialog window.

We are now in Sketcher (Figure 33). Two references have been chosen for us (the back and top surfaces of the object). We are going to create the U-shaped figure shown in Figure 34. Note that there is no sketched line across the top of the U - there is no inside or outside. Thus, it is technically called an *open* sketch (as opposed to a *closed* sketch for our previous feature). There are some restrictions on the use of open sketches which we will run across in a minute or two.

You might prefer to set your display mode to *Hidden Line* at this point.

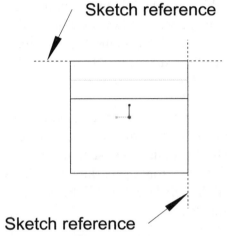

Figure 33 References for cut sketch

Helpful Hint
In general, try to keep your sketches closed - you will have fewer problems that way.

Use the RMB pop-up menu to select the **Line** command. Start your sketch at vertex 1 in Figure 34 - the cursor will snap to the reference. Then drag the mouse down and pick vertex 2 (note the V constraint), and middle click twice to end the **Line** command. Some weak dimensions will appear. Do nothing about them yet because, since they are weak, they are liable to disappear anyway. If we make them strong, this will cause us extra work dealing with Intent Manager. Click somewhere on the background to turn off the red highlighting.

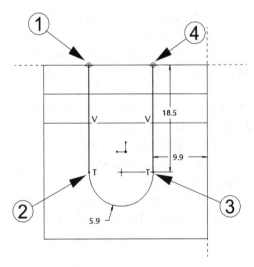

Figure 34 Sketch geometry

> **Helpful Hint**
> Wait until the shape of the sketch is finished before you start worrying about the
> dimensioning scheme or dimension values.

Use the RMB pop-up menu again and select the ***3-Point/Tangent End*** command. Pick on
the end of the sketched line (vertex 2) and drag the mouse downwards in the direction of
tangency. Once the arc has been established, drag the cursor over to the right (the arc will
rubber-band while maintaining the tangency constraint) and click at vertex 3. (If you drag
straight across to vertex 3 you will get a 3-point arc which is not automatically tangent at
vertex 2.) You should see two small blips that indicate when vertex 3 is at the same
height as the center of the arc. Left click to create the vertex 3. Use the RMB menu to
pick ***Line*** again.

Now left click at vertex 3 and draw a vertical line up to snap to the reference at vertex 4,
making sure that you have a tangent constraint (T) at vertex 3. Our sketch is complete.
Use the middle mouse button to return to Select mode. Your dimension values may be
different from those shown in Figure 34. Your dimensioning scheme may even be
slightly different. It will be easier to see this if you go to hidden line display instead of
shading.

All the dimensions should be weak. Drag them to a better location if necessary (off the
part). Don't be afraid to resize your display so that you can see everything clearly.
Compare the dimensioning scheme with the one in Figure 35. We want to have a
horizontal dimension of 15 from the reference at the back of the part to the center of the
arc of the U. If you do not have that dimension, we'll have to add one manually. This will
illustrate a case where we will override the Intent Manager.

To create your own dimension, select the
Dimension command from the right toolbar
(or the RMB pop-up). Click on the vertex
at the center of the arc (it will highlight)
then click again on the dashed reference
line at the right. Now middle click in the
space above the part where you want the
dimension text to appear. Set the value as
shown in the figure. It's that easy! Note
that this dimension shows immediately in
pale yellow (almost white) since it is
strong. One of the weak linear dimensions
should be gone. Middle click to get back to
Select.

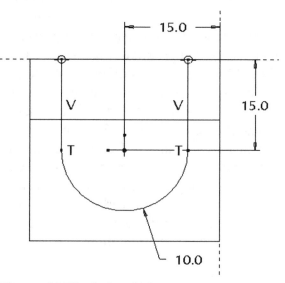

Figure 35 Final sketch for cut

We now have the implicit constraints and dimensioning scheme we want. So now we can worry about the dimension values. Get in the habit of dealing with your sketches in that order (shape, constraints, dimension scheme, dimension values). Modify the values of the dimensions to match those in Figure 35.

Recall the hint above about open vs closed sketches. The sketch we have just produced will be able to produce the desired cut, but it is not the best we can do. The behavior of features constructed using open sketches is unpredictable. The danger lies in the possibility that something or someone may come along later to modify this part and add something to the top of the block earlier in the model tree. In that case, the cut feature would likely fail due to the uncertainty in what to do across the open ends of the sketch. So before we accept this sketch, let's explore the diagnostics a bit.

First, turn on the *Shade Closed Loops* and *Highlight Open Ends* buttons. Since the sketch is currently open it will not shade; the two ends will show the measles. Now select the *Feature Requirements* button. In addition to a couple of checked items, there are a couple that are not satisfied. One is a warning, and one is an error. The message at the top indicates the sketch is not appropriate for the current feature (an extruded solid - note that we have not indicated yet that this is going to be a cut). Close this window and create a line across the top of the sketch to close it. Now the sketch will shade, the measles disappear, and the *Feature Requirements* function will indicate all is well.

The sketch is now complete, so click on the *Done* button in the toolbar[9]. If you are in hidden line display, return to shading display.

The feature will now be previewed. A couple of new buttons have appeared on the dashboard. First, in the **Depth Spec** pull-up list, there are a few more options available (Figure 36). For this cut, we would like the sketch to be extruded through the entire part, so pick the *Through All* option. Note that the dimension for a blind extrusion disappears from the screen. To the right of this area, click the *Flip* button to make the extrusion go through the part. The *Remove Material* button needs to be selected - finally we indicate that we are making a cut. Now, there are two yellow arrows attached to the sketch. The one perpendicular to the plane of the sketch shows the direction of the extrusion. The other shows which side of the sketched line we want to remove material from. These should be set as shown in Figure 37.

---

[9] This is one of the few times when a middle click does not mean "Accept", which is a good thing since inadvertent middle clicks happen often when you are in Sketcher.

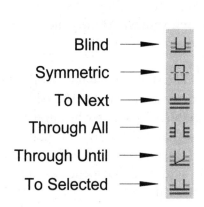

Blind
Symmetric
To Next
Through All
Through Until
To Selected

Figure 36 More Depth Spec options in the dashboard

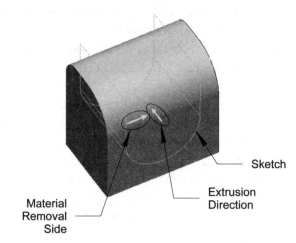

Sketch

Extrusion Direction

Material Removal Side

Figure 37 Defining cut attributes (direction and material removal side)

Now select the *Verify* 👓 button in the right area of the dashboard. If you have the *Remove Material* button set wrong, Pro/E will create a protrusion instead of a cut[10]. Turn *Verify* off.

Another common error with cuts is having the material removal side set wrong (the second yellow arrow in Figure 37). If you do that for this part, you will end up with Figure 38. Make sure the material removal arrow points to the inside of the U. Plus, you should explore the **Placement**, **Options**, and **Properties** menus on the dashboard before you leave.

We are finished creating this feature, so select the *Accept* button at the right end of the dashboard. The part should now look like Figure 39 when in default orientation. The cut will be highlighted in red as usual, as the last feature created.

Save the part. We will need it in this condition for the next chapter.

---

[10] Even worse, if we had left the sketch open, the feature would fail and you would be launched into a **Troubleshooter** dialog window. The source of this problem is the open sketch for the U. This sketch is ambiguous since when the sketch starts out from the sketch plane, the vertices at the ends are out in the open air; Pro/E does not know how to create the solid to attach it to the existing part. This problem does not occur with a cut as long as the open ends of the sketch stay outside or on the surface of the part. You might come back and explore this later.

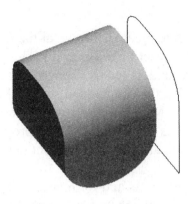
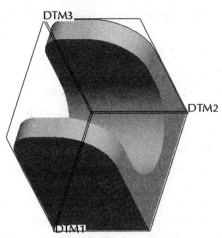

Figure 38 Removing from the wrong side of the sketch

Figure 39 Cut feature completed

Using Part Templates

You will recall that in the block part created earlier, the first thing we did was to create default datum planes. These (plus the named views based on them, which we didn't create this lesson) are very standard features and aspects of part files, and it would be handy if this was done automatically. This is exactly the purpose of part templates.

A template is a previously created part file that contains the common features and aspects of almost all part files you will ever make. These include, among other things, default datum planes and named views. Pro/E actually has several templates available for parts, drawings, and assemblies. There are variations of the templates for each type of object. One important variation consists of the unit system used for the part (inches or millimeters). Templates also contain some common model parameters and layer definitions[11].

A template can be selected only when a new model is first created. Let's see how that works. Create a new part (note that you don't have to remove the block - Pro/E can have several parts "in session" at the same time) by selecting

File > New

or using the "Create New Object" button. The **New** dialog window opens. The

Part | Solid

options are selected by default. Enter a new name, like *exercise_1*. Remove the check mark beside *Use default template* (we normally don't do this, but we should have a look

---

[11] Model parameters and layers are discussed in the *Advanced Tutorial*.

at what is available) and then select *OK*.

In the **New File Options** dialog window, the default template is shown at the top. It is likely "inlbs_part_solid" (unless your system has been set up differently). This template is for solid parts with the units set to inch-pound-second. It seems strange to have force and time units in a CAD geometry program. Actually, this is included so that the part units are known by downstream applications like Pro/MECHANICA which perform finite element analysis (FEA) or mechanism dynamics calculations. These programs both require force, mass, and/or time in their operation and are very picky about units!

Note that there are templates available for sheet-metal parts and for metric units (millimeter-Newton-second). While we are mentioning units, be aware that if you make a wrong choice of units here, changing units of a part is possible after it has been created (see *Edit > Setup > Units*).

There are only two model parameters in the default template. *DESCRIPTION* is for an extended title for the part, like "UPPER PUMP HOUSING". This title can (eventually) be called up and placed automatically on a drawing of the part using, you guessed it, a drawing template. Similarly, the *MODELED_BY* parameter is available for you to record your name or initials as the originator of the part. Fill in these parameter fields ("Wildfire Exercise #1" and your initials) and select *OK*.

The new part is created which automatically displays the default datums. They are even named for you (we will see how to name features in lesson 3): instead of DTM1, we have **RIGHT**. **TOP** replaces DTM2, and **FRONT** replaces DTM3. The part also contains a coordinate system, named views (look in the Named Views List), and other data that we'll discover as we go through the lessons. The named views correspond to the standard engineering views. Thus, it is important to note that if you are planning on using a drawing template that uses these named views, your model orientation relative to the default datums is critical. The top-front-right views of the part are the ones that will be automatically placed on the drawing later. If your model is upside down or backwards in these named views, then your drawing will be too. This is embarrassing and not likely to win favor with your boss or instructor!

Now, having created this new part, you are all set up to do some of the exercises at the end of the lesson. Do as many of these as you can. Perhaps do some of them in different ways by experimenting with your sketch orientation, Sketcher commands, and so on.

This completes Lesson #2. You are strongly encouraged to experiment with any of the commands that have been presented in this lesson. Create new parts for your experiments since we will need the block part in its present form for the next lesson. In the next lesson we will add some more features to the block, discover the magic of relations, and spend some time learning about the utility functions available to give you information about the model.

Questions for Review

Here are some questions you should be able to answer at this time:

1. What is meant by a blind protrusion?
2. What is the purpose of the sketching reference?
3. How do you specify the name of a part?
4. Give as many of the Sketcher implicit rules as you can.
5. How do you save a part?
6. What is a template?
7. What is your system's default template?
8. Where does your system store your part files when they are saved?
9. What is meant by the *active* part?
10. How does Sketcher determine the radius of a fillet created on two lines?
11. What happens if you delete any of the constraints (H, V, etc.) on a sketch?
12. In an extrude, what happens if you set the thickness of a thickened sketch greater than the radius of a filleted corner of the sketch?
13. What is meant by *Linking* to a sketch?
14. In Sketcher, what is the difference between gray, white (pale yellow), and red dimensions?
15. In Sketcher, how do you create an explicit dimension? Is this weak or strong?
16. In Sketcher, how do you indicate where you want the dimension text placed?
17. What are the commands available for diagnosing errors in sketches?
18. How do you turn on the Sketch grid?
19. What are three ways to create a strong dimension?
20. How do you create a weak dimension (trick question!).
21. In Sketcher, how do you create a radius dimension? A diameter dimension?
22. In Sketcher, what dimension is created if you left click on an arc or circle, then on a planar reference, then middle click to place the dimension?
23. What kind of dimensions are created in Sketcher for the sloping line in the figure at the right if, after you have selected the line, you middle click in regions A, B, or C?

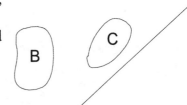

24. When would you normally create a sketch embedded within a feature, as opposed to a separately created curve?
25. What, in Pro/E terminology, is meant by "Direct Modelling"?
26. What is the default direction for the normal to a datum plane? A solid surface?
27. What is the purpose of the *Pause* button on the feature creation dashboard? What about the *Preview* check box? How is *Preview* different from *Verify*?
28. In Sketcher, what is the difference between a geometry element and a construction element? What types of elements does this refer to?
29. What are the nine explicit constraints in Sketcher?
30. What are two ways of finding out if a sketch is open or closed?
31. How can you find overlapping entities in a sketch?
32. What are the measles?

Exercises

Here are some simple shapes that you can make with simple extrusions. They should give you some practice using the Sketcher drawing tools and internal rules. Choose your own dimensions and pay attention to alignments and internal constraints. The objects should appear in roughly the same orientation in default view. Have a contest with a buddy to see who can create each object with the fewest number of dimensions. This is not necessarily a goal of good modeling, but is a good exercise! Feel free to add additional features to these objects.

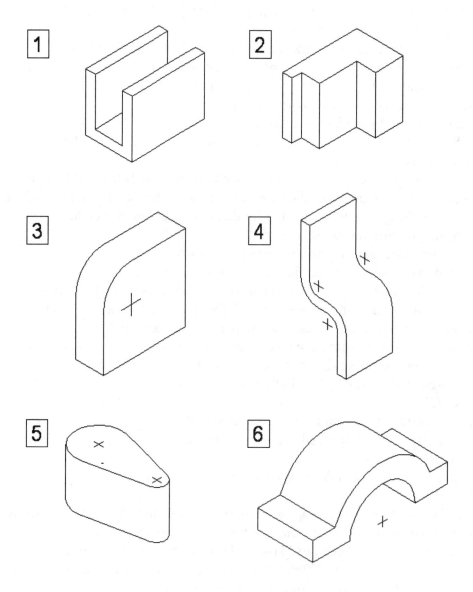

These parts are a bit more complicated, requiring two or more simple extruded features (protrusions or cuts). Think about these carefully before you try to make them.

1.

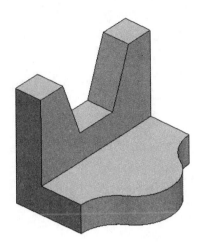

2.

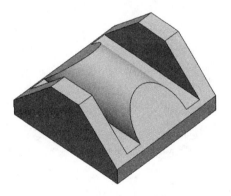

3.

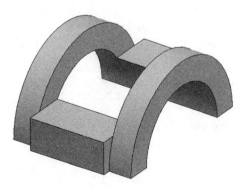

This page left blank.

Lesson 3

Creating a Simple Object (Part II)

Synopsis

Placed features (hole, round, chamfer) are added to the block created in Lesson #2; customizing the model tree; naming features; modifying dimensions; implementing *design intent* using relations; more Sketcher tools and options.

Overview of this Lesson

We will continue with the creation of the model you started in Lesson 2. We are going to add three new features to the block: a *hole*, a *chamfer*, and a *round*. These features do not require Sketcher since their geometry is more-or-less predetermined. We only have to specify where they go - they are *placed* on the model, rather than sketched. Then, we will explore some more of the interface tools using the model tree. We will look at several ways to modify part dimensions, and then introduce the use of *relations* to adjust the geometry automatically. Finally, we will open up the sketch of the cut we made last lesson and look at how a feature's dimensioning scheme is used to implement *design intent*. Along the way we will come across some new tools and functions in Sketcher.

When we are finished this lesson, the block part should look like Figure 1. Although not obvious from the figure, there are a number of different ways we can create this simple geometry. This goes to the subject of *design intent*, which will be discussed towards the end of the lesson.

Here are the major steps we will follow, which should be completed in order:

1. Retrieving a Part
2. Adding a Hole
3. Adding a Chamfer
4. Adding a Round
5. Customizing the Model Tree
6. Naming features
7. Modifying Dimensions

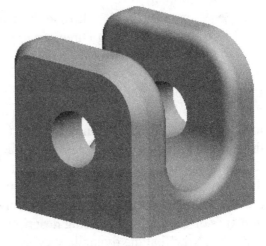

Figure 1 Final part geometry

8.   Adding Feature Relations
9.   Implementing Design Intent in Sketcher

We will be seeing a lot of new menus and dialog windows here. As usual, we will not discuss all commands and options in detail although some important modeling and Pro/E concepts will be elaborated. You should quickly scan each new menu/window to familiarize yourself with the location of the available commands and options.

Retrieving a Part

If you haven't already, login to the computer and bring up Pro/Engineer. If you are already in Pro/E, make sure there are no parts in the current session (select *File > Erase > Current*; then select *File > Erase > Not Displayed* to remove any other parts in the session).

Helpful Hint

If you need to change the default directory, use the commands:

File > Set Working Directory

and select the path to the desired directory for your *block.prt* file from the last lesson OR (even easier) select the Folder Tree in the Navigator window than use the ***Set Working Directory*** command available in the RMB pop-up menu.

You can retrieve the block part we worked on last lesson using one of the following command sequences:

➤   in the pull-down menus, select ***File > Open***

OR ➤   use the ***Open*** shortcut button on the top toolbar

OR ➤   open the Folder Browser by clicking on the Working Directory in the Navigator.

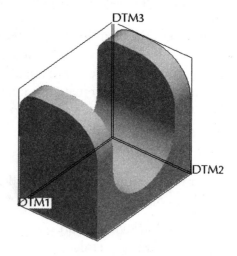

If you use either of the first two methods, in the dialog window that opens make sure you are looking at the desired working directory (shown at the top). In all cases there is a ***Preview*** button at the bottom. This will be useful when your directory starts to fill up with part files by making it easier to select the file you want (especially if you are not very careful in using descriptive file names!). Note that the dynamic view controls (spin, zoom, pan) work in the preview window, which can be resized by dragging on the

Figure 2 The **block** part at end of previous lesson

horizontal sash. Also, it is easy to customize the displayed list of files by requesting only part files, assembly files, drawings, and so on. You can also change a setting that allows you to see all versions of a file (see the section *Pro/E Files Saved Automatically* at the end of this lesson).

With **block.prt** highlighted in the file list select the *Open* button (or double-click the name). Pro/E will bring the part into the session, as shown in Figure 2. Close the Model Tree window if it is currently open and position the part in the default orientation.

Creating a Hole

The next feature we'll add to the block is the central hole. The major difference from the extruded features (protrusion and cut) we made before is that those were *sketched* features whereas a hole is a *placed* feature. It's shape is pretty much already defined, and all we have to do is tell Pro/E its size and where to place it on the model. Some other examples of placed features are rounds, chamfers, shells, pipes, and draft features. We will add some of those later this lesson. Although it sounds like a hole feature should be simpler than an extrusion, there are many variations of this feature. Some examples are shown in Figure 3.

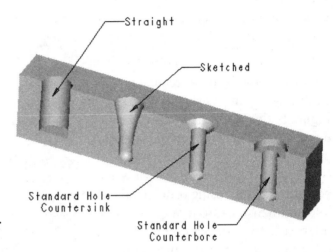

Figure 3 Example hole types

A *straight* hole is a simple cylindrical hole with a flat bottom, essentially what you get with an end mill. A *sketched* hole involves the use of Sketcher to define the hole cross sectional shape or profile. This shape is revolved through 360° to create the hole. This obviously gives considerable freedom in the hole geometry which is handy for holes with several steps or unusual curved profiles. The *standard* holes can be countersunk, counterbored, neither, or both! Notice the shape at the bottom of the holes. Standard hole sizes are built-in for common bolts and thread specifications, and can be either tapped or clearance holes. Standard holes can also be tapered. If you pick a common thread specification, this will automatically create a note (that can be included in a drawing, for example).

After its type and diameter, the next important variation in hole geometry is its depth. This is defined using one of the depth specifications shown in Figure 4. These are essentially the same as we saw previously for the cut feature. The *Blind* option drills the hole to a specified depth. *Thru Next*[1] will create a hole until it passes through the next

---

[1] The unusual spelling of *Through* is an artifact of manual drafting practice.

surface it encounters. A *Thru All* hole, as you would expect, drills through everything. Finally, a *Thru Until* hole goes up to a designated surface, edge, or point. If the hole is created "both sides" from the placement plane, then the hole depth can be defined separately in each direction.

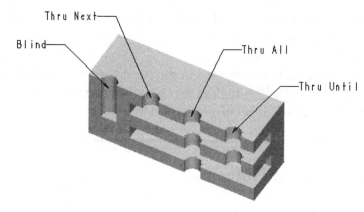

Figure 4 Hole depth options

A final requirement for defining the hole is the method for specifying where the hole is to be created, that is, its placement. As shown in Figure 5, this can be a *linear* dimensioning scheme (on the left) or a *radial* dimensioning scheme (on the right). Linear placement will position the hole using orthogonal linear dimensions from selected references to its center point. The references are typically surfaces of the part or datum planes. Radial placement requires an axis, a radial distance from the axis, and an angular distance from a planar reference. Another common placement option (not shown) is

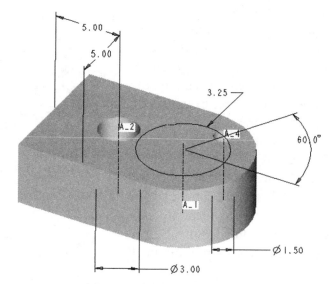

Figure 5 Hole dimensioning schemes: linear (left) and radial (right)

coaxial, where the center of the hole is placed on an existing axis.

The **Hole** command is one of the more automated commands in Pro/E, and a lot happens here very quickly. Go through this slowly, and take time to explore some of the options and pull-up menus. As you select different options for the hole, the true size and shape will be previewed on the part.

If you create holes with threads, the actual thread will not be shown on the part. This would become computationally expensive if there were many holes. Instead, a cosmetic thread is created, which appears as a purple cylinder around the hole showing the major thread diameter. Full thread details are stored with the part, however, and can be placed on a drawing.

In the right toolbar, select the *Hole* command in the placed features toolbar. This will open the dashboard shown in Figure 6. The default settings are for a **Simple** hole. The default depth is blind, that is, with a specified depth. The *Depth Spec* button on the

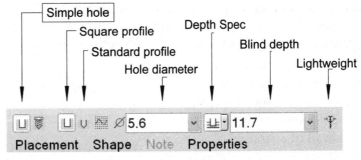

Figure 6 The *Simple* hole dashboard

dashboard lets you easily change this. The square profile button (default) creates a flat bottomed hole. The standard profile (not to be confused with a Standard hole described below) creates a conical bottom to the hole, as would occur if a normal drill bit was used. If you pick the standard profile shape, some additional buttons will appear that specify how the depth dimension is to be interpreted (shoulder or tip), and create a countersink or counterbore on the hole. For the latter, opening the *Shape* slide-up panel will allow you to specify dimensions. Also in the *Shape* panel, if you create a **Thru All** hole, you have the option of specifying an exit countersink. The *Lightweight* option will only be relevant when you have a model with hundreds (or thousands) of holes[2].

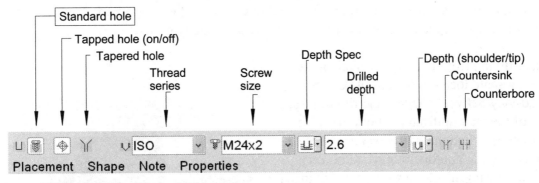

Figure 7 The *Standard* hole dashboard

The alternative to a Simple hole is a **Standard** hole, obtained by selecting the second icon from the left (see Figure 7). A standard hole lets you specify a thread series (UNC, UNF, etc.), standard screw size, and a thread depth. Other options are for turning thread tapping on or off, and for creating a tapered thread. The nominal hole diameter is set automatically when you pick the screw size. It also lets you add a counterbore or countersink to the hole. All the hole information is placed in a note which becomes part of the feature definition. What is in the *Note* drop-down menu? Compare this to the *Properties* pull-up and contents of the *Shape* menu. In the latter, note the option for

---

[2] A lightweight hole contains all the hole data but is represented graphically by a single axis line and an orange circle on the placement plane and also have a special icon in the model tree. The purpose of lightweight features is to conserve memory. This will only become relevant if you have a model with hundreds or thousands of holes. The Lightweight setting is a toggle that can be changed later. Mass property calculations do not include lightweight holes.

turning on and off the display of the thread surface. This is a cosmetic feature (a purple cylinder) that helps to differentiate between identify threaded holes and plain holes in complex models. This is a way of conserving memory, much like lightweight holes.

For a Simple hole, another option for the hole shape is called a **Sketched** hole, Figure 8. Instead of a straight cylindrical hole, this lets you define the cross sectional profile of the hole (on one side since it is axisymmetric) using Sketcher. This is useful for creating stepped holes. If the hole shape is complicated and used often, the sketch can be loaded from a separate file. An example of a sketched hole is discussed in Lesson #11.

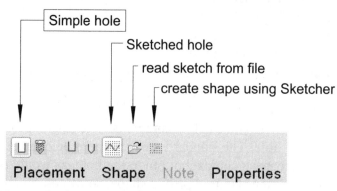

Figure 8 The *Sketched* hole dashboard

For now, all we want is a *Simple, Square, Thru All* hole using *Linear* placement on the front surface of the block. This is the easiest hole imaginable to create that uses almost all default settings, so there is not much we need to change in the dashboard. As you perform the following, follow the prompts in the message window.

Click on the front face of the block at the approximate location of the hole center (mid-way between the left and right faces, 1/2 of the way up from the bottom). This surface is called the *placement reference* for the hole[3]. You do not have to be very accurate with this since we will be setting exact dimensions next.

A hole preview will appear as shown in Figure 9. Notice that Pro/E has automatically figured out which way the hole should go. This feature preview has five drag handles whose functions are as follows (you may have to zoom in on the hole to distinguish between these):

- center location (white square)
- diameter (white square)
- distance to reference #1 (green diamond)
- distance to reference #2 (green diamond)

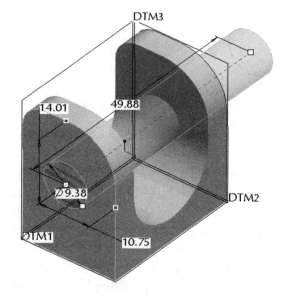

Figure 9 Default hole preview showing drag handles

---

[3] For a *coaxial* hole, the placement references are the surface where the hole will be located, and an axis from another feature.

> ▸   depth (white square with black dot)

You can modify the hole geometry and placement by selecting one of the handles and dragging them across the part. A selected drag handle also has its own RMB pop-up menu. If you accidentally click on a surface instead of a drag handle, the hole primary reference (placement surface) will change. Not to worry - just left click back on the front face of the block. Try moving the center of the hole and changing its diameter or depth. The default placement type is *linear*. The green location drag handles are used to select two edges, axes, planar surfaces or datum planes for linear dimensions to locate the hole center. We will use the right and top surfaces of the block for these references. All you have to do is drag each of the appropriate handles and drop it on either the right or top surface of the block, as in Figure 9 above. Each time you select a surface, be sure (using preselection) to drop the drag handle on the *surface* not the *edge*[4]. Once you have attached the handles to the references, double click on the dimension values to change the diameter to **10** and the linear distances to **10** from the right surface and **15** from the top (to center the hole on the front face). To change the depth from a blind hole to a through all hole, use the ***Depth Spec*** button on the dashboard (or RMB on the depth drag handle). The hole preview will stop at the back surface of the part; the depth dimension disappears.

This completes the definition of the hole. Before you accept the feature, select the ***Verify*** button to see the hole. Also, examine the contents of the **Placement** and **Shape** pull-up menus to see how other hole options may be selected. As you move the cursor over reference fields in these menus, the appropriate edge/surface on the model will highlight.

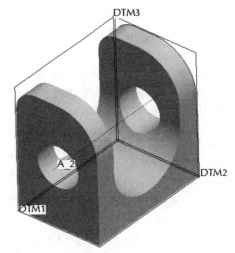

If all is well, accept the feature. If the preview shows something wrong, you can correct any of the element definitions by selecting the appropriate area or data field in the dashboard and making your corrections. Assuming the hole is correct, accept the feature. Your block should now look similar to Figure 10. Note that an axis line has been added

Figure 10 Hole created

automatically down the center of the hole (A_2 in Figure 10).

There are obviously a lot of options to explore with the Hole feature. You are encouraged to come back and explore these later. To that end, there is an exercise included at the end of the chapter.

_____

[4] We prefer to use surfaces for references instead of edges because they are more robust. That is, they are less likely to be changed or removed later in a design revision.

Creating a Chamfer

A chamfer is another example of a placed feature - the only reference it needs is the edge (or edges) on which it will be placed.

We will use the object/action command style here. Using preselection (pick object - surface - edge with the left mouse button or use the selection filter), pick the two edges of the block shown in Figure 10. Remember that to pick multiple entities, after the first is selected you can hold down the CTRL key to include additional entities in a selection set. It doesn't matter which edge you pick first. When the edges are selected, they will be highlighted in red.

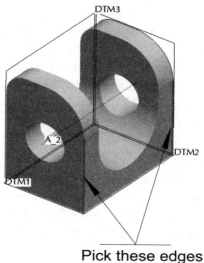

Pick these edges
for Chamfer.

With the edges highlighted, pick the ***Chamfer*** tool in the right toolbar. Be careful to get this one and not the ***Round*** tool button which looks very similar.

Figure 11 Picking two edges simultaneously for chamfer

A lot of things will happen on the screen at once. First, the **Chamfer** dashboard will open at the top of the screen (Figure 12). Also, the edges of the chamfer will be shown in preview yellow on the model. Two drag handles will be attached to these edges. See Figure 13.

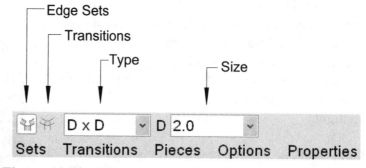

Figure 12 The ***Chamfer*** dashboard

Let's explore the dashboard a bit. The chamfer icon is on the top left corner. In the top row, the two icons at the left end determine the dashboard mode of operation. In "edge sets" mode, you determine the collection or set of edges that will all have the same chamfer properties. It is possible to create multiple chamfer sets within the same feature, each with different properties. The next button is used to enter "transition" mode. As the icon indicates, this mode is used to determine the geometry of chamfers that intersect or meet at corners. There are a number of ways that transition geometry can be set up[5]. None of these are necessary here since we do not have intersecting chamfers. The first pull-down list contains the options for setting the chamfer dimension type. The default (DxD) is an equal leg chamfer. The final text field contains the value of the indicated dimension D. This value is also indicated on the screen next to the previewed chamfer.

---

[5] Chamfer and round transitions are discussed at length in the *Advanced Tutorial*. We will not investigate them here.

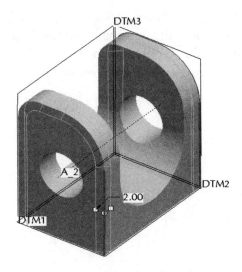
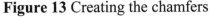

Figure 13 Creating the chamfers

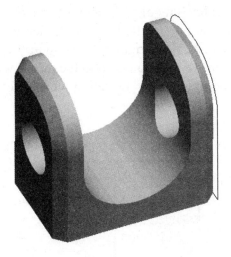

Figure 14 Chamfers complete

You can change the chamfer dimension either by moving the drag handles, double clicking the value on the screen and typing in a new value, or by entering a new value in the dashboard. What happens if you make the chamfer too big (try sizes of 4, 5, and 6)? Set the final chamfer distance to **2**.

Before you accept the chamfer, have a look in the pull-down menus on the dashboard. The **Sets** menu shows our current set (*Set 1*) and the contained edges in the References collector just below, with dimension type and value indicated. If we had multiple sets, they would be listed here. The **Transitions** pull-up is currently empty.

We have basically used all the defaults to create this equal length chamfer. Note that Pro/E has placed the chamfer by following along the tangent edge chain starting from the single straight edges we first selected. To override this tangent-following behavior, use the *Details* button. Use the *Verify* button on the dashboard at the right to see how the final geometry will appear. Finally, *Accept* the feature. The block should now look like Figure 14.

Creating a Round

Rounds are very common placed features that are created in the same way as a chamfer. Rounds are normally considered *cosmetic features*, and are therefore added to the model quite late in the regeneration sequence. Because they are so easy to create and make the model look more realistic (in shaded mode or rendered images), newcomers tend to go overboard in adding rounds to their models. However, be warned that misuse of rounds can have several detrimental effects on the model.

The first is their appearance in drawings. If a model has many rounds, the display of tangent edges showing the round extents can clutter up the drawing considerably, as in the left side of Figure 15. On the other hand, if the display of tangent edges is turned off (which is standard practice), then important information about the part may sometimes be lost, as in the right side of Figure 15. A partial solution to this problem is to temporarily remove the rounds from the model when creating the drawing (which then shows the "virtual sharps" or defining edges for the rounds).

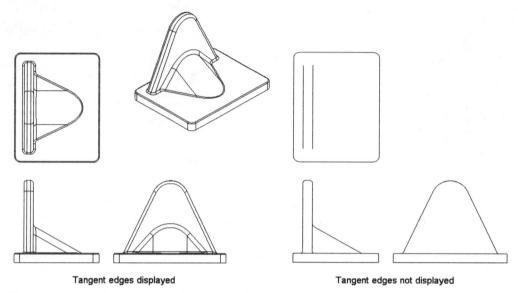

Tangent edges displayed   Tangent edges not displayed

Figure 15 Problems caused by rounds in drawings

The second effect of rounds is felt if the model is used for Finite Element Analysis (FEA). In FEA, the presence of rounds leads to a substantial increase in the modeling effort, primarily in creating the number of elements required to represent geometry ("meshing"). This can drastically increase the model size and computational cost. Rounds do not usually have a large effect on the stress magnitudes in a part (unless they are at critical zones, especially fillets), so this increase in modeling effort is wasted (or may preclude the FEA modeling entirely). FEA models are often "de-featured" by eliminating unnecessary cosmetic features like rounds.

Finally, when a lot of rounds are present on a model, it is easy (but not good practice) to accidentally pick a tangent edge as a reference for a subsequent feature. Creating this type of parent/child relation will usually cause problems.

In these cases (drawings, FEA, or avoiding inadvertent references), it will be handy to have the rounds organized in the model near the end of the regeneration sequence, and in some sort of orderly presentation so that they can be easily and temporarily removed from the model (*suppressed*, see Lesson #5).

We have added all the key features to our block model, so now is a good time to add a final round feature. Using preselection, pick the edge shown in Figure 16. Now select *Round* toolbar button at the right (be careful not to pick *Chamfer*, which looks almost the same) OR use the RMB pop-up menu and pick *Round Edges*.

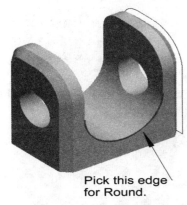

Pick this edge for Round.

Figure 16 Creating a round

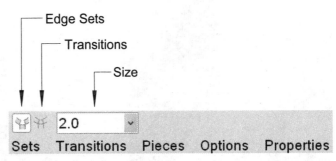

Edge Sets

Transitions

Size

2.0

Sets Transitions Pieces Options Properties

Figure 17 The ***Round*** dashboard

The **Round** dashboard appears as shown in Figure 17 and the round is previewed on the model (Figure 18) with yellow lines, a couple of drag handles, and a dimension (the round radius). The default round follows the tangent edge chain from the selected edge all the way around the model.

The dashboard looks and operates much the same as the chamfer dashboard. Selected edges to receive rounds are organized into edge sets (top row, left icon). A single round feature can contain several edge sets. You can use the transitions options to specify the type of geometry where rounded edges meet at corners.

Open the ***Sets*** drop-down menu to see the default settings for this edge/set. The round is *circular* (as opposed to *conic*, ie elliptical). The shape is a *rolling ball* round. Read the tool tip pop-ups for descriptions of these settings. The references pane lists the edges in the present set. The ***Transitions*** pull-up is currently empty.

Even for simple rounds (with no transitions), you will find that there are considerably more options than there were for chamfers. A major variation available is the ability to create rounds whose radius changes along their length (*variable radius rounds*). The round extent can also be determined by other features (edges or datum curves). In this tutorial, we do not have time to explore all these options - you could spend an entire book chapter just studying rounds[6]!

---

[6] The *Advanced Tutorial* spends half a chapter on rounds, including variable radius rounds, surface rounds, and transitions, and still does not cover all the options.

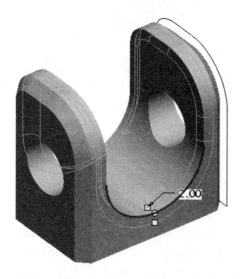

Figure 18 Previewed edges and drag handles for simple round

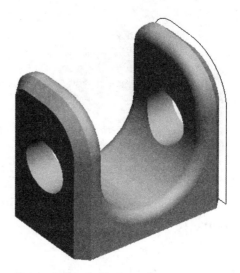

Figure 19 Completed round

For our purposes, this round is fine, Set its radius to **2.0** and *Accept* the feature. The model should now look like Figure 19. Save it now, before we do any more explorations.

Exploring the Model

Configuring the Model Tree

Open the Navigator window. The model tree should be displayed. If not, pick the left tab on the Navigator menu.

In the model tree, click the "+" signs beside the protrusion (EXTRUDE 1) and the cut (EXTRUDE 2). The tree now lists the sketches which were used with each of these sketched features. The other features do not have this because they were placed. The bottom entry in the tree is the *insertion point*. The next feature added to the model will be added to the tree here. We will find out in Lesson 5 how to move the insertion point around in the model, and what effect that has.

Review the features currently listed in the model tree. This is the regeneration sequence. Selecting a feature in the model tree will cause it to highlight on the model in the graphics window. To turn this highlight off, click anywhere on the graphics window. You may have to use the *Repaint* button on the top toolbar if your screen gets a bit cluttered.

To give us some more information about the features, we would like to add some columns to the model tree. Select the *Settings* tab just above the model tree and pick *Tree Columns*. This opens up the **Model Tree Columns** dialog window (Figure 20). Have a look in the *Type* pull-down list. Select the default option *Info*. Then, in the left pane double click on **Feat #** and **Feat Type**. The *Width* control below the right pane will control the display of the selected column listed in the pane. Press the *Apply* button, then

OK. The new columns are added to the model tree in the Navigator window (Figure 21). You might like to drag the right edge out a bit to see the entire tree. The column width can also be modified by dragging on the column separator bars.

Figure 20 Configuring the Model Tree

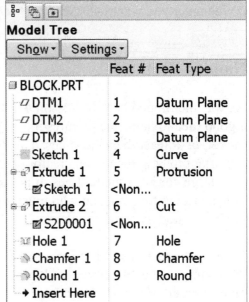

Figure 21 Model Tree with added columns

Select the *Settings* tab on the Navigator toolbar, then select *Tree Filters*. This opens the dialog window shown in Figure 22. Turn on the checks beside **Annotations** and **Suppressed Objects**. It will be helpful while you are learning Pro/E to have everything turned on so that you won't miss anything. Open the other tabs (*Cabling, Piping, NC*) to see what other information Pro/E can display in the model tree. Looks pretty complicated! Due to space and time constraints, we won't be dealing with any of these other items in this tutorial. Once again, *Apply* these settings (they won't change the model tree for this part) and select *OK*.

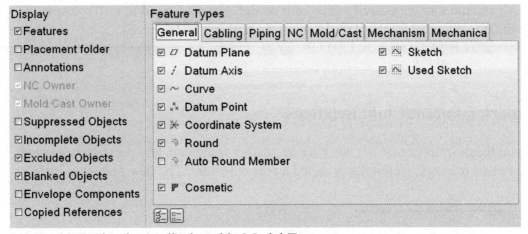

Figure 22 Setting items displayed in Model Tree

We want to save these settings so that the model tree will always be displayed this way. In the *Settings* tab, select *Save Settings File*. Go to the working directory and use the default name for the configuration file (**tree.cfg**). This name is already in the file name text box at the bottom of the window. Go ahead and save this file now. You can retrieve it whenever you want with *Settings > Open Settings File*[7].

Naming Features

As was mentioned back in Lesson #1, it is a good idea to name the features in a model, or at least the major ones. This is important to help the model creator deal with large complex model trees. It is also indispensable for someone who must use a model created by someone else.

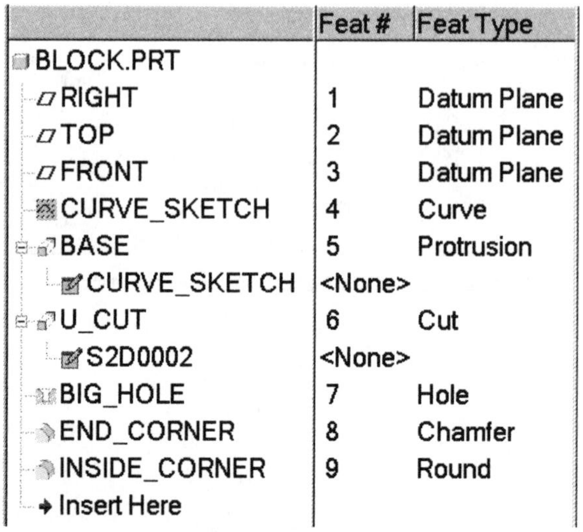

Naming the features is quite easy. Select the feature in the model tree - it highlights on the screen. If you click twice on the feature in the model tree or use *Rename* in the RMB pop-up, the text field opens to let you change the default name to something more meaningful. Do that now with the features in the model tree, using names

	Feat #	Feat Type
BLOCK.PRT		
RIGHT	1	Datum Plane
TOP	2	Datum Plane
FRONT	3	Datum Plane
CURVE_SKETCH	4	Curve
BASE	5	Protrusion
CURVE_SKETCH	<None>	
U_CUT	6	Cut
S2D0002	<None>	
BIG_HOLE	7	Hole
END_CORNER	8	Chamfer
INSIDE_CORNER	9	Round
Insert Here		

Figure 23 Named features

similar to those in Figure 23. The name is not case sensitive (as you type it in), and will be converted to all upper case.

Notice that even with only the name displayed in the model tree, the feature icon tells you what type of feature it is.

Helpful Hint

Just a reminder to periodically save your model. Now is a good time. Try using the keyboard command CTRL-S (hold down the Ctrl key and press S).

Exploring Parent/Child Relations

As you recall from Lesson #1, when a new feature is created, any previously created feature that it uses for reference is called a *parent* feature. The new feature is called a

---

[7] You can use the configuration setting *mdl_tree_cfg_file* so that the next time you launch Pro/E, the *tree.cfg* file will be read automatically. See the Appendix or the Advanced Tutorial for an introduction to configuration settings.

child. It is crucial to plan for and keep track of these parent/child relations. Any modification to a parent can potentially change one or more of its children. This may be precisely the desired model behavior and is the reason why we set up parent/child relations on purpose. However, with poor (or no) planning, changes to the parent may result in unintended (and unwanted) changes in the children. In the extreme case, deleting a parent will normally result in deletion of all child features that reference it (and their children...). In these cases, Pro/E will ask you to confirm the deletion. If you don't want to delete the child, you will have to change its references using techniques discussed in Lesson #5. Sometimes, if you are not careful about modifications to a parent, the child will be unable to regenerate. This is a symptom of a poor feature selection and/or referencing scheme. So it is important to be aware of what parent/child relations are present when new features are added. Be aware of the intent of your part geometry and build the model accordingly.

As you might expect, parent/child relations can become quite complicated when the model starts to accumulate features. This is a good reason to keep your models as simple as possible, and to think about your modeling strategy *before* you start creating anything! A parent can have many children, and a child can have several parents. Choosing (dare one say *designing?*) the best parent/child scheme for a part is a major difference of Pro/E from previous CAD programs. A clearly thought-out and implemented parent/child scheme is crucial to having flexible and robust models. Poor planning of the model will almost guarantee big problems later on if the model must be changed in any way. Fortunately, Pro/E provides a number of utility functions to help you manage the parent/child relations in a model. These include changing the dimensioning scheme and/or replacing current relations with new ones (called *rerouting*). In the worst case, reference elements of a feature can be *redefined*. We will be discussing these functions at length in Lesson #5. For now, you might keep as a general rule that, as in many things, simpler is better.

To reinforce these ideas, let's explore the parent/child relations of the cut. Select this in the model tree (or use preselection to select it in the graphics window). Now hold down the right mouse button and in the pop-up menu select

Info > Reference Viewer

Turn off the **System** checkbox in the **Reference Types** list, then close the filters pane on the left. What is left is a feature graph (Figure 24). The current object is in the middle, the parents at the left, and the children at the right. This shows that the BASE feature is providing three references for the cut. Meanwhile, the cut is supplying twelve references for the round feature.

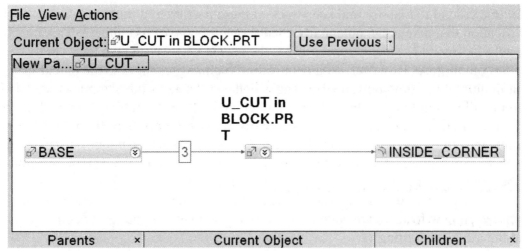

Figure 24 The **Reference Viewer** window for the cut

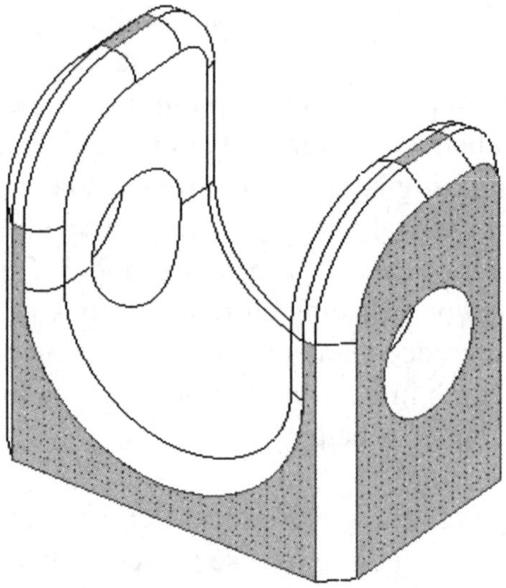

Expand the reference list beside BASE by clicking on the ▼ symbol. Each of the three surfaces is listed. If you select these in turn, they will highlight on the model. When selected, using the RMB pop-up and selecting *Info > Reference Info* will open an information window describing the nature of the reference. Look for the sketching plane and the section dimensioning references.

There is only one child feature of the cut - the round on the edge - although the cut provides twelve reference edges.

The feature *BASE* must have other children as well. Select it in the parent pane, hold down the right mouse button and select *Set As Current*. The

Figure 25 Parent references for cut

feature *BASE* appears in the Current Object area. It has several children but it is interesting to note that the round does not appear on the child list. We already know that the round is a child of the cut. Evidently, the parent/child relations explicitly reported by Pro/E are only one generation deep (no grandchildren or grandparents!).

The *BASE* feature has one parent (the sketched curve), and several children. You recall we used this curve to specify the shape to be extruded to make that first protrusion. The shape of the curve has been copied into the sketch attached (in the model tree) to *BASE*. If we were to *Unlink* the sketch in the first extrude, we would expect that the three datums (which were parents of the sketch), would become listed parents of the extrude. Let's try that. Close the **Reference Viewer** window. You should become comfortable using this window since it will be important in deciphering model structure.

Select the first extrude in the model tree. In the RMB pop-up menu, select *Edit*

Definition. We are now in the extrude dashboard. Select the *Placement* slide-up panel and then the *Unlink* button. A warning window will open to tell us what is about to happen - in this case exactly what we want. Select *OK* and then accept the extrusion. The geometry will not change, but there is a subtle change in the model tree - the sketch associated with the BASE feature is now S2D0001 instead of CURVE_SKETCH. Furthermore, examining the base feature parent/child information shows the curve is no longer a parent and has been replaced by the datum planes, exactly as we anticipated.

Put the model back in default orientation.

Modifying Dimensions

There are numerous ways that you can change the shape of the model. You will do this most often by modifying its dimensions, as we saw briefly in Lesson #1. There are (at least) three ways of doing this. Let's experiment with the sketched curve. (We can mess around with this all we want without worrying about damaging the model, since in the last section we unlinked the curve from the extrude!) Select it in the model tree and if necessary pick *Unhide* in the RMB menu.

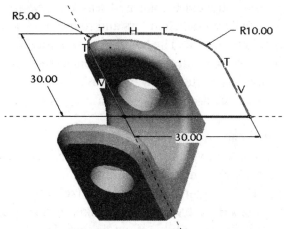

In the graphics window, double-click on the sketched curve. All the dimensions used in the sketch are shown. Put the mouse cursor over the line on the right edge - the cursor arrow loses its tail. Holding down the left button causes the cursor to change again. Now dragging the mouse will cause the line to move. The movement of the line will be consistent with the existing dimensions and constraints on the sketch - tangency points must be maintained, vertical lines stay vertical, and so on. The only thing that

Figure 26 Modifying dimensions of curve

changes is the dimension for the width of the sketch. Drop the line by releasing the left mouse button. What color is the affected dimension? What happens if you grab one of the corner fillets? What happens if you grab a vertex where a fillet meets an edge? If you double click directly on the dimension value, you can type in precisely the desired value. Do that now, using the values shown in Figure 26.

If you left click somewhere else on the screen, the yellow dimensions disappear and the blue curve is shown in its original shape. Double click on the curve again. The shape with modified dimensions is still there.

New dimensions do not take effect until you *Regenerate* the model, using the button in the top toolbar OR selecting *Edit > Regenerate* OR pressing **CTRL-G** on the keyboard. The new curve displays in blue, without any change in the protrusion (again indicating that it is not a parent of the protrusion).

Two other ways of modifying dimensions involve selecting the feature (do that now with the sketched curve) in either the model tree or on the screen and holding down the right mouse button. In the pop-up menu that appears, select *Edit*. This will display all the dimensions as before. Double click on a dimension to change its value. Don't forget you have to *Regenerate* the model for the new value to take effect. What happens if you enter a negative number for the height or width dimensions? What is the value the next time you launch the *Edit* command?

We have found that we don't need the sketched curve in the model. Select it (either in the model tree or on the screen), hold down the right mouse button, and select *Delete* from the pop-up menu. You will have to *Confirm* this deletion.

We would like to make the *BASE* feature wider. Select it (double click on the end surface in the graphics window) and change the dimension 20 to a new value of **30**. *Regenerate* the part. It should look like Figure 27. Notice that the other features have all adapted to this change in the base feature - the cut is longer (it was a *Through All* cut), and the chamfers and round have also lengthened. The hole has maintained its distance from the right reference surface of the block, just the way it was dimensioned.

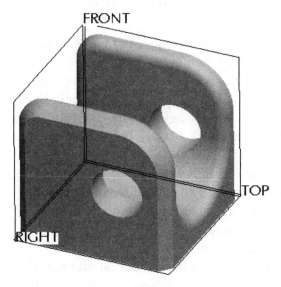

Figure 27 Modified *BASE* feature

What can go wrong here? Before we experiment, you should probably save the part. Now, double click on the *BASE* protrusion again and notice the size of the two rounded corners on top of its sketch. What happens if we try to make the sketch narrower than the sum of these two radii? We should expect trouble if we do that. Try it - say by entering a value of 12.5 for the width of the part. Zoom in on the top of the sketch for the protrusion and observe the shape. What happens when you *Regenerate*? A warning window appears indicating a problem (the *BASE* feature cannot regenerate with the crossed sketch) and a number of features are shown in red in the model tree. The first failed feature is bold. We won't explore error recovery techniques right now, so select *Cancel*.

You might try some other "silly" dimensions (for example, make the diameter of the hole bigger than the height of the block), to see what Pro/E will do - in particular, what messages does it give you? Try changing the location of the hole so that it is completely off the left end of the block. As long as datum axes are turned on, you can still find it using preselection. What happens if you decrease the height of the *BASE* feature to 20? In particular, what happens to the round? If you get into serious trouble here, just erase the part from the current session (*File > Erase > Current*), and retrieve the previously-saved part (You did save it, right?) from disk (*File > Open > block.prt*). Before you proceed, return the dimensions to their original values and *Regenerate*.

Can we set up the model to ensure that the hole always stays in the center, regardless of the width of the block? We'll find out in the next section.

Note that when the dimensions are changed, Pro/E will still maintain all the geometric constraints that you set up during feature creation. A simple example of this is alignment or snapping to references - the edges of the cut were aligned with the upper surface of the block, for example. If the block height is increased, the top edges of the cut sketch move with the top surface of the block. If a feature is *completely* defined by this type of constraint (ie. all geometry is defined with alignments to references), then you will not be able to modify it directly by its dimensions since it has none! We saw this in a cut feature in the *tut_base* part in Lesson #1. You will only be able to affect it via its parent(s) dimensions.

The type of constraints on the geometry discussed in the last paragraph are built into the model during sketching of the feature. There is another way that we can define dependancy between dimensions of different features that is equally powerful - these are feature relations.

Creating Feature Relations

A *Relation* is an explicit algebraic formula that allows a dimension to be automatically computed from other dimensions in the part (or in other parts in an assembly) or from a numeric formula. This is an important way of implementing design intent. We will set up two simple relations to ensure that the hole in the block is always centered on its width, and mid-way between the top and bottom faces.

Turn the datum planes and axes off, close the model tree, and put the model in the default orientation. If you double-click on the hole, you will see its location dimensions: 10 from the right surface, 15 from the top surface. What we are going to do is create two formulas that will be used to compute these values based on the current dimensions of the block. There are a couple of ways to do this. One way is very quick, but you won't see the available options or commands for dealing with relations. So, we will do it the long way around first! From the pull-down menus, select

Tools > Relations

The **Relations** dialog window opens. The relations toolbar buttons are shown in Figure 28.

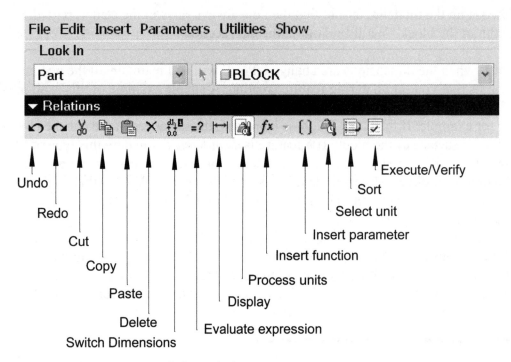

Figure 28 The **Relations** dialog window

Also, the dimension text on the hole showing the numerical values has been replaced with some symbols "dxx". See Figure 29. The "d" indicates a dimension; the number "xx" is a unique number defined by Pro/E, basically in the order that dimensions are added to the part.

The *Switch Dimensions* button in the **Relation** window toolbar is a toggle that switches between symbolic and numeric display of dimensions. Try that now. Note what the dimension symbolic names are in your model - the dimensions **d16** and **d17** in Figure 29 - for locating the hole. Your symbolic names may be different.

We need to find out the symbolic dimensions for the width and height of the **Figure 29** Symbolic dimensions of hole and protrusion protrusion. Click on the front surface of the block. Its dimensions should now also show up on the screen. Take note of the symbolic names for the width and height of the block (dimensions **d6** and **d7** in Figure 29).

IMPORTANT: Your dimension labels might be numbered differently from these. Make a note of *your* labels!

> **Helpful Hint**
> Make sure the *Look In* setting at the top of the **Relations** window is set to *Part*. Otherwise, relations get attached to features and may be harder to find in the model later.

Now for the actual relations. In the text area in the **Relations** window, type in the following lines (see Figure 30) (**use your own dimension labels!**):

> */* hole centered at half width*
> *d16 = d6 / 2*

The first line of the relation, starting with /*, is a comment line that describes the nature of the relation. This comment is not mandatory, but is a very good idea for clarity. You can put any text here that you like (multiple lines starting with /* are legal, too; blank lines are ignored). The next line defines the relation itself - the distance from the end face to the center of the hole is half the width of the block.

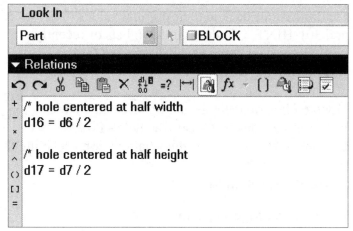

Figure 30 Relations for centering the hole

Here is another way to enter dimension symbols into the **Relations** window. Select *Switch Dimensions* so that they are showing up in numerical form. Now type in the next line of text:

> */* hole centered at half height*

In the next line, instead of entering the dimension symbol text directly, pick directly on the hole dimension from the top of the block (15). The appropriate symbol (like **d17** in Figure 29) will appear in the Relations editor. Type in an equals sign (or pick it from the palette at the left) then pick on the height dimension for the block (30). The symbol (like **d7** in Figure 29) will appear. Complete the relation as shown in Figure 30. Notice that by using this method, we don't need to first look up the symbolic names.

Select the *Execute/Verify* button in the relations toolbar. This will confirm that the relations are correct (or at least that they contain no syntax errors). Before you leave the

Relations dialog window, in the pull-down menu select

Show > Info..

This opens a Browser page that lists all the relations in the part. It also reports the values computed by the relations. A lot of other information is presented that deals with mass properties of the part, which we will discuss later in these lessons. Close the Browser page, then accept the **Relation** dialog window with *OK*.

Note that the relations haven't taken effect yet. Select the *Regenerate* button on the top toolbar. The hole should move to the center of the block. Double-click on the block and change the width and height dimensions to *60* and *40*, respectively. *Regenerate* the part. If all goes well, the hole should be exactly centered on the block. Change the dimensions back to their original values (30 and 30). HINT: Use the pull-down lists of recently used dimensions beside each dimension field. *Regenerate* the part.

Figure 31 Centered hole using relations

Double-click on the hole and try to change either of the dimensions that locate the hole - Pro/E won't let you! And it even tells you what relation is driving that dimension.

More about relations:

Relations can take the following forms:

> /* explicitly define a dimension
> **d4 = 4**
>
> /* explicitly define a parameter
> **length_of_block = 30**
>
> /* use a parameter
> **d6 = length_of_block**
> **d12 = length_of_block / 2**
>
> /* set up a limiting value for a dimension
> **d4 > 2**

Explicitly defined dimensions are just that - they create constant values for dimensions that cannot be overridden. The right hand side of a relation can contain almost any form of arithmetic expression (including functions like sin, cos, tan, ...). The inequality form can be used to monitor the geometry during regeneration of the part. If the inequality is violated, then Pro/E will catch the violation and show you a warning message.

These are the simplest form of relations - simple assignments. There are a number of built-in functions that can be used in relations (like locating entities in a model, logical branching, and so on). Relations can be used almost like a programming language. For example, relations can be used to solve systems of simultaneous equations involving part parameters, or be used to perform design calculations that yield dimensional values. Very high level functionality can be obtained using a module of Pro/E called Pro/PROGRAM (see the *Advanced Tutorial*).

All the relations for a part go into a special database that is consulted/executed when the part is regenerated. These relations are evaluated in a top-down manner, so that the order of relations is important (just like the order of feature creation). You can't have two relations that define the same dimension, and a relation is evaluated based on the current values on its right hand side. If one of the right-hand side values is changed by a subsequent relation, then the dimension using the previous value will be incorrect. Pro/E has a utility function that will let you reorder the relations to avoid this. When re-ordering, Pro/E assumes that each relation is preceded by a single comment line that will be moved with the relation when the database is reordered.

Considering Design Intent

The notion of *design intent* arises from the fact that there are always alternate ways of creating the model. Even for our simple cut, there are a number of possible dimensioning schemes that would all describe the same geometry. We must choose from these alternatives based on how we want the feature to relate to the rest of the part (or to itself) and how it will respond to changes elsewhere in the model. This is called *design intent*.

Our design intent can be implemented by a combination of feature selection and creation order, explicit constraints, parent/child relations, feature relations, and the dimensioning scheme. We have seen some of these methods. Let's go back and see how the dimensioning scheme of a feature can be used to implement design intent. Use preselection to select the U-shaped cut. When this is selected, use the RMB pop-up menu to select *Edit Definition*. This opens the extrusion dashboard. On the far left, pick the *Placement* drop-down panel, then the *Edit* button. This takes us to Sketcher with the sketch for the cut displayed (Figure 32). You might like to go to wireframe mode here and you can close the model tree.

Design Intent Alternative #1

The dimensioning scheme we used before expresses a design intent as follows:

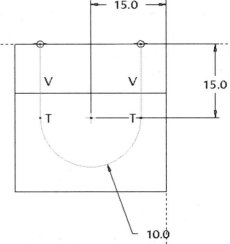

- center of cut is 15 from the back of part
- radius of cut is 10

Figure 32 Sketch of cut with first design intent

● center of U-shape is 15 from top of part

Design Intent Alternative #2

Suppose we wanted a different design intent as follows (see Figure 34):

● center of cut is 15 from the back of part (same as before)
● radius of cut is 10 (same as before)
● clearance from bottom of cut to the bottom of the part is 5

We saw previously that decreasing the height of the block caused the existing cut to pass through the bottom of the part. Our new intent is that the bottom of the U should always be exactly 5 from the bottom of the block. We can easily set this up using a different dimensioning scheme in the sketch.

In the Sketcher toolbar at the right (or RMB pop-up), select the ***Dimension*** button. Click once on the arc (not the center) and once on the bottom edge of the part. These will highlight in red. Move the cursor to the side and middle click at the location where you want the dimension text to be placed.

Since we are now over-dimensioning the sketch, the **Resolve Sketch** window will open (Figure 33). Recall that Intent Manager will not ask for confirmation if it wants to delete a weak dimension - it just does it. All the existing dimensions, however, are strong. Intent Manager won't delete any strong dimension or constraint without asking. The **Resolve Sketch** window shows the conflicting dimensions and these are highlighted in red on the screen. The dimension currently selected in this window will have a yellow box around it on the screen. At least one of the three

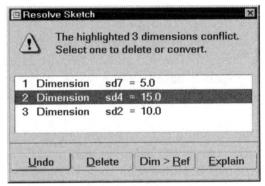

Figure 33 Resolve Sketch window showing conflicting dimensions

dimensions is no longer necessary. A dimension we can afford to lose is the 15 dimension. Select it and press the ***Delete*** button at the bottom[8]. The modified sketch with our new design intent implemented is shown in Figure 34. Accept the new sketch and the feature.

---

[8] You can also convert this to a *reference dimension*. Reference dimensions cannot be used to change the sketch geometry, but just indicate values in the sketch. In Pro/E jargon, they are *driven* dimensions rather than *driving* dimensions.

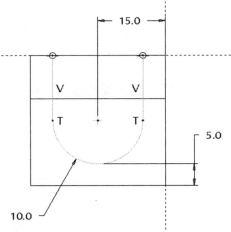

Figure 34 Sketch with second design intent

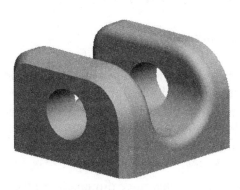

Figure 35 Design Intent #2

With this new design intent, change the height of the block to **20** and ***Regenerate***. If you recall, this is the value we used before that resulted in the part splitting into two pieces. That won't happen this time, due to our intent (Figure 35). Change the height back to **30**.

Design Intent Alternative #3

Let's try one more variation on the design intent. Suppose we wanted the following:

- ● ensure a thickness of 5 between the vertical sides of the cut and the front and back surfaces of the block
- ● clearance from bottom of cut to the bottom of the part is 5 (same as previous)

Select the cut feature again, and use the right mouse button to select ***Edit Definition***. Re-enter the sketch (using the RMB pop-up, select ***Edit Internal Sketch***) and pick the ***Dimension*** command again. Add the dimensions shown in Figure 36. You will have to deal with the **Resolve Sketch** window again, and delete some of our previous dimensions. You will also have the opportunity to delete constraints here (which we don't want to do).

Don't leave this sketch just yet - there are more tools to investigate.

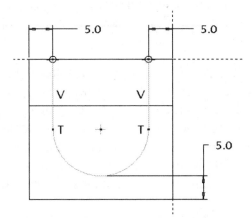

Figure 36 Sketch showing third design intent

More Sketcher Tools

The *Modify* Command

We have seen how to modify an individual dimension by double-clicking on it. You can also change the sketch by grabbing a sketched entity and dragging it with the mouse. Here is yet another way.

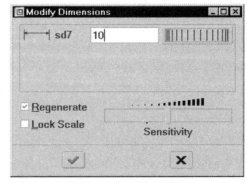

Figure 37 The **Modify** window

Click on the clearance dimension at the bottom of the cut. Now select the *Modify* button in the toolbar. The **Modify Dimensions** window appears (Figure 37). To the right of the dimension value is a thumbwheel. Drag this with the left mouse button. Experiment with the Sensitivity slider. Return the dimension to its original value (5**.0**) by typing it into the data field and hitting *Enter*.

Now hold down the CTRL key while you left click on the other dimensions in the sketch. These will be added to the **Modify** window. Check the box beside *Lock Scale*. Now drag the thumbwheel beside any of the dimensions. All dimensions are changed simultaneously, in the same proportion.

Helpful Hint

The *Lock Scale* option is particularly useful when you are sketching the first feature in a part. Recall that the numerical values created for the first feature are chosen at random. If you try to modify the dimensions one at a time, you will probably destroy the shape of the sketch. If your sketch is more or less the right shape, you can change all the dimensions simultaneously using *Lock Scale* without changing the shape of the sketch. This is a great time-saver.

Remove the checks beside both *Lock Scale* and *Regenerate*. The latter option will delay the simultaneous and/or immediate regeneration whenever a single dimension is changed. This is sometimes necessary when you want to change several dimension values at the same time, but don't want to regenerate until all new values are entered. This would avoid trying to regenerate to a geometry with some old and some new dimensions, which might be incompatible. When you are finished experimenting, return the dimensions to the original values and close the **Modify** window (or select the X symbol).

Sketcher Relations

We would like to ensure that the thickness of the part at the front and back are equal. Using Design Intent #3 from above, we have two dimensions that we want to make equal. We could do that using a relation defined at the part level as we did before. There is another way here that is quicker.

While you are in sketcher, in the top pull-down menus select

Info > Switch Dimensions

The dimension labels on the screen will change to their symbolic values, with an "s" in front indicating they are sketch dimensions. Note the dimension at the top right (**sd8** in Figure 38).

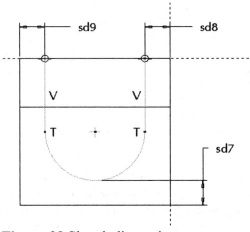

To very quickly enter a relation, make sure you are in Select mode and double-click on the thickness dimension on the top left (**sd9** in Figure 38). Instead of typing in a numeric value, just type in the symbolic name of the other dimension on the top, **sd8** in Figure 38. A message window asks if you want to add the relation

Figure 38 Sketch dimensions

sd9 = sd8

Middle click to accept this. Select

Info > Switch Dimensions

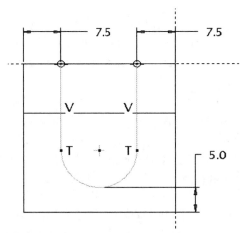

again to get the numerical display back. Now, try changing the value of the top left dimension. You can't. Change the value of the other dimension to **7.5**, as in Figure 39. Both dimensions change, indicating that the relation has executed.

Figure 39 Final sketch for cut

Sketcher Preferences

There are a number of options for how you want Sketcher to behave. To investigate these settings, select (in the top pull-down menu)

Sketch > Options

This brings up a dialog window containing three tabs. Selecting the tabs will open the windows shown below. Come back to these and experiment with the settings later.

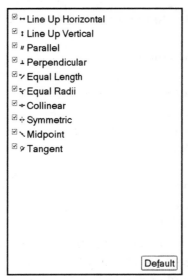

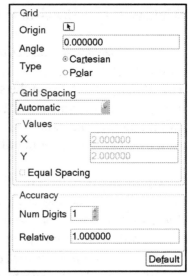

Figure 40 Sketcher options: **Miscellaneous**

Figure 41 Sketcher options: **Constraints**

Figure 42 Sketcher options: **Parameters**

Using *Undo*

Another useful command in Sketcher is *Undo*  located at the top of the screen. Each time you select this command, you move backwards through any changes you have made in the sketch, one at a time. You can move forward again (with some restrictions) using *Redo* .

We have now finished with Sketcher for this lesson, so accept the sketch (it should look like Figure 39) and complete the cut feature. The final part should look like Figure 43.

We are (at last!) at the end of this lesson - it's been a long one. Before you leave, make sure that you save the current part with

> *File > Save*

or use Ctrl-S. You can now exit from Pro/E.

Figure 43 Final part geometry

Pro/E Files Saved Automatically

Have a look at the files in your default disk space or Pro/E working directory. You should see files listed that include the following forms:

block.prt.1   block.prt.2   block.prt.3   . . . .

Each time you save a part (or drawing or assembly), a new file is created with an automatically increasing counter. Thus, you always have a back-up available if something goes very wrong. On the other hand, this can eat up your disk space very quickly since the part files can get pretty large. If you are sure you do not need the previous files, you can remove them. You should, of course, copy final part files to another storage location anyway for back-up.

Other files written to your disk space might include the following:

trail.txt.??
> This is a record of all keystrokes, commands, and mouse clicks you made during a session[9]. For an advanced user, this may be useful to recover from catastrophic failures! Each new session you launch starts a new trail file, with an automatically incremented counter. These files are often stored somewhere else on your system, away from your working directory.

feature.lst
> The same list of features obtained using *Info > Feature List*

feature.inf
> The data about features obtained using *Info > Feature*

rels.inf
> All the dimension relations in the part or assembly file

reviewref.inf
> Information on parent/child relations

and other *.inf files.

Unless you have a good reason to keep these, remove them from your disk space as soon as you leave Pro/E (and not before!). Some programs are available for download from the Web (some free) that will automatically purge these files from your directories.

In the next lesson we will look at a number of new features, including revolved protrusions, mirrored copies, and more Sketcher tools that will extend our repertoire of part-creation techniques. In the meantime, here are some questions for you to think about. Some review material we have covered and others will require you to do some exploring on your own.

---

[9] Trail files are not created by the Student Edition.

Questions for Review

1.   What elements are required to define a simple hole?
2.   What is meant by linear placement of a hole?
3.   What is the difference between the terms "protrusion" and "extrusion"?
4.   What are two methods of obtaining a model's feature list?
5.   What commands are used to name features?
6.   Suppose you have a very complex part with many features and you want to identify/locate (ie. show graphically) a specific feature in the model. How would you do it?
7.   When might you want to turn off *Regenerate* in the **Modify Dimensions** dialog window?
8.   Once a feature has been created, how can you change its dimensions?
9.   What do we call an equation that computes a dimensional value?
10.   What is the difference between a standard profile and a standard hole?
11.   What are the "junk" files that Pro/E creates in your disk space? How do you get rid of them?
12.   How can you go back and edit a previously defined relation?
13.   How can you find out the internal symbolic names for feature dimensions?
14.   What happens to the relations if you delete a feature whose dimensions appear (a) on the right side, or (b) on the left side of a relation?
15.   What is the difference between the **Feature Number** and the **Internal ID**?
16.   What does it mean when the stem (tail) of the cursor arrow disappears?
17.   What is the meaning of gray dimensions? What about the yellow, red, green, and white ones?
18.   How can you strengthen a dimension? What does this mean?
19.   Where did we see the *Lock Scale* option? What does it do?
20.   How do you over-ride the default dimensions placed by Intent Manager?
21.   How do you change the location of the dimensions (on the screen) after they have been placed by Intent Manager?
22.   What does the right mouse button do in Sketcher?
23.   How can you create a polar grid in Sketcher? How do you set the origin of the grid?
24.   What is the keyboard shortcut to *Regenerate*?
25.   Find out how to turn off the constraints presented by Intent Manager (not just turn off the display, but actually get rid of them).
26.   What is the minimum number of Sketcher References needed by Intent Manager? The maximum number? What do these do?
27.   Are the following sets of references sufficient or not for defining the Sketch (can the sketch be "fully placed")?
      a.   a single vertical reference line
      b.   a single point at the center of a circle
      c.   a pair of parallel lines
28.   In your own words, describe what is meant by "design intent." How was design intent implemented in the part created in this lesson?
29.   Examine some simple everyday objects and describe how you might implement design intent in a computer model of the object. Make some freehand sketches to illustrate.

30. How many different variations of the RMB pop-up menus can you find in Sketcher? When creating Holes?

Exercises

On the next page are some simple shapes you should be able to make using the features covered so far. When complete, the shapes should be approximately in the positions shown in default view. Before starting in on any new part, take a few minutes to plan your modeling strategy. For example, where should the datum planes be located? This will pay dividends in the ease with which you can model the part, and particularly with how you will be able to modify it afterwards.

❶

❷

❸

❹

❺

❻

❼ Hint:
   This part can be made with just two features (a
   protrusion and a cut), although this requires fairly
   complicated sketches and so would not be good
   modeling practice.

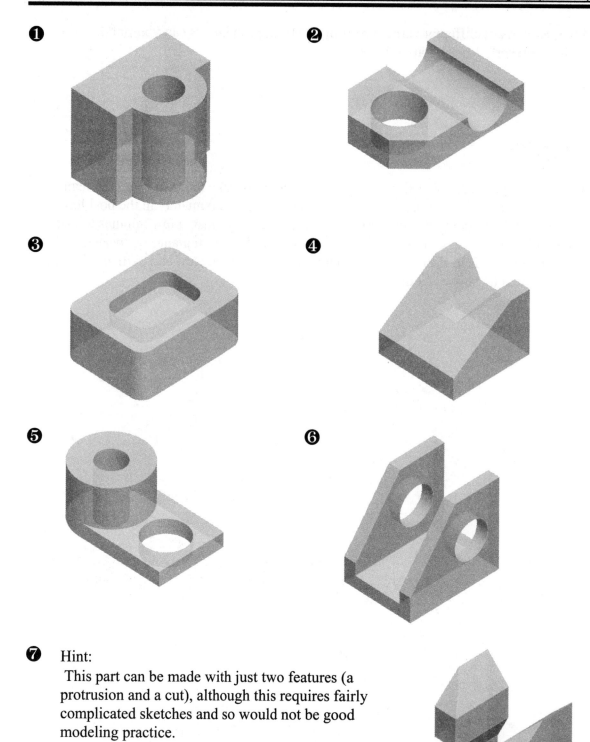

These parts are a bit more complicated, and use more of the features covered this lesson (holes, chamfers, rounds).

8.   9.

10.   11.

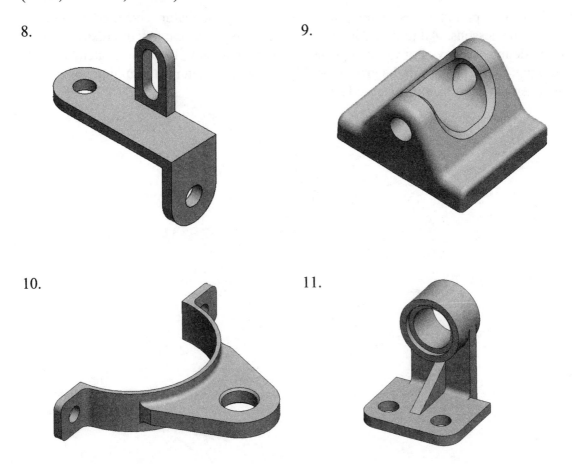

12. Create the "hole sampler" block shown here in cross section, containing a variety of holes. Although these may be standard holes, cosmetic threads are not shown. Go ahead and create threads if desired.

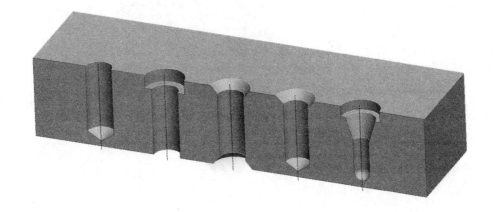

Project

Here is the first part in our assembly project. It uses only the features covered in the previous two lessons. All units are in millimeters. As usual, take a few minutes to plan your modeling strategy. For example, where should the datum planes be located? How should you orient the part in the Front-Top-Right system of datums (assuming you are using a template). Which is the base feature?

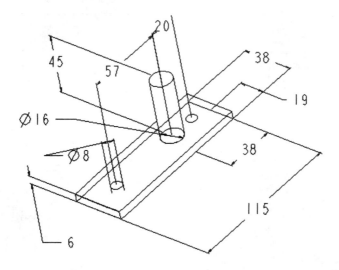

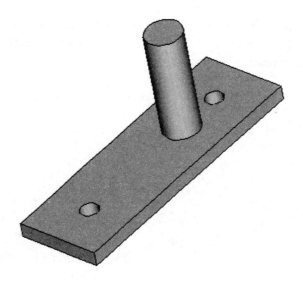

Lesson 4

Revolved Protrusions, Mirror Copies, Model Analysis

Synopsis

A new part is modeled using a number of different feature creation commands and options: both sides protrusions, an axisymmetric (revolved) protrusion, a cut, quick rounds, and chamfer edge sets. More Sketcher tools. Mirrored features. Error recovery. Model analysis functions.

Overview of this Lesson

This lesson will introduce you to an important feature geometry (a revolved protrusion), and give you some practice using features introduced in the first two lessons. Because Sketcher is such an important tool, we will spend some time exploring more tools and functions, and discussing how it can be used most effectively. The part modeling steps should be completed in order. Remember to scan through each section before starting to enter the commands - it is important to know what the goal is when you are going through the feature creation steps. If you can't

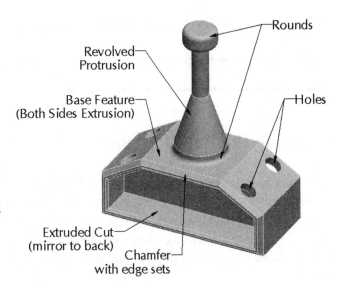

Figure 1 Finished part

finish the part in one session, remember to save it so that you can retrieve it later and carry on. The finished part should look like Figure 1. Here are the steps:

1.   Creating the base feature
2.   Adding a revolved protrusion
3.   Adding and mirroring a cut
4.   Adding and mirroring holes

5.   Adding rounds and chamfers
6.   Model analysis tools
7.   Exploring "What Can Go Wrong?"

IMPORTANT:

Be sure to complete the last section. You will learn a lot about how Pro/E works, beyond which button to push. This is important for your proficient use of the program.

As usual there are some Questions for Review at the end, some exercises, and another part for the project.

The instructions are going to be a bit more terse this lesson, especially for commands we have covered previously. You should be getting in the habit of scanning both the command menus and the message line in the command/message window. Remember, if the mouse seems to be dead, then Pro/E is probably waiting for you to respond to a prompt via keyboard entry. By now, you should also be fairly comfortable with the dynamic view controls obtained with the mouse.

So, get started by launching Pro/E as usual. Close the Browser and Navigator windows. Study the object in Figure 1 carefully before proceeding.

Create a solid part named *guide_pin* using the *Create New Object* button or select:

File > New > Part | Solid | [guide_pin]

Use the default part template.

Creating the Base Feature

The rectangular block at the base of the part will be our first solid feature, also sometimes called the *base feature*. We will be creating the base feature so that the **FRONT** and **RIGHT** datum planes can be used for mirroring of features we will create later. This is an example of the planning ahead you must do. This one was easy - only "one move ahead." Like good chess players, good modelers are always looking many "moves" ahead.

Helpful Hint

Whenever you have symmetry in a part, it is a good idea to use the datum planes on the plane(s) of symmetry. That way, they will be available for mirroring and serving as references for symmetric features.

Thus, we will create the first feature as a *blind, symmetric* extruded protrusion: the sketch will be on FRONT and the protrusion will extend a specified distance on both sides of the sketching plane. Rather than creating the sketch first and then launching the extrude command as we did for the block of lesson #2, we will create the sketch within the extrusion (an *internal* sketch). Thus, select the ***Extrude*** tool in the right toolbar. With the cursor in the graphics window, hold down the RMB and select ***Define Internal Sketch***. Now you need to select a sketch plane and reference plane. Choose **FRONT** as the sketch plane. The RIGHT datum is automatically chosen as the Right orientation reference. This is what we want, so just middle click to accept the dialog and enter Sketcher. The sketching references have been selected automatically for you.

Before we start the sketch, recall the sequence we want to follow with Sketcher:

1. make sure the **desired references** are selected; if you missed any on your way in to Sketcher, use the RMB pop-up menu to select ***References*** and add them. You can do this any time you are in Sketcher. Also, a reference is automatically added if you dimension to it or constrain an edge or vertex to it.
2. **sketch the shape** using the chosen references for alignments, constraints, etc.;
3. **strengthen dimensions or constraints** created by Intent Manager you want to keep;
4. **add constraints** if required to implement your design intent;
5. **change the dimension scheme** so that it implements your design intent;
6. **modify the dimension values** to those desired for the feature.

The final sketch we want to create is shown in Figure 5; the finished feature is shown in Figure 6. We'll get there in several steps, corresponding to the sequence just given.

Step 1 - Selecting References

The first step has been done for us - as we entered, Sketcher picked the only two references possible at this time. With these identified, you can turn off the datum planes and coordinate system, as they will not be needed for a while. Some time you should try entering Sketcher with datum planes turned off to see what happens.

Step 2 - Sketch Geometry

Use the RMB pop-up menu to select the ***Line*** drawing command. Letting the cursor snap to the references, you can create the entire sketch using a single polyline (left click, left click, ... seven times). See Figure 2. Middle click (twice) to leave ***Line*** mode and return to ***Select*** mode (why twice?). Intent Manager will put all the weak constraints and dimensions on the sketch in gray. Don't worry if the constraints don't match the desired ones just yet. Also, since this is the first feature of the part, dimension values will be chosen based on a default setting for model size. Some dimensions and constraints will be the ones you want; others won't. **DO NOT bother modifying these dimension values yet - this will result in wasted effort.** What we are interested in first is getting the shape and proportions of the sketch right.

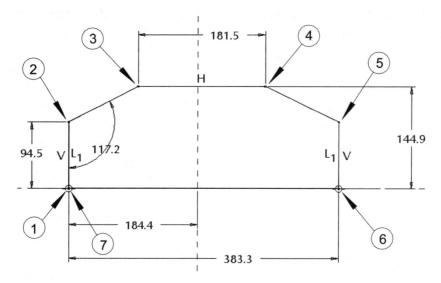

Figure 2 Creating the sketch for the base feature (constraints and dimensioning scheme not completed)

Step 3 - Strengthen Constraints and Dimensions

Move the dimensions off the part (pick to highlight in red, then drag with the left mouse button) and observe the constraints and dimensions that have been created by Intent Manager. Compare these to the desired constraints shown in Figure 5. In this step we select aspects of the sketch we want to keep - we do this by making them strong. Select one you want to keep. When it is highlighted in red, use the right mouse button pop-up menu and select *Strong*. It will change from the weak color (gray) to the strong color (pale yellow). Continue doing this for any constraints and dimensions corresponding to those in Figure 5. We are still not worried about dimension values.

Step 4 - Specify Constraints

Now we can implement any missing constraints that have not been deduced by Intent Manager. This follows after step 3 because as we add our new constraints, previous weak dimensions and constraints can be deleted by Intent Manager. The constraints and dimensions we made strong in the previous step are immune from this.

We can implement a left-to-right symmetry about the RIGHT datum (the vertical reference) as follows. Use the flyout on the *Line* button to select the *Centerline* button, *OR* use the RMB pop-up menu and select *Centerline*. Sketch a vertical centerline on the vertical reference. When the centerline appears (yellow dashed line), if your sketch is already close to being symmetric about this line, Sketcher may automatically apply the symmetry constraint and you may notice a change in the (weak) dimensioning scheme. *Repaint* your screen to look for the small symmetry constraint arrows. These are weak (gray) so they may be hard to see. If these are missing, read on...

If your current sketch is missing some of the constraints shown in Figure 5, we can set some or all of these explicitly. Select the **Constraints** button in the right toolbar. This flyout contains the nine explicit constraint options shown in Figure 3. Examine these carefully, and add any constraints on your sketch so that it matches the desired figure. For example, for the symmetry constraint, select the symmetry constraint button (lower left) and read the message window. Click on the vertical centerline and

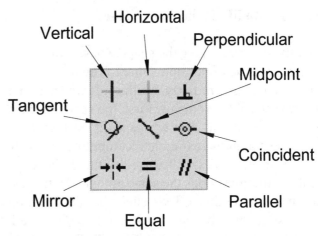

Figure 3 Explicit constraints on Sketcher toolbar flyout

then the two lower vertices. Note that with symmetry constraining the sketch, the dimensioning scheme has probably changed. Check out the symbols that indicate the symmetry. If necessary, repeat this process for the two vertices on the top edge of the sketch. The sketch also contains an equal length constraint on the vertical edges. If required, add this to your sketch. The sketch constraints should now look like Figure 4.

Step 5 - Finish the Dimensioning Scheme

So far, the shape and constraints are set the way we want, but the dimension scheme and values probably are not. Again, compare to the dimensioning scheme shown in Figure 5. If any of these dimensions are missing, create them explicitly. Pick the **Dimension** command from the right toolbar (or RMB pop-up). Recall that these

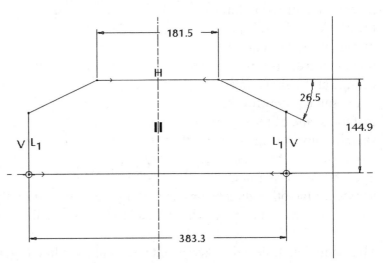

Figure 4 Sketch with desired constraints and dimension scheme

will be strong dimensions and Intent Manager will remove redundant weak dimensions automatically.

To dimension the angle, click on the two intersecting lines and middle click where you want to place the dimension text. Sketcher assumes that if two lines intersect you must want to dimension the angle between them. When you are finished adding dimensions, middle click to return to **Select** mode.

Step 6 - Modify Dimension Values

Finally, once you have the shape, constraints, and dimensioning scheme you want, you can modify the dimension values. The initial dimension values chosen by Sketcher for the base feature are fairly arbitrary. If we tried to modify dimensions one-by-one, there are two possible problems. First, the shape of the sketch may become grossly distorted, and we will lose its desired shape (at least temporarily). Second, it is possible that Sketcher might have trouble recomputing the sketch because we may be requesting incompatible values. What we want to do is keep the shape of the sketch the same, while scaling all dimensions the same amount. In the last lesson, we found a very useful command to do this. CTRL-click with the left mouse button to select all the linear dimensions (not the angle[1]). Select *Modify* in the RMB pop-up menu. The three selected dimensions will appear in the **Modify Dimensions** window.

Now, check the *Lock Scale* option (since we want to change all dimensions simultaneously).

Select the dimension for the block width and enter **20** into the data field. The other dimensions will change at the same time in the same proportion so that the shape of the sketch is not damaged. Now uncheck the *Lock Scale* option. Enter new

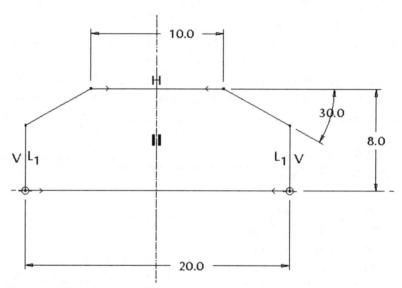

Figure 5 Final sketch for base feature

values for the other dimensions according to Figure 5. Finally, close this window and change the angle dimension (hint: double-click on the dimension).

This should complete the sketch and it should look like Figure 5. So, select the *Done* button (the check mark ✔) at the bottom of the Sketcher toolbar.

You should review this Sketcher sequence again - using it properly can save a lot of frustration.

We now see a preview (in yellow) of the protrusion. The default is a one-sided, blind protrusion (turn the datum planes back on to see where our sketch was on FRONT). On the dashboard, open the **Depth Spec** pull-up list, and select the *Both Sides* option. The blind dimension value specifies the total depth (symmetric about the sketch plane). Enter

---

[1] Come back later to find out what happens if you drag a selection box around the entire sketch to select all dimensions, including the angle dimension. This is much faster and ensures that you do not accidentally miss a dimension for scaling.

a value of **10** (either in the dashboard or on the dimension shown in the graphics window). The preview should look like Figure 6.

You can now *Verify* the protrusion. Assuming everything is satisfactory, *Accept* the feature.

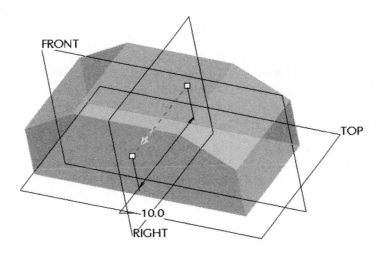

Figure 6 Base feature preview (*both sides, blind*)

Creating a Revolved Protrusion

We'll now add the vertical axisymmetric shape onto the top of the base feature. In 3D solid modeling terms, this is a "revolved solid", created by taking a 2D sketch and rotating it around a specified axis. In Pro/E, we can use revolved features to create protrusions or cuts. The angle (or 'depth') of the rotation is adjustable using the same type of options as an extrusion (blind, up to surface, one or both sides, and so on). For this part we will do a one-sided, blind (360°) revolve. Only a half cross-sectional shape is required. See Figure 7. Depending on the feature shape and model geometry, the sketch can be either an open or closed curve (closed curves are safer). The axis of the revolve can either be included in the sketch of the section, or can be specified externally.

For this feature, we will again use an internal sketch so select the *Revolve* tool in the right toolbar. The **Revolve** dashboard looks the same as the **Extrude** dashboard, and offers the same options (thin feature, remove material, depth spec, and so on). Open the *Placement* slide-up panel (observe the option to specify an external revolve axis) and select *Define*. Select **FRONT** as the sketching plane. Set up the RIGHT datum plane as the Right sketch orientation reference, then middle click or select *Sketch*.

Notice the two automatically chosen sketch references. The sketch we are going to create is shown in Figure 9. This is essentially the right half of the cross section of the revolved feature. We want the lower vertex on the sketch to lie precisely on the top of the block. The easy way to do this is to make the top surface a reference. You may want to spin the object to see this surface. (If you do, there is a button in the top toolbar to reorient your view of the sketch back to the standard view.) In the top pull-down menu, select

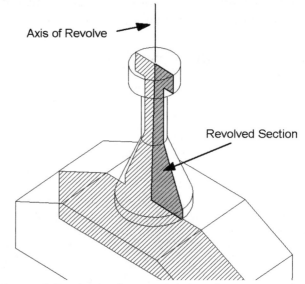

Figure 7 Section to be revolved to form protrusion

Sketch > References

(or find the ***References*** command in the RMB pop-up menu).

Spin the model and left click to select the top surface now. This will create another horizontal reference in the sketch (see Figure 8). The one on the TOP datum can be deleted. The reference status should still be "Fully Placed." If it reads "Unsolved Sketch", just push the ***Solve*** button on the right.

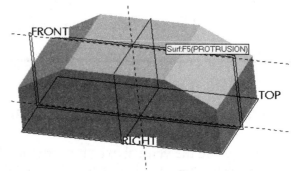

Figure 8 Adding the top surface of the base feature as sketching reference

Create the sketch shown in Figure 9 (display of H and V constraints has been turned off for clarity). Remember the desired sequence for efficient use of Intent Manager:

- select the appropriate references (done that!);
- sketch the desired shape (doing that!)
- strengthen any constraints or dimensions you want to keep;
- add explicit constraints;
- add your own dimensions to get the scheme you want;
- modify dimension values to get desired size.

Here are a few more tips for using
Sketcher effectively:

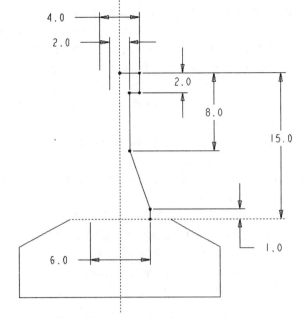

1. While you are sketching lines,
    if a constraint appears in red,
    you can turn it off
    immediately (that is, prevent it
    from "sticking") by clicking
    the right mouse button.

2. The axis of revolution can be
    specified on an internal sketch
    using a centerline. To place a
    centerline along the vertical
    reference hold down the right
    mouse button in the sketch
    window and select *Centerline*. **Figure 9** Sketch for revolved protrusion
    Click once on the vertical
    reference; the centerline will automatically snap to vertical when you click to create
    the second point on the reference.

3. Revolved features are usually specified using diameters rather than radii. To
    dimension a diameter of a revolved feature (the horizontal dimensions in the
    sketch): left click on the sketched line or vertex, then on the centerline, again on the
    same line/vertex, then middle click to place the dimension text.

4. When you are modifying the dimension values, it is sometimes beneficial to do the
    smaller dimensions first. This ensures that the geometry will stay close to the
    desired shape throughout the changes.

Helpful Hint

If you have several construction lines in the sketch (they all have the same line style
as a centerline), which one becomes the axis of revolution? You can choose the one
you want by selecting it (highlights in red) then holding down the right mouse
button to find the *Axis of Revolution* command. The axis of revolution will become
yellow.

You might like to check out the *Feature Requirements* function at this time. It contains a
warning about open ends (turn on the *Highlight Open Ends* button). In this case, the
feature will regenerate, but to be more robust you should probably close the sketch.

After finishing the sketch, select the *Done* button. In previous releases of Pro/E, Sketcher
would warn you if you tried to leave without creating a centerline (axis of revolution).
Since Wildfire 2.0 you can select the axis externally, so this does not happen. Having an

external reference for this might be handy if several features were going to be revolved around the same reference (if the reference moved, so would all the features). The external axis is chosen back in the **Placement** slide-up panel. If you are going to use an internal centerline as the axis, you should get in the habit of always creating the revolve centerline first when you enter Sketcher. It is then available for creating diameter dimensions. If you forget to do this, just select the *Define* button to re-enter Sketcher.

You should now be back in the Revolve dashboard. The default is a blind protrusion, which in this case means that the angle of the revolve is specified. It should be 360°. If you left the sketch as an open curve, Pro/E must know which side of the curve is to be made solid. That is the meaning of the arrow shown in Figure 10 (at the bottom of the revolve).

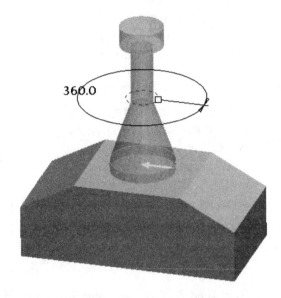

All elements should now be defined. *Verify* the part (it should look like Figure 10) and select *Accept*. Note that if you used an internal centerline, an axis has been defined as part of the feature. Although it doesn't appear in the model tree, the axis can still be used as another feature's reference (for example, for a coaxial hole).

Figure 10 Preview of revolved protrusion

Adding and Mirroring a Cut

We'll now use an extruded cut feature to create a pocket on one side of the base. We will then mirror it to the other side of the base. Our design intent here will be to leave a 1 unit thick wall around the pocket[2]. While we have created a cut feature before, we will use a new useful tool in Sketcher to create this geometry.

Select the *Extrude* button in the right toolbar; its dashboard opens. Before we forget, click on the *Remove Material* button on the dashboard to produce the cut. Then, activate Sketcher using *Placement > Define*. You should now be in the **Sketch** menu. Select the front surface of the block as the sketching plane, then select the top surface of the block as the TOP orientation reference. Middle click to enter Sketcher.

When you arrive in Sketcher, references will have been already picked. We will now create our sketch using only a single dimension - the thickness of the wall around the pocket!

---

[2] Incidentally, what are your units? These are the units of the default template. We'll introduce part units and how to change them in Lesson #8.

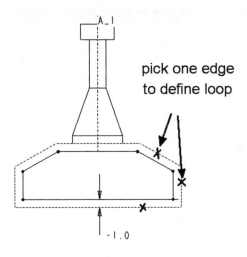

Figure 11 Picking edge to define loop

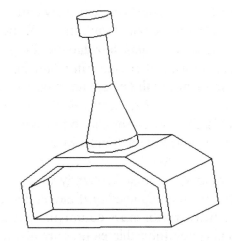

Figure 12 Pocket added using cut feature

On the flyout from the *Use Edge* button in Sketcher, select the *Offset* button ⬜ . In the
TYPE window, select the *Loop* option. Pick on one of the right or bottom edges as
shown in Figure 11, or you can pick on the front surface of the block. A small arrow will
appear on one of the edges showing an offset direction. Read the message window. If
the arrow is pointing outwards, enter an offset value of *-1*, otherwise enter *1*. The sketch
for our pocket is now complete, as in Figure 11. Notice the symbols on each sketched
line, which indicates it was produced by an offset. Select the *Done* button.

The Pro/E default is a blind cut, with the material removal side on the interior of a closed
sketch. All we have to do is set the depth. Enter a value of **4** and *Accept* the feature. The
resulting pocket should look like Figure 12.

Creating a Mirror Copy

Since the part is symmetrical, we can easily create the pocket on the back of the base by
mirroring the first one. We only need a couple of mouse clicks to do this. For the
following, in order to see a new function for locating features, turn off the display of the
datum planes. The cut should already be highlighted in red as the last feature created. If
not, just select it.

Select the *Mirror* button in the right toolbar. This opens the Mirror dashboard. See the
message window. We want to mirror this pocket through the **FRONT** datum plane,
which is currently turned off. To select this plane, we'll do something a little different. In
the top toolbar, select the *Search* button ⊞ .

The **Search Tool** dialog window opens (Figure 13). Here you can select references by datum or surface, and by name, ID, or feature number, and many other variations. The *Look For* data field has already been selected for us. Press the *Find Now* button. All the datum planes in the model are now listed at the bottom. In this list, select **FRONT** (it shows on the model), then the >> button to move it to the selected window, and finally select *Close*.

The *Search* command is handy if, as in this case, the feature is not displayed or if the model becomes very complicated with many datum planes and/or features. It is also helpful if the features are all named.

Before we accept the feature, open the *Options* panel in the dashboard. This contains a single toggle that determines whether the mirrored feature is dependent on the original. For example, if we changed the offset value of the original cut (currently 1.0) then we control whether the mirrored cut would also change (dependent) or not (independent).

Unfortunately, there is no Verify function here, so just accept the new feature (middle click a couple of times). The result is shown in Figure 14.

By the way, have you saved the part recently?

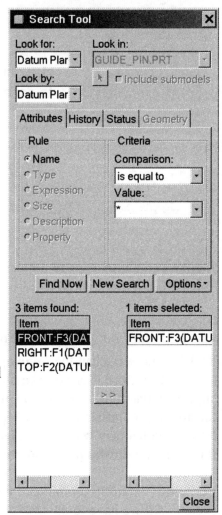

Figure 13 The Search tool

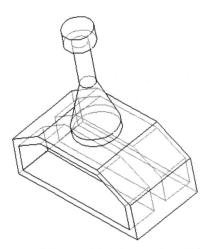

Figure 14 Part with mirrored pocket

Creating Holes

We already came across the hole feature in Lesson #3. We are going to add four holes as shown in Figure 1. We are going to do something a little different here with the depth specification, plus use the mirror command a couple of times after creating the first hole. For something a bit different, starting in the pull-down menu, select

Insert > Hole

The **Hole** dashboard opens. The default is a *Simple* hole. For the primary reference (the placement plane), make sure the correct surface is preselected (highlighted), then click on the sloping surface of the base at approximately the position where we want the hole center to be. This is shown ("placement plane") in Figure 15. Use the green drag handles to select the **FRONT** datum plane (reference #1) and the upper edge of the end surface of the base (reference #2) for the linear references. This is one time where

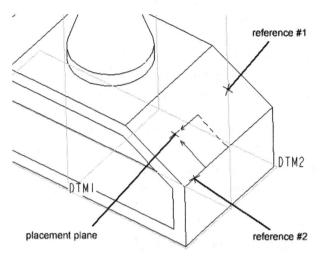

Figure 15 Placement plane and linear references

we must use an edge as a dimensioning reference, which we normally want to avoid. (Why?) The distance from each reference will be *3*. Set the hole diameter to *2.0*.

In the **Depth Spec** list, select *To Next* ("Drill up to next surface"). All the depth specification options are also available if you select the drag handle on the end of the hole and use the RMB pop-up menu. As might be expected, this creates the hole until it passes through the next surface it comes to, wherever that is. Do not be alarmed if the preview of the hole goes all the way through the part. The only restriction on *To Next* is that the sketch or hole must be entirely within the terminating surface. That is, if only part of the sketch or hole intersects the surface, the feature will just keep going through! We will see some examples of the

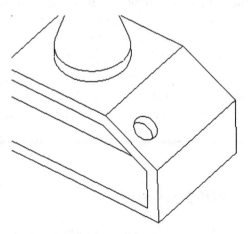

Figure 16 First hole

problems this might cause when we get to the last section of this lesson.

In this part, *To Next* means that the hole doesn't go all the way through the part. A blind hole may have achieved the same geometry, but would not be in keeping with our design intent. Why?

You can now *Verify* the hole. Assuming all
is well, *Accept* the feature. See Figure 16.
Notice that the hole feature automatically
contains an axis (not shown in Figure 16).

We can use the *Mirror* command to make
copies of the hole. For practice, turn off the
datum planes and use the *Search* command
again. First, mirror the single hole using
FRONT as the mirror plane.

Repeat this process to mirror both holes to
the left side of the part at the same time.
Using the CTRL key, select both holes,
then launch the *Mirror* command. The
mirror plane is RIGHT. Accept the feature.

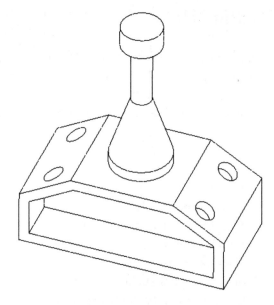

Figure 17 Holes added to base using *Mirror*

The part should now look like Figure 17.
Once again, this figure does not show the axes created with each hole.

Having Problems Mirroring?

If you have trouble creating mirrored features, it is likely that your underlying geometry
is not perfectly symmetrical about the mirror plane. We should not have that problem
here, because we used the symmetry constraints on our base sketch, and a both-sides
blind protrusion, which is also automatically symmetric. If you ever do have problems,
you may have to double check the geometry to ensure that its dimensions are exactly
correct. We will investigate this potential problem later on in this lesson. Geometric
conditions at the location of the mirrored featured must be "legal" for the creation of the
feature. For example, if the left side of the block did not have the same slope as the right
side at the location of the hole, we should expect problems trying to do the mirror
operation from right to left (since the hole must be perpendicular to the surface).

Creating Rounds

We will use a very handy short cut to add a couple of simple rounds to the top of the
guide pin, and the edge where the shaft meets the base. Technically, these are called a
round and a fillet, respectively. (A round removes material from an edge, while a fillet
adds material.)

For the first round, use preselection to pick the edge where the base of the revolved
protrusion meets the block (Figure 18). Note that only half the circular edge needs to be
chosen - the feature will follow the tangent edge all the way around. The selected edge is
highlighted in red. Now hold down the right mouse button, and select *Round Edges* in

the pop-up menu. The display will show a preview of the fillet in yellow. Set the radius to **0.5** by entering the value, or using the drag handles. To accept the fillet, just middle click. That's fast! (How many mouse clicks?)

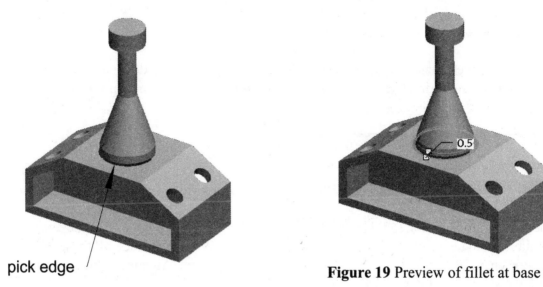

pick edge

Figure 18 Creating fillet at base

Figure 19 Preview of fillet at base

Let's do the same for the edges at the top of the shaft. Use preselection once again to highlight a single edge. Then use CTRL-click to select the second edge (see Figure 20). Once again, hold down the right mouse button and select **Round Edges** in the pop-up menu. Both edges will preview (Figure 21). The radius will be set initially to the value we used for the previous round.

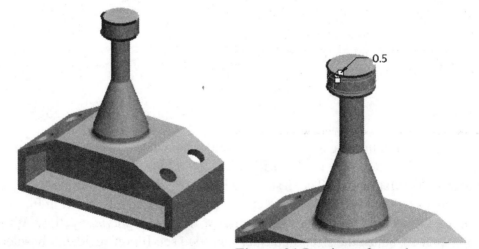

Figure 20 Selecting edges at top

Figure 21 Preview of rounds at top

If you look in the **Sets** slide-up panel in the dashboard, you will see one set listed, containing two edges. All edges in the set have the same properties. Note that we could have put all rounds into the same set here. What would that imply about our design intent?

This round feature is OK for now, so just middle click. If you are in wireframe mode and the tangent edges are not visible, select

> *Utilities > Environment*
> *Tangent Edges > Dimmed*
> *OK*

You might experiment with the image (shading, hidden line, no hidden, etc.) to see what the rounds look like in different displays, in particular the appearance of the tangent edges.

Using Edge Sets with *Chamfer*

The last feature addition to this part is a chamfer all around the edge of the pocket and the parallel outside edge on the front and back of the base. We will include all these edges in a single chamfer feature by organizing them in two edge sets. All edges within each set have the same size. Edge sets are also used in the round feature. The main trick with edge sets is making sure a chosen edge is in the set you want it to be. Doing this is largely a matter of being careful when you are selecting the edges, and watching the screen carefully. The reason edge sets are useful is that the model tree can be simplified considerably by having multiple chamfered (or rounded) edges contained in the same feature. So, all chamfers or rounds of the same size can be modified simultaneously with a single dimension. Furthermore, when rounds or chamfers meet at corners, you can control the transitions between them. This can only be done for chamfers or rounds contained in the same feature.

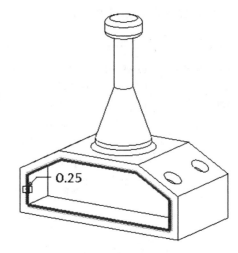

Figure 22 Chamfer edge set #1

You might find the following easier to do in hidden line or wireframe display. In shaded mode, some of the edges may not be really clear. Start by selecting the *Chamfer* command in the right toolbar. The dashboard is now open. You can immediately start selecting edges. Hold down the CTRL key and pick the six edges shown in Figure 22. The edges will highlight in red and the chamfer will show in preview yellow. When the last one is picked, adjust the size to **0.25** for this edge set. If you accidentally select a wrong edge, just pick it again.

Now, left click on an edge going around the outside of the base - see Figure 23. **As soon as you left click (without holding down CTRL), Pro/E assumes you are starting a new edge set.** The previous set is still shown in preview. Now holding down the CTRL key you can continue to pick edges for the second set. Set the dimension for this set to **0.5**.

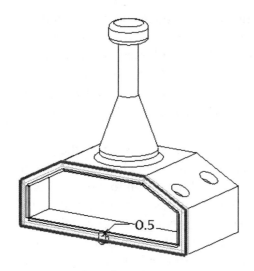

Figure 23 Chamfer edge set #2   **Figure 24** Chamfer completed

Open up the **Sets** slide-up panel. The two sets are listed, with the edges of the highlighted set shown in the pane below. Selecting Set1 or Set 2 will highlight the various edges on the model.

There are no Transitions here (the next dashboard panel button), since none of the edge sets intersect.

Verify the feature, and *Accept* it. See Figure 24. Save the part.

Open the model tree and observe that the last feature is the chamfer, containing all 12 edges. The previous two features were the rounds. Notice the listing of the mirrored holes and the mirrored pocket. It might be a good idea to come back later and rename all these Mirror features in the model tree to help distinguish them.

Now, in preparation for what we are going to do later (some things to make Pro/E fail!), we will try to mirror the chamfer to the edges of the pocket on the back face of the base using mirror plane **FRONT**. This seems like a reasonable kind of thing to do, but is kind of like poking the sleeping giant. Notice that if you pre-select the chamfer, the *Mirror* button on the right toolbar is not available. We'll have to do something a bit different here. Starting in the pull-down menus:

> *Edit > Feature Operations*
> *Copy > Mirror | Select[3] | Dependent | Done*

When you select the chamfer by picking on any of the chamfered surfaces, they will all highlight, since they all belong to the same feature. Middle click. When it comes to specifying the mirror plane, select **FRONT**. Now the problems start! Pro/E is unable to

---

[3] Incidentally, never use the *All Features* option here if you want a mirror copy of an entire part. There is a much more elegant way of doing this using a dummy assembly.

create the mirrored feature and a **Failure Diagnostics** window opens up. Click on the *<Overview>* field. This tells us how we can get some more information about fixing this problem. *Close* the information window. In the RESOLVE FEAT menu at the right, we have seen the *Undo Changes* command before - this comes up if a dimensional change has led to a regeneration failure. The problem here is different (and *Undo Changes* is not available anyway). To find out some more, select *Investigate > Show Ref*. This brings up the **Reference Viewer** window that we have seen before. In the list of parents, expand the list for the cut 'Extrude 2' (click on the + sign). This brings up a list of all the references of the failed feature - the edges of the pocket. If you right click on any listed edge and select *Entity Info*, you will see a statement a few lines down to the effect that the edge is "not in geometry." Hmmm ... it appears that Pro/E just won't let us do this mirror operation. We need to back out of this command. Close the **Reference Viewer** window. In the **RESOLVE FEAT** menu, select *Quick Fix > Delete > Done*. This doesn't delete the original chamfer, just our attempted copy (the failed feature).

To get the chamfer on the back pocket we have two options:

1.   Delete the existing chamfer and create a new one containing edge sets with edges on both front and back surfaces, or
2.   Redefine the existing chamfer by adding new edges to the feature (this involves commands discussed in Lesson #5).

For now, you might as well try the first of these two. With the new chamfer with edges on both sides, the part is completed.

Saving the Part

Don't forget to save your part:

File > Save

(or use CTRL-S) and if you have been saving regularly, get rid of previous copies of the part file by using

File > Delete > Old Versions > [guide_pin]

and press the enter key (or middle click).

Model Analysis Tools

Quite often, you need to find some information about a part - distances between points, surface area, center of gravity, moments of inertia. There are lots of tools available in Pro/E to query the model. Let's start with something simple. In the pull-down menus, select:

Analysis > Measure > Length

This opens the dialog window shown in Figure 25. If you select any edge on the model, its length will appear in the window and on the screen. Select an edge of one of the holes (remember these are ø2). Is the reported length the full circumference or only half? What does this tell you about how Pro/E stores circular shapes?

Try selecting

Analysis > Measure > Diameter

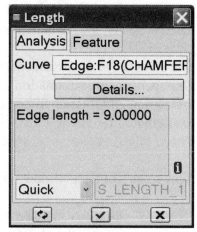

Figure 25 Obtaining a length measure

then pick on the cylindrical portion near the top of the shaft. The diameter shows in the Measure window. Even more interesting is to pick on the conical part of the shaft. This reports the diameter at the pick point. What happens if you pick on the round at the base of the pin (this is curved in two directions)?

If you select *Measure > Area*, you can select individual planar or curved surfaces (they highlight in pink) or the entire model (click the part name in the model tree). See Figure 26. This might be useful to calculate paint quantities. You can also obtained projected area by specifying a projection plane or direction.

Figure 26 Area of surface

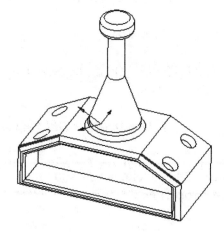

Figure 27 Angle between edges

By selecting *Measure > Angle*, you can find the angle between the sloping edges at each end of the block (Figure 27). *Distance* lets you find the distance between any two entities. Figure 28 shows the measurement of the (shortest) distance between the tangent edge of the round and the chamfer on the front of the part. Select the *Definition* tab in the **Distance** window to help select these. You can also obtained projected distance.

The *Transform* measurement will produce a 4X4 homogeneous transformation matrix which describes the translation and rotation of one coordinate system relative to another.

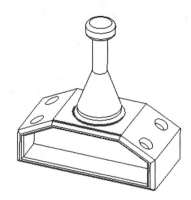

Figure 28 Distance between curves

Now select (in the pull-down menus)

Analysis > Model > Mass Properties

This opens the window shown in Figure 29. Press the *Compute* button at the bottom left.

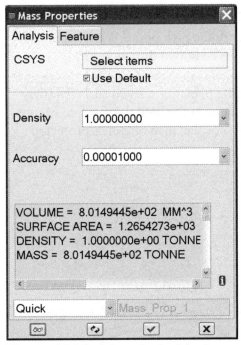

Figure 29 Model analysis showing mass properties

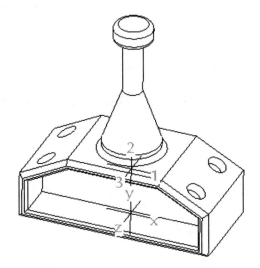

Figure 30 Part center of gravity and principle axes

The mass property data uses an assumed density for the solid (which can be changed). The results include the volume of the part, surface area, and mass. A bit farther down in the results is the location of the part center of gravity (relative to a specified coordinate system). The location of the center of gravity is shown graphically on the object (Figure

30). The axes 1-2-3 refer to the principle axes of the solid. The results also include the mass moments of inertia about these axes, and the radius of gyration of the solid about each axis. This data is useful for dynamic analysis of the part.

Other types of model analysis are cross section properties, one-sided volume (on one side of a selected plane), clearance between entities, determining if any edges are shorter than a specified length, or any thickness values are greater or less than specified values (important to molded plastic parts).

Exploring the Model, or "What Can Go Wrong?"

Now comes the fun stuff! Here are some things you can try with this part. These explorations are very important, so DO NOT SKIP THIS SECTION!! We will review some of what we covered in Lessons #2 and #3. More importantly, some things we'll try here will show you how Pro/E responds to common modeling errors such as the failure to mirror the chamfer earlier in this lesson. Being comfortable with these methods to respond when an error occurs is an important aspect of your modeling proficiency. A common tendency among newcomers to Pro/E is to retreat from these errors and try to create the model in another (usually more familiar but less efficient) way. This will not expand your knowledge of modeling practice, or allow you to anticipate errors before they happen. Spend the time to learn this now, and it will save you much time later.

Here are the exercises:

1.   We found out before how to name the features of a part. Do that now for the *guide_pin*, using whatever names you like. Obtain a feature list using
        Info > Feature
    or
        Info > Model
    What is the difference between these lists?
2.   Make the following dimensional changes to various features of the model. (HINT: preselect the feature, use RMB pop-up menu and select ***Edit***). ***Regenerate*** the part after making each dimensional change. Observe what Pro/E does and see if you can explain why. You can usually recover from any errors that might occur by selecting ***Undo Changes***, or ***Quick Fix > Delete***. If things really go wrong, you should be able to use ***File > Erase > Current***, and retrieve your stored copy of the part file.
    ▸   change the radius of the round on the base of the revolved protrusion to the following values: (*0.75, 1.5, 3.0*). For each value, see if you can predict what Pro/E will do before you actually execute the regenerate command. Reset to the initial value (0.5) after these modifications.
    ▸   change the diameter of the first hole to the following values: (*1.0, 3.5, 4.0, 5.0*). Again, try to predict how Pro/E will handle these changes. Reset to the initial value (2.0) after these modifications. Try changing the diameter of one of the mirrored holes on the back of the part. When you click on this hole, where do the placement dimensions show up on the screen?

- ▸ change the location of the first hole from 3 to **1.5** away from the datum plane **FRONT**. Where does the hole now terminate? Why? Now change the same dimension to **5**. What happens and why? Reset to the initial value after these modifications.
- ▸ change the location of one of the holes from 3 to **(1.5, 1.0)** away from the edge reference on the end of the block. Where does the hole now terminate? Now change the same dimension to **(7.0, 8.0)**. What happens? Reset to the initial value after these modifications.
- ▸ change the height of the base block from 8.0 to **6.0**, then to **4.0**, then **3.0**. Explain what happens and reset to the initial value after these modifications.
- ▸ change the depth of the base block (10.0) to **(9.0, 8.25, 8.0)**. What happens each time? Reset to the initial value after these modifications.
- ▸ change the length of the base block to **(16.0, 12.0)**. Shade the view. What happens each time? Reset to the initial value after these modifications.
- ▸ change the diameter of the base of the revolved protrusion (6.0) to the following values: **(8.0, 9.0, 9.5)**. What happens and why? Reset to the initial value after these modifications.
- ▸ change the radius of the rounds on the top of the revolved protrusion to the following: **(0.75, 1.5)**. What happens? Reset to the initial value after these modifications.
- ▸ change the edge offset dimension for the pocket to the following: **(2.0, 3.5)**. What happens? Reset to the initial value after these modifications.
- ▸ change the depth dimension for the pocket to the following: **(4.5, 5.5)**. Reset to the initial value after these modifications.

3. Set up a relation so that the distance of the holes from the datum **FRONT** is such that the hole is always centered on the depth of the pocket. Add another relation that will give a warning if the web between the two pockets down the center of the part becomes less than 1.50 thick. Your relations will look something like this (your dimensions symbols will probably be different from these):

```
/* hole centered on pocket depth
d38 = (d5 - d14) / 2
/* narrow web warning - message is generated if false
(d5 - 2*d14) > 1.5
```

Check these relations by changing the depth of the base feature from 10 to 20. Then change the depth of the pocket to 9.5. Follow the prompts in the message window. When the part is regenerated, open the **Relations** dialog window. Reset the values to remove the relation violation.

4. Examine the parent/child relations in the model. What are the parents of the pocket? What are the children of the pocket? Do the relations added in question 3 change the parent/child relations?

5. Delete the front pocket and all its children. Now, try to create it again. What happens to the holes? Since this new feature will be added after the holes, you might anticipate some changes in the model. This points out again the importance of feature creation order.

6. Explain why centering the base feature (the block) on the datums was a good idea.

7. Try to delete the revolved protrusion. What happens?

8.   Try to delete one of the holes. What happens?

That's a lot of exercises and is enough to think about for this lesson. Select *File > Exit*.
When you quit Pro/E, you might also have to check out your disk space usage and delete
any files that you don't want to keep (for example: trail.txt).

In the next lesson we will discuss Pro/E utilities for dealing with features, including
examining parent/child relations in detail, suppressing and resuming features, editing
feature definitions, and changing the regeneration order. These are often necessary when
creating a complex model, and to recover from modeling errors or poor model planning.

Questions for Review

1.   When sketching with Intent Manager, why should you deal with and set up your constraints before setting up the dimensioning scheme? Why do you set the dimension values last?

2.   What surfaces can be legally chosen as sketching planes?

3.   In Sketcher, how do you easily create an arc tangent to a line at an endpoint?

4.   What does the *Thru Next* depth specification do? What is a requirement for this?

5.   In Sketcher, where are the *Trim* and *Extend* commands? What do they do?

6.   What elements are required to create a **revolved protrusion**?

7.   What is meant by a **linear** hole? What are the alternatives?

8.   What is meant by a **dependent** copy?

9.   What is the difference between a round and a fillet?

10.   What types of chamfer are available?

11.   When you are creating a mirrored copy can you:
    ▸   select more than one feature to mirror at once?
    ▸   select more than one mirror plane at the same time?

12.   What happens when a chamfer meets a round at the corner of a part?

13.   What happens when two rounds of different radii meet at a corner of a part?

14.   The figure at the right shows a sketch of two four-sided polygons. What is the difference between these polygons? Notice the difference in format of the "width" dimension, and the appearance of the vertical line on the far right.

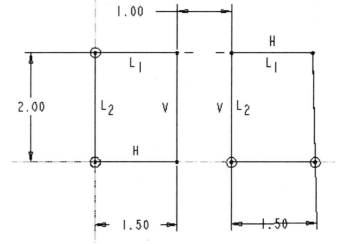

Figure for Question 14

15.   Where do the placement dimensions of a mirrored feature appear under *Edit*?

16.   What are the options for setting the depth of a blind, both-sides protrusion?

17.   Could the rounds we made on the top of the guide pin be created as part of the **revolved protrusion**? What advantages/disadvantages would there be in doing that?

Exercises

Here are some simple parts to make that use the features introduced in this lesson.

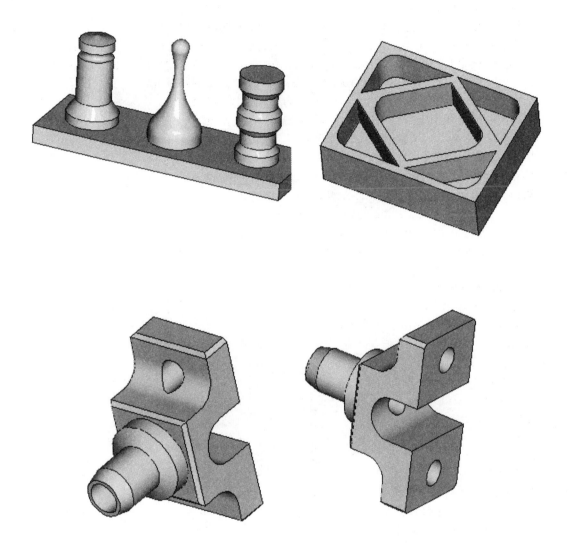

There are some more parts on the next page.....

These parts will be a bit more challenging. HINT: at this stage, keep your features as simple as possible, and plan ahead!

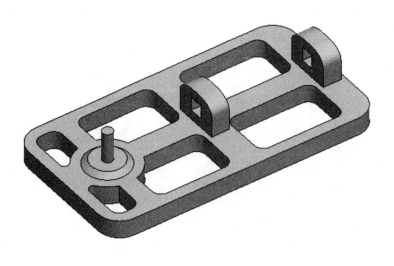

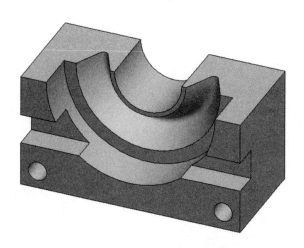

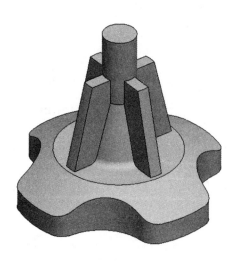

Project

Here is another part for the vise project, using features introduced in this lesson (a revolved protrusion, some mirrored cuts, and some rounds). All units are in millimeters.

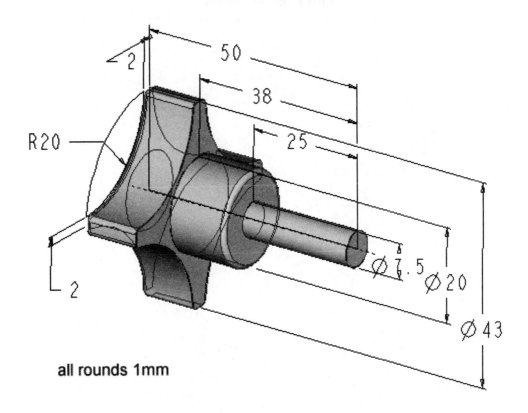

all rounds 1mm

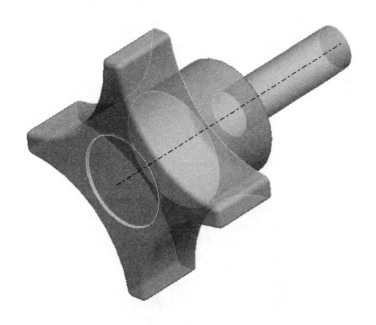

This page left blank.

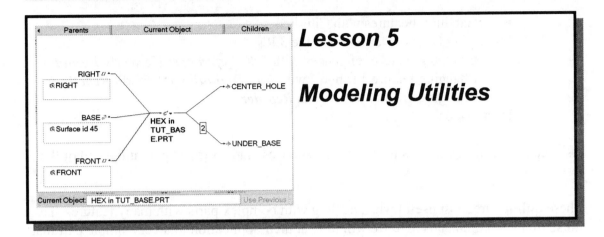

Synopsis

Utilities for exploring and editing the model: finding relationships between features, changing references, changing feature shapes, changing the order of feature regeneration, changing feature attributes, changing the insertion point, suppressing and resuming features.

Overview of this Lesson

In this lesson we will discuss Pro/E utilities for dealing with existing features. When you are creating complicated models, it is almost inevitable that you will have to change the geometry and/or structure of your model at some point. If your model becomes even moderately complex, you will need to know how to modify the model data structure and/or recover from poor model planning. This could be because you discover a better or more convenient way to lay out the features, or the design of the part changes so that your model no longer captures the design intent as accurately or cleanly as you would like. Sometimes, you just run into difficulty trying to modify the model (usually caused by the logical structure of the features) or have made errors in creating the model. This lesson will cover ways of obtaining information about parent/child relations, suppressing and resuming features, editing feature definitions and references (the commands formerly known as the 3 R's - *Redefine*, *Reroute*, and *Reorder*). We will also introduce Insert Mode for adding new features to the model early in the regeneration sequence. We have seen some of this before, so it will let you review that material.

The lesson is in four sections:

1. Obtaining Information about the Model
   ‣ Regeneration Sequence
   ‣ Obtaining a Feature List and Using the Model Tree
   ‣ Getting Information about a Specific Feature
   ‣ Parent/Child Relations
2. Suppressing and Resuming Features
   ‣ Single Features

       ▸   Handling Features with Children
3.   Modifying Feature Definitions - the 3 R's
       ▸   Changing feature references with **Edit References** (formerly **Reroute**)
       ▸   Changing feature attributes with **Edit Definition** (formerly **Redefine**)
       ▸   Changing creation order with **Reorder**
4.   Insert Mode

As usual, there are Questions for Review, Exercises, and a Project part at the end of the lesson.

These utilities are most useful when dealing with complex parts with many features. To illustrate these commands here we will look at their application to a very simple part that will be provided for you. This part has a number of modeling "errors" that must be fixed. With parts this simple, it might actually be easier to just create a new part and start over again (you may find it necessary to do that occasionally anyway). However, when parts get more complex, and contain many features, starting over will not be an option and these utilities will be indispensable.

In order to do this lesson, you will need a copy of the file *lesson5.prt.1* that is available on the enclosed CD or from the SDC Web page (go to **http://www.schroff1.com**). Use your Web browser to download this file and copy it to your Pro/E working directory - full instructions to do this are on the Web page.

Once you have the part file, launch Pro/E, retrieve the part and continue on with the lesson. The part should look like Figure 1 in default orientation.

This model contains the default datum planes and four features. The base feature is a rectangular block. The other features are another solid protrusion and two cuts. The features are named as shown in Figure 1.

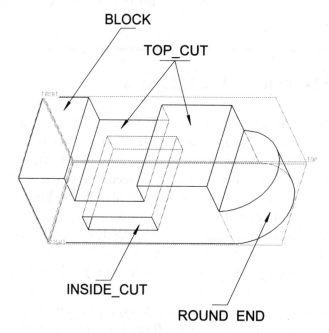

Figure 1 Initial part for Lesson #5

Obtaining Information about the Model

Once your model gets reasonably complex, or if you "inherit" a model from another source such as we are doing here, one of the important things to do is to have a clear idea of the structure of the model. Which features were created first? Which features depend on other features? How do the features reference each other? Answers to all these questions are available!

The Regeneration Sequence

The order of feature creation during part regeneration is called the *regeneration sequence*. Features are regenerated in the order in which they appear in the part database[1]. (We will talk about changing the order of the regeneration sequence in a later section of this lesson.) To observe the regeneration sequence select the following commands, starting in the pull-down menu:

> *Tools > Model Player*

Enter a **1** in the **Feat #** box to go to the first feature. Then press the ***Step Forward*** button to step you through the creation of the model one feature at a time. The model player window will tell you which feature is currently being created. As you progress through the sequence, the menu gives you a chance to get more information about the current feature, including its dimensions.

For example, when you get to feature #6, select ***Feat Info*** in the **Model Player** window. This opens a Browser window with a page that gives you lots of information about the feature. Look for the following: *feature number* (#6), the *internal feature ID* (52), the ID's and feature numbers of the parents and children of this feature, the *feature type* (an extruded cut), dimensions. One of the data panels has scrollable text. Note that the depth of this feature is 10. This will be important later on. Also, note the difference between the feature number (the placement within the regeneration sequence) and the feature ID (Pro/E's internal bookkeeping). It will be possible to change the feature number, but, once created, you can never change a feature's ID.

Close the Browser window and continue through the regeneration sequence until you have all seven features. Then select ***Finish***.

The Feature List

You can call up a table summary of all the features in the model by selecting:

> *Info > Model*

This brings up the Browser page shown in Figure 2. At the top is shown the system of units for the model. Below this is a table that lists all its features. Information for each feature includes: the feature number and ID in the first two columns, a name for the feature (defaults to feature type), the type of feature, and current regeneration status. There are two action buttons for each feature which will highlight the feature on the model, or open up the feature information page we saw previously. If you have many

---

[1]This is called "history-based" modeling. Some modeling programs do not have this mode of operation - they regenerate everything simultaneously.

features, it is a good idea to name them - there is nothing worse than seeing a whole bunch of features all identified with just "Hole" or "Cut" in this table.

By the way, whenever you see a Browser window like this in Pro/E, you can easily print or save it by using the buttons at the top of the Browser window. This may be useful for design documentation. *Close* the Browser.

The Model Tree

The model tree was introduced earlier and you have probably seen it many times by now. If it is not currently displayed, open it by clicking on the textured button on the left sash. You

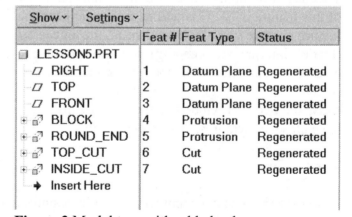

Figure 2 The Browser page for **Model Info**

should see the columns shown in Figure 3. If those are not visible, either load the model tree configuration file we made earlier (*tree.cfg*) or use

Settings > Tree Columns

to add and format columns. The usual columns you will use are *Feat #*, *Feat Type*, and *Status*. Also, while we're here, select

Settings > Tree Filters

This brings up a dialog window with a number of checkboxes for selecting items to be displayed in the model tree. For example, remove the check mark beside **Datum Plane**, then select *Apply*.

Show ˅	Settings ˅	Feat #	Feat Type	Status
▢ LESSON5.PRT				
⊿ RIGHT		1	Datum Plane	Regenerated
⊿ TOP		2	Datum Plane	Regenerated
⊿ FRONT		3	Datum Plane	Regenerated
⊞ BLOCK		4	Protrusion	Regenerated
⊞ ROUND_END		5	Protrusion	Regenerated
⊞ TOP_CUT		6	Cut	Regenerated
⊞ INSIDE_CUT		7	Cut	Regenerated
➜ Insert Here				

Figure 3 Model tree with added columns

This might be useful if the part contains many datum planes which are cluttering up the view of the model tree feature structure. Turn the datum plane display back on. Turn on the check boxes beside **Annotations** and **Suppressed Objects** and exit the window with *OK*. (What happens if you *Close* this window instead?). The model tree should now look like Figure 3.

Left click on any of the feature names shown in the left column of the model tree to see it highlighted in the model. (If the feature doesn't highlight, make sure that **Highlight Geometry** is checked in the *Show* menu just above the model tree.) This is an easy way to explore the structure of the database and the features in the model. But the model tree can do much more!

Hold down the right mouse button on one of the features listed in the model tree. This pops-up a menu containing the following commands:

- ▸ Delete
- ▸ Group
- ▸ Suppress
- ▸ Rename
- ▸ Edit
- ▸ Dynamic Edit
- ▸ Edit Definition
- ▸ Edit References
- ▸ Create Driving Dimension AE
- ▸ Pattern
- ▸ Insert Here
- ▸ Setup Note
- ▸ Info
- ▸ Edit Parameters

We have seen the *Edit* (for changing dimension values) and *Delete* (for removing features) commands before, as well as the *Info > Model* commands. The other commands *Edit Definition* (or *Redefine*), *Edit References* (or *Reroute*), and *Suppress* are among the main topics in this lesson, and are discussed at length below.

Parent/Child Relations

Using the commands given above, you can find out the regeneration sequence and internal ID numbers of parent and child features. There are several commands for exploring the parent/child relations in the model in considerably more detail. Select feature #5 in the model tree (ROUND_END) or preselect in the graphics window. Hold down the right mouse button and select:

Info > Reference Viewer

The **Reference Viewer** window opens. In the filter pane on the left, turn off the check box beside **System**, then close the filter pane and expand the graphic area to see the feature names. Click the down arrow beside BLOCK to display the four surface references, as shown in Figure 4.

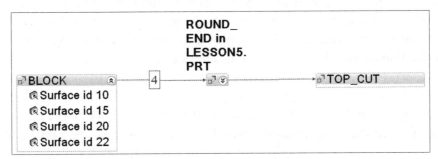

Figure 4 Graphic display in **Reference Viewer**

Click on each of the four surfaces listed. As each is selected, the reference surface will highlight on the model. If you open the RMB pop-up for each surface and select *Info > Reference Info*, an information window will open describing the nature of the reference (sketching plane or dimension reference, among other things).

On the children side, we see that the feature TOP_CUT is a child of the rounded end protrusion. What is the nature of this reference? Position the mouse cursor on the line joining the features - a pop-up information box will appear giving some information about the relation. Let's explore this a bit more. Highlight this feature in the children list, then hold down the right mouse button and in the pop-up menu select *Set as Current*.

The **Reference Viewer** window now shows TOP_CUT as the current object, and lists its parents and children. Expand these lists (Figure 5). Notice the surface listed under ROUND_END in the parents area. Select this surface and it

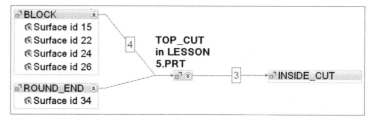

Figure 5 The Reference Viewer window for the feature TOP-CUT

is highlighted on the model. The reference information message (hold the cursor over the connecting line) tells us that this was used as the horizontal sketcher reference for the cut feature #6 (TOP_CUT). This will be important to us later. The other four parent surfaces of TOP_CUT correspond to the following:

1. (Surface id 15) the front of the block - sketching plane
2. (Surface id 24) top of block - dimensioning ref used for aligning/dimensioning the cut
3. (Surface id 22) right end of block - dimensioning ref used for aligning/dimensioning the cut
4. (Surface id 26) left surface of block - dimensioning ref used for dimensioning reference

If you repeat this process for the inside cut (use *Set Current* and expand the parent features), you should see the following references:

1. the front of the block - sketching plane
2. the right horizontal surface of the top cut - horizontal reference plane
3. left vertical surface of the top cut - alignment/dimension reference
4. right vertical surface of the top cut - alignment/dimension reference
5. the Top datum plane - dimension reference

Now that we have explored the model a bit, you should have a good idea of how it was set up. Before we go on to ways that we can modify the model, let's have a look at a useful utility for dealing with features. Select *Close* in the **Reference Viewer** window.

Suppressing and Resuming Features

When you are working with a very complex model, it will often happen that many of the model features are irrelevant to what you are currently doing. Or, you want to avoid accidentally picking on some features as a reference for a new one. There is a command available that will temporarily remove one or more features from the regeneration sequence (and hence the model display). This is called *suppressing* the feature(s). It is important to note that this does not mean deleting the feature(s), it just means that they are skipped over when Pro/E regenerates the model. This will speed up the regeneration process thus saving you time. On some systems, it may also noticeably speed up the screen refresh rate when doing 3D spins and shading.

When a feature is suppressed, it generally means that all its children will be suppressed as well. To bring the feature back, you can *resume* it. Let's see how suppress and resume work.

Preselect the feature INSIDE_CUT (or select it in the model tree). Hold down the right mouse button, and in the pop-up menu select

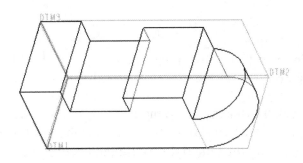

Figure 6 Part regenerated with cut suppressed

Suppress

Confirm the operation with *OK*. The part will regenerate without the cut as shown in Figure 6.

Check out the new feature list:

Info > Model

Observe the feature status. Call up the model tree (make sure that *Settings > Tree Filters > Suppressed Objects* is checked). Notice the small black square beside the name of the suppressed feature.

You will note that the suppressed feature no longer has a feature number (but it still has an ID), and the last column shows its status as suppressed. To get the feature back into the geometry, issue the commands (starting in the pull-down menu)

Edit > Resume > Resume Last Set

Now, try to suppress the TOP_CUT. Select it in the model tree, hold down the right mouse button and select *Suppress*. A warning window appears. Move it out of the way to see the model. The TOP_CUT is highlighted in red, the INSIDE_CUT is highlighted in green - it is a child of the TOP_CUT. You will have to decide what to do with it. Select *Options*. This opens the **Children Handling** dialog window (Figure 7). This window allows you to find information about the children (references and so on), as well as set options for how each child should be handled. The default action is to suppress all children with their parents. For now, select this with *OK* to suppress both cuts together. You should see the part as shown in Figure 8.

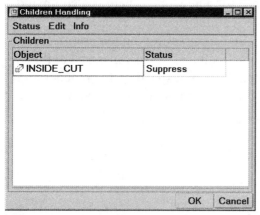

Figure 7 The Children Handling window

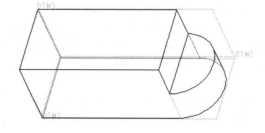

Figure 8 Part with both cuts suppressed

Check the display in the model tree. Both features have the small black square indicating their suppressed status. Try to resume the INSIDE_CUT by itself. Select it in the model tree, hold down the right mouse button and select

Resume

Both the selected feature and its parent (the other cut) are resumed - you can't resume a child without also resuming it's parent(s).

Using suppress and resume can make your life easier by eliminating unnecessary detail in a model when you don't need it. For example, if your part is a valve, you don't need all the bolt holes in the flange if you are working on some other unrelated features of the valve. If you are setting up a model for Finite Element Modeling (FEM) for stress analysis, for example, you would usually suppress all fine detail in the model (chamfers, rounds, etc.) in order to simplify it. Suppressing features also prevents you from inadvertently creating references to features that you don't want (like two axes that may coincide, but may be separated later). Finally, suppressing unneeded features will also speed up the regeneration of the part.

Features that are suppressed are still included in the part data base, and will be saved with the part (with their suppressed status) when you save your model to a disk file.

Helpful Hint

A trick used by advanced users who are dealing with very complicated parts is to suppress a large number of features before storing a part file. This reduces the file size, sometimes significantly. This can be useful when sending the part by email. When the file is read in again, the features are resumed by the new user. Be aware that this may be contrary to company policy (see next hint!).

Helpful Hint

When you inherit a part made by someone else, always check for suppressed features when you first open it. You may be (unpleasantly) surprised at what you find!

When we get to drawings and assemblies in the last lessons, remember that suppressed features are carried over into these objects as well. That is, a suppressed feature will stay suppressed when you add its part to an assembly, or display the part in a drawing. Suppressed features in a part may even prevent the assembly from regenerating since some important references may be missing (although there are tools available in assembly mode to deal with this all-too-common occurrence).

Suppressing versus Hiding

Hold down the right mouse button on any of the datum planes. In the pop-up menu, you will see another command - *Hide*. Select that now. The datum plane disappears from the graphics window. All the datums in this part have children, so clearly we have not suppressed the datum, only removed it from the display. Observe that the datum icon in the model tree is now on a gray background. This indicates its hidden status. You can *Unhide* it using the same pop-up menu.

Hide and *Unhide* only work for non-solid objects (datum planes, curves, points). You cannot *Hide* a solid feature (but you can *Hide* a component in an assembly).

Modifying Feature Definitions

In previous lessons, we have used the *Edit* command to change dimension values. We need some tools to let us modify the basic structure of the model. So, now we will look at ways to modify the parent/child relations in the part, and to modify the geometric shape of some features.

Suppose we want to take the original *lesson5.prt* and modify it to form the part shown in

Figure 9. This involves the
following changes (some of these
are not visible in the figure):

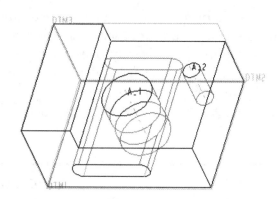

1.   delete the rounded end
2.   change the shape of the inner
       cut
3.   change the dimensioning
       scheme of the inner cut
4.   change the references of the
       inner cut
5.   change the shape of the cut on
       the top surface
6.   change the feature references   **Figure 9** Final modified part
       of the top cut
7.   increase the depth of the part
8.   change the depth attribute of the top cut
9.   add a couple of vertical holes

Some of these changes will require modifications to the parent/child relations that were
used when the part was created. This will also result in a cleaner model.

If you haven't gone through Section 1 of this lesson on obtaining model information, now
is a good time to do so, since a good understanding of the existing parent/child relations
is essential for what follows.

To see what we are up against, try to delete the rounded end of the part (the first thing on
our "to do" list) by preselecting it, holding down the right mouse button and selecting

> ### *Delete*

You will be notified that the feature has children (shown in green) and asked what you
want to do with them. In the warning window, select *Options*. This opens the **Children
Handling** window we saw before. The default action is to delete the children. In this
window, select the child TOP_CUT. It will now highlight on the model. To find out how
it is related to the parent, hold down the right mouse button and select

> ### *Show References*

You can now step through the references used to create TOP_CUT. As you step through
these with *Next* in the **SHOW REF** menu at the right, they will highlight in green on the
model. Watch the message window as you do this. The first reference is the sketching
plane. The next is the horizontal sketching reference for TOP_CUT. The surface used
was the upper surface of the rounded end - this is the parent/child connection that has
interfered with our plan to delete the rounded end. We could change that reference now
(using *Reroute*), but we'll deal with that possibility later. We could also delete the child
along with the parent. We would then have to decide what to do with the children of the
children (that is, the inside cut) and so on! Keep selecting *Next* in the **SHOW REF** menu

to step through the rest of the references for TOP_CUT. When you have gone through them all, select

> ### *Done/Return*

in the **SHOW REF** menu. You are back to the **Children Handling** window. In the RMB pop-up menu for TOP_CUT, there are a couple of commands (*Replace References*, and *Redefine*) which we will discuss shortly.

In the **Children Handling** window, select the INSIDE_CUT and, in the RMB pop-up menu, select

> ### *Show References*

You will see the sketching surface, the sketching reference surfaces, and a couple of dimensioning references.

In the **Children Handling** window, the Status column options for the two children are *Delete* or *Suspend*. The former will remove them from the model immediately (along with the parent). *Suspend* will keep them in the model, but the next time the model is regenerated, these features will fail regeneration and require special processing (like recreating or reassigning the necessary references that have been lost) to keep them in the model.

Cancel the deletion command that we launched previously. Clearly, this is not going to be as easy as it first looked. We'll deal with our desired changes one at a time, and not necessarily in the order given above. For example, before we can delete the rounded end, we have to do something about its child references. Some careful thought and planning is necessary here. When you get proficient with Pro/E, you will be able to manage these changes more efficiently. Our main tools to use here are: *Edit Definition, Edit References*, and *Reorder*. The first two commands were previously called *Redefine* and *Reroute*, respectively, and still appear with those names in a few places in Pro/E.

① Changing the shape of a sketch (*Edit Definition*)

The first thing we'll do is change the shape of the inner cut from its current rectangular shape to one with rounded ends. This requires a change in the sketch geometry of the feature. We'll take the opportunity to change the dimensioning scheme as well.

The *Edit Definition* (aka *Redefine*) command allows you to change almost everything about a feature except its major type (you can't change an extrude into a revolve). Preselect the INSIDE_CUT (on the screen or in the model tree) and in the right mouse pop-up menu select *Edit Definition*.

The feature dashboard will open, exactly as we saw it as the feature was being created. The feature is shown in preview yellow. The *Remove Material* button is selected and the **Depth Spec** is set to *Through All*. In the dashboard, select the **Placement** tab, then *Edit* (or use the RMB in the graphics window and select *Edit Internal Sketch*). You will automatically be taken into **Sketcher** where we can proceed to modify the sketched shape of the cut. You might like to go to wireframe or hidden line display here, and close the model tree. The desired final shape is shown in Figure 10.

First, delete the vertical sketched lines at each end. Highlight both lines, open the right mouse button pop-up menu and select

>   ***Delete***

Now add two circular arcs: use the right mouse button pop-up menu to select

>   ***3 Point / Tangent End***

and sketch the arcs at each end. Now change (if necessary) the dimensioning scheme to the one shown in Figure 10.

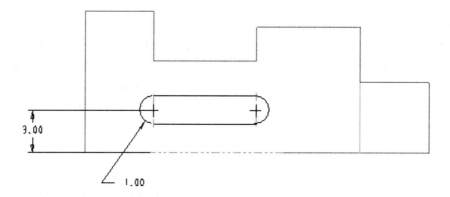

Figure 10 New sketch for the inner cut

Note that the ends of the straight part of the slot are still aligned with the vertical faces of the top cut. We will deal with those later. Accept the sketch. In the dashboard, select ***Verify*** if desired, then ***Accept*** the feature. If all went well, you should get the message

>   "Feature redefined successfully."

in the message area at the top of the screen.

② Changing a Feature Reference (*Edit References*)

Recall that the horizontal sketching reference for the inner cut was on the right side of the top cut, and we are planning on changing the shape of the top cut to remove that surface. We will have to change the reference for the inner cut to something else. This is done using the ***Edit References*** (aka ***Reroute***) command.

Preselect the inner cut, and use the pop-up menu to select ***Edit References***. You will be asked if you want to *"roll back"* the model. Rolling back means temporarily returning to the part status when the inner cut was created. In a complicated part, this would suppress all features created after the one we are interested in. This is a good idea, since then it will not be possible to (accidentally) select a new reference that is "younger" than the cut (ie. created after it). Unless you can think of a really good reason not to, you should **ALWAYS ROLL BACK THE PART!** It is curious that this is not the Pro/E default (although if you have a seriously complex model, this situation might change!) - you will have to enter a *y* (or click the *Yes* button) to cause the roll back to occur. This doesn't do anything for this simple model at this time because the cut was the last feature created.

The front surface of the block is highlighted in green on the part. The message window indicates that this was the sketching plane. The vertical and horizontal references of the sketch are shown. On the window right side, the **REROUTE REFS** window has opened. The command *Reroute Feat* is already active.

The general procedure in a reroute operation is to step through all the references for the feature being changed. In the **REROUTE** menu on the right, as you step through the sequence of current references, you have the options of selecting an alternate reference, keeping the same reference, or obtaining feature/reference information. As you step through the references, they will be highlighted on the part. Read the message in the message window - it will tell you what the currently highlighted reference is used for. For the inner cut, we want to do the following (observe the various prompts as we go through here):

1.   Prompt: "Select an alternate sketching plane." We want to keep the same sketching plane, so just select *Same Ref*.
2.   Prompt: "Select an alternate horizontal reference plane." This is the one (notice the green highlighted surface) we want to reroute to a different reference so select *Alternate*. A good one (that is, one that is not likely to change in the future) is the top surface of the block; an even better one is the horizontal datum plane (TOP). Click on either of these now.
3.   Prompt: "Select an alternate dimensioning reference." For all remaining references, we want to keep all the same alignment and dimensioning references (select *Same Ref* three more times).

When you have cycled through all the references, you should get the message

"Feature rerouted successfully"

If you have rolled back the part, any features suppressed during the roll back will now be resumed.

Go and check with *Info* > *Parent/Child* and click on the inside cut to confirm that the horizontal surface of the top cut is no longer referenced. There should still be a couple of references to the top cut, though. These are alignment constraints in the sketch of the inside cut. We'll still have to change these if we are going to modify the top cut as planned.

③ Changing the Sketcher Constraints (*Edit Definition*)

As we saw earlier, the ends of the straight part of the inner cut are aligned with the vertical faces of the top cut. These alignments are still at work in the sketch. See Figure 11. To change these alignments, we need to redefine the sketch. A quick way to get directly into Sketcher is to open the feature listing in the model tree, select the feature sketch **S2D0001**, and with the RMB pop-up select *Edit Definition*. This has the added advantage of bypassing the dashboard both on your way in to the sketch and on your way out, saving a few mouse clicks.

Turn off the datum plane display. We want to do something with the sketch references so in the pull-down menu select

> *Sketch > References*

Click on the left edge of the part. This should add an entry in the **References** window. Now, in the **References** window, select the other listed surface references (these will both be to feature #6, the top cut) and select the *Delete* button. The other two vertical references (shown in Figure 11) should disappear. Now select *Solve*. The sketch's **Reference Status** is still **Fully Placed**. Close the references window.

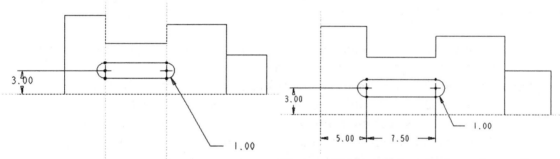

Figure 11 Old alignment references in the inside cut sketch

Figure 12 New dimensioning scheme for the inside cut sketch

Change the dimensioning scheme to the one shown in Figure 12. Make sure the arcs are tangent to the horizontal lines. Intent Manager will do some of this for you automatically. Close out Sketcher to accept the redefined feature.

To make sure that there is now no relation between the top cut and the inside cut, preselect the TOP_CUT and, using the right mouse pop-up, select

> *Info > Reference Viewer*

The inner cut should no longer be listed as a child!

④ **Changing a Feature Reference (*Edit References*)**

Recall that the rounded end is a parent of the top cut via supplying the horizontal sketching reference. We need to break this connection before we can delete the rounded end (which is on our "to do" list). This calls for another reroute operation. Pick on the top cut, use the right mouse pop-up, and select *Edit References*. Roll back the part. Notice that the inside cut disappears (temporarily). Keep the same sketching plane (*Same Ref*), but select a new horizontal reference (*Alternate*) like the top of the block or the horizontal datum. This is all we have to reroute, so select *Done* in the **Reroute** menu window (bypassing the remaining references). You should get the message

"Feature rerouted successfully"

Select the rounded end and with

Info > Reference Viewer

observe that it now has no children. Go ahead using the right mouse pop-up and select

Delete

to remove the feature from the model.

⑤ **Changing Feature Attributes (*Edit Definition*)**

We want to change the shape of the top cut to get rid of the step. We will also change its depth attribute. To see why this is necessary, select the BLOCK feature in the model tree, right click and select *Edit*. (Or just double click on the feature in the graphics window). Change the depth of the block from 10 to *15* and *Regenerate*. As you recall, the top cut had a blind depth of 10, so it doesn't go all the way through the new block as shown at the right.

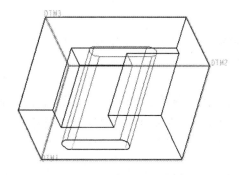

Figure 13 Block width increased to 15

Let's change both the shape and depth of the top cut at the same time. Select it in the model tree, use the right mouse pop-up and select

Edit Definition

In the dashboard, change the **Depth Spec** option (or in the **Options** slide-up panel) from *Blind* to *Through All*. This fixes one problem. Now, to change the shape of the feature, select

Placement > Edit (or use RMB menu command *Edit Internal Sketch*)

Using the Sketcher tools, change the shape of the cut to a simple L-shape as shown in Figure 15. With the Intent Manager, you should be able to do this very quickly. Here are a couple of Sketcher tools to make this easier.

Select the *Dynamic Trim* tool ⌇⌐. As the icon implies, hold down the left mouse button and drag the mouse cursor through the two lines you want to get rid of. See Figure 14. Middle click to get back to Select mode.

Now you can drag the right end of the horizontal line over to the right vertical reference of the sketch. To make sure the vertex sticks to this reference, open the Sketcher constraints fly-out menu and pick the *Coincident* constraint. Click on the vertex, then on the dashed reference line. You should now have the sketch shown in Figure 15. Make sure your dimensions match the figure.

When the sketch is complete, return to the feature dashboard.

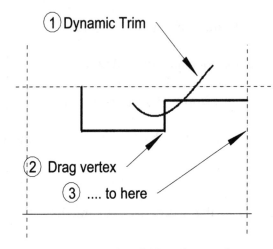

Figure 14 A couple of Sketcher tools

Verify the part, and if it looks all right, select *OK*. The modified part is shown in Figure 16.

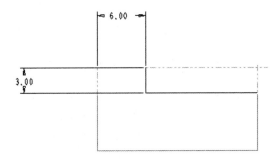

Figure 15 New sketch for the cut

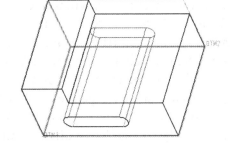

Figure 16 Part with redefined cut

⑥ Changing the Regeneration Sequence using *Reorder*

It is sometimes convenient or necessary to change the order of the features in the regeneration sequence. For example, an advanced technique involves grouping adjacent features in the regeneration sequence so that the group can be patterned or copied. The major restrictions on reordering features are:

♦   a child feature can never be placed before its parent(s)
♦   a parent feature can never be placed after any of its children

The reasons for these restrictions should be pretty self-evident. Fortunately, Pro/E is able to keep track of the parent/child relations and can tell you what the legal reordering positions are. To see how it works, in the pull-down menu select

Edit > Feature Operations > Reorder

and click on the inside cut, then *Done*. Observe the message area. This cut (feature #6) was originally a child of the top cut (#5), but that relation was modified above. Thus, we should be able to create the cuts in any order, after the block (#4). In this simple part, there is only one legal possibility, that is, reorder the selected cut (currently #6) before the top cut (currently #5). This is what Pro/E tells you in the message window. In a more complicated part, Pro/E would tell you where the legal positions in the regeneration sequence are, and you could specify a *Before* or *After* placement for the reordered feature. Go ahead and complete the reorder: select *Confirm* and then call up the model tree. Note that the feature numbers of the cut and slot have now changed, but the internal ID's are still the same. Close the **FEAT** menu with *Done*.

Pro/E has made the *Reorder* command quite a bit easier by allowing you to drag and drop features in the model tree. Try that now by reordering the top cut. Click on the feature in the model tree and slowly drag the cursor upwards. The mouse icon changes slightly as you move back up the list to show you where legal reordered positions are. In this part, of course, there is only one valid position. You might try out this mode of reordering sometime when you get a more complicated part. You can reorder features both upwards and downward in the model tree.

⑦ Changing the Insertion Point

New features are typically added at the end of the regeneration sequence (notice the "Insert Here" arrow in the model tree). Sometimes it is necessary to create a new feature whose order you want to be earlier in the sequence. You could do this by creating it and then using the reorder command, being careful that you don't set up parent references to features after the targeted reorder position. Also, you would have to be careful not to create any new features that could interfere with existing features (like cutting off a reference surface). There is an easier way!

In the pull-down menu, just select

Edit > Feature Operations > Insert Mode > Activate

You will be asked to select which feature to insert after. Pick on an original surface of the block (not one created by either of the cuts) or pick the block in the model tree. The part will automatically roll back by suppressing all features created after the block. Notice the new position of the "Insert Here" arrow in the model tree.

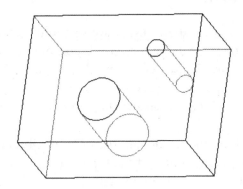

Create two *Through All* circular holes in the part as shown in the figure (the diameters are 2 and 5; placement is approximately as shown).

Figure 17 Two holes inserted after block feature

Insert mode will stay on until you turn it off by selecting

Edit > Feature Operations > Insert Mode > Cancel

You will be asked about resuming the features; accept the default [Y, or middle click]. Call up the **Feature List** or model tree to see that the two holes have been added to the model after the block and before the cuts.

You have probably guessed that you can also activate insert mode by dragging the ***Insert Here*** arrow back up in the model tree. Try it! You can move the insertion point around pretty much anywhere in the model tree. There is one place it won't go - can you find it? All the features after the insertion point are automatically suppressed. If you resume any of these features, the insertion point will advance to the last feature resumed in the model. This is a handy way to step through a model (much like using the model player) - just move the insertion point to where you want to start stepping through the model, then just ***Resume*** the feature below the insertion point.

Conclusion

The modeling utilities described in this lesson are indispensable when dealing with complex parts. You will invariably come across situations where you need to redefine, reroute, or reorder features. The information utilities are useful for digging out the existing parent/child relations, and discovering how features are referenced by other features. The more practice you get with these tools, the better you will be able to manage your models. As a side benefit, having a better understanding of how Pro/E organizes features will cause you to do more careful planning prior to creating the model, with fewer corrections to be made later. This will save you a lot of time!

In the next lesson, we will investigate the use of datum planes and axes, including creating temporary datums called "make datums". We'll also discover yet more tools and commands in Sketcher.

Questions for Review

1.   How can you find out the order in which features were created? What is this called?
2.   How can you find which are the parent features of a given feature?
3.   How can you find the references used to create a feature?
4.   How can you find any or all other features that use a given feature as a reference?
5.   What is the difference between the Feature # and the internal ID?
6.   What is the command to exclude a feature temporarily from the model?
7.   What happens to the parents of a suppressed feature? To the children?
8.   Is it possible, via a convoluted chain of parent/child relations, for a feature to reference itself?
9.   What happens to suppressed features when the model is saved and you leave Pro/E?
10.   If you are given a part file that you have never seen before, how can you determine if it contains any suppressed features? What about hidden features?
11.   In Sketcher, how many variations of the right mouse pop-up menu can you find? In what modes are these active?
12.   How can you restore previously suppressed features?
13.   How can you change the sketch references when you are in Sketcher?
14.   How many features can you suppress at once?
15.   Can you resume a parent without resuming its children?
16.   Is there any aspect of a feature that cannot be modified using *Edit Definition*?
17.   What is the difference between *Edit, Edit References, Edit Definition*? Which is the most general command?
18.   What is meant by "rolling back the part?"
19.   How can you remove unwanted alignments in a sketch?
20.   What symbol in the model tree indicates suppressed features?
21.   What are the two fundamental rules of reordering?
22.   Are there any restrictions on the insertion point in *Insert Mode*?
23.   What happens if Insert Mode is on when you save a part and then later retrieve it?
24.   How do you get out of insert mode?
25.   What are the following buttons used for in Sketcher?

a)   b)   c)   d)

Exercises

Here are some simple parts to model using the features we have covered up to here. Before you start creating these, think about where you will place them relative to the datum planes, what type and order you should select for the features, and how you should set up parent/child references and dimensioning schemes.

1.

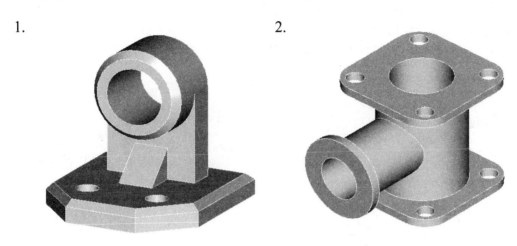

2.

3.

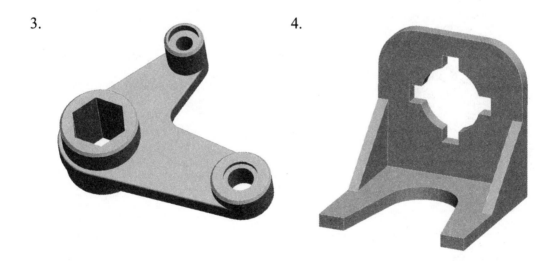

4.

Project

Here are three small parts for the project. All dimensions in millimeters. For the acorn nut, you might like to investigate alternate Sketcher environments (see **Sketch > Options | Parameters** when you are in Sketcher), including a polar grid, and the use of centerlines as construction aides (straight lines and/or circles). Note that the hexagon on the nut requires only one dimension to give its size.

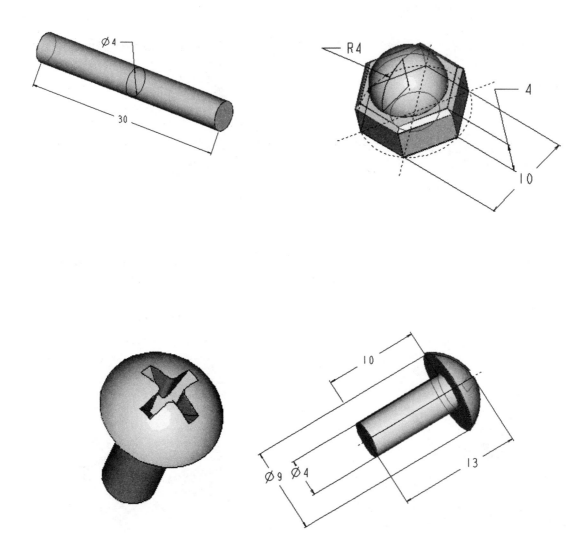

Lesson 6

Datum Planes and Sketcher Tools

Synopsis

The mysteries of datum planes and 'make datums' are revealed! What are they, how are they created? How are they used to implement design intent? More tools in Sketcher are introduced.

Overview of this Lesson

In this lesson we are going to look at some new commands in Sketcher for creating sections. We will also use relations within Sketcher to control the geometry. Our primary objective, though, is to look at the commands used to set up and use datum planes. Some of these datum planes, like the default ones (**RIGHT**, **TOP**, and **FRONT**), will become references for many features, or will appear similarly on the model tree. Others, called *make datums*, are typically used only for a single feature and are created "on-the-fly" when needed. These will appear on the model tree embedded in the feature for which they were created. Along the way, we will discuss some model design issues and explore some options in feature creation that we have not seen before.

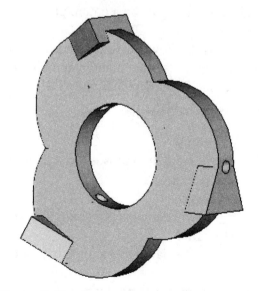

The part we are going to create is shown in the figure at the right. As you can see, the part consists of a three-lobed disk with a central hole. Three identically-shaped triangular teeth are spaced at 120 degrees around the circumference. Each tooth includes a central radial hole that aligns with the central axis of the disk. Although there is no indication of it in the figure, each of these tooth/hole shapes will be created differently using different datum plane setup

Figure 1 Final part - three tooth cutter

procedures. We will see what effect this has on the model at the end of the lesson[1].

Here is what is planned for this lesson:

1.   Overview of Datum Planes and Axes
2.   Creating a Datum Plane and Datum Axis
3.   Create the Disk with Hole
4.   First Tooth - using an Offset constraint
5.   Second Tooth - using Normal and Tangent constraints
6.   Third Tooth - using Make Datums
7.   Effects on the Model
8.   Things to Consider about Design Intent

As usual there are some Questions for Review, Exercises, and a Project part at the end of the lesson.

Overview of Datum Planes and Axes

Datum features (planes, axes, curves, points and coordinate systems) are used to provide references for other features, like sketching planes, dimensioning references, view references, assembly references, and so on. Datum features are not physical (solid) parts of the model, but are used to aid in model creation. Datum planes or axes extend off to infinity. By default, Pro/E will show visible edges of a datum plane or the datum axis line so that they encompass the part being displayed. It is possible to scale a datum plane differently so that, for example, it will extend only over a single feature of a complex part. This would be done to reduce screen clutter. When we use the word "datum" by itself, we usually mean a datum plane.

Let's consider how a datum plane can be constructed. In order to locate the position and orientation of a datum plane, you will choose from a number of constraint options. These work alone or in combination to fully constrain the plane in space. The major options for datum planes are:

Through
      the datum passes through an existing surface, axis, edge, vertex, or cylinder
      axis
Normal
      the datum is perpendicular to a surface, axis, or other datum
Parallel
      the datum is parallel to another surface or plane

---

[1]A better way to create this part would be to create a single lobe, tooth, and hole, then group these together. The group can be copied around the central axis, creating a "pattern." We will have a look at patterns in the next lesson.

Offset (linear)
> the datum is parallel to another surface or plane and a specified distance away

Offset (rotation)
> the datum is at a specified angle from another plane or surface

Tangent
> the datum is tangent to a curved surface or edge

Some of these constraints are sufficient by themselves to define a new datum plane (for example, the **Offset(linear)** option). Other constraints must be used in combinations in order to fully constrain the new datum. When you are constructing a new datum, Pro/E will automatically pick an appropriate option (based on the entity selected) and show you the results of the currently set constraints by using a preview.

Construction of a datum axis is similar, with the following constraint options:

Through
> the axis is through a selected vertex, edge, or plane. May require addition constraints.

Normal
> the axis is located using linear dimensions and is normal to a selected plane

Tangent
> the axis is tangent to the selected reference at a specified point

Center
> the axis is normal to and through the center of a selected planar circular edge or curve

We won't have time to explore all the variations of these options in this lesson. The general procedure is pretty similar for all options, however. With the preview capability in Wildfire it is quite easy to figure out what to do after you have seen the general procedure a few times.

Let's see how this all works. Start Pro/E in the usual way, and clear the session of any other parts. Start a new part called *cutter* using the default template. The default datum planes are created for you as the first features in the part. You can delete the datum coordinate system feature for this part since we won't need it and it just clutters up our view (or just turn off its display with *Hide*).

After the default datums are created, new datum planes and axes are created using either the toolbar buttons on the right of the graphics window (the ones without the eyeballs) or using the *Insert > Model Datum* pull-down menu at the top.

Creating a Datum Plane and Datum Axis

First, we will define a datum axis that will
be the central axis of the cutter. This will
be at the intersection of the existing datums
RIGHT and **TOP**. Using the CTRL key,
select both these datum planes. They
should both be highlighted in red. Now,
select the *Datum Axis* button in the right
toolbar. This creates the datum axis A_1, as
shown in Figure 2. This is the appropriate
axis for Pro/E to make if you pick two
intersecting plane surfaces, so it skips over
the **Datum Axis** dialog window. Let's have
a look at that window.

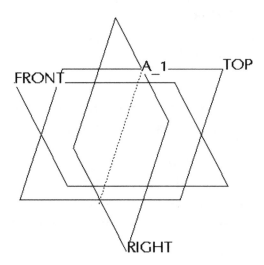

Figure 2 Datum axis A_1 created

With A_1 highlighted in red, use the RMB pop-up menu
and select *Edit Definition*. This opens the **Datum Axis**
dialog shown in Figure 3. We see the two datums,
RIGHT and TOP, each with the constraint *Through*.
This fully constrains the axis. Note that you can rename
the axis feature using the **Properties** tab. Also, the
Display tab lets you change the displayed axis length.
Come back later to investigate these options. For now,
close the window with *OK*.

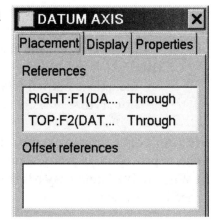

Figure 3 Datum Axis dialog
window

In the procedure we just did, we selected the new datum
references first, then launched the datum creation
command. This is an example of object/action
execution. Alternatively, we could have launched the
Datum Axis tool first to open the dialog window, then picked on each of the datums and
set the associated constraints shown in Figure 3 to *Through*. This would be an
action/object procedure. You can use whichever method you are most comfortable with -
they have the same final effect on the model. Once you get more experience with the
commands (that is, understand the defaults), you will probably find object/action to be
more efficient.

Our next task is to create a new datum plane that passes through the axis A_1 we just
made, and is at a specified angle to the RIGHT datum plane. We will use this as a
reference in a couple of features later on in the part.

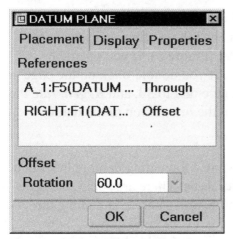

Figure 4 Datum Plane dialog window

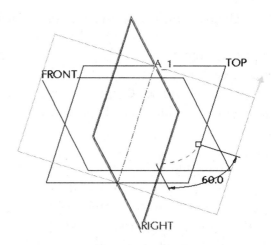

Figure 5 Datum plane with *Through* and *Offset(rotation)* constraints

We will use action/object for this. With nothing highlighted in the graphics window, select the *Datum Plane* tool in the right toolbar. The **Datum Plane** dialog window(see Figure 4) opens at the right. We need to specify the references for the new datum. If the axis was preselected it will already be listed. Otherwise, pick on the axis A_1. This is added to the reference collector in the dialog window with a *Through* constraint. Click on the listed constraint to see a hidden pull-down constraint list; the only alternative now is *Normal*. Leave it set to *Through*. Now, holding down the CTRL key, select the RIGHT datum. This is now listed as well, with an *Offset* constraint. The *Offset(rotation)* constraint is the only one that makes sense with the existing *Through* constraint. The datum is previewed on the graphics window (Figure 5), with a drag handle to control the value of the offset angle. This value is also shown in the dialog window. Set the value to *60*. A negative value would rotate the other way.

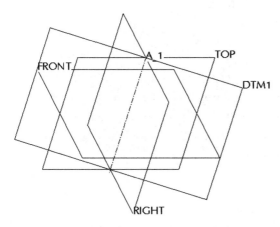

Figure 6 Datum plane DTM1 created at 60 degrees from RIGHT

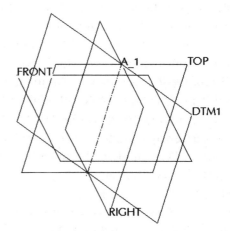

Figure 7 Datum plane DTM1 changed to 30 degrees from RIGHT

In the **Display** and **Properties** tabs of the dialog window you can change the normal direction (the yellow arrow) and name of the feature. Leave these alone and select **OK**. The new datum plane DTM1 will be added to the model (Figure 6). If you open the model tree, you will see features A_1 and DTM1 there. If you double-click on the edge of DTM1, you will see the offset angle dimension. Change that to **30**, and **Regenerate** the part (Figure 7). This angle dimension is how we control the orientation of the datum plane.

These two examples have illustrated the general procedure for creating datum planes and axes. You might like to come back and experiment with these. There are some short cuts available that can save you some time (like preselecting features before launching the **Datum** command). To use the shortcuts, you need to have a very good grasp of how Pro/E will utilize defaults and the references you give it. You should also spend some time exploring the various constraint options for each chosen feature - these are available in a pull-down list beside each feature in the dialog window. Possibly because datums do not result in solid geometry, new users tend to find them a little tricky to deal with and, as a result, often do not make very effective use of them. Remember that we are creating a model, not just a solid. Datums are often crucial elements of the model structure.

We will leave datums for a bit now, so that we can create the base feature of the cutter. We will be creating several more datums as we go through this lesson.

Creating the *Cutter* Base Feature

Our base feature is a solid protrusion that will look like the figure shown at the right. We are going to go through the sketching procedure slowly here to illustrate a few new tools and techniques.

Our plan of attack is to sketch this shape on the FRONT datum plane. Since the part is symmetric front to back, we will make this a **Symmetric, Blind** protrusion. It also makes sense to center the feature where the datums TOP and RIGHT meet. The reason for DTM1 will be clear when we get into the sketch - it provides a reference for locating the geometry.

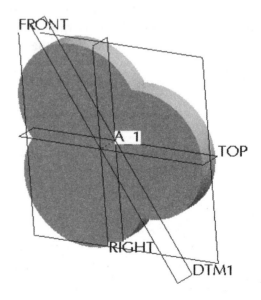

Figure 8 Base feature - a **Both Sides** protrusion

The sketch basically consists of three circular arcs. We'll call these the first, second, and third arcs, starting at the right and going counterclockwise.

Select the ***Extrude*** tool. Its dashboard opens up. Change the **Depth Spec** to ***Symmetric*** (also known as ***Both Sides***), and set its value to *2*. Note that we can do this even before we have created the sketch. Now launch Sketcher using ***Placement > Define***. Click on the FRONT datum as our sketching plane. The RIGHT datum becomes our orientation reference facing the right side of the screen. Middle click to enter Sketcher.

In Sketcher, two references have been chosen for us. We want to add DTM1 (which is visible on edge) as a reference. In the pull-down menu, select

> ***Sketch > References***

(or use the RMB pop-up and select ***References***) then pick DTM1 and then ***Close*** the **References** window.

The center of each of the three arcs is the same distance away from the axis A_1. We can implement this intent in Sketcher by creating a construction circle. Use the RMB pop-up menu to select ***Circle***, and draw the circle shown in Figure 9. Set the diameter to *8*. You may have to use the ***Refit*** command here. Click on the circle so that it highlights in red and open the RMB pop-up menu. Select the ***Construction*** command. This changes the line style to dashed. This curve can now be used as a sketching reference and will not contribute to solid geometry of the feature. You can toggle a construction line back to a physical edge using the RMB pop-up command ***Solid***.

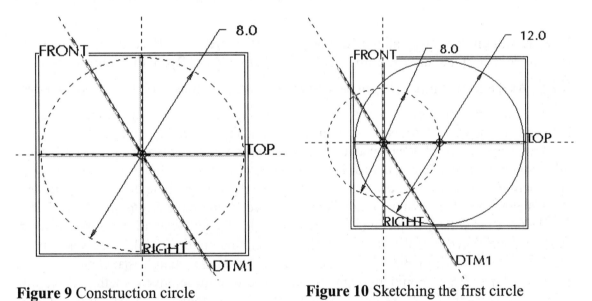

Figure 9 Construction circle   **Figure 10** Sketching the first circle

Now (use RMB pop-up) select the ***Circle*** command again and draw the first circle, shown in Figure 10. Its center can be snapped to the intersection of the construction circle and the reference on TOP. Set the new circle diameter to **12**.

Select the ***Circle*** command again to draw the second circle. Its center can be snapped to the intersection of the construction circle and the reference on DTM1. Drag out the circle until the "equal radius" (with the same radius as the larger circle) constraint snaps in. Look for a red R_1. Complete the circle - see Figure 11. You might turn the datum planes off now, since the screen is getting a bit cluttered.

Select the *Circle* command for a third time. The center we want is on the construction circle and directly below the center of the second circle. The cursor should snap to this position. Watch for the small red blips that indicate vertical alignment. Once again, drag out the circle until the R_1 constraint snaps. The sketch should look like Figure 12. Weak constraints are shown in gray, so may be hard to see.

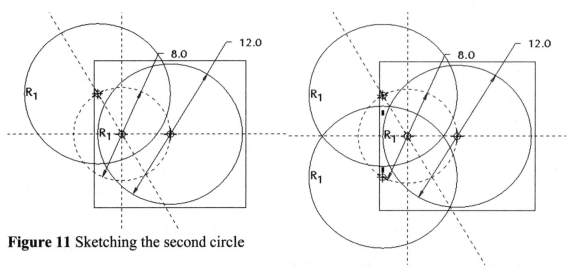

Figure 11 Sketching the second circle

Figure 12 Sketching the third circle

Now we want to trim away all the geometry inside the three arcs. Here are a couple of tools to do that. First, there is a nifty tool on the *Trim/Divide* flyout that looks like this

. As the icon implies, all you have to do is swipe the mouse pointer across the edge segments you want to remove - this is *Dynamic Trim*. The edge will be trimmed back at both ends to the nearest intersection point or vertex. Try it! See Figure 13. Note that the dynamic trim command does not affect the construction lines. When using this tool, one thing you will have to watch out for is the presence of very small line fragments left behind after trimming. You can usually spot these either by the blue dots on the vertices or by dimensions that seem to go nowhere. Better yet, turn on the *Highlight Open Ends* and *Shade Closed Loops* functions in the top toolbar. To get rid of all these fragments at once, you may have to resort to another trick for deleting entities. Make sure *Select* is picked in the Sketcher menu. Then left click and drag out a rectangle that encloses all the offending lines. They should highlight in red. If you want to remove something from this selection set, use the CTRL key when you pick the item to toggle its selection status. For example, in this sketch we do not want to delete the construction circle, so remove it from the selection set. Also, beware of deleting constraints that you want to keep - remove them from the selection set as well. Hold down the right mouse button and select *Delete*. The selected entities are all gone! You may have accidentally deleted some Sketcher constraints (like vertical alignment of the centers of the second and third circle). Intent Manager is able to generate other constraints to keep the sketch solved. If these are not the ones you want, use the Constraints tool to explicitly create the ones you do want. Note that with two sketched entities selected, the RMB pop-up menu contains the relevant constraints possible for those entities. This is another example of object/action, this time dealing with the setting up of sketch constraints. The completed sketch should look like Figure 14. It should only require two dimensions.

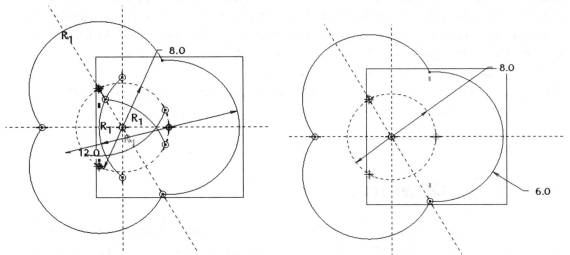

Figure 13 Some lines removed using *Dynamic Trim*

Figure 14 Completed sketch

To test the flexibility of this sketch (and if the constraints are doing what we want), try changing either of the dimensions. For example, change the diameter of the construction circle to 6 and/or the radius of the arc to 8. Try some other values. If the sketch is robust, it should be able to regenerate correctly for a wide range of dimensional values.

If you have accidentally deleted an alignment constraint, you will likely see one or more "0.0" dimensions on the sketch. To see what these refer to, change the dimension value to something small, like 1.0. This will modify or shift the sketch slightly to show where the desired alignment has been lost. Restore the desired constraint(s) using the *Coincident* constraint ⊙. Make sure you return the dimensions to the values shown in Figure 14.

Accept the sketch. If you missed it before, set the depth to **2**. In the extrude dashboard, *Verify* the feature. The solid should be symmetric about FRONT (check the right side view). If everything looks like Figure 8 above, *Accept* the feature.

Creating a Coaxial Hole

We'll create the large center hole using some new options in the hole dialog window. Preselect the axis A_1. If you have trouble picking this, try setting the **Filter** at the bottom right to *Datums* or select the axis in the model tree. Now, with A_1 highlighted, select the *Hole* command in the right toolbar. A one-sided blind hole is now previewed. Change the diameter to *8.0*. Open the **Placement** slide-up panel (Figure 15). Since we entered the command with A_1 preselected, Pro/E assumes that we want a *Coaxial* hole. It still needs

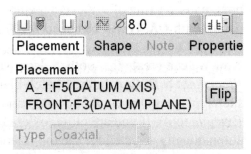

Figure 15 Creating a *Coaxial* hole

to know what surface the hole should be defined on. The **Placement** collector should be highlighted (yellow). With the CTRL key pressed, select the FRONT datum on the screen. The hole is still one-sided and blind. In the **Shape** slide-up panel, change the depth spec to *Through All* . In the same panel, change the Side 2 depth spec also to *Through All*. The preview now shows the hole coming in both directions off FRONT, with no depth dimension.

That completes the hole, so you can *Accept* the feature. Have you saved the part yet? Now is a good time.

First Tooth - Offset Datum

The first tooth will be the one at the right (3 o'clock position). The design intent for this tooth is that the inner side of the tooth will be a specified distance away from the disk axis. We will create a datum plane at the desired distance that we can use as a sketching plane. The tooth will be extruded outward (for a fixed distance) to the outer edge of the disk. Then we will place a hole, also on the new datum plane, using the both sides option to go radially inward and outward.

Start by selecting the *Datum Plane* button on the right toolbar. Then pick the RIGHT datum plane. This reference will be listed in the dialog window on the right, with the default constraint *Offset*. Note that this is a translation. On the yellow preview of the new datum, you will see a single drag handle. Drag this out to the right. The dimension shows the offset distance from the reference. The offset dimension is also given in the dialog window.

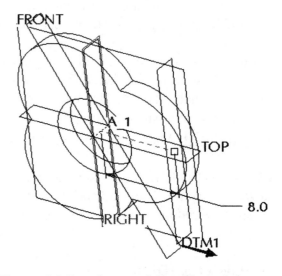

Figure 16 Creating an *Offset(linear)* datum

If you wanted to go to the other side of **RIGHT**, you could enter a negative offset or drag the handle to the opposite side. For now, enter a value of *8*. Accept the new datum with *OK*. It will be called **DTM2**.

Now we can create the tooth. Select the *Extrude* command. In the dashboard, select *Placement > Define*. In the **Sketch** dialog window, select the new datum DTM2 as our sketch plane. (This would be automatic if DTM2 was highlighted when you launched the *Extrude* tool). If you are close to default orientation, the TOP datum will likely be automatically selected for the top orientation reference; if not, set that up now.

In Sketcher, the two references TOP and FRONT have been chosen for us already. We want to add a couple more to this list. In the pull-down menu (or RMB pop-up), select

Sketch > References, then pick on the front, then the back, surfaces of the base feature. We prefer to use surfaces for references instead of edges. You can delete the reference FRONT.

Make the sketch shown in Figure 17. Notice that the top line in the sketch aligns with the horizontal reference and observe the dimensioning scheme. This sketch implements a design intent where the width of the tooth is determined by the overhang beyond the side of the disk. Can you think of different ways of using references and dimensions to create different design intents for this sketch?

Let's add a relation to make sure the two overhangs are the same. We'll do this the fast way presented in a previous lesson. Put the mouse cursor over the horizontal dimension on the right and note the dimension symbol label, *sdx*. Now double-click on the overhang dimension on the left. Enter the dimension symbol for the right overhang distance. You will be asked to confirm adding this relation to the sketch. As usual, when you have created relations you should test them to make sure they are working properly. Try to change the value on the left - you can't. Try changing the one on the right - they should both change. Return the value to the one shown in Figure 17.

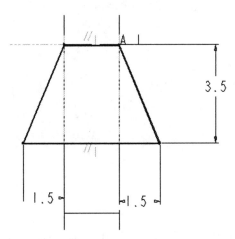

Figure 17 Sketch of first tooth

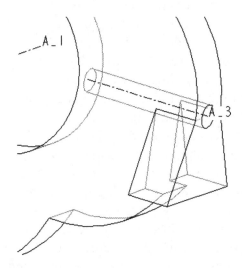

Figure 18 First tooth and hole complete

When you have a completed sketch, leave Sketcher, select a *Blind* depth of *2*, and accept the feature. Turn the display of the datums back on.

Create the small hole using the new datum plane DTM2 as a placement surface. This is a straight, linear hole. Once you have selected DTM2 as the placement plane, drag the two green linear placement handles to the FRONT and TOP datums (anywhere on the displayed edges of these datums will do for an attachment point). Rather than setting the placement dimensions to zero, open the **Placement** panel in the hole dashboard and for the offset references change *Offset* to *Align*. The hole diameter is *1.0*. In the **Shape** slide-up panel, set both the Side 1 and Side 2 depths to *To Next*.

Note that in one direction, a *Through All* depth would have gone completely through the other side of the disk, which we don't want. *To Next* extends the hole until it passes through the next part surface. The yellow hole preview may not show the hole depth correctly, so use the *Verify* button on the right of the dashboard. *Accept* the hole.

The tooth/hole combination should now be complete and look like Figure 18.

Second Tooth - Normal and Tangent Datum

The second tooth is the one at the top left of the part (on arc #2). The intent demonstrated here is to have the planar outer surface of the tooth tangent to the arc of the disk and to extrude the tooth inwards towards the center of the disk. So, we will create a datum to give us a flat sketching surface at the outer edge and tangent to the disk. We can make use of our existing datum **DTM1** which passes through the center of the disk and the second arc.

With nothing highlighted, select the *Datum Plane* button in the right toolbar. Select the curved surface of the cutter on the side of the second arc (you may have to set the selection filter to Surface). It highlights in red. A preview datum will show up in yellow. The default is a **Through** constraint, going through the central axis of this surface. Hold down the CTRL key and click on **DTM1**. The preview datum is now normal to DTM1 and still through the center of the surface. In the **Datum Plane** dialog window, go to the curved surface reference and click on the *Through* constraint. In the pull-down list, select *Tangent*. The previewed datum now moves to be tangent to the cutter and normal to DTM1 - exactly what we want.

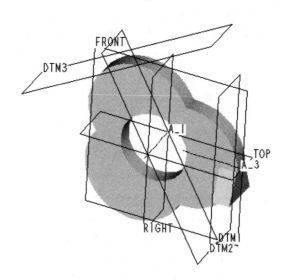

Figure 19 Tangent datum plane for second tooth

See Figure 19. Accept the new datum by selecting *OK*. The new datum is called DTM3.

Next we'll create a one-sided solid protrusion on the new datum plane. Select the *Extrude* tool and launch Sketcher from the dashboard. Pick DTM3 as our sketching plane. The yellow arrow shows the direction of view onto the sketch plane. Flip this so that it points away from the center of the cutter[2]. The sketch orientation reference is DTM1 and it should face the Top of the sketch. Now select the *Sketch* button.

The cutter will re-orient. You might like to give the part a small spin to make sure you

---

[2] The default solid protrusion is created towards you off the sketch (coming out of the screen). The default solid cut is created away from you (into the screen).

understand its orientation. You may also find it easier to sketch when the display is set to wire-frame or hidden line. We're going to create the sketch shown in Figure 20.

Pick the following five sketching references: DTM1, both sides of the disk, and the two outer edges of the first tooth. Now create the sketch shown in Figure 20. This sketch only needs one new dimension because the lines and vertices snap and/or align to the various references. When the sketch is complete, leave Sketcher and choose a **Blind** depth specification and enter the value **2**.
Verify that the tooth is the correct geometry and **Accept** the feature.

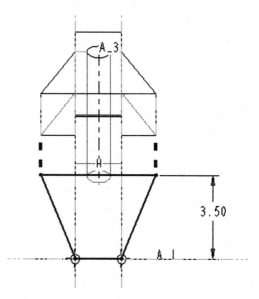

Create another **Straight Linear** hole using the outer planar surface of the tooth as the primary reference (placement plane). Use the datums **FRONT** and **DTM1** for the linear placement references and **Align** to each. The hole has a diameter of **1**. Specify a **Blind** depth and enter a value of **8.0**. Once again, if any of the dimensions are hard to pick on the screen, you can set these in the dashboard or the slide-up panels. The completed tooth looks like Figure 21.

Figure 20 Sketch for second tooth

IMPORTANT NOTE:
Although this results in exactly the same solid geometry as the first tooth, notice our change in design intent. This tooth is to go a specific depth into the disk measured inwards from the circumference rather than outwards from the center. In this way, the tooth will be tangential to the disk regardless of the disk's size. Similarly, the hole's depth is a fixed value into the disk. At the present time, the hole goes through the surface of the inner hole. We will examine the effects of this later.

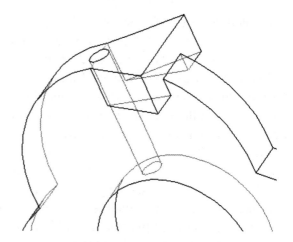

Figure 21 Second tooth completed

Third Tooth - Using Make Datums

The model is getting pretty cluttered up with datum planes which is making it more difficult to pick things out on the screen. One way to deal with this, of course, is to just turn off their display. This gets rid of them all, which cleans up the display but may make selecting them more difficult (you could always use **Search** to find them or use the model tree). A more selective way of controlling their display is to **Hide** them. Do that now with datum DTM1 - select the datum and then at the bottom of the RMB pop-up menu select **Hide**. The datum disappears (but not its children!). Do the same with DTM2 and DTM3 (use CTRL-click to select them both at the same time). The default datums should still be visible. Open the model tree and observe the gray box on the icons for these datums that indicates they are hidden.

All the datums we have created up to now have taken their expected place on the model tree, and could be used as parents for many other features. If a datum is only going to be used once to create another feature, it seems wasteful to create one that will be a stand-alone permanent feature on the model tree. Furthermore, we would likely want to Hide it to get it out of our way just as we did with the previous three datums. The solution used by Pro/E for both these problems is a *make datum*. This is a datum that is created just when needed ("on-the-fly"), and then is automatically hidden when the feature using it is accepted. Make datums are sometimes called "datums-on-the-fly" for precisely this reason. The official terminology for make datums in Wildfire is "asynchronous datums" which is a bit of a mouthful. We will continue to use the old terminology. One other new facet of make datums is that they are listed on the model tree, but in a special way which we will soon discover.

The rules and methods for constraining a make datum are the same as if it was a regular one. What determines whether a plane is considered a make datum is *when* it is made. All our previous datums were created *before* we launched the commands that used them as references. For example, for the first tooth we created DTM2 first, then picked Extrude, then identified DTM2 as the sketching plane. For a make datum, this sequence would be changed: pick the extrude command first, then when we are asked to identify a sketching or reference plane, make the datum "on-the-fly". This is sort of a "just-in-time" delivery notion.

We are going to do other things in a slightly different order for the third tooth, by creating the hole first. However, a hole requires a planar surface for its placement plane. We don't have such a plane at the desired angle. So, we will create the hole using a make datum to act as the placement plane.

Proceed normally to start the hole creation - that is, select the **Hole** toolbar button. You are asked (see the message area) to select a placement plane - but there isn't one in a suitable orientation. Here is where we will make the datum on-the-fly. Select the **Datum Plane** toolbar button. The Hole dashboard is grayed out (technically speaking, it has been *paused*), and the **Datum Plane** dialog window appears. We need to specify the constraint references for the new datum. Select the reference A_1 of the cutter. This is entered in the **Datum Plane** window with the default constraint *Through* (just what we want). Now

CTRL-click on the TOP datum. It is added to the collector in the **Datum Plane** window with the *Offset* constraint with some rotation angle assumed. Change this angle to 30 degrees below the TOP datum, as shown in Figure 22 (you may have to use a negative angle). When this feature is finished, select *OK*.

We can continue on with our hole creation. Select the *Resume* button ▶ at the right end of the dashboard (the only button active) to return to the hole creation. A previewed hole will appear on the new datum plane (which is called DTM4). Set the diameter to *1.0* and the **Depth Spec** to *Through All*. Now drag the green linear reference drag handles to FRONT (you can drag to anywhere along the displayed edge) and A_1. In the **Placement** slide-up panel, change *Offset* to *Align* for both references. The hole preview is shown in Figure 23.

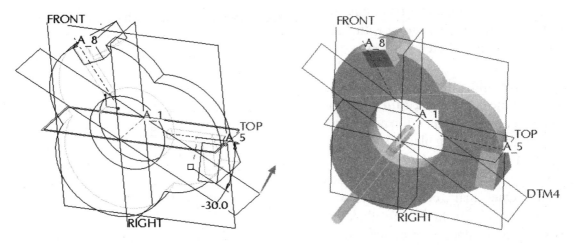

Figure 22 Creating the Make Datum   **Figure 23** Creating the hole on DTM4

When the hole is accepted, there is no sign of the make datum we just created, although the hole does have an axis. Open the model tree. The other datums are all there (some are hidden), but the make datum DTM4 is not. However, the last feature on the model tree must be the hole we just created. Open the hole feature by clicking on the "+" sign, and there is our hidden DTM4 along with the hole that used it. If you select it in the model tree, it highlights on the model. Right click on DTM4 in the model tree and select *Edit*. You will see the angle dimension associated with this make datum. You will also see this if you edit the hole itself.

Now create the last tooth. This will also be a sketched protrusion on a make datum that is perpendicular to the axis of the hole (that's why we made it first) and tangent to the cutter surface. Select *Extrude > Placement > Define*.

The **Sketch** window is waiting for us to specify the sketching plane. Move it (the Sketch window) out of the way and select the *Datum Plane* button, or pick *Insert > Model Datum > Plane*. Select the axis of the hole we just made, and (using CTRL-click) the surface of the cutter where the hole comes out. In the **Datum Plane** dialog window, set the constraints for these references in the pull-down lists to *Normal* (for the axis) and *Tangent* (for the surface). The preview should show a datum plane at the correct location and orientation. See Figure 24. Accept this datum with *OK* and return to the **Sketch** window.

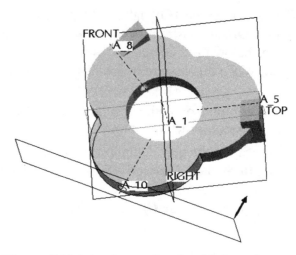

Figure 24 Make datum for the third tooth

Set the view direction away from the center of the cutter using *Flip* or clicking on the yellow view direction arrow on the edge of the sketching plane. Use the **FRONT** datum as the *Left* orientation reference plane for the sketch. Now select *Sketch*. Once again, check your view orientation relative to the part. Pick the existing tooth edges as references, plus the front and back of the cutter body. Since these are all parallel, you are still only **Partially Placed**. For the final sketch reference, pick axis A_1. Sketch the tooth as shown in Figure 25. Note that, in order not to fill in half the hole through the tooth, we must sketch around the

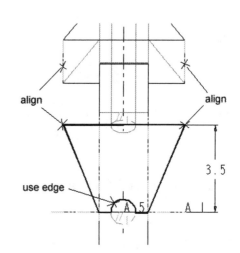

Figure 25 Sketch of third tooth

circumference of the hole. The *Use Edge* button ▢ is handy for this. Select this command and pick on the curved edge of the hole. You may have to pick edges on each side of the circle. Use *Dynamic Trim* to get rid of unwanted edges. Make sure you have a closed sketch with no open ends.

When you are finished with the sketch, select a *Blind* depth of *2*. We have now finished constructing the part, which should look like Figures 26 and 27.

Open the model tree and check how the last tooth is represented. In particular, where is the datum we used for the sketching plane and how is it shown? Save the part!

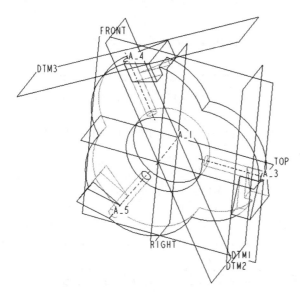

Figure 26 Finished part - wireframe showing datums

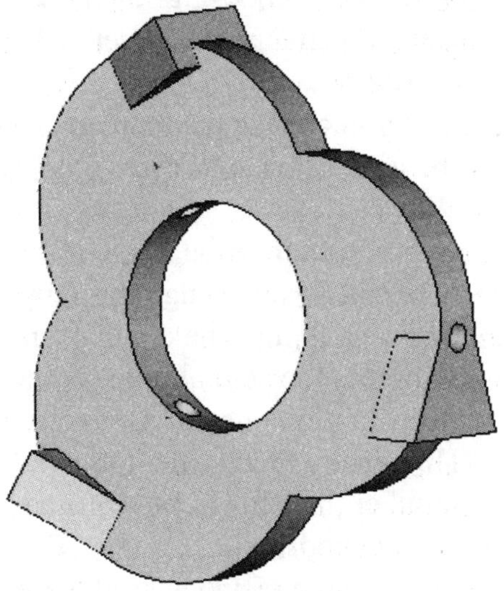

Figure 27 Completed part

Exploring the Model

We have created three geometrically identical teeth using three different modeling strategies. Let's see what happens when we start to play with the dimensions of the features. Try the following and see if you can explain what is going on. Before you try any of this, save the part so that you can recover from any future disasters! In each case, change the geometry back to the original before making a new modification.

1. Change the radius dimension of the first circle of the disk (currently 6.0) to values of **5.0** and **8.0**. What happens to each of the tooth/hole features? Why?
2. Change the diameter dimension of the construction circle (currently 8.0) to values of **4.0** and **12.0**. What happens? Why?
3. Change the diameter of the large coaxial hole to 0.5. What happens? (This is easier to see in hidden line.) Why?
4. What happens if you try to *delete* the datum **DTM1**? What about **DTM2**? Don't actually delete the datums.
5. Turn all the datums off. Use the *Search* command to find **DTM1**. What happens if you try to change the angle of the datum **DTM1** to 45°?
6. Check the parent/child information window (the *Reference Viewer*) for the first cutter tooth and explain what you see there. In particular, how can this feature appear as current object, as well as in the parents and children columns? What references are causing this relation?
7. Examine the other parent/child relationships in the model. It is possible that, rather than being related only through the width alignment, some of the tooth/holes refer to other features in ways that were not intended. A possible reason for this is when you were selecting references, the picks were made to axes or edges of previously created features rather than the datum planes or surfaces. How you can be more

selective in choosing references?

8. Can you change the offset of **DTM2**? What happens if you specify an offset of *6.0* or *12.0*?

9. Can you change the diameter of the hole going through the third tooth? Where does the dimension appear for this? What happens if you set this diameter to *1.5* and *2.0*? Why?

10. Can you change the angle of the Make Datum used to create the third hole? What happens if you change this angle to 60°?

11. Can you change the depth of the second and third teeth easily?

12. Suppress the central hole. What happens to the small radial holes? How far through does the first one go? Does anything happen to the third tooth? Why?

13. How many independent dimensions are there in this model? What is the minimum number that should be required? Set up the model so that only these dimensions can be modified.

14. Of the three methods used to create the teeth, which one would you say is the "best"? Keep in mind our three modeling objectives (simple, robust, flexible).

Considering *Design Intent*

You should be able to see once again that capturing the design intent is an important part of feature-based modeling and the model creation strategy. In this lesson we have added an important new consideration to this strategy - datum planes. Design intent involves consideration of the following:

  ▸   What is the design function of the feature?
  ▸   How does this influence the modeling strategy?
  ▸   How does the design function of a feature relate to other features?
  ▸   Which features should be unrelated in the part?
  ▸   How can you set up references and dimensioning schemes so that the parent/child relations reflect the above?
  ▸   How can you create the model so that it is driven by as few dimensions as possible? Will this necessarily always be desirable?
  ▸   When should you use relations internally in the part to drive the geometry automatically, depending on the critical design dimensions?

Design changes are inevitable. Therefore, you should try to design the model so that it will be easy to make the kinds of changes you expect in as direct a manner as possible. This is hard to do if you know only a few methods to create new features since your choices will be limited. You can often create the correct geometry, but it may be very difficult to modify or change later. Furthermore, it is often difficult to foresee exactly how you might want the model to change later. One thing is for sure, if you just slap-dash your features together, sooner or later you will run into a serious modeling problem that can become a nightmare for making design changes.

In the next lesson we will look at commands for creating patterned features (linear and radial patterns) and several ways of making feature copies. There will be more discussion of feature groups. We'll also see some new Sketcher tricks and a new type of protrusion (*Thin*).

Questions for Review

Several of these questions will require you to do some exploring of the program on your own.

1. What are the constraint types for creating datum planes? How are these different for make datums?
2. What are the constraint types for creating datum axes?
3. What combinations of constraints will lead to a completely constrained datum plane? Draw some freehand sketches to illustrate these.
4. What references are required to create a coaxial hole?
5. For a **Symmetric** solid protrusion, do you specify the depth in each direction, or the total depth? What about for a **Symmetric** cut?
6. What is the easiest way to create a datum plane parallel to a previous one at a specified distance away? What is this called?
7. Suppose you want to create a datum plane at an angle to another datum. You want to use the **Through** placement option, but there is currently no part edge or axis to use as a reference. How can you create the desired datum?
8. Does the order of selection of **Through** and **Offset(Rotation)** matter?
9. What is the difference between **Through All**, **To Next**, and **Up to Surf** when specifying an extruded feature's depth? For the last two, what happens if the extruded sketch does not completely intersect the specified surface?
10. Compare the advantages and disadvantages of using permanent datums and make datums.
11. If you want to *Edit* a feature created using a make datum as a sketching plane, where does the sketch show up?
12. Can you use the *Edit Definition* function on a hidden feature (like a make datum)?
13. When the model starts to get cluttered up with surfaces, edges, datums, and axes, how can you make sure that you are making an alignment to the desired entity?
14. Can the dimensions of a make datum (offset distances or angles) be controlled using relations?
15. What is the difference between the symbols "**dx**" and "**sdx**"?
16. Are other feature dimensions available for use in Sketcher relations?
17. Find a simple mechanical part and try to "reverse engineer" the design intent. How would you implement this in Pro/E?
18. Where and how do make datums show up in the model tree?
19. Can you use a make datum as a reference for another make datum? That is, can make datums be *nested*?
20. Is there an axis equivalent to a make datum (sort of a "make axis") that behaves in the same way as a make datum? That is: you make it on-the-fly, it is automatically included in the feature group, and its display is automatically hidden.
21. Does the *Dynamic Trim* tool affect construction lines?
22. How can you change the display extent of a datum plane or axis?
23. Can the *Search* command be used to locate Make Datums?

Exercises

Here are some objects for you to make. Don't worry about exact dimensions, but datums and make datums will come in handy for these!

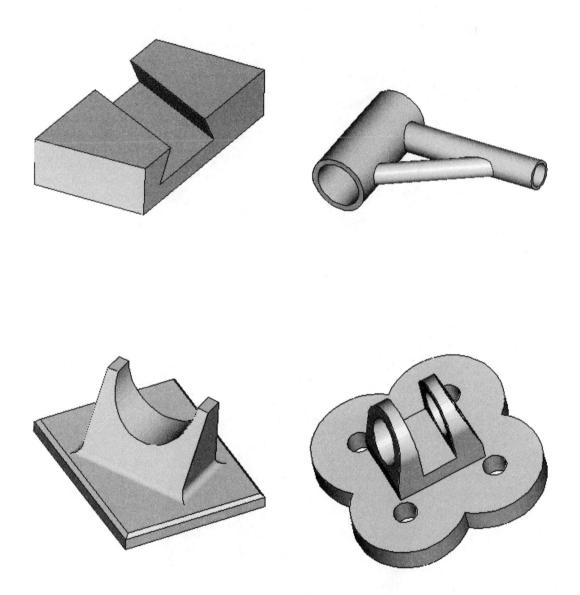

Project

Here is another part for the project. More pictures with dimensions are shown on the next page (all dimensions in millimeters). As usual, study the geometry carefully, and plan your modeling strategy before starting to create anything! Feature creation order is important to make this part as simple as possible.

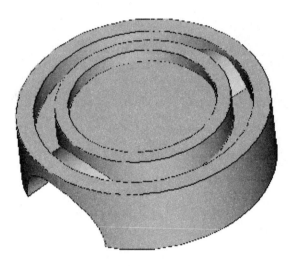

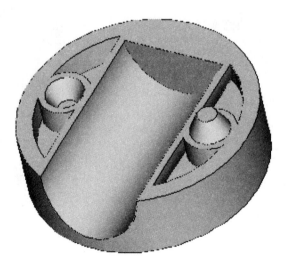

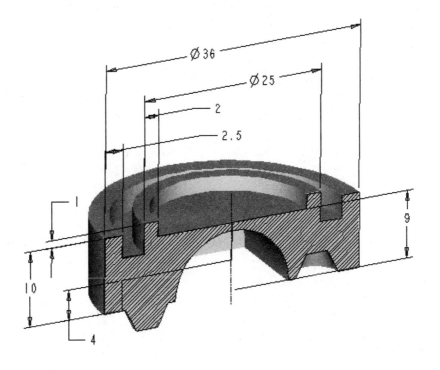

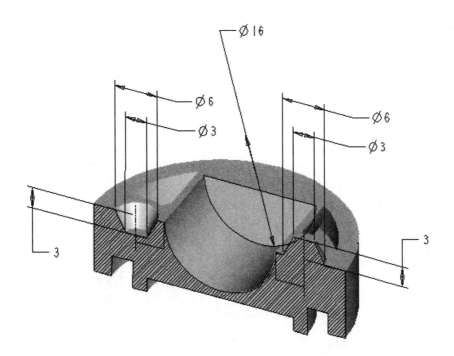

This page left blank.

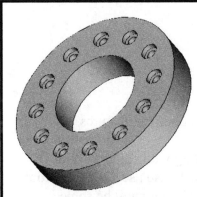

Lesson 7

Patterns and Copies

Synopsis

Naming dimension symbols. Dimension patterns in one and two directions. Creating a standard counterbored hole; hole notes. Radial patterns of placed and sketched features. Group patterns. Using the Copy command with Paste and Paste Special. Creating dependent and independent copies. Copies using translation, rotation. The Sketcher palette of defined shapes.

Overview of this Lesson

Models often contain repetitive instances or copies of the same geometric form. In Pro/E terms, these are called *patterns*. The name suggests a regular, geometrically repeated placement of features. We will find that patterns can do a lot more than this, including changing the shape of a feature as it is patterned. There are numerous options available when creating patterns. In this lesson we will look at the simpler and more commonly used pattern types.

When only a single duplicated feature is desired, it may make more sense to copy it rather than create a pattern. The copy command also allows more freedom in selecting references for the duplicated feature, including making it partly or completely independent of the original. Copies can also be made by translation or rotation (or a combination of these).

Patterns and copies work on individual features and on features arranged in groups. We'll look into the formation of groups a bit later in the lesson. To demonstrate the use of patterns and copies, we will be creating several different parts. The parts are totally independent of each other, so you can jump ahead to any one of these:

1.　Patterned Features
   ▸　simple uni-directional patterns
   ▸　bi-directional patterns
   ▸　radial pattern of holes with relations
   ▸　patterns of grouped features

> ▸ radial patterns of sketched features
2. Copied Features
>   ▸ using the *Paste* command
>   ▸ using the *Paste Special* command
>   ▸ creating translated and rotated copies
3. Design Considerations
>   ▸ some things to think about when designing with complex features

The use of named dimension symbols is helpful when dealing with patterns (and elsewhere in Pro/E). We will see how to do that first. We will also use a Sketcher tool called the **Palette** that provides pre-defined shapes. As usual, there will be some Questions for Review, Exercises, and a Project part at the end.

Patterned Features

Patterns are created by making duplicates of an existing feature - called the *pattern leader*. There are eight kinds of patterns in Pro/E:

> ▸ dimension
> ▸ direction
> ▸ axis
> ▸ fill
> ▸ table
> ▸ reference
> ▸ curve
> ▸ point

In this lesson we will look at dimension patterns only[1] - there are enough variations of these to keep us busy for a while. The simplest dimension pattern is created by incrementing a single dimension that locates the pattern leader on the part. Each increment of the pattern dimension produces a new *instance* of the feature at the incremented location. Patterns are even more powerful than just creating multiple instances: it is possible to form the pattern in two directions simultaneously and to change the geometry parametrically of each instance in the pattern. While the dimension that locates the feature is incremented, other dimensions of the pattern leader can be incremented so that the instances change size and/or shape. It is even possible to change size and shape of an instance without changing its location (see the exercises!). All instances in the pattern can be modified simultaneously, if set up to do so.

---

[1] See the on-line help for pattern tables, direction, axis, and fill patterns, reference patterns, pattern relations, *Identical*, *Varying*, and *General* patterns. These are also discussed in the *Pro/E Advanced Tutorial* from SDC.

Naming Dimension Symbols

Create a new solid part called ***pattern1*** using the default template. ***Delete*** (or ***Hide***) the default coordinate system. Create a base feature using an extruded protrusion. The Sketch plane is the TOP datum. As shown in Figure 1, the part is a 12 X 20 X 2 rectangular solid.

Now create an extruded protrusion near the front left corner of the base feature. This is a cylindrical protrusion of diameter 2 and height 1. See Figure 2 for the dimensions and be sure to use the identical dimensioning scheme. This protrusion will be our pattern leader for the next several exercises.

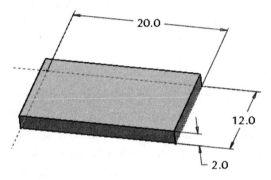

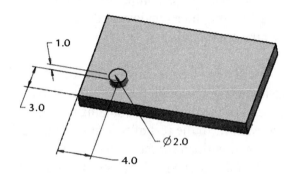

Figure 1 Base feature for part *pattern1*

Figure 2 Dimensions of the pattern leader

In preparation for the pattern exercises, it will be helpful (though not necessary) to change the symbolic names for the dimensions shown in Figure 2. To see the current names, double click on the protrusion and select

Info > Switch Dimensions

The symbolic names "***dxx***" will be displayed. Let's make those symbols a bit more meaningful. Preselect the horizontal dimension (4.0 in Figure 2). When it highlights in red, use the RMB pop-up and select ***Properties***. Scan over the contents of the **Dimension Properties** dialog window that opens. At the top of this window, the name of the dimension symbol is shown. Enter a new name here - "***L_X***". Select ***OK***. Notice on the part that the "***dxx***" symbol has changed to "***L_X***".

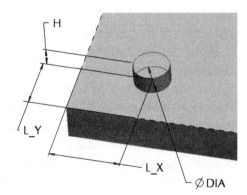

Figure 3 Renamed dimension symbols

Change the depth dimension (3.0 in Figure 2) text to "***L_Y***".

Change the protrusion diameter (2.0 in Figure 2) text to "***DIA***".

Finally, change the protrusion height dimension (1.0 in Figure 2) to "*H*". The protrusion dimensions should now look like Figure 3.

You can use almost any alphanumeric symbol for a dimension (note that upper case "X" and "Y", for example, are reserved symbols). Keep the name short and don't use spaces or punctuation. If a renamed symbol is used in a relation, Pro/E will automatically update the relation to use the new symbol.

Creating a Uni-directional Pattern

Turn off the datum planes and preselect the cylindrical protrusion. With this feature selected, one of the right toolbar buttons has become live. This is the *Pattern* tool ▦. You can launch the command with this button, or by using the RMB pop-up command in either the graphics window or the model tree. Choose one of these options to launch the *Pattern* command.

You will now see the dimensions associated with the protrusion[2] and the **Pattern** dashboard opens, with the Pattern tool symbol in the top row. The pull-down list at the left end of the dashboard contains the eight types of patterns. Leave this set to the default *Dimension*. In the rest of this row of the dashboard, the "1" and "2" refer to the first and second directions for the pattern. In the dashboard, move your cursor slowly across the four text areas and read the pop-up messages. Two of these text areas are for entering the number of instances in each pattern direction. The other text areas tell you which dimensions are being incremented in each direction. The default contents are: Direction 1 (2 instances, No Items), Direction 2 (2 instances, No Items). The item collector for Direction 1 is selected (yellow box).

Pattern #1 - Click on the horizontal dimension (4.0) for the protrusion. A text box appears which allows you to enter the increment to be used with this dimension. Enter a value of *6.0*. This means the next instance will be 6.0 units over to the right from the pattern leader (that is, the 4.0 dimension is incremented by 6.0). The position is indicated by a small black circle. The one after that will be another 6.0 units over, and so on. In the dashboard, find the box for the number of instances to be created in the first pattern direction. Enter *3* in this box. We have now provided enough information (dimension to be incremented, increment size, number of instances) to create our first simple pattern. The location of the three instances are indicated by the small black dots. *Accept* the pattern definition (shortcut: middle click). The part should look like Figure 4. All three protrusions are highlighted in red as the last feature(s) created.

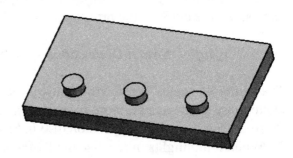

Figure 4 Simple pattern #1

---

[2] If the dimensions are still in symbolic form, select *Info > Switch Dimensions*.

If you double-click on the second or third protrusion in this pattern, you will see all the dimensions associated with that instance. In particular, you can see the increment 6.0, and the number of instances. Change the increment from 6.0 to *4.0*, and the number of extrudes from 3 to *4*. Now *Regenerate*. Change the increment back to *6.0* and *Regenerate*. For this feature, you can even run the pattern off the right end of the part (in which case, observe the warning in the message window). This may

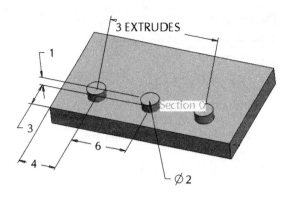

Figure 5 Pattern #1 dimensions

not always be possible, especially if the feature being patterned was created with an open sketch. Running the pattern off the part can be a subtle error to catch if you are creating a pattern of cuts or holes (so pay attention to the message window).

Open the model tree and expand the pattern. You will see each feature instance listed.

Pattern #2 - Let's play with this simple pattern some more. In the model tree, select the pattern and in the RMB pop-up select *Edit Definition*. This re-opens the pattern dashboard and shows all the dimensions for the pattern leader.

Open the **Dimensions** panel. Our dimension "*L_X*" is indicated in direction 1. Select this and use the RMB pop-up, select *Remove*. In its place, click on the dimension 3.0 for the protrusion - this is the dimension "*L_Y*". Enter an increment of *6.0*. In the dashboard, specify *2* instances. *Accept* the pattern. See Figure 6.

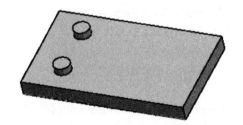

Figure 6 Simple pattern #2

So, the Direction 1 does not always have to be in the same direction on the part. In fact, the 1st and 2nd pattern directions are not physical directions at all, but more logical ones. The 'directions' are a way of organizing which dimensions will be incremented together. It may even be that the feature being patterned does not move at all, but just changes shape and size (see the pyramid exercise at the end of the lesson).

Can a pattern go only in the "*X*" and "*Y*" directions? Let's find out.

Pattern #3 - Highlight the pattern in the model tree and using the RMB pop-up, select *Edit Definition*. Open the **Dimensions** panel. The "*L_Y*" dimension is listed in Direction 1. Click in the panel for Direction 1 and then CTRL-click on the horizontal dimension to add it. Set the increment to *6.0*. The panel should look like Figure 7. *Accept* the pattern (Figure 8). So, we are not restricted to incrementing a single dimension in pattern "direction". For that matter, we can increment in more than one physical direction at once. Let's explore this a bit more.

Direction 1

Dimension	Increment
L_Y:F7(EXT...	6.0
L_X:F7(EXT...	6.0

Figure 7 Pattern dimensions for pattern #3

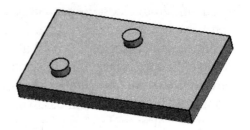

Figure 8 Simple pattern #3

Pattern #4 - Once again, select the pattern in the model tree and *Edit Definition*. Open the **Dimensions** panel. *Remove* the "*L_Y*" dimension using RMB. Holding down the CTRL key, click on the protrusion diameter dimension in the graphics window. Set an increment of *1.0*. Hold down the CTRL key and click on the height dimension. Set the height increment to *3.0*. Change the number of instances to *3*. The panel should now look like Figure 9. Accept the pattern and the model should look like Figure 10. The instances are created as before, but this time their diameter and height also change. Furthermore, it doesn't matter what order you specify the pattern dimensions shown in Figure 9. We could have picked the diameter dimension first, for example. Clearly, you can do more with patterns than just make duplicates!

Direction 1

Dimension	Increment	
L_X:F7(EXT...	6.0	
DIA:F7(EXT...	1.0	
H:F7(EXTR...	3.0	

Figure 9 Pattern dimensions for pattern #4

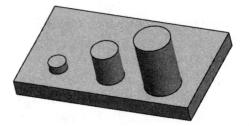

Figure 10 Simple pattern #4

Creating a Bi-directional Pattern

So far, we have not done anything with the second pattern direction. Select the pattern in the model tree and in the RMB pop-up select *Delete Pattern*. This removes the pattern instances but leaves the leader. (Be careful not to pick *Delete*, which gets rid of everything but asks for confirmation first).

Pattern #5 - Highlight the cylindrical protrusion. In the RMB menu, select *Pattern*. Click on the horizontal dimension (4.0) and enter an increment of *6.0*. In the dashboard enter the number of instances as *3*. Now, still in the dashboard, click in the item collector for the second direction (farthest right box) that currently says "Click

Direction 1

Dimension	Increment
L_X:F7(EXT...	6.0

☐ **Define increment by relation**

Edit

Direction 2

Dimension	Increment
L_Y:F7(EXT...	6.0

Figure 11 Pattern dimensions for pattern #5

here to add items." When you click on the area, it turns yellow which means it is active. Now select the "**L_Y**" dimension (3.0) for the protrusion. Enter an increment of **6.0** and specify **2** instances.

Open the ***Dimensions*** slide-up panel (Figure 11). It shows "***L_X***" for Direction 1 and "***L_Y***" for Direction 2, along with their increments. ***Accept*** the feature (Figure 12).

Let's modify the pattern one more time.

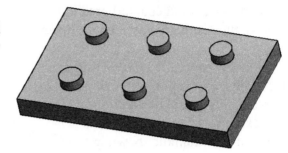

Figure 12 Simple pattern #5

Pattern #6 - Select the pattern in the model tree and ***Edit Definition***. Click on the Direction 1 box that says "1 Item". It turns yellow (active). Hold down the CTRL key and add the diameter dimension (increment **1.0**) and the height dimension (increment **2.0**). Observe the colors of these dimension. Now click on the Direction 2 item collector that says "1 Item". Using the CTRL key, add the height dimension (increment **4.0**). Open the **Dimensions** slide-up panel to see all the pattern dimensions. See Figure 13. Notice that a dimension, like "**H**" in this case, can be used in both directions of the pattern. ***Accept*** the pattern, which should look like Figure 14.

Direction 1

Dimension	Increment
L_X:F7(EXT...	6.0
DIA:F7(EXT...	1.0
H:F7(EXTR...	2.0

☐ Define increment by relation

[Edit]

Direction 2

Dimension	Increment
L_Y:F7(EXT...	6.0
H:F7(EXTR...	4.0

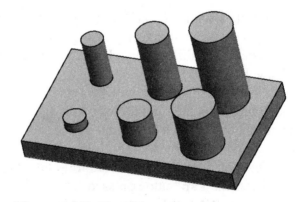

Figure 14 Pattern #6

Figure 13 Pattern dimensions for pattern #6

We'll leave this part now. ***Save*** it and perhaps come back to it later to explore more simple pattern options. After you have saved it, select ***File > Erase > Current***. This removes the model from memory (takes it "out of session").

Creating a Simple Radial Pattern

A common element in piping systems and pressure vessels is a bolted flange. Here is how to create a pattern of bolt holes. To demonstrate this, we'll explore the *Hole* dashboard to create a standard counterbored hole. In addition, we will set up a couple of relations to control the geometry based on the specified number of holes.

Start a new part called *flange* using the "inlbs_part_solid" template. (Note: Units *must* be in inches for this exercise!) Create the circular disk with central hole shown in Figure 15. We will need a central axis for the counterbored hole placement so you have a number of options: a) create a solid protrusion of two concentric circles, b) create a solid circular disk and add a coaxial hole, or c) revolve a rectangle around a central axis aligned with the datums. Each of these options will create the axis

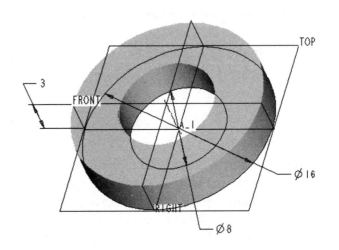

Figure 15 Base feature of flange

automatically. Pick whichever of these options you are *least* familiar with - might as well get some practice! The outer diameter is *16*, the hole diameter is *8*, and the disk is *3* thick. Note that the disk is constructed on **TOP**.

Now we'll create a single counterbored hole in the disk. This will be the pattern leader. In order to specify the pattern using an angular dimension, we choose a *Diameter* placement scheme (requiring an angle from a reference plane, and a diameter dimension for the flange bolt circle).

Select the *Hole* tool in the right toolbar. Moving across the dashboard from left to right, do the following:
- pick the *Standard Hole* button
- leave the **Tap** button pressed
- select a **UNC** thread type
- set size **1-8** (it's way down at the bottom of the hole list)
- set the depth to **Through All**

and finally
- press *Counterbore*.

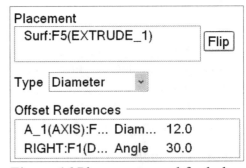

Figure 16 Placement panel for holes

Pick on the surface of the top of the protrusion at about the 5 o'clock position. A hole will be previewed. Open the *Placement* slide-up panel. Change the Primary placement type from *Linear* to *Diameter*. See Figure 16. Click in the offset references pane. Drag one green hole placement handle to the axis of the protrusion - a diameter dimension appears; drag the other to the RIGHT datum - an angle dimension will appear. Change the diameter dimension to *12* and the angle dimension to *30* as shown in Figure 17.

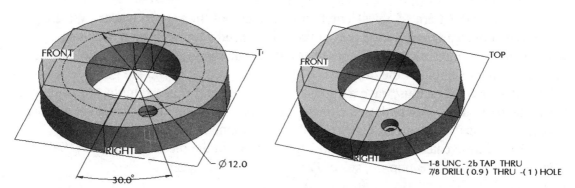

Figure 17 Placement dimensions for counterbored hole

Figure 18 Completed hole with note.

Open the **Shape** slide-up panel. Note the default diameter and depth of the counterbore. Change the thread depth from *Variable* to *Thru Thread*. Leave the checked box beside *Include Thread Surface*.

Open the **Note** slide-up panel. This shows the text of a note that will be attached to the hole in the database. This can eventually be displayed on the part drawing. Open the **Properties** panel. This contains a table showing all the parameters associated with this hole.   *Accept* the feature.

If you have been in shaded mode, go to ***Hidden Line***. Note that Pro/E does not show the physical thread of a hole (that would take too much CPU resource!), but uses a visible indicator to show that a thread is defined. This purple cylinder is called a *cosmetic* thread, and indicates the thread major diameter. The hole appears (Figure 18) with the thread note, as might appear in a drawing (except note that the counterbore dimensions are missing).

Open the model tree and expand the entry for the hole. The note is listed there[3]. To move the note, select it in the model tree, use the RMB and select *Move*. You can click anywhere on the screen to drop the note. See what happens when you spin the model. To turn off the display of the note, select ***View > Display Settings > Datum display*** and deselect the option **3D Annotations**. Or, find the *AE Display* button (*Annotation Element*) in the top toolbar (beside the datum visibility buttons). Curiously, you cannot use a Hide command for this note.

You can create 3D notes for other features as well. These notes can contain any text and are useful ways to attach documentation to the model. In the model tree, select the base feature, and in the RMB pop-up menu, select ***Setup Note > Feature***. This opens the **Note** window. Basically, you need to enter the note text, then select the *Place* button to

---

[3] You may have to turn on the display of annotations in the model tree using ***Settings > Tree Filters***.

tell Pro/E how and where to attach the note. Come back later and try this (you will have to turn 3D Annotation display back on). For now, just **Cancel** the dialog.

Now, back to our pattern of holes. The first hole becomes the pattern leader. We are going to make a pattern of 8 instances of the hole spaced equally around the flange. That is, to create each instance, we will increment the angular placement of each hole by 45°. This is another example of the importance of planning ahead: if you are going to use a dimension pattern, you must have a dimension to increment! For example, we could not create the bolt circle if we had used a linear placement for the pattern leader (or at least it would be very difficult) or especially not if we had aligned it to either FRONT or RIGHT[4]. As we create the pattern, follow the prompts in the message window. Select the hole and in the RMB pop-up, select **Pattern**.

This is actually a uni-directional pattern in disguise. There is only one dimension to increment - the angle to the pattern leader. Click on the 30 dimension, and enter an increment of **45**. Change the number of instances to **8**. **Accept** the pattern. See Figure 19.

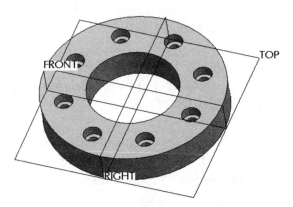

Figure 19 Pattern of holes

Open the model tree to see how the pattern is listed there. Turn on the 3D Annotations button. Does every hole inherit the thread note of the pattern leader? Examine the note carefully - it also contains the number of holes in the pattern.

Setting up Pattern Relations

Suppose we wanted to change the number of holes on the flange - this would change all the angular dimensions. Do we have to recreate this pattern from scratch? The answer is no - we can use relations! In the pull-down menu, select

> **Tools > Relations**

Click on the 2nd hole in the bolt pattern (the one at about 3-o'clock). You should see all the dimensions that control the pattern as in Figure 20. Note that some hole dimensions have been removed from this figure for clarity.

Take note of the symbols for the following dimensions (your symbols might be different): angular dimension between holes (*d11*), the angle of the first hole from RIGHT (*d5*), and the number of holes (*p12*).

_____

[4] The **Axis** pattern type allows you to create a radial pattern around any axis or straight edge, even if the feature does not directly reference it. This pattern type is discussed in the *Advanced Tutorial*.

With these symbols identified, enter a couple of relations as follows (using your own symbols, of course, and remember that you can easily pick off the dimensions on the graphics window just by clicking on them):

/* angular separation of holes
d11 = 360 / p12
/* location of first hole from RIGHT
d5 = d11 / 2

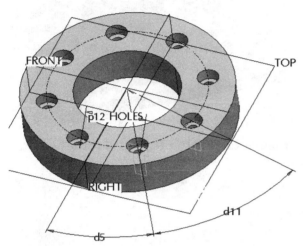

Figure 20 Critical pattern dimensions for setting up some relations

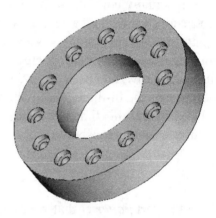

Figure 21 Hole pattern modified for 12 bolts

Note that the second relation uses a value computed by the first relation. In the database, all relations are evaluated top-down. Before you leave the **Relations** menu, select **Switch Dims** to return dimensions to numeric values. Also, select the **Verify** button. Select **OK**. You must select **Regenerate** for the relations to take effect. The only dimension that will change this time is the angle to the pattern leader. This pulls the entire pattern around slightly. Double click on any of the holes and change the number of holes to **12**, then **Regenerate** the part. See Figure 21. Check again for 6 holes, 5 holes. Don't forget you have to regenerate after each modify. In each case, the correct number, separation, and pattern leader placement are automatically determined.

Double click on any of the holes, and change the diameter of the counterbore to **2**. **Regenerate** the model. Note that all pattern members change. With the diameter of 2, try to create a pattern of **16** holes, then **20** holes. What happens? Note that the pattern members are allowed to intersect each other. This is the result of a setting in the **Options** panel in the pattern dashboard. We will explore this a bit later (meanwhile, you might check out the online help topic "About Pattern Regeneration Options").To turn off the display of the cosmetic thread, select the pattern leader and **Edit Definition**. Open the **Shape** panel and deselect **Include Thread Surface**.

If you want to play with this part later, then **Save** it now. Otherwise, select **File > Erase Current**.

A Pattern of Grouped Features

The patterns we have seen up to now have involved a single feature as pattern leader. Sometimes, a geometric shape that you want to pattern requires several features to create. In order to pattern these, they must first be grouped together.

We are going to create the part shown in Figure 22. The pattern leader is on the left in the front row. Each instance in the pattern actually consists of three features: a protrusion, a hole, and a round. We will use a pattern to set up two rows with the dimensions of the features incrementing along each row, and between rows. This is the same as the bi-directional pattern we did before, but this time involving three features simultaneously.

Figure 22 Pattern of grouped features

Open the part **_pattern1_** that we used before. Delete the previous pattern, keeping the pattern leader (the cylindrical protrusion). Create a **_Through All_**, coaxial hole (diameter **_1.0_**) on the axis of the protrusion, and a round (radius **_0.25_**) on the edge around its base. The dimensions are shown in Figure 23.

Before we can create the pattern, we have to group all the features (circular extrusion + hole + round) into a single entity - called (no surprise!) a *group*. Note that grouped features must be adjacent to each other in

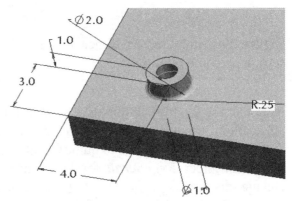

Figure 23 Pattern leader composed of circular protrusion, hole, and round

the model tree. Select the three features (with the CTRL key) and in the RMB pop-up menu, select **_Group_**. The three entries in the model tree will collapse under a single new entry called a LOCAL_GROUP. With this highlighted, in the RMB pop-up menu, select **_Rename_** and type in a new name like "holder". Expand the entry in the model tree to see the three original features. Note the icon that indicates a group.

With the group highlighted, in the RMB pop-up menu select **_Pattern_**. The pattern dashboard opens and you should see all the dimensions associated with the group as shown in Figure 23. We now can select the various dimensions we want to increment in the first and second directions. Select the following (remember to hold down the CTRL key while selecting dimensions to get them in the same collector!):

First Pattern Direction
1.   pick on the 4.0 dimension, and enter the increment *6.0*. This will increment the location of the group along the plate.
2.   pick on the diameter of the protrusion 2.0, and enter the increment *1.0*
3.   pick on the height of the protrusion 1.0, and enter the increment *1.0*
4.   pick on the diameter of the hole 1.0, and enter the increment *1.0*
5.   enter the number of instances *3*

Now left click on the item collector for the second direction.

Second Pattern Direction
1.   pick on the 3.0 dimension, and enter the increment *6.0*. This will increment the location of the group to the next row.
2.   pick on the height of the protrusion 1.0, and enter the increment *4.0*
3.   pick on the protrusion diameter 2.0, and enter the increment *1.0*
4.   pick on the hole diameter 1.0, and enter the increment *1.0*
5.   enter the number of instances *2*

For a summary of all this, open the **Dimensions** slide-up panel. *Accept* the pattern. It should appear as in Figure 22.

What dimensions are available for modification (this may depend on which feature you pick)?

What happens here if you try to create a group off the end of the plate by extending the pattern? Change the direction 1 increment to *10* to find out. How do you recover from this?

Open up the model tree to see how a group pattern is represented. Then, save the part and erase it from the session.

Radial Patterns of Sketched Features

A common modeling problem involves creating radial patterns of sketched features. The radial hole pattern we did earlier was of a placed feature, and was pretty easy. For sketched features, we must be a bit more sophisticated in order to create an angular dimension which can be incremented to produce the pattern. The most common way of doing this is by using a make datum in the creation of the pattern leader[5]. We set up the feature so that the make datum is used as a reference for the sketch. The make datum is typically created using *Through* (the axis of the pattern) and *Offset(rotation)* (from a datum passing through the axis). Then, we can increment the rotation angle to form the

---

[5] We prefer to use a make datum because we don't want the screen cluttered up by a bunch of duplicated datum planes - remember that a make datum is automatically hidden.

pattern. It is crucial when creating the sketch of the feature that there are **no** references, alignments, or dimensions to entities (datums, edges, surfaces) in the part other than the make datum, the axis of the radial pattern, or other axisymmetric features. References to other features will usually not survive a large angular increment of the patterned feature, causing the pattern to fail. This is the most common problem that new users encounter when creating radial patterns.

There are two types of radial patterns, which are determined by how the make datum is used. In the first, the feature is sketched on a plane that goes through the radial pattern axis (or one parallel to this); the feature extrudes in a direction perpendicular to the axis. In this type, a make datum is used as the *sketching plane*. In the second type, the feature is sketched on a plane that is normal to the axis and extrudes parallel to it. The make datum is used as the *sketching reference plane*. We will see examples of both types here.

Radial Pattern using Make Datum as Sketching Plane

The first part we will make is (very approximately) the geometry of a turbocharger rotor (see Figure 29). We will take this opportunity to introduce a new feature variation - a *Thickened* extrusion[6], and a new arc type in Sketcher.

Start a new part called **turbo**. Use the solid part template for **millimeter-Newton-seconds**. Close the model tree.

Our base feature is a revolved solid protrusion. Sketch this on **FRONT**. The sketch is shown in Figure 24. Sketch all the straight edges first. The curved edge in this sketch is a *conic arc* (use the 𝒫 button on the end of the arc fly-out). Click at the two arc end points and drag out the arc until each end shows a tangent constraint; then drop the arc. The conic dimension (0.4 in the figure) is not a radius but a parameter (rho) used to define the conic section. For a perfect elliptical curve, this parameter should be 0.414... (enter this value as [**SQRT(2)-1**] and note the use of

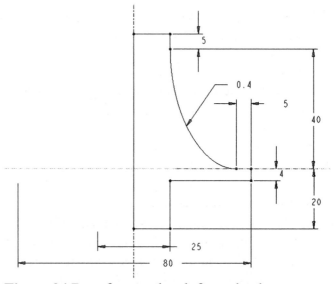

Figure 24 Base feature sketch for turbocharger

the built-in math function). This expression is automatically inserted as a sketch relation. Notice that the constraints are turned off in the figure here for clarity. Don't forget the centerline (lined up with **RIGHT**). Create this sketch and then revolve it through 360° to

---

[6] This is another recent change in terminology in Wildfire. Previously, this was known as a *Thin* solid.

get the shape shown in Figure 25.

Now we will make our first turbocharger blade to serve as pattern leader. We are going to create a sketching plane through the axis of the revolved base feature at an angle to **RIGHT**. We can then create the pattern instances by incrementing this angle. Since the sketching plane is through the axis, the extruded blade will be normal to the axis. We are also going to use a new type of feature that we haven't seen before - a *Thickened* feature (instead of *Solid*). All we have to sketch is a single line representing the cross section shape of the blade.

Figure 25 Base feature

Select the *Extrude* tool, then select *Placement > Define*. We want to make a datum-on-the-fly here, so move the Sketch window out of the way and pick the *Datum Plane* tool. Pick on the axis of the revolve. This appears as a *Through* constraint. Holding down CTRL, select the **RIGHT** datum. In combination with the previously selected axis, this gives us the correct Offset(Rotation) constraint. Change the *Offset* rotation value to *60* degrees. Accept this with *OK*.

Back in the **Sketch** window, select the **TOP** datum with orientation **Top**. Then select *Sketch*. We are now in Sketcher looking directly at the make datum. For our sketching references, select TOP, the revolve axis, and the top surface of the base feature (we can use this surface because it will be constant for all instances in the pattern). Create the sketch shown in Figure 26. This consists of a single vertical line and a circular arc[7]. When the sketch is complete, select *Accept* in Sketcher.

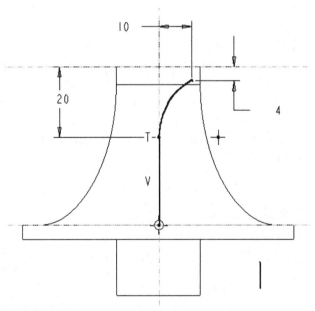

Figure 26 Sketch for *Thin* protrusion - turbocharger blade

Since this was an open sketch, the preview consists of a single surface. A direction arrow points away from this surface that indicates the side Pro/E will add material. This obviously won't work here to create a solid.

---

[7] No claims are made here about the aerodynamic suitability of this blade shape, other than it's probably far from ideal!

Pick the **Thicken** button 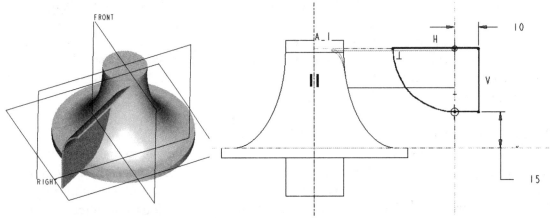 on the dashboard, and specify a thickness of **1.0** (remember we are in mm). Beside this data field is a button that lets you specify which side of the sketched line to add material (either side, or both). Watch the preview carefully as you cycle through these options. We want to thicken the sketch equally on both sides here. For the depth specification, select **Blind** with a value **60**. Verify the blade shape (see Figure 27) and **Accept** the feature. In the model tree, select this extrude (note that it contains the hidden make datum) and rename it "**blade**".

Figure 27 Completed blade   **Figure 28** Revolved cut to trim blade

Before we complicate the part with the pattern of blades, we will create a revolved cut. Launch the **Revolve** tool. The feature is sketched on another make datum that is **Through** the revolve axis and **Parallel** to one of the vertical flat surfaces of the blade. For the sketching orientation reference, select **Top > TOP**. In Sketcher, select as references the top edge of the blade, the outside edge, and axis (for the axis of revolution). Create the sketch shown in Figure 28 (don't forget the revolve axis). You might wonder why it needs to extend past the end of the blade. Come back later to change the dimension 10 to 0 and regenerate - don't do this now! Revolve this cut through 360° and accept the feature. Don't forget the **Remove Material** button!

We are now ready to pattern the blade. In the model tree, select the blade, and in the RMB pop-up menu, select

Pattern

Select the angle (60) used to create the make datum sketching plane. Enter an increment of **30** for this dimension. In the dashboard, set the number of instances to 12. That's all there is to this pattern. **Accept** the feature.

Figure 29 Completed pattern of blades

Open the model tree to observe where the pattern is. Recall that we created the pattern *after* we created the revolved cut, yet it appears immediately following the pattern leader in the model tree. That is, patterns are created "in place." This was actually fortunate, since it allowed us to create the sketch for the revolved cut on a fairly simple view without a lot of additional clutter. Try opening the sketch of the cut now to see what it looks like with all 12 blades in view.

Why could we not use a vertical surface of the blade as the sketching plane for the revolved cut? Try that and see what problem arises. This will be more obvious if you make the blades thicker. You might dress this part up with a coaxial hole and some rounds.

Let's look at another variation of radial patterns using a make datum. Save this part and then erase it from the session.

Radial Pattern using Make Datum as Reference Plane

In this example, the feature extrusion direction for the pattern leader is parallel to the axis of the radial pattern. We must do something a bit different from the turbocharger. The main idea is the same - incorporate a make datum created using ***Through*** and ***Offset(rotation)*** into the sketch references. The angle parameter can then be incremented to produce the pattern. In the turbocharger, the make datum was the sketching plane; in this part, the make datum will be the sketching horizontal reference plane.

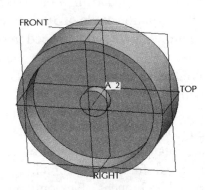

Figure 30 Base feature

Start a new part **wheel_rim** using the default part template. Our base feature is again a revolved solid protrusion (Figure 30). The sketch plane is **TOP** and the axis of the revolve goes through **RIGHT**. The sketch is shown in Figure 31. Revolve the sketch through 360° and accept the feature.

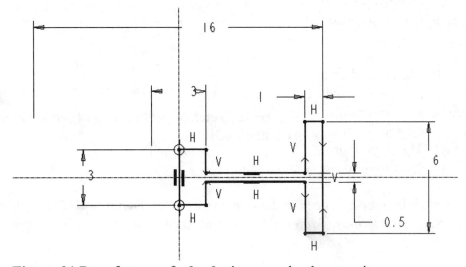

Figure 31 Base feature of **wheel_rim** - revolved protrusion

We will create a pattern of cuts through the web of the wheel (Figure 34). The pattern leader will be a both-sides extruded cut, sketched on **FRONT** (the extrusion direction is therefore parallel to the axis of the wheel - compare this to the turbocharger where the extrusion direction was perpendicular to the axis). We want to pattern this feature around the axis of the base feature.

The most common error for this type of feature pattern (although it seems reasonable enough) is to use a *fixed* datum as the sketching reference plane, then a centerline in the sketch through the wheel axis and at some angle to this datum. If you then try to pattern this feature past 180° of rotation, the pattern will fail. This is because of the inner workings of Pro/E's geometry engine. Try it sometime! We will use a much more robust way of creating the radial pattern.

Select the *Extrude* tool and *Placement > Define*. For the sketching plane pick **FRONT**. For the sketching reference plane, *Remove* the default RIGHT datum plane using the RMB pop-up in the *Reference* collector. Instead, select the *Datum Plane* tool and create a make datum *Through* the axis of the wheel and *Offset* from the **TOP** datum. Enter an offset rotation angle of *30* degrees. The reference should face *Top*. Accept the make datum with *OK*, and proceed into Sketcher.

We are now looking at **FRONT** with the make datum **DTM1** facing the top of the screen. The edge views of **RIGHT** and **TOP** are rotated a bit. We must be very careful now about picking sketch references. Pick only on **DTM1** and the axis of the wheel (when selected, you will see a small X there). You may have to spin the model a bit (or use the Search tool) to select the axis. Notice in the reference window that we are fully placed (press *Solve*).

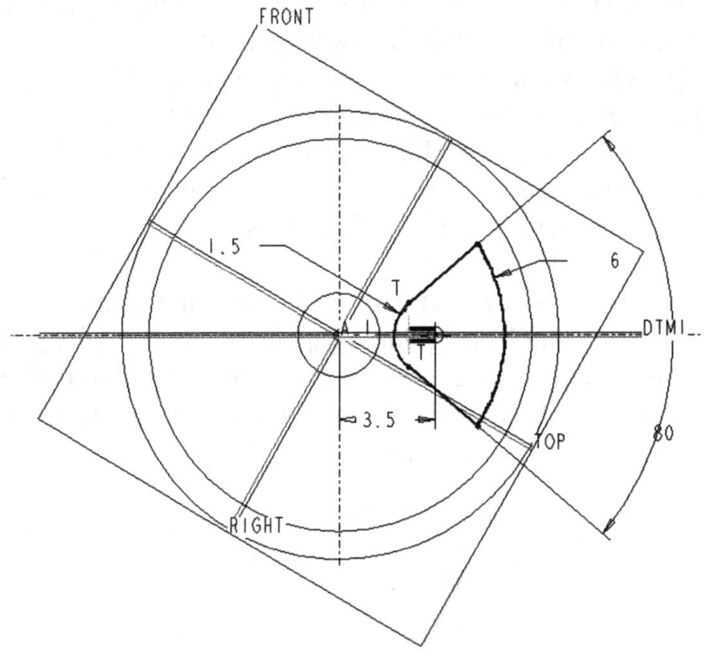

The sketch for the cut is shown in Figure 32. Be sure to avoid any dimensions or constraints that involve the fixed datums **TOP** and **RIGHT**. If you turn

Figure 32 Sketch of pattern leader (note rotation of TOP and RIGHT)

them off, you don't have to worry about this.

When the sketch is complete, back in the dashboard set the Depth Spec *Through All* on both sides. Select the *Remove Material* button and *Accept* the feature. See Figure 33.

We can now pattern the cut. Open up the model
tree and right click on the extruded cut. This
contains the make datum reference. In the RMB
pop-up menu, select ***Pattern***. In the dimensions
on the screen, find the 30° dimension we used
to locate the make datum reference plane from
the TOP datum and click on it. Enter the
increment *72°*, and up in the dashboard specify
5 copies. There is nothing to do in the second
direction. Open the ***Options*** panel and select
the ***Regeneration Option(Identical)***. This
means that all instances in the pattern will have
the same shape and use the same references. We
are finished defining the pattern, so select
Accept. The pattern should now be created as
in Figure 34.

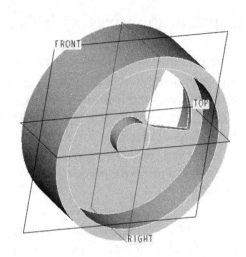

Figure 33 Pattern leader completed

What happens if you try to make a pattern of 6 cuts at 60° increments? How about 8 cuts
at 45° degree increments? Would you say this is a *robust* model? Go back to the pattern
dashboard using ***Edit Definition*** and in the ***Options*** panel, change the regeneration option
to ***General***. At the expense of somewhat increased processing time, this allows pattern
instances to change geometry (and intersect). Now try the pattern of 8 instances.
Obviously this wheel would not work, but we have successfully decoupled the pattern
creation from the shape of the pattern instances, making a more robust model. We could
now go back to the pattern leader and change its geometry without fear that the pattern
will fail.

This concludes our discussion of patterns.
There are many more things you can do
with patterns, and some more advanced
techniques. For example, instead of simply
incrementing dimensions between
instances, you can use pattern relations to
develop formulas that will control the
instance placement and geometry. Another
tool called a pattern table allows you to
place instances at non-uniformly spaced
locations driven by dimension values stored
in a table like a spreadsheet. A pattern fill
will duplicate features (like holes) in a
regular geometric pattern in order to cover
a region bounded by a datum or sketched
curve. These advanced pattern functions
are discussed in the *Pro/ENGINEER
Advanced Tutorial* from SDC.

Figure 34 Wheel_rim with radial pattern of
cuts.

Save the part and erase it from the session.

Copying Features with *Paste* and *Paste Special*

In the previous sections, we saw how to create a multiple-instance dimension-driven pattern of a single feature or a group of features. The pattern was created by incrementing one or more of the feature's existing dimensions. The **Copy** command allows more flexibility in terms of placement and geometric variation (you aren't restricted to the dimensions or references used to create a pattern leader, for example), but only creates one copy at a time. There are several options available with *Copy* (including copying features to a different part), and we will create several different simple parts to illustrate these.

There are two versions of the *Copy* command in Wildfire. The original version, that has been around for a long time, is still available in the *Edit > Feature Operations* menu. This has been superceded by a more Windows-like Copy/Paste command structure that gives easier access to all the copy options. We will not investigate the older command style here.

When only a single copy of a feature is desired, the first and main consideration is whether or not copying is actually more efficient than simply creating a new feature from scratch at the desired new location. If the feature is simple enough (like a simple hole), this may actually be quicker. However, if a copy is truly desired, the following must also be considered:

- Should the copied feature be dependent or independent of the original feature?
- Will the copied feature use the same references as the original?
- Will the copied feature use the same dimension values or different ones?
- Which dimensions will be driven by the parent and which will be independent?
- Is the copied feature created by simple translation or rotation (or some combination) of the original?

As you can see, there are quite a few options available. We will explore a number of possibilities. The main option, after identifying the feature to be copied, is to choose one of the following operations:

Paste - creates independent copies using the copied feature's dashboard interface to specify new references
Paste Special - allows choice of new references, variable dimensions, translation, rotation, and more. The copied feature can be independent, partially dependent, or fully dependent (default) on the original feature.

Copying using *Paste*

Our first example of Copy/Paste will result in the part shown in Figure 35. The tab with hole on the top left edge is the original extrusion. The tabs on the top right and the right side are copies. This would be difficult to do with a pattern due to the change in reference surfaces and orientation of the two copied tabs. For this example, we will use the *Paste* command, which will result in the three tabs being independent of each other.

Figure 35 Part with original and two copied tabs

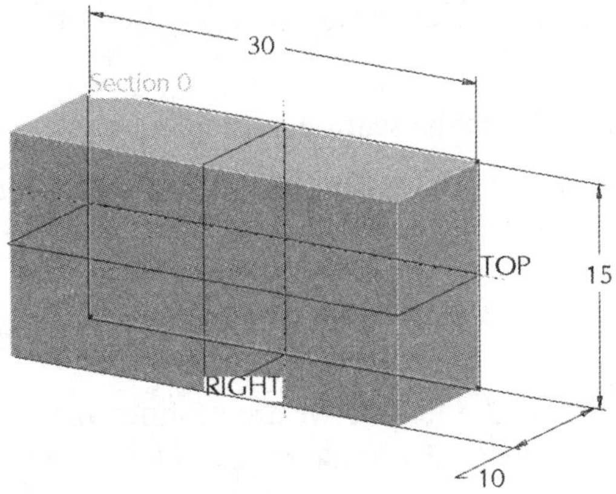

Figure 36 Base feature

Start by creating a new part called **featcopy** using the default template. Create the extrusion shown in Figure 36. This is sketched on the FRONT datum and centered on the datum planes RIGHT and TOP.

Now create the first tab using an extrusion sketched on the FRONT datum. Use the top of the block as the top reference for Sketcher. The vertical reference is RIGHT. The sketched shape of the tab is shown in Figure 37. You will have to close the sketch across the bottom (you can't have a mix of open and closed curves in a single sketch). The feature has a blind depth of 3. The finished tab is shown in Figure 38.

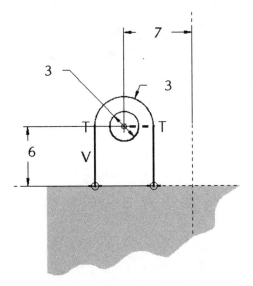

Figure 37 Sketch for first tab

Figure 38 First tab completed

Select the tab extrusion (either in the model tree or on the screen). With the tab highlighted in red, select the *Copy* button 📋 in the top toolbar, or in the top pull-down menu select

Edit > Copy (notice the standard Windows keyboard shortcut CTRL-C).

This places the feature in the clipboard. Now select the *Paste* button 📋 in the top toolbar (don't confuse this with *Paste Special* which is right beside it), or in the pull-down menu select

Edit > Paste (notice the keyboard shortcut CTRL-V).

Because the feature we are pasting was created using the dashboard, that now opens and we must specify some required references for the new pasted feature. The missing references are indicated by the red lettering on the slide-up **Placement** panel. Open that. Notice the red dot in the data field for the sketch. Select the *Edit* button. Missing references in the Sketch dialog window are indicated by the red dots. The first required reference is the sketch plane - this should be FRONT. The second is the sketching reference - pick on the top of the block and set this to face the top of the screen. Now press the *Sketch* button.

We are now looking at the sketching plane. If you move your cursor you will see a dark red outline of the sketch. Drag that to a position to the right of the first tab, and left click to drop it. We can now use the usual Sketcher tools to complete the placement. For example, constrain the bottom edge of the sketch to the top of the block and dimension the center of the hole to the RIGHT datum. See Figure 39. Accept the sketch and specify a blind depth of 3 as before (this is actually brought along from the original).

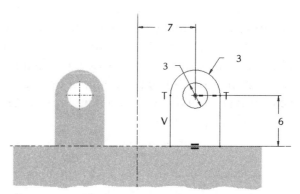

Figure 39 Pasting the copied feature

Let's copy the original tab once more. Select the first tab again, then *Copy* (CTRL-C) followed by *Paste* (CTRL-V). Once again the extrude dashboard opens with missing references indicated with red. Open the *Placement* slide-up panel (or use the RMB and select *Edit Internal Sketch*). As before, select the FRONT datum as the sketching plane but this time select the block's right vertical surface as the TOP sketching reference plane. This will maintain our sketch orientation. Now select the Sketch button. The dark red outline of the sketch appears attached to the cursor. Place that so that the bottom edge aligns (more or less) with the surface of the block.

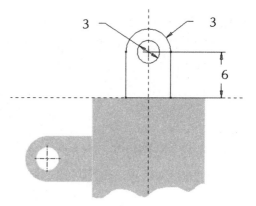

Figure 40 Pasting the second copied feature

Use the *Constraints* command in Sketcher to fix the bottom edge onto the block surface, and align the center of the hole with the TOP datum. See Figure 40. Accept the sketch and the feature with the default blind depth of 3.

To show that *Paste* produces independent features, go to the first tab and use *Edit* to change the hole diameter from 3 to **1**. On the second tab, change the height dimension from 6 to **10**. On the third tab on the end, use *Edit Definition* to change the blind depth to **Up To Surface** and pick on the front surface of the block. After regeneration, the part should look like Figure 41. You can also examine the parent/child relations for each tab to check that they are independent of each other.

Figure 41 Exploring independence of copied features created using *Paste*

So, the *Paste* command uses the dashboard interface for the copied feature, and automatically creates independent copies. This may be useful in taking features from one model to another[8].

It is possible to relate pasted features together either using relations or by using the geometry of the original feature as a reference in the pasted feature. For example, in our first copied tab, we could either specify a relation for the height dimension (setting it equal to the corresponding dimension in the original) or we could have selected the hole axis in the original as a reference for placing the sketch in the copied feature (thus eliminating the height dimension in the copy). If you want to make the copied feature dependent, it is probably advisable to use the *Paste Special* command instead.

Save the current part and remove it from your session.

Copying using *Paste Special*

Unlike *Paste*, which is used primarily to create independent copies, the default operation for *Paste Special* results in dependence of the copied feature on the original. This mostly involves the dimensions of the feature, although other elements (such as annotations) are also involved. There are several variations of *Paste Special*, hence more options to consider and we will have a look at some. The first copy we will make with *Paste Special* will use all defaults. Remember that this results in a dependent copy. An important point to note is that, once created, the dependent status can be changed to various forms of independent status. However, once declared to be independent, a copied feature cannot be redefined as dependent (unless additional steps are taken such as

---

[8] If you are going to be using the same feature in many models, you may want to create a ***User Defined Feature*** (UDF) that can be stored in a feature library. UDF's operate much like the Paste portion of a Copy/Paste operation. UDF's can be set up to be independent, partially or fully dependent on a master. This is discussed in the *Advanced Tutorial*.

creating relations).

Create a new part called **featcopy2** using the default template. The base feature is an extruded protrusion, with the sketch created on TOP with the right reference being RIGHT. Once you are in Sketcher, select the *Palette* tool. This opens the dialog window shown in Figure 42.

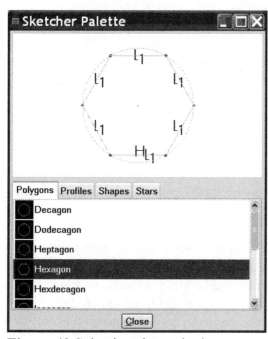

Figure 42 Selecting shapes in the Sketcher pallette

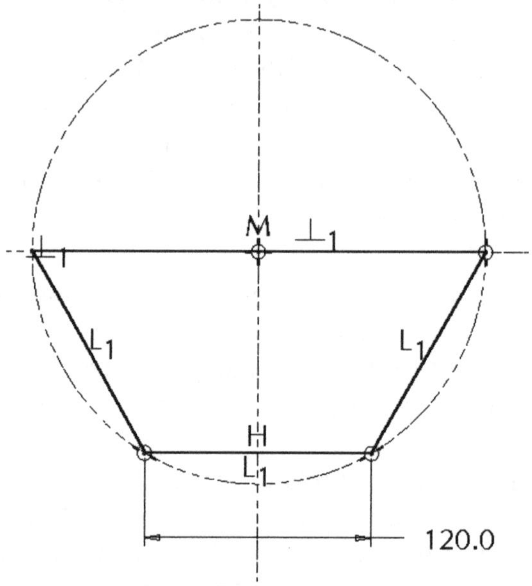

Figure 43 Modified sketch of hexagon

The **Sketcher Palette** tool allows you to select from a number of pre-defined shapes as indicated by the tabs. In the **Polygons** tab, select the **Hexagon** shape with the LMB. This opens a preview of the shape at the top. Double-click the hexagon shape.

Back in the graphics window, drop the hexagon shape onto the sketching plane by clicking with the LMB. Check out the indicated (in white) drag handles for location, rotation, and scale of the sketch. You can also specify the scale and angle of the sketch in the small dialog window at the right. Enter a **Scale** value of **120** and close that window and the palette window. Use the Sketcher *Constraints* command to align the center of the hexagon with the sketching references. As shown in Figure 43, create a single line across the center of the hexagon, and delete the sketched lines on the top half of the hexagon. Accept the sketch, and (IMPORTANT) set the symmetric **Blind** depth of the extrusion to **120**. Accept the feature.

We will have need of a datum axis defined at the intersection of FRONT and RIGHT. Create that now.

The feature we are going to copy is an extruded cut created on the right surface of the base feature. Launch the *Extrude* command and select this surface for the sketching plane. Select the TOP datum as the top sketching reference. Once you are in Sketcher, select the datum axis for the second sketching reference. Open the *Palette* tool again. In the **Shapes** tab, select the **Cross** shape. Double-click on this and then drop the shape (or just drag it from the palette window and drop it) onto the sketching plane. Enter a **Scale** value of **20**. Use the *Constraints* command to align the crossed centerlines of the cross sketch with the sketching references. The sketch should be driven by only two dimensions - see Figure 44 (constraint display has been turned off). Accept the sketch. In the Extrude dashboard, set the **Blind** depth to **20**, and don't forget to select the **Remove Material** button and flip if necessary. The finished feature is shown in Figure 45. To make it easier to refer to the original feature, rename it to **Cross**. We will use this feature to explore several variations of the *Paste Special* command, paying particular attention to the different levels of dependency between the original and copied features.

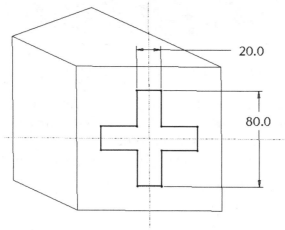

Figure 44 Sketch selected from the palette

Figure 45 Original extruded cut

Paste Special Example #1 (default)

Select the cross feature (highlight in red), then pick the *Copy* command in the top toolbar. Now select the *Paste Special* command.

A new dialog window opens as shown in Figure 46. For our first example of *Paste Special*, we will accept all the

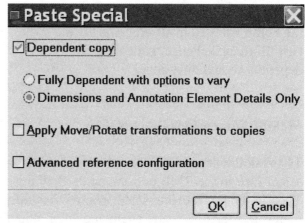

Figure 46 The **Paste Special** dialog window

defaults in this window[9]. As you move your cursor over the window, a pop-up and the message window will give you a bit more information about each option. Do not change any settings yet, and accept the settings shown in Figure 46 with *OK*.

The feature dashboard opens and we must now specify the new references for the copied feature. Missing references are indicated using red. This behavior is the same as for *Paste* command. We will see at the end, however, that the copy will be dependent on the original (unlike *Paste*).

Open the **Placement** slide-up panel and select the *Edit* button. Select *Yes* in the warning window. For the new sketching surface, select the front surface of the base. The sketching orientation reference is again the TOP datum, to face the top of the

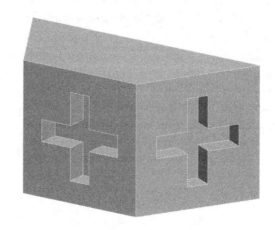

Figure 47 The copied extruded cut

screen. Now select *Sketch* and you will now reorient to the sketch view. The cross sketch will show in dark red, and you can drop it on the sketching plane. Use the *Constraints* tool to align the cross centerlines with the sketch references. Accept the sketch. The original blind depth (20) has been carried over from the original. The final copied feature is shown in Figure 47.

Select the original cross, and edit the height dimension to **60**. Change the width to **10**. *Regenerate* the part. The new geometry is shown in Figure 48. Note that the copy is also changed, indicating its dependence on the original.

Select the copied feature, and change the height dimension from 60 to **80**. Change the width from 10 to **40**. *Regenerate* the part. Both cuts change, indicating that the dependence is bidirectional.

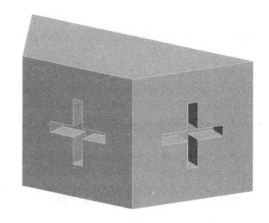

Figure 48 Dependency of the copied cut

Making Dimensions Independent

To break the dependency on selected dimensions of the copy, highlight the copy and select *Edit* in the RMB pop-up menu. Pick the blind depth dimension to highlight in red. Then in the RMB menu, select *Make Dim Indep*. In the Confirmation window pick *Yes*, then select the dimension again and enter a new value for the depth. *Regenerate* the part.

---

[9] It is possible to change the defaults shown in Figure 46 using the system configuration file, *config.pro*. The ones shown are the unmodified default settings.

The depths of the two cuts are now independent of each other, while the other dimensions remain dependent. Experiment with the dimensions of the two cuts to prove the dependent/independent status. When you are finished, delete the copied cut and change the dimensions of the original cross to height **60**, width **20** and depth **20.**

Paste Special Example #2 (using the Varied Items table)

Highlight the cross feature and select *Copy* and *Paste Special*. In the **Paste Special** dialog window, select the radio button **Fully Dependent with Options to Vary**, then *OK*. Nothing seems to have happened! However, if you select the copied feature in the model tree, you will see it highlight in the model superimposed on the original. In the RMB menu, select *Edit* and change the height dimension from 60 to **80**. As you do this, a message will appear asking you to confirm the addition of this dimension to the **Varied Items table**. Select *Yes* and enter the new value. Now pick the width dimension 20. Add this to the table as well,

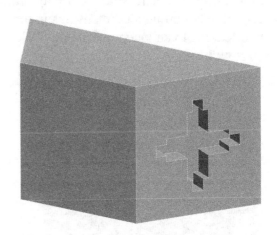

Figure 49 Copied cut with modified dimensions

and enter a new value of *10*. *Regenerate* the part. The second cross appears superimposed on the first one (Figure 49).

To see the varied items table, select the copied cut. In the RMB menu, select

Copied Feature > Varied Items

This opens the dialog window shown in Figure 50. This window allows us to add (or remove) dimensions and other references that have been specified to vary between the original and the copy. We can see the two dimensions we previously picked to be variable. Let's add a new reference - a new sketching plane.

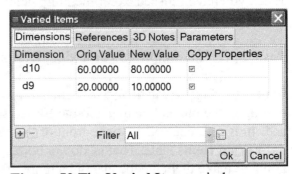

Figure 50 The **Varied Items** window

Go to the second tab, *References*. You are asked if you want to roll back the model - select *Yes*. Another menu opens at the right. This is the **Reroute** menu we saw previously for the *Edit References* command discussed in Lesson #5. It allows us to step through the references used in the original cut and select either new references or keep the old one. As you step through these, keep your eye on the message window at the bottom as the references highlight on the part. The first reference is for the sketching plane (shown in green). Select *Alternate*, and pick on the front surface. It now appears in the **Varied Items** window. Proceed through the rest of the references (there are three), keeping *Same*

Ref for all. In the Varied Items window, select *OK*. You must confirm a direction for a
reference before the feature is regenerated - the green and red arrows show the normals to
the old and new references, respectively. The copied feature now appears on the front
surface of the base as in Figure 51. If you *Edit* the height and width dimensions you will
see that these are independent. One dimension that is still dependent is the blind depth.
Change the depth of the original cut to **40** to prove the dependency. Select the depth of
the copy and add it to the Varied Items table. You should now be able to modify any of
the three dimensions for either cut without affecting the other feature, as indicated in
Figure 52. By putting all dimensions in the Varied Items table we have essentially
converted this to an independent copy. We could have done that much simpler with *Paste*
to start with!

Figure 51 Copied cut with varied
dimensions and sketching plane

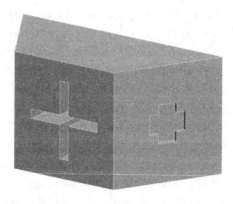

Figure 52 Copied cut independent of
original

When you have finished experimenting, delete the copied cut and return the dimensions
of the original cross to those shown in Figure 44, with a blind depth of 20.

Paste Special Example #3 (Breaking, Restoring, and Removing dependence)

Repeat the *Copy > Paste Special* command used in the previous example. Use the RMB
pop-up in the model tree to get to the Varied Items table (Figure 50). Change only the
sketching reference plane to the front of the block as before, using the *References* tab in
the **Varied Items** table. That is, do not bother to put any dimensions in the table - we are
going to make them independent in a more efficient way and all at once.

Select the copied feature in the model tree and in the RMB menu, pick

Copied Feature > Break Dependence

You can now change any dimensions of the original or copied feature. Try it! They will
regenerate with the new dimension(s) without affecting the other. The dependence of the
features is clearly broken.

Select the copied feature in the model tree, and in the RMB pick

Copied Feature > Restore Dependence

The dimensions of the copy will once again take the values from the original feature.

If you select (in the model tree RMB menu)

Copied Feature > Remove Dependence

a warning window appears indicating that the dependence will be removed permanently. If you select *Yes*, notice the change in the copied feature name in the model tree.

Once again, delete the copied feature and return the dimensions of the original cross to those shown in Figure 44.

Paste Special Example #4 (using Advanced Reference Configuration)

Select the cross feature, then *Copy > Paste Special*. In the Paste Special window, leave *Dependent copy* checked and select the option *Advanced Reference Configuration > OK*. This opens the dialog window shown in Figure 53.

In the left pane of this window are the references used by the original feature. The purpose of this dialog is to allow us to replace one or more of the original references with new ones for the pasted feature. If you select any of the references listed in the left pane, it will highlight on the model. If you pick a different reference, it will be used in the pasted feature. For example, select the surface reference used in the original feature (as shown in Figure 53). This is the sketching plane reference. Now pick on the front surface of the base. The other references can be used as-is by the pasted feature. Accept the dialog. We must confirm the direction of a reference surface, and then the pasted feature is added to the model.

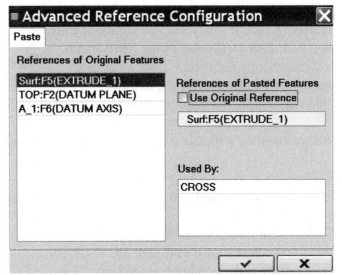

Figure 53 Specifying new references with the Advanced Reference Configuration window

Check that the copied feature is dependent on the original (and *vice versa*) by changing some of the dimensions.

Another way to change the dependency of the copied feature is by selecting the feature in the model tree and in the RMB menu picking

Make Sec Indep

This makes all dimensions used in the section sketch independent of the original. This does not affect the blind depth dimension (since that is not in the sketch). Check it out! If you want to make the depth independent, highlight it and use the *Make Dim Indep* command in the RMB menu.

Delete the copied cut and return the dimensions of the original to those in Figure 44.

Paste Special Example #5 (making an independent copy)

Select the cross feature, then *Copy > Paste Special*. Turn off the option for a dependent copy. Use the *Advanced Reference Configuration* option to change the sketching plane to the front surface of the base. Middle click to accept the copy.

Check out the feature information (*Info > Reference Viewer*) of the original and copied features to confirm that they are no longer related. In fact, if you select the copied feature then pick *Edit Definition* in the RMB menu, you can change the feature from a cut to a protrusion by deselecting the *Remove Material* button, and flipping the extrude direction. See Figure 54.

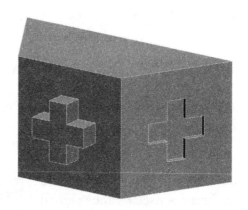

Figure 54 Fully independent copy (cut redefined as protrusion)

We are finished with this part, so you can erase it and remove it from your session.

Paste Special Example #6 (Translated and Rotated copies)

To demonstrate a translated copy, we will use the part shown in Figure 55. The vertical plate with hole on the left is the original, and the one on the right will be a dependent copy. Start by creating a new part **featcopy3** with the default template. Create a rectangular solid protrusion on **TOP** that is **10 x 20 x 2 thick**. Line up the left face of the block with the **RIGHT** datum, and the back face with **FRONT**.

Figure 55 Part with copied feature

For the first vertical plate, the sketching plane is a make datum that is *Offset* from **RIGHT** by *5*. Use the selection filter if you have trouble picking this. Select the top of the rectangular base as the *Top* reference plane. Then sketch the protrusion as shown in Figure 56. Note the sketching references. The hole is included in the protrusion - Pro/E will know where to add material, and where to leave the hole. Also, the sketch must close across the bottom since you can't have a mix of open and closed curves in the same sketch. The extrusion has a *Blind* depth of *1*. The part should look like Figure 57.

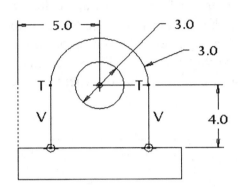

Figure 56 Sketch for vertical plate

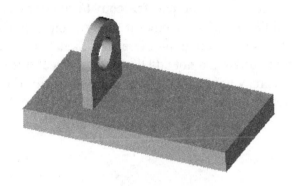

Figure 57 First feature completed

Now, we are ready to copy the feature. We want the copy to be 10 units to the right of the first. If the geometry of the first feature changes, we want the copy to change too. Highlight the vertical plate, then select *Copy > Paste Special*. Keep the **Dependent** copy option selected, and check the box to *Apply Move/Rotate Transformations > OK*. A new dashboard opens. Read the message line at the top. On the middle line, the first two buttons are for translating (default) and rotating the copied feature. The feature collector beside these (with the red dot) is waiting for us to specify a reference for the translation. The translation will be normal to a selected surface, or along a selected edge. Pick the RIGHT datum plane. A drag handle appears on the previewed feature - drag this out to 10 units. Accept the feature with a middle click.

How does the copy appear in the model tree? What happened to the make datum in the copied feature? How can you change the translation distance? (HINT: Pick various elements in the model tree and use the *Edit* command in the RMB pop-up.) What happens if you try to *Edit* the hole diameter on the first protrusion? Or the height dimension on the copy? What happens if you suppress the original? The copy?

Select the **Moved Copy** item in the model tree and in the RMB pick *Edit Definition*. Open the **Transformation** slide-up panel. This lists our first translation. If you pick *New Move*, you can now add a second translation by picking a new reference (plane or edge) and translation distance. Try it to move the copy 1 unit farther away from FRONT.

Can you make the copied plate independent of the original? (Hint: Where else have you seen the command *Make Sec Indep*?) Can you suppress or delete the original?

You can now either *Save* this part or *Erase* it.

Now, we will use a rotated copy to create the part shown in Figure 58 - a large circular pipe with two pipes joining it off-axis. At the same time, we will see a situation where feature creation order can be used to advantage (or foul you up!).

The original side pipe is on the left, the rotated copy is on the right. It can be obtained by a 180° rotation around the big pipe axis.

Create a new solid part **featcopy4** using the default template. Start by creating a circular solid *both-sides* (symmetric) protrusion from the sketching plane **TOP**. Use **RIGHT** and **FRONT** as sketching references. Sketch a circle with a diameter of *20* and set *blind* depth of *20*. Do not add the inner surface of the pipe at this time - we will do that later. This may not be an obvious thing to do (for now!) but we have a situation where feature creation order is important as discussed below.

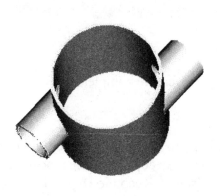

Figure 58 Part with Rotated copy

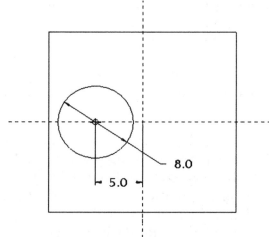

Figure 59 Sketch for side pipe

For the first side branch, create a one-sided solid protrusion. Use **FRONT** as the sketching plane (**Top** reference **TOP**) and sketch an *8* diameter circle *aligned* with TOP and with a center *5* from RIGHT (Figure 59). Check the feature creation direction arrow. Make the protrusion with a *blind* depth of *15.* This will extend it outside the circumference of the main pipe.

Create a *Straight, Coaxial hole* on the axis of the side pipe. The hole diameter is *7.* Use the placement plane **FRONT**. We want *Through All*. The part should look like Figure 60.

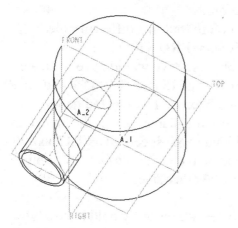

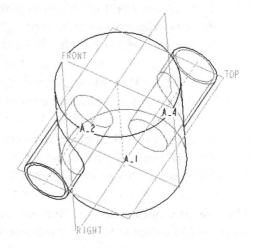

Figure 60 First pipe (Note the vertical pipe is still solid)

Figure 61 Rotated copy completed

Now we will create a rotated copy of both the sidepipe extrusion and the coaxial hole. Select these in the model tree (holding down the CTRL key), then select *Copy > Paste Special*. Turn off the *Dependent copy* option and check the *Apply Move/Rotate Transformations* option, then *OK*. In the dashboard that opens, select the second button on the middle line for a rotation. Now select the main axis of the large pipe as the rotation reference. Drag the rotation around to 180° and accept the feature. How do the two copied features appear in the model tree?

Since we have created an independent copy, check that you can change any dimensions of the copied features.

Now we can add the central *Hole* of the main pipe. Make it a *Straight, Coaxial* hole from the placement plane **TOP**. Make it *Through All* in both directions, with a diameter of *19.* This completes the model, so *Save* it now. We are going to explore it a bit, which might mess it up.

Exploring the Model

Now, you may be wondering why we left the central hole until last. Let's experiment with the *Edit* command (RMB pop-up menu), changing diameter dimensions of both the original and the copy. You can also modify the rotation angle. You should be able to modify both branch pipes with no problem. What happens if you modify the diameter of the main pipe to *12* and hole to *11?* The part will certainly regenerate, but is clearly wrong. However, the error is relatively easy to fix. Consider what would happen if we had used the following "obvious" sequence (what is important here is the order that features are created - you might like to sketch each feature in the following sequence as it is added to the part (or actually make a new part) in order to visualize the problem that would arise):

1.   **create main pipe** - same geometry as before.
2.   **create central hole** - same geometry as before (but in a different order).
3.   **create side branch** - We couldn't do this from **FRONT** since that would be inside the pipe (that now has the inner hole in it). We would have to create a **Make Datum** outside the pipe using an offset of 15 from **FRONT** and create the branch towards the main pipe using **To Next** or **To Selected** depth.
4.   **create the side branch hole** - We could use the planar face of the branch as the placement plane for a coaxial hole with a depth specified as **To Next** (through the next part surface encountered, ie the inside surface of the big pipe). Note that a *Thru All* would go out the other side.

These steps would create the same original geometry. However, we would have a big problem if we tried to reduce the diameter of the main pipe to anything less than 18, as we did above. Why? At step 3, the side branch solid protrusion would not totally intersect the surface of the main pipe as required by the **To Next/Selected** depth setting. The part would not regenerate at all, and we would have to spend some time fixing the model. This is a more serious problem than we have with the current model, which is therefore more robust. Once again, we see the need to plan ahead!

Design Considerations

We have covered a lot of ground in this lesson, and hopefully added a lot of ammunition to your modeling arsenal! We have also seen how the feature creation options can control the behavior of the model. So, now is a good time to say a few more words about part design.

One modeling decision you often have to make involves the balance or trade-off between using a few very complicated features or many simple ones. You must consider the following when trying to put a lot of geometry into a single feature:

- How easy will it be to modify the part/feature later?
- If the geometry is very complex, it is generally easier to create a number of simpler features that would combine to give the same resulting geometry.
- Using more, but simpler, features generally will give you more flexibility.
- Having a higher feature count increases the need for a carefully managed parent/child network.
- If you plan to do some engineering analysis of the part, for example a finite element analysis, then minor features such as rounds, chamfers, small holes, etc., will only complicate the model, perhaps unnecessarily. They will also lead to increased modeling effort downstream. These features are normally added last. We saw in Lesson #5 how they can be temporarily excluded from the model (called *suppressing* the feature), as long as they are not references (parents) of other features.
- If the entire part is contained in a single feature, some major changes to the part may not be feasible using that feature.
- What is the design intent of each feature? How should each feature be related

to other features (via the parent/child relations)? Don't set up unnecessary interdependencies between features that will restrict your freedom of modification later.

♦   You must be very careful with references. Sometimes these are essential elements of the design intent; sometimes you will fall into the trap of using a reference as a convenience when setting up a sketch, where this is not in the design intent. If you try to modify the feature later, you may find that the reference will get in the way.

When creating the patterns and copies, we discovered the ways that duplicated features could be modified, either during feature creation or after the fact. We also saw some of the ramifications of feature order in the model.

These considerations should be kept in mind as you plan the creation of each new part. It is likely that there are many ways in which to set up the part, and each will have different advantages and disadvantages depending on your goals. The more you know about the Pro/E tools, and the more practice you get, the better you will be able to make good decisions about part design. Good planning will lead to an easier task of part creation and make it easier to modify the geometry of the part later. Like most design tasks, the model design is subject to some iteration. We discussed in Lesson #5 some of the tools that Pro/E provides (the three R's) to allow you to change the structure of your model if it becomes necessary or to recover from modeling errors.

Most importantly, since design is increasingly becoming a group activity, make sure your model will be easy for someone else on your design team to understand. They may have to make modifications while you are away on vacation and you want them to be happy with you when you get back!

In the next lesson we will see how to create an engineering drawing from a Pro/E part. This will include view layout, section and detail views, and dimensioning. We will also create a couple of parts that will be needed in our assembly in the following two lessons.

Questions for Review

1. When creating a revolved protrusion, does the sketch have to be open or closed or can it be either?
2. When creating a revolved cut, does the sketch have to be open or closed or either?
3. What essential element is common to all revolved features?
4. Suppose you are creating a revolved protrusion and you align a vertex of the sketch with an existing feature surface. What happens if you try to create a 360 degree revolve and the aligning surface doesn't exist for the full revolution?
5. What is the first feature in a pattern called?
6. What is meant by a "radial" hole?
7. How do you turn off the note that comes with a standard hole?
8. How can you tell if a hole has a thread on it?
9. What dimensions are available for patterning a feature?
10. How could you create a spiral pattern of holes?
11. How could you create a radial pattern of rectangular cuts (extruded parallel to the radial pattern axis) so that the orientation of the cuts (a) changes with each instance to stay aligned with a radial line or (b) stays constant relative to the fixed datums?
12. What is the difference between independent and dependent copies?
13. What is the easiest way to create a pattern of several related features?
14. Is it possible to create a copy that is translated and rotated at the same time? What is the effect of changing the transformation order?
15. Comment on the rule of thumb in solid modeling: "Add material first, subtract material last." Do you think this would generally lead to good modeling practice?
16. What happens if you try to mirror one instance in a patterned feature?
17. What happens if you try to pattern a feature created using a make datum as a sketching plane?
18. What are the available variations for selecting references for specifying the translation direction and distance when making a copy?
19. Are there any dimensions of a pattern leader you cannot increment in the pattern?
20. What happens if you try to make a mirror copy that intersects the original feature. Is this even possible?
21. Can you make a pattern of patterns? A group of patterns? A pattern of groups?
22. What is the main difference between *Paste* and *Paste Special*?
23. What is the easiest way to create the following:
    a. An independent copy using the same references.
    b. A dependent copy with new references.
    c. A copy that uses some dimensions of the original but has some that differ.
    d. A copy that is always identical to the original but shifted sideways and vertically in the model.

Exercises

Here are some parts to practice the features you have learned in this lesson.

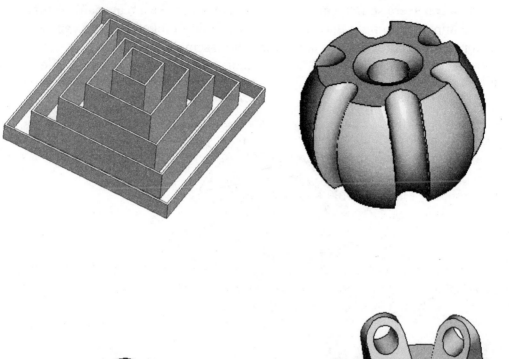

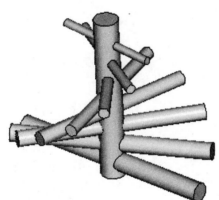

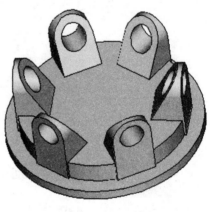

Project

This is the most complex project part. All dimensions are in millimeters. Some dimensions may be missing (because of implicit Sketcher rules or because the figures get too busy!). You can exercise some poetic license here and make a reasonable estimate for these. The important thing is that the assembly should fit together - you can easily edit dimension values later when you are putting the assembly together.

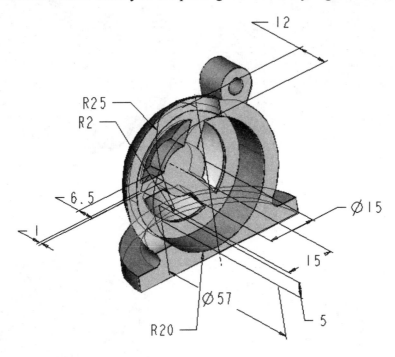

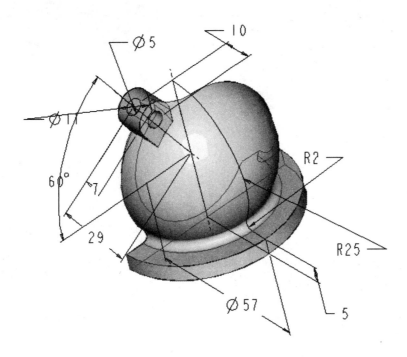

To help you visualize the part, these are close to full scale views of the Panavise part.

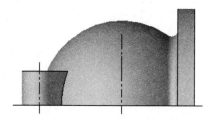

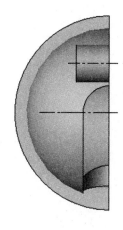

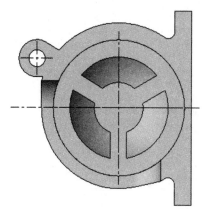

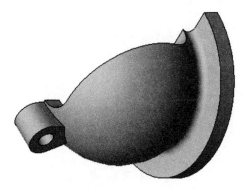

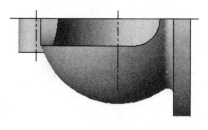

This page left blank.

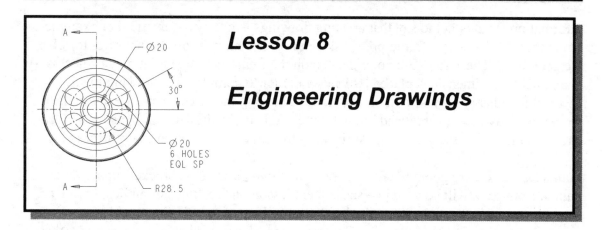

Synopsis

Overview of Drawing Mode environment. The Drawing Ribbon and Drawing Tree. Associativity. Shown vs created dimensions. View selection, orientation, and layout, section and detail views, dimensioning and detailing. Using a drawing template. Notes and parameters.

Overview of this Lesson

Although some changes in practice are on the horizon[1], the primary form of design documentation is still the 2D engineering drawing. The drawing must contain complete and unambiguous information about the part geometry and size, plus information on part material, surface finish, manufacturing notes, and so on. Over the years, the layout and practices used in engineering drawings have become standardized. This makes it easier for anyone to read the drawing, once they know what the standards are. Fortunately, Pro/E makes creating drawings relatively easy. You will find that all the standard practices are basically built-in - if you accept the default action for commands, most aspects of the drawing will be generally satisfactory. There are a number of commands we will see that are necessary to improve the "cosmetics" of the drawing.

Doing drawings with Pro/E lets you concentrate on *what* to show in the drawing instead of dealing with the drudgery involved in *how* to show it. For example, when creating views of an object it is virtually impossible to create views of a part that is not physically realizable - we don't have to worry about any 3-pronged blivots (see the Introduction). Even if the shape is possible, we don't want any visible or hidden lines in the wrong position (or missing entirely) on the drawing. This kind of mistake is easy to do with 2D CAD ("D" as in drafting) programs. The solid model contains all necessary and sufficient information in order to define the part geometry. Therefore, by getting all this information into the drawing, it is very difficult to create a drawing with inaccurate

---

[1] Some product development processes can go directly from the computer model to the manufacturing plant floor. A recent standard (ASME Y14.41) has been introduced for the annotation of 3D models. This standard is supported by Wildfire 2.0 and later.

information. That is not to say that creating drawings is totally automatic. For example, remember that when Pro/E interprets a sketch it fires a number of internal rules to solve the geometry. These rules are not indicated on the final drawing, and it may be necessary to augment the dimensions placed by Pro/E in order to complete the drawing to an acceptable industry standard. So in addition to showing the dimensions already in the model, we may have to create additional dimensions in the drawing. It is also possible, and sometimes necessary, to add additional graphical elements or notes to the drawing.

In this lesson, we are going to create drawings of two parts: an L-bracket support and a pulley. Both parts will be used in a subsequent lesson on creating assemblies, so don't forget to save the part files. We will also discover the power of bidirectional associativity, mentioned in the tutorial introduction. Here is what's on the agenda (these should be completed in order):

1. Exploring the Drawing Mode Environment
    ▸ layout of the interface
    ▸ exploring the ribbon tabs and drawing tree
    ▸ dimension types (model *vs* draft)
    ▸ exploring associativity
2. The L-Bracket
    ▸ creating the part
      • changing part units
    ▸ creating the drawing
      • layout (sheet setup)
      • layout (creating views)
      • annotation (showing dimensions)
      • annotation (cosmetic changes)
      • annotation (adding a note)
    ▸ changing the part/drawing - exploring associativity
    ▸ publishing the drawing
    ▸ drawing templates
3. The Pulley
    ▸ creating the part
    ▸ creating the drawing
      • layout (selecting the sheet)
      • layout (creating a section view)
      • layout (creating a detailed view)
      • annotation (showing dimensions)
      • annotation (cosmetic changes)
      • annotation (using parameters in notes)
      • annotation (creating dimensions)

This will be a pretty basic lesson on part drawings and we will only have time to cover the main topics. Even at that, this is a long lesson. The *Advanced Tutorial* from SDC contains more information on advanced drawing commands and functions, such as multisheet drawings, using multiple models, tables, repeat regions, formats, annotation elements, and creating drawing templates. As usual, there are some Questions for

Review, Exercises, and some Project parts at the end.

Before we get started, you need to make sure that the following files are available in your working directory

drwdemo.prt
drwdemo.drw
tut_Aformat.frm

These are on the enclosed CD or can be downloaded from <www.schroff1.com>.

The Drawing Environment

We will start by having a look at the various interface areas and drawing tools. Launch Wildfire (or clear everything out of your current session by closing all windows and selecting *File > Erase > Not Displayed*), turn off display of all datums, make sure the necessary files (*drwdemo.prt*, *drwdemo.drw*, and *tut_Aformat.frm*) are in your working directory, and open the file *drwdemo.drw*.[2]

Drawing Interface

The drawing interface is shown in Figure 1. The main drawing area shows a simple drawing of a single part. Contents of this drawing are discussed below. The major changes to the screen are the appearance of a set of commands near the top, the *Drawing Ribbon*, and a *Drawing Tree* that appears in the Navigator. These are shown in boxes in Figure 1 and are the major tools that you will use when in drawing mode. The ribbon functions in a similar way that the dashboard does in part mode. The ribbon contains six tabs (*Layout*, *Table*, *Annotate*, and so on); each tab has an associated set of groups of commands. The operation of the ribbon and the drawing tree are linked. We'll explore this some more in the next section.

Minor changes have occurred in the Menu bar and in the top toolbar. The pull-down menus have been repositioned to the top-right corner, and commands in each pull-down list are slightly different from part mode. Some buttons have disappeared from the toolbar, others have appeared. At the bottom of the screen are some controls for drawing sheets and some information about the current drawing (drawing scale, type and name of the active model, sheet size). The Model Tree appears in the Navigator as usual and the selection filter is above the top right of the drawing area. The filter now refers to elements that would appear in a drawing.

---

[2] Note that the part file must be available. We have placed this in the working directory along with the drawing. This is not strictly necessary but having it elsewhere complicates things. The optional format file, on the other hand, is usually stored in a system formats directory along with some standard formats. Creating your own format file is a form of customization that is discussed in the *Advanced Tutorial*.

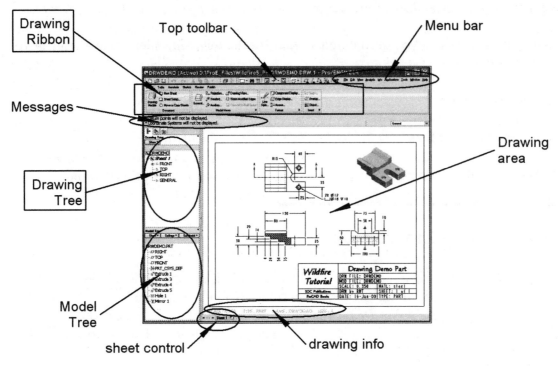

Figure 1 The Drawing Mode default interface

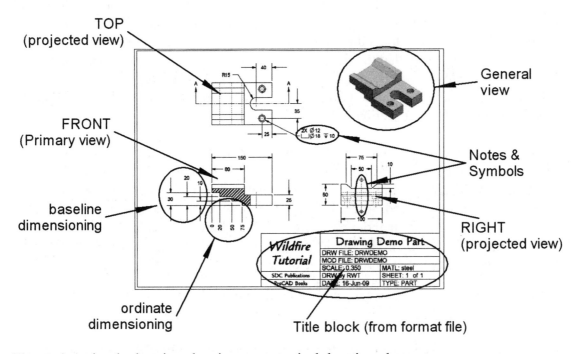

Figure 2 A simple drawing showing some typical drawing elements

A fairly simple engineering drawing appears in the drawing area (see Figure 2). The drawing sheet includes a title block that is defined in a drawing format file. Some of the information in the title block is filled in automatically using parameters contained in the model. The drawing itself shows the standard orthographic views (TOP-FRONT-RIGHT) as well as a general view. The latter is becoming more common on engineering drawings in order to give the reader a quick look at the 3D shape of the object. The front view contains a full section, with a hatch pattern indicating that the part is made of steel (also indicated in the title block). The part has been annotated with dimensions and notes. There are several styles of dimensions shown here, including baseline and ordinate dimensions. Not visible immediately is the fact that some of the dimensions have come from the model, while others were created in the drawing. This very important point will be discussed some more later.

Try changing the model display (*Hidden*, *No Hidden*, and *Shading*) using the buttons in the top toolbar or in *Tools > Environment*. You will find that only the general view on the drawing responds to these changes (you may have to do a *Repaint* after each, or just do a quick scroll wheel jog). This is because this view has been left to follow the environment (the default) while the three other views have been specifically set (select the general view and use the *Properties* command in the RMB pop-up menu, then select the category *View Display*).

Mouse Controls in Drawing Mode

The middle mouse button function has changed a bit. Instead of controlling spin as in part mode, it is now used to pan. The scroll wheel controls zoom as usual. Try these out. If you are zoomed way in on the drawing, there is a *Refit* button in the top toolbar.

As always, the RMB pop-up menu is context sensitive. Try picking some items on the drawing and see what is in that menu. If you accidentally make a change in the drawing, just load a fresh copy from the working directory.

Drawing Ribbon and Drawing Tree

We'll spend a few minutes exploring the functions in the various groups in the ribbon at the top. We will not be using all of them but it may be helpful in the future to know what and where these commands are. As always, Wildfire allows us to launch commands in a number of ways (ribbon, RMB menu on a highlighted item in the drawing or model trees, pull-down menus, or RMB menu on a selected element in the drawing itself). The commands available will change depending on the status of the ribbon (ie which tab is selected) and what is currently highlighted in the graphics window.

As mentioned above, the ribbon and drawing tree functions are linked. The information displayed in the drawing tree will depend on which of the ribbon tabs has been selected. Regardless of which tab is selected, the top level organization in the drawing tree is the drawing sheet. It is common practice (and usually necessary) for drawings to contain multiple sheets; our demo drawing here has only one sheet. The next level of organization is the view. Each view will contain drawing elements that will change depending on which ribbon tab is currently selected.

There are six tabs on the ribbon. You can select any tab at any time and are not restricted to a particular sequence. However, they are organized from left to right in generally the same order that your workflow will occur. Selecting each tab opens a new set of groups of commands. Within each ribbon group, some command buttons will display only with an icon, some will have a text label. How these are displayed will depend on a number of factors (configuration settings, display size and resolution, customized settings, ...). Some buttons may appear as large icons while others are small. When you mouse-over any of the buttons in the groups you will see a pop-up showing the command name and a brief explanation. Some groups also have a pull-down panel at the bottom containing infrequently used commands. As usual, buttons that are not relevant at any given moment are grayed out.

The six tabs on the drawing ribbon are as follows:

Layout

When you first enter a drawing, you start by determining which model(s) you are going to display, details of drawing sheets (formats, sheet sizes), and setting up which views will appear on each sheet.

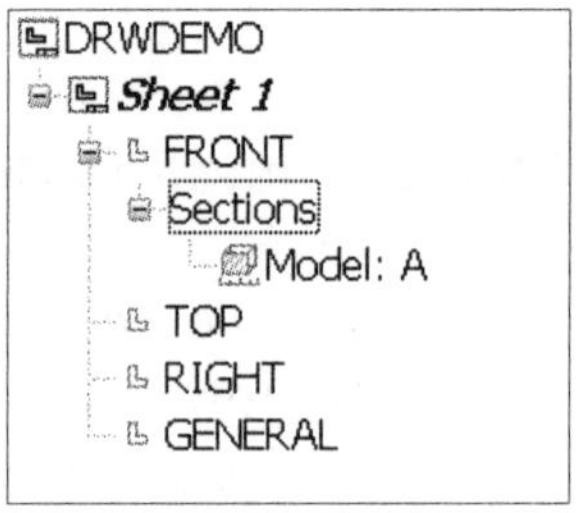

Figure 3 Drawing tree with **Layout** selected

When **Layout** is selected, the Drawing tree shows the views in the drawing, Figure 3. In the current drawing, the various views have been renamed to correspond to normal practice in order to make it easy to select the desired view. If a view in the drawing tree is selected, it will be surrounded by a dashed red highlight box in the drawing. Expanding a view in the drawing tree, shows details of specific aspects of the view, such as the section "A" shown in the FRONT view.

Table

This tab is for creating things like the title block, but more often for drawing elements like Repeat Regions and Bill of Materials (BOM). When you select this tab, the drawing tree indicates the tables in the drawing (Figure 4). In the present case, the only table is the one in the title block. We will not be doing any tables in this Tutorial, but this is covered in the *Advanced Tutorial*.

Figure 4 Drawing tree with **Table** selected

Annotate

You will be spending most of your time in this tab. It has the largest set of groups and individual commands. Selecting this tab changes the drawing tree to once again show the views on the drawing and, at the next level in the tree, the various annotations and datums associated with each view. This will likely be the most detailed set of data concerning the drawing you will see.

For example, in the TOP view, open the annotations and datums groups. See Figure 5. Selecting any of these entries in the drawing tree will highlight them in red on the drawing. Note the symbolic names of the model dimensions given here. If you expand the annotations under the FRONT view, Figure 6, you will see that there are two types of

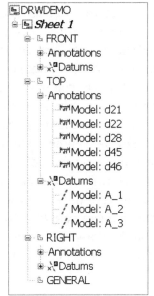

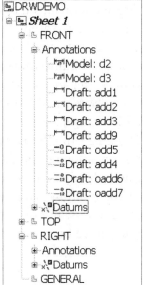

Figure 5 The drawing tree with **Annotate** selected

Figure 6 The drawing tree with Annotate selected

annotations. Model annotations are based on dimensions and parameters that come from the 3D model itself. Draft annotations are created in the drawing. For example, the draft dimension **add9** in the Front view was necessary due to an explicit constraint being used in the sketch for the base feature of this part. Such constraints do not show on the drawing and we frequently must create some dimensions to make the drawing complete. The baseline and ordinate dimensioning schemes were also set up in the drawing itself (even though model dimensions already exist), which result in these becoming draft annotations. Note the symbolic names of these dimensions and the different icons in the tree. Other types of draft annotations are notes.

Sketch

These six groups contain commands for creating graphical drawing elements. The functionality of this is very similar to Sketcher. We will not be using these commands here, but you should come back some time to play with these functions.

Review

These commands let you check the status of the drawing prior to release. For example, you can make sure that information in drawing tables is updated, the model is regenerated, and so on. You can obtain information about the model (measured quantities such as distance or area). A handy command in the *Query* group is *Highlight By Attributes* (also available in the top toolbar) which opens the window shown in Figure 7. Set the checkbox for *Dimension* in the **Item Type** area. When you select the *Highlight* button at the bottom, the model and draft dimensions will be highlighted in a different color. By changing the settings in the dialog window, you can highlight only specific types of annotations. For example, you can determine if draft geometry or notes have been placed on the drawing that do not come from the model itself. Close the **Highlight** dialog window.

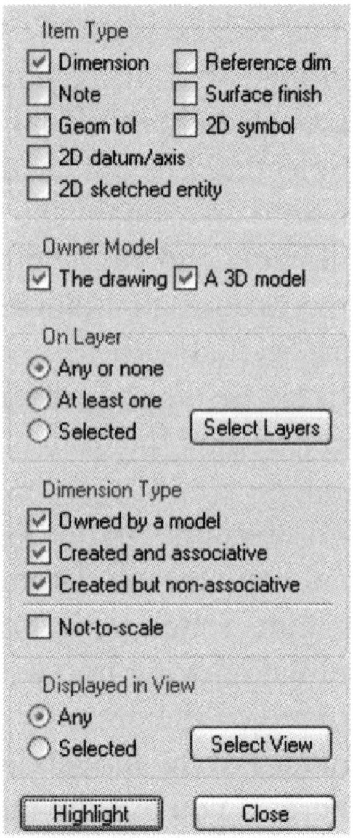

Figure 7 The Highlight menu

Publish

When this is selected, the Navigator minimizes (and in fact no longer contains either the drawing tree or model tree). In the first group in the ribbon you can determine the type of output you want (typically either sending to a printer or storing as a file in a specific format). The second group lets you preview the output before actually producing it.

This completes your introduction to the drawing ribbon tools. In the following, when a particular command or button is to be selected, its ribbon tab and group will be identified as **tab(group)**. For example, the *Preview* button is located in **Publish(Finish)**.

Before we start making our first drawing, there are a couple of important concepts we should go over: dimension types (model and draft) and associativity between the drawing and the model.

Shown vs *Created* Dimensions

The drawing in Figure 2 illustrates a number of ways for laying out the dimensions, including baseline and ordinate dimensioning, and the addition of notes and symbols. Although it is not obvious from the figure, most of these dimensions come from the part model itself where they are used in sketches or locating features like holes. When placing the annotations on the drawing, all we have to do is "show" these dimensions (with the opposite operation being to "hide" them). Such *model dimensions* cannot be created or destroyed in the drawing, since they belong to the model. They are sometimes called *driving dimensions* since they control the model geometry. We will see this in the next section on the topic of associativity.

On the other hand, we may have to create some dimensions on the drawing that do not currently exist in the part. These exist only in the drawing and are called *draft dimensions* or, because their values are determined by the model, they are also known as *driven dimensions*. Draft dimensions could be necessary for a number of reasons, including the fact that we prefer a different dimensioning scheme (ordinate, for example) than was used in the model or we must account for explicit constraints that have been used in feature sketches. This somewhat elaborate terminology is hopefully made a bit more clear in the following table.

Table 8.1 The Mysteries of Model vs Draft Dimensions

The type of dimension indicated in the drawing tree is ...	Model	Draft
Where does the dimension value originate?	part or assembly	drawing
How do we get the dimension onto the drawing?	Show	Create
What is the relation of the dimension to the model?	Driving	Driven
What is the form of the symbolic name for the dimension on the drawing?	*dxx*	*adxx* or *oadxx*

To see the symbolic names (last row in the table above), in **Annotate(Parameters)**, select the command *Switch Dimensions*. This causes all the dimensions (and parameters in the title block) to display on the drawing using their symbolic names. We can pick out which are model dimensions and which are draft dimensions. Another way to do this is with the *Highlight* button in the top toolbar (or in the **Review** tab). Yet another way to determine the symbolic name is with a simple mouse-over - the driving dimensions will indicate which feature they come from while the driven dimensions do not (can not since their references could be two different features!).

Dimension Properties

Select *Switch Dimensions* again to return the dimension display to numerical values. Select the vertical dimension **50** that appears in the right view. As you mouse-over the dimension or extension lines (not the numerical value), a pop-up should identify it as "d1:F5(EXTRUDE_1)", meaning symbolic dimension *d1* of feature #5 called "Extrude 1" - check the model tree. With this selected, in the RMB pop-up menu, select *Properties*. This opens the window shown in Figure 8. In the **Properties** tab, you can see the symbolic name and the nominal value. Check out the other options available here (decimal places, tolerance, decimal/fractional format). Select the **Display** tab. This lets you set non-default display properties. In particular, note the text string "@D" in the pane on the right. This string means, effectively, "print the nominal value of the driving dimension". The notation "@S" here would cause the symbolic value to be printed. The third tab in the **Properties** window is *Text Style*. This dialog gives you control over the text font, size, color, orientation, etc. of the dimension. Close the dialog window with *OK*.

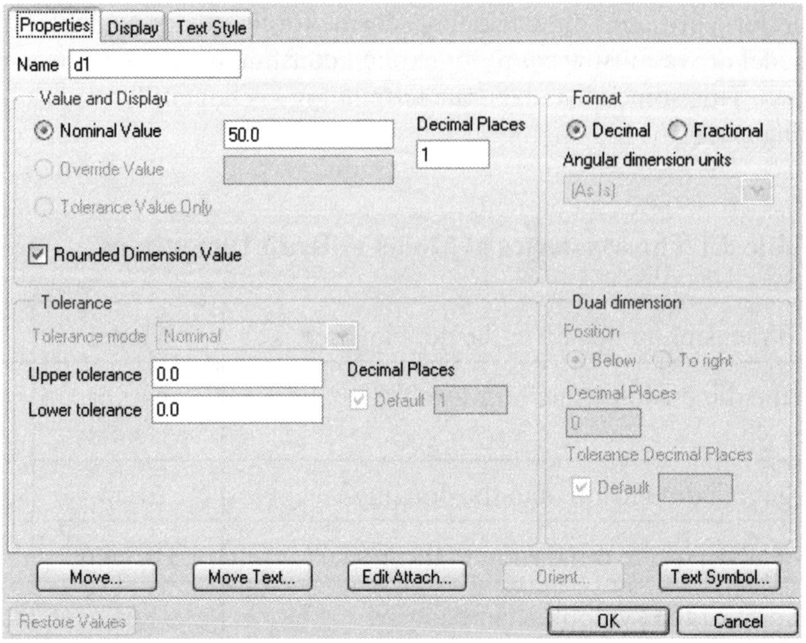

Figure 8 The **Dimension Properties** window

Select the leader note on the hole in the TOP view. A mouse-over on the leader indicates that this note is for dimension *d28* of the hole feature #9. This is actually the dimension for the diameter of the counterbore that the leader is touching (the outer circle). Now open the *Properties* window with the note selected. In the **Properties** tab, the symbolic name (d28) and nominal

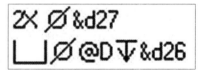

Figure 9 Display text for the hole note

value (18) are indicated. Compare this to the note on the drawing. The value is buried inside the note text. How does this happen? Go to the **Display** tab and check out the pane on the right. See Figure 9. Observe that the "@D" notation occurs after the counterbore and diameter symbols on the second line. The other symbolic dimensions preceded with an ampersand, "&d27" and "&d26", are for the hole diameter and counterbore depth, respectively. The ampersand means "display the value" of the following model parameter. Note that only one "@D" can appear in the dimension text, since the dimension text is "owned" by only one model dimension (d28 in this case). This notation was created by entering the text directly in the pane, with help from the *Text Symbol* button at the bottom right to open a pallette of commonly used symbols. You can put any text into this pane. Close the **Properties** window with *OK*.

Exploring Associativity

Our last exploration of the drawing environment involves the concept of associativity. This was mentioned in the Introduction, but we now get to see what it is all about.

Once again select the vertical dimension **50** in the right view. Change this to **80** by selecting *Modify Nominal Value* in the RMB pop-up (or by selecting *Properties*). If you clear the red highlight by clicking on the drawing background, the dimension should appear in green. This is the indication that the nominal value has changed but the model has not been updated. Before you do that, have a look at the vertical dimension 25 in the front view. What dimension type is this? (Hint: use a mouse over). You can update the model in any of four ways: (1) select *Edit > Regenerate Model*, (2) use the keyboard shortcut CTRL-G, (3) go to **Review(Update)** and select *Regenerate Model*, or (4) with nothing highlighted, use a RMB on the background and select *Regenerate Active Model*. Pick one!

When the model regenerates, the FRONT, RIGHT, and general view all change. This indicates that the dimension we chose to modify is driving the geometry. The drawing and the model are associated through the driving dimensions. Since the dimension is associated with both the model and drawing, changing its value in either place will result in a change in the geometry.

Meanwhile, the vertical dimension *add9* on the FRONT view (that was 25) is now 40. Try to select this dimension and change it back to 25. You can select it but there is no way to modify its value - with the **Annotate** tab selected, try the RMB pop-up menu, and *Properties* command. The nominal value data field is grayed out. It has been driven by the change in the model.

This concludes our introduction to drawing mode. There is a lot to learn here. In the following we will create a couple of drawings from scratch. We will discover yet more options and drawing functions.

A final thing you should keep in mind is that although the drawing file is able to display and call up information about the part model, the drawing file does not contain the model. This still resides in the part file. If you move the drawing file to another machine and don't take the part file with it, the drawing will not open. Because the drawing and part are so tightly linked, most systems are set up so that if the drawing file makes changes in the model (using the driving dimensions) then the part file is automatically saved when the drawing file is saved. This way the drawing and model are always in sync. Eventually, you are liable to come across a situation when the drawing and model are out of sync (due to file mismanagement, for example) and you will receive warning and/or error messages.

Close the demo drawing window (and part window if you had that open), and remove everything from your session using *File > Erase > Not Displayed*.

The L-Bracket

Creating the Part

First, we'll create the part shown in
Figure 10. Call this part **lbrack** and
use the default template for a solid
part. (We're going to change the
part units in a minute.) Study this
figure carefully. When you create
the part, make sure that the back
surface of the vertical leg is aligned
with **FRONT**, the lower surface of
the horizontal leg is aligned with
TOP, and the vertical plane of
symmetry through the upper hole is
RIGHT. An obvious choice for the
base feature is a both-sides solid
protrusion in the shape of a
backwards "L" (as seen from the
right side) sketched on **RIGHT**.
This will allow us to mirror the
second small hole and align the
larger one with **RIGHT**. Notice the
dimensioning scheme for the holes.
Go ahead and create this part now.

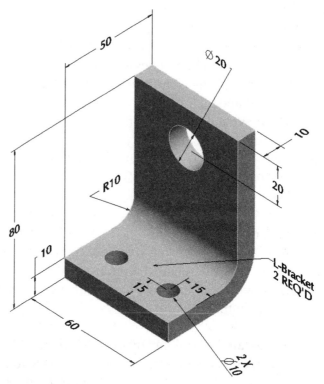

Figure 10 The L-bracket part (dimensions in mm)

Changing Part Units

The model units are important so that the scale factor for showing the views on the
drawing sheet will be correct. Wildfire will try to pick a reasonable scale based on the
actual size of the object and the physical size of the drawing sheet.

Note that the units in Figure 10 are given in millimeters, whereas in a standard Pro/E
installation, the default template uses inches. This is a common "oops" when creating a
model, since the units are not topmost in our mind when we first start the part (or when
you inherit a model from another source). Here's how to change the part units (if you
have to). Select (from the pull-down menu)

> *File > Properties*

This opens the **Model Properties** window. This shows the current status of a number of
attributes of the model. In the top group, in the row indicating the current units pick
change at the far right. The **Units Manager** window opens, as shown in Figure 11. This
lists the common unit systems in Pro/E (and its companion Pro/MECHANICA used for
finite element analysis). The current units are indicated by the red arrow pointer. Select

the line containing the unit system

millimeter Newton Second

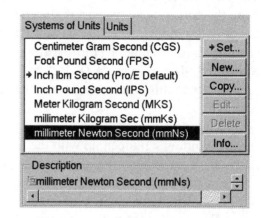

and then *Set*. A warning dialog opens. When you change the units of a model, you have two options that will affect all linear dimensions:

Figure 11 The **Units Manager** window

Convert dimensions - This leaves the model the same real size as the original. For example, a 1 inch long bar will be converted to a 25.4mm long bar. The dimension number changes. This is normally what we mean when we "change units."

Interpret dimensions - This keeps the dimension numbers the same, but interprets them in the new units. In our example, the 1 inch long bar becomes a 1mm long bar. This is how we recover from the "oops" mentioned above.

Managing units is especially important if you are going to produce an assembly of parts, as we will do in the next two lessons. It is also critical to be aware of units when you are working in a design group, since some people may be working in inches while others are in millimeters. Parts downloaded from the web also come in all varieties. You may be aware of some classic blunders that have occurred over the years due to mix-ups in the interpretation of units or people making assumptions about units used by others.

If you have used the dimension values in the figure above, then you want to pick the second option here (*Interpret dimensions*) and select *OK*. *Close* the Units Manager window, then *Close* the **Model Properties** window. When this is applied, double-click on the protrusion to verify that the dimension numbers haven't changed.

Don't forget to save the part in the working directory! We are now ready to create the drawing. Leave the part in hidden line display mode.

Creating the Drawing of the L-Bracket

① **Create the Drawing File**

Select the following:

File > New > Drawing

Replace the default name with **lbrack** - we generally keep the drawing name the same as the part name.

IMPORTANT: Turn off the option **Use default template**. We will deal with drawing templates a bit later. Select *OK*.

The **New Drawing** menu will open up (see Figure 12).
Note the currently active part is automatically selected as
the drawing model. Keep the defaults for the template
(**Empty**) and orientation (**Landscape**), but change the
Standard Size option to **A** (8-1/2" by 11" in landscape
mode). When this window is complete, accept the entries
with *OK*.

A new window will open up with the title *LBRACK
(Active)*. This will overlap or cover the part window,
which is still open but pushed to the back. You can switch
back and forth between the part and drawing windows
using *Window* (in the pull-down menu). Current windows
are listed at the bottom of the menu. If several windows
are in view, only one of them will be active at a time
(indicated by the word **Active** in the title).

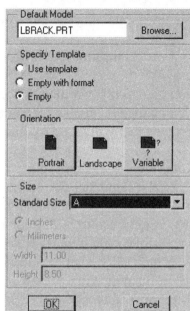

Figure 12 The **New Drawing**
menu

In the drawing window, the drawing ribbon is now
displayed, with the default **Layout** tab selected. The
drawing tree shows that there is one sheet. The information area at the bottom of the
screen shows the model type and name, and the sheet size. The scale value doesn't mean
much yet since we haven't set up any views.

② **Adding Views**

In **Layout(Model Views)**, select *General* (or use the RMB pop-up menu either in the
drawing area or in the drawing tree, select *Insert General View*). Read the prompt in the
message window. The view we will place first will be our primary view. It will be the
front view of the part, so select a center point a bit left and below the center of the sheet,
as shown in Figure 13. The **Drawing View** dialog window also opens (Figure 14).

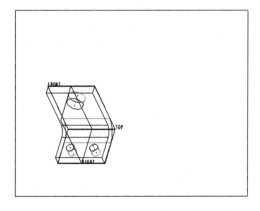

Figure 13 Placing the primary view

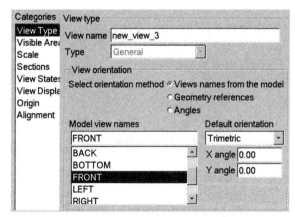

Figure 14 The **Drawing View** window

The **Drawing View** window contains all the options for creating (and changing properties) of views on the drawing sheet. This includes view type and orientation, section views, edge display, scale, and so on. Browse through the various items listed in the **Categories** area. As each is selected the window contents will change, showing the options available with that category. For example, note in the **Scale** category, a default sheet scale has been determined (in this case 1.0). We can come back later to change the sheet scale if desired. Don't change any of the default settings for now.

Select the **View Type** category. We want to set the desired orientation of the primary view. This will be the front view of the bracket. In the **Model view names** list, select **FRONT** from the list of views defined in the model (shown in Figure 14). Now select *Apply* at the lower right, then *Close*.

Notice that the view has a dashed red box around it. This means that it is the currently selected view. Click anywhere else on the sheet to turn off the selection highlight. Turn off the datum display and *Redraw*. Your drawing should look like Figure 15.

Now we want to add the right and top views. These could be created using the *General* button and selecting the RIGHT and TOP named views in the **View Type** lists. However, this will not automatically align these new views with the primary view. We want to create projected views off the primary.

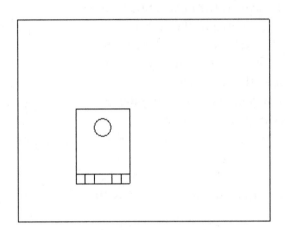

Figure 15 Primary view placed and oriented

Select the primary view so that it is highlighted with the red box. Now in the RMB pop-up menu, select *Insert Projection View*. You will now see a sliding yellow border that will always align with the parent view. Position the mouse somewhere to the right of the primary view and click. Voilà! The right side view appears. To create the top view, we once again select the primary view (this is what we want to project from) and use the RMB pop-up command *Insert Projection View.* Click above the front view to get the top view. Pretty easy!

If you don't like the spacing of your views, you can easily move them. By default, views are locked in place where you created them. In order to move any of the views, this lock must be turned off. You can do this in one of two ways:

- select *Tools > Environment*, and turn off *Lock View Movement*

or
- select any view, entry in the drawing tree, or even the drawing background, then in the RMB pop-up, uncheck *Lock View Movement*

When you move views, Pro/E will ensure that your projected views stay aligned. Select the right side view - it will be surrounded by a red border and have a drag handles at the corners and enter. Click anywhere on the view and drag to move the view. Try to move the view up, down, left, and right on the screen (you can't move up or down since the view must align with the front view). Left-click again to drop the view at the new location. Try moving the top view. Finally, try moving the front view. You should see the other views move to maintain the correct orthographic alignment.

Click the **left**-mouse button on an open area of the screen (ie not on another view) when you are finished moving the views to turn off view selection. Turn the view lock back on using the RMB pop-up menu.

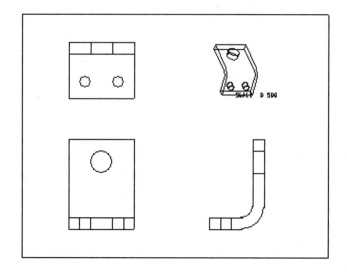

Figure 16 All views placed for L-brack

Let's add a fourth view that shows the part in 3D. Note that this is not a projected view but a general one. We'll scale this one down to half size. In the RMB pop-up menu, select

> ***Insert General View***

then click in the top right corner of the sheet. The view will appear. In the **Drawing View** window, under the **View Type** category, select the **Default Orientation**, then *Apply*.

Select the category **Scale**, and change the **Custom Scale** to *0.5* and once again select *Apply > Close*.

③ Setting View Display Mode

The default view display (hidden line, wireframe, etc) is determined by the view display of the part in the model window. Of course, we don't normally use shaded images in a drawing. Thus, it is possible that your drawing is displaying all edges as solid lines (hidden line and visible lines the same). To make sure hidden lines are treated correctly, select all four views (using the CTRL key), then in the RMB pop-up menu, select **Properties**. (You can also do this one view at a time by double clicking on it.) In the **Drawing View** window (you are automatically in the *View Disp* category panel since you selected multiple views) set the following

> ***Display Style (Hidden)***
> ***Tangent edges (None)***

then press *Apply > Close*. These view display settings are now fixed properties of the views and not affected by the top toolbar buttons or the display style in the part window. The drawing should now appear as in Figure 16.

④ **Adding Dimensioning Detail**

In the drawing ribbon, select *Annotate(Insert)*. Then select the button *Show Model Annotations* (or just use the RMB pop-up in the drawing area to select *Show Model Annotations*). Note in passing that this pop-up menu is different from the one we got with a different ribbon tab selected.

The **Show Model Annotations** window opens. The **Type** pull-down list (default to **All**) lets us select specific types of annotations (dimensions, notes, datums, etc.) that might exist in the model. The tabs at the top (currently grayed out) would be available if we had annotations of the respective types in the model. The message in the window directs us to select either views, components, or features, and to pick the desired view where we want the annotations to go.

Let's start by selecting the entire part. Go to the Model Tree in the Navigator and select the part name. All of the part dimensions are now listed with check boxes in the window, and appear in dark red on the drawing on various views. As you mouse-over the check boxes, the dimensions will show on the drawing in cyan. You can individually select check boxes for dimensions you want to appear, or pick the button at the lower left to select them all, as in Figure 17. The dimensions will turn yellow. Then select the *Apply* button at the lower right. The dimensions change to gray.

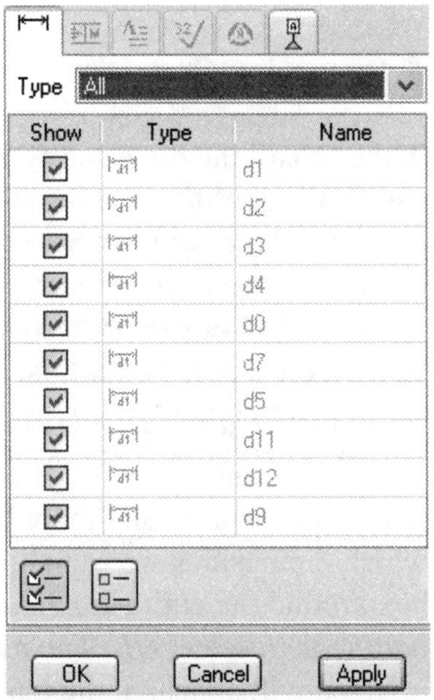

The **Show Model Annotations** window now lists all the datum axes in the model (the tab on the far right has been selected automatically). Once again, experiment with the various check boxes, turning on the ones you want to keep. Note that these include axes in the general view at the top right. You likely won't need all of them since some may be aligned behind others in a particular view. Then select *Apply*. The axes now appear in gray.

Figure 17 Window for Show Model Annotations

Finally, accept all the annotations with *OK*.

Observe what has happen on the drawing (axes show in brown, dimensions in yellow), and in the drawing tree. Each view now contains both annotation and datum elements.

We selected to show all the dimensions at once. This is a potentially hazardous thing to do - think of a part or assembly that might have hundreds of dimensions! We got away with that procedure this time because there aren't too many dimensions in this drawing.

For more complicated parts, you might like to show the dimensions by individual feature, all dimensions in a given view, or a specific feature in a chosen view. Some experience with these options is necessary to make good choices here, otherwise you'll spend a lot of unproductive time cleaning up the drawing.

Take a moment to think back to how you created the part. The dimensions put on the drawing using **Show** are exactly the ones you used in your features. These are (no surprise!) called *Shown* dimensions. Another type of dimension can be created in the drawing, naturally called *Created* dimensions, which we will discuss a bit later. **The lesson here is to use the dimensions in feature creation that you want to appear on the drawing**[3]. So, you should know something about drawing standards and how you want the dimensions laid out in the drawing *before* you start to create the solid model - a point often missed by many. This is often a point of contention between designers (who make the models) and detailers (who create the detailed drawings).

In the next drawing, we will see a more systematic way of adding the dimensions rather than showing them all at once. This will always be the preferred way of defining annotations.

⑤ Dimension Cosmetics

Although all the dimensions are now on the drawing, and Pro/E does the best job it can to determine where to place the dimensions (which view, and so on), there is a lot we may need to do to improve their placement and appearance. For example, some of the dimensions may be a bit crowded. To fix this, in **Annotate(Arrange)**, select the ***Cleanup Dimensions*** button or use the same command in the RMB pop-up menu. This opens the window shown in Figure 18. We have to identify which dimensions we want cleaned. Draw a selection box around the entire drawing with the left mouse button, then select ***OK***. The number of dimensions affected will appear at the top of the **Clean Dimensions** window and these will appear in dark red on the drawing. Notice that dimensions using leaders are not affected. The default spacings (an offset of 0.5 is the spacing in real inches from the edge of the part to the first dimension line, the increment of 0.375 is

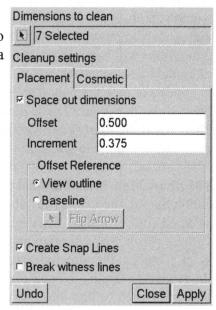

Figure 18 Cleaning up the dimension layout

---

[3] This is a good topic for a philosophical discussion. Some users differentiate between "design" intent (dimension scheme used to create the computer model) and "manufacturing" intent (dimensions appearing on the drawing), maintaining that sometimes these are different. If you want to start a lively discussion among hard-core Pro/E users, ask them if it is better to use "Shown" dimensions or "Created" dimensions in a drawing.

between parallel dimension lines) are drawing standards. Pick on the *Apply* button. All the dimensions should spread out and appear in dark red. The faint dashed gray lines are called the *snap lines*. As you proceed to modify the drawing layout, the dimensions will snap to these locations to help you maintain the spacings set in *Clean Dimensions*. These snap lines are a convenience only and will not be printed with the drawing.

Depending on your view placement and dimensioning scheme, Pro/E might have some trouble with dimension placement (for example, too little room between views). Look in the message window for error messages and warnings. *Close* the **Clean Dimensions** window. All dimensions should now be in yellow.

The drawing should look something like Figure 19 (your dimensioning scheme may be slightly different from this, depending on how you created your model).

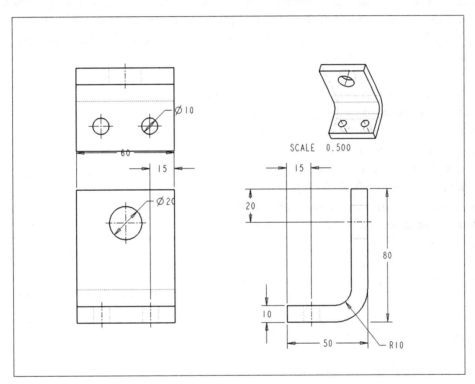

Figure 19 Dimensions placed and *Clean*ed

There is a lot more we can do to modify the display esthetics of the dimensioning detail. To start with, some of the dimension placement locations chosen by Pro/E may need to be touched up a little. It is probably necessary to switch some of the dimensions to a different view, and you may want to modify spacing and location of dimensions on views, direction of dimension arrows, and so on. For example, the location dimensions for all the holes should be on the view that shows the circular shape of the hole. For the two small holes, this is the top view. For the large hole, this is the front view. Most of these cosmetic modifications can be made using the mouse buttons as follows.

Pick (left click) on one of the dimensions you want to modify. For example, you might select the dimension giving the thickness of the plate as shown in the right view. (See Figure 20). Note the small square "handles" on the dimension components. Left-click on any handle in order to drag it to the desired position. If you select the handle directly under the dimension value, you can move it practically anywhere. The extension lines and arrows will automatically follow. Notice the effect of the snap lines.

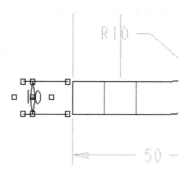

Figure 20 "Handles" for modifying dimension cosmetics

While dragging this around, if you want to flip the dimension arrows (ie. put them inside/outside the extension lines), just ***Right-click*** (while you are holding down the left button). When you select a dimension with a leader, clicking the RMB will cycle through a number of arrangements for the leader line and dimension arrowhead placement.

When the dimension is where you want it, ***left-click*** to drop. You can continue to left-click on the handles to move the dimension, extension lines, dimension line, and arrows until you get exactly the appearance you want. ***To accept the final placement and format, click the left mouse button somewhere else on the screen or select another detail item.*** The modified dimension will turn yellow.

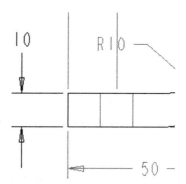

Figure 21 Modified dimension cosmetics

The final configuration might look something like Figure 21.

To modify more dimensions, continue the sequence:

- ◆   left-click on a dimension,
- ◆   drag on the handles as desired using left-mouse,
- ◆   right-click to flip arrows if desired,
- ◆   left-click to accept

until you are satisfied with the layout. If you want to move a dimension to another view, after you have picked out the dimension, hold down the right mouse button and select ***Move Item to View*** from the pop-up menu, then left-click on the desired new view. You can also use (in the pull-down menu) ***Edit > Move Item to View***.

Also available in the pop-up menu are a number of other cosmetic modification commands. The major ones are fairly self-explanatory

Try to lay out all the dimensions so that your drawing looks similar to Figure 22. The dashed offset (snap) lines created when we cleaned the dimensions can be removed by selecting ***Delete*** from the pop-up menu. You don't really need to do this for hard copy, since Pro/E will not print snap lines.

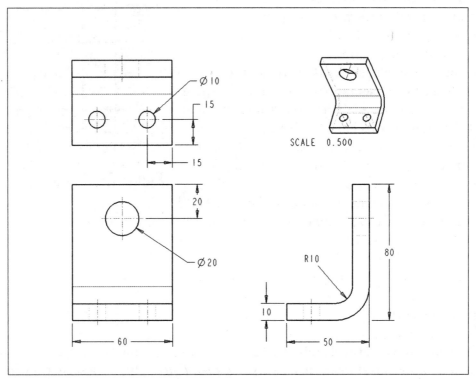

Figure 22 L-bracket final drawing

Do not be concerned at this time if the yellow extension lines are touching or crossing the model. As you probably know, this is a "no-no" in engineering drawings. Pro/E will clean up the extension lines when a hard copy is generated. Pro/E will also look after all the line weights and line styles (for visible and hidden lines, center lines, dimension and extension lines, and so on) according to standard engineering drawing practice.

⑥ Creating a Note

Let's add a short note on the drawing (we will talk about title blocks in the next section). You may have to move the other views up a bit to fit this in (you can do that after the note is created, if necessary). In **Annotate(Insert)**, select the ***Note*** button ![A note button] . Observe the defaults in the **Note Types** menu (see the message window as you mouse-over these options)

No Leader | Enter | Horizontal | Standard | Default

and select the ***Make Note*** command at the bottom of the menu. Read the message prompt, then select a location a little below the right side view. An input window opens where you can type in the note text, and a small **Text Symbol** window opens from which you can select special characters. Pressing the enter key will advance you to the next line of text in the note. Pressing the enter key on a blank line will complete the note. Type in something like the following:

> ***ALL DIMENSIONS IN mm***
> ***Drawn by Art O'Graphic***
> ***6 July 2009***

In the menu at the right, select ***Done/Return***. If you left click on the note, you can move it around by dragging. If it is selected, you can pick the ***Properties*** command in the RMB pop-up. This lets you change the text and text font, and even load text from an external file or create a hyperlink.

Figure 23 The Symbol palette

Save the drawing using the default filename; Pro/E will automatically append a *drw* extension to the file name.

> ***File > Save***

Exploring Associativity

One of the most powerful features of Pro/E is its ability to connect the part model and the drawing in a bidirectional link. This is called *associativity*. Here is a scenario where this is very useful.

It's late Friday afternoon and your boss has just reviewed the design and drawings of the L-bracket, and has decided that a few changes are needed as follows (before you go home!)

- ♦ the height must be increased to 100 mm
- ♦ the diameter of the large hole must be changed to 30 mm
- ♦ the top of the bracket must be rounded in an arc concentric with the large hole
- ♦ the manufacturing group wants the drawing to show the height of the large hole off the bottom of the part, which should be 70mm

Hmmmm... You could do this by going back to the part and modifying/changing. BUT..there is an easier way! To really see the power of what you are about to do, resize the drawing and part windows so that both are visible. Make sure the **DRAWING** window is active. If not, click on the drawing window and select ***Window > Activate*** in the pull-down menu (or use the shortcut CRTL-A).

Select the diameter dimension of the large hole. In the RMB pop-up menu, select ***Modify Nominal Value***. Enter a new value of ***30***. Click somewhere off the dimension and it will show in green. Similarly, select the height dimension and change it to ***100***. Now, in the top pull-down menu, select (or use the shortcut key CTRL-G)

Edit > Regenerate Model

The drawing should change to show the new geometry. Even better, as soon as you activate it, the part window also shows the new geometry. In the part window double click on the protrusion and change the width of the bracket from 60 to *80*, then *Regenerate*. Change back to the drawing window and activate it - it shows the new shape too. These actions show that there is a *bidirectional* link between the drawing and the part. If changes are made to an item in either view of the model, the other is automatically updated. The same holds true when you deal with assemblies of parts, and drawings of those assemblies.

* VERY IMPORTANT POINT *

New users often find that changes they have made to a drawing get lost somehow. The following will help you avoid the "What happened to my drawing?" syndrome.

Consider what Pro/E needs to maintain associativity between part and drawing. In order to update the part when a dimension is changed on the drawing, then the part itself must be "in session" (but not necessarily in its own window) whenever the drawing is[4]. Therefore, to bring up the drawing (read it from disk), the part file must also be available (on disk or already in session). The part will be brought into session, if necessary, even if it is not displayed in its own window. Think of the drawing file as a set of instructions for how the part model should be represented in the drawing. **The drawing file does not itself contain the part.** Furthermore, when the drawing file is read from disk, the part file must be in the same location relative to the drawing file (and have the same name) as it was when the drawing was created (usually the same directory) - otherwise Pro/E doesn't know where it is and cannot load it. You cannot load the drawing as an independent object[5]. The same holds true for assemblies: when you want to work on an assembly, all its constituent part files must be available to be read in as required. You can see that for complicated projects, file management might become an issue.

Consider also that if you change a dimension on the drawing, this makes a change in the part file loaded in session. It does not immediately change the part file on disk. To make the change "stick" you have to save the part file! The same holds for some other drawing entities like section definitions[6].

Before we forget, change the width of the bracket back to *60*. In the drawing, select the dimension to highlight it, right click to bring up the pop-up menu, select *Modify Nominal Value*, enter in the new value *60*, select *Regenerate Model* as before.

---

[4] Check out *Info > Session Info > Object List*

[5] You can create model-less drawings that consist of "dumb" 2D entities like lines, circles, notes, and so on. This is what CAD was like many years ago.

[6] A configuration option *save_modified_draw_models_only* (default = Yes) lets you automatically save the part file whenever you save the drawing file.

One thing we can't do in the **DRAWING** window is change the basic features of the part (like creating new solid features, or changing feature references). For that you have to go back to the **PART** window. Do that now, so that we can add the cut to round off the top of the bracket.

First, if necessary, **Reroute** the large hole (select it and in the RMB menu select **Edit References**) so that the horizontal dimension reference is **TOP** instead of the upper surface of the bracket. The distance above this reference should be **70**. If the hole disappears off the bottom of the part (the axis is still visible), modify its dimension value to -70. If you scroll back a few lines in the message window[7], you will see a warning that was produced when the hole was regenerated (something like "Hole is entirely outside the model").

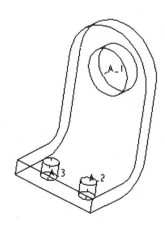

Figure 24 The modified L-bracket

Now create a circular arc cut, concentric with the large hole and aligned with the left and right sides of the bracket. The part should look like Figure 24 when you are finished. Don't forget to save the new part.

Now we have to touch up the drawing a little. Change back over to the drawing window. The new circular arc should be shown there.

First, the drawing scale is a little too big for the sheet. Double-click on the **Scale** value shown on the bottom line of the graphics window and enter **0.8**. You might like to reposition the views. Notice that this change in scale affects the orthographic views (that are using the sheet scale) and not the 3D general view (that has its own scale).

Next, you may note that the large arc isn't dimensioned. Actually, a dimension isn't needed for the arc since we know the block width. And anyway, because of the way the feature was created, it has no dimensions in the model, so there is nothing to **Show**! Since the dimension is not strictly necessary, we will create a *reference dimension* in the drawing. In the **Annotate(Insert)** group select the button **Reference Dimension** and then left click on the arc in the front view. Use the MMB to place the dimension - it will appear with the symbol REF to indicate it is a reference dimension[8]. Select **Return** in the **ATTACH TYPE** menu. You might like to clean up the dimension cosmetics a bit. In Pro/E language, the dimension we just added is called a *created* dimension (as opposed to a *shown* dimension). These do not have to be reference dimensions (which is why there are two versions of the **New Dimension** command).

---

[7]Check out **Info > Session Info > Message Log**

[8] Your system may be set up to show reference dimensions in parentheses.

You should also change the text in the note. Left click on the note, then in the RMB pop-up menu select *Properties*. The text will appear in the text editor window. Change the first line to something like

SCALE 0.8, DIMENSIONS IN mm

Select *OK* when you are finished and don't forget to save the drawing.

Publishing the Drawing

In addition to saving the drawing on your hard disk, it will be likely that you need to create images of the drawing for distribution or printing. These are done using the **Publish** options in the drawing ribbon. Obtaining hard copy may depend on the details of your local installation (for example, to obtain large format plots). See your system administrator for information on this. However, there are two possible ways that might work. Go to the **Publish** tab in the drawing ribbon.

The **Configure** group is where you specify what you want - a hard copy print, a DXF or IGES format drawing file, a PDF format document, a TIFF image, and so on - and create the settings for the output. Select the output type first, then the *Settings* button.

Check the **Print/Plot** radio button, and then select the *Settings* button. If you are running under Windows, in the **Destination** tab of the new window, select *Printer(MS Printer Manager)*, then in the **Model** tab make sure that *Plot (Full Plot)* is set. Then select *OK* for the printer configuration.

Now go to the **Finish** group and select *Preview*. This will confirm exactly what will be printed. Now pick the *Print* button. This should bring up your normal Windows print control dialog. Use it as you usually would to select the printer and printer properties (quality, speed, color, page size, etc). Some experimentation may be required here to get margins, orientation, and so on set just right.

If you do not have a plotter attached directly, wish to archive the drawing image, or want to send the drawing to someone who cannot read the native Pro/E file you can print directly to a pdf file by using the **PDF** radio button in the **Configure** group. This setting will automatically print the entire sheet. Check out the options available under *Settings*. These include the print resolution (dpi), color choice, treatment of hidden lines, security features (like passwords), and so on. You should probably go for the highest resolution possible (disk space is cheap!). The default output file will be *lbrack.pdf* in the current working directory (unless this has been over-ridden by your system administrator). Once you have the settings you want, publish the drawing as usual using the *Finish* button. Once you have a pdf file of the drawing, there are a number of things you can do with it: email it to someone, view or print it with a pdf-file viewer (like Adobe Acrobat), whatever.

Using Drawing Templates

For our first drawing, we did a number of operations manually. Many of these are common to all part drawings. Fortunately, there is a way to do much of this tedious drawing creation automatically.

First, make sure the current drawing has been saved, then remove it with *File > Erase > Current*. Note that this does not delete the drawing from your hard disk but just removes it from the current session (takes it out of memory). You should be back in the part window.

Create a new drawing called *lbrack2*. Once again, uncheck the box beside **Use default template** (we want to pick our own) and select *OK*. In the **New Drawing** dialog window, check the button beside *Use template* and select an **A** sized drawing by picking *a_drawing* in the **Template** area. This does the following:

- creates the drawing sheet (A size)
- orients the model
- places the standard views (top, front, right) for a multiview drawing
- scales the views to give you room for detailing

When you select *OK* and enter the drawing window, everything should be set up for you as shown in Figure 25.

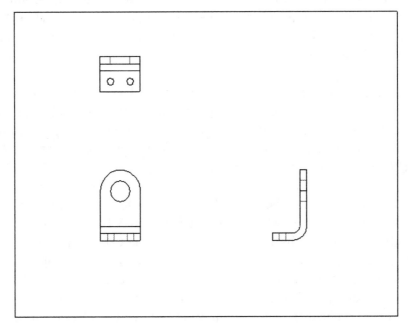

Figure 25 Drawing created using the default template

How does Pro/E know what standard views you wanted? The views that are shown on the drawing are determined by the layout of the template[9]. The drawing template refers to

---

[9] Creating your own templates is discussed in the *Advanced Tutorial*.

standard views defined in the part (that were likely created with the part template). The drawing views are based on the default datum planes TOP, FRONT, and RIGHT and the associated Saved Views. The orientation of the part in the drawing is therefore determined by how we orient the geometry of the part relative to the datums. If your part is upside down in the model, then the drawing views will be upside down too. Another good reason to plan ahead!

Now, there may be a good reason to have the orientation of the part different in the model than in the drawing. If you still want to use the part and drawing templates, here is how to reorient the drawing views created automatically. Double-click on the front (primary) view. In the **Drawing View** window, select *Category(View Type)*. In the view orientation area, select the view **LEFT**, then the *Apply* button. A confirmation window will ask if you want to modify the orientation of the children views (these are projections of the primary view). Select *Yes*. All three views will change, maintaining the specified orthographic projection relation between views. Change the primary view back to our original **FRONT** view.

With the views created, go ahead and finish detailing the drawing for practice. Try to do this on your own, but refer back to our previous procedures if necessary.

On to the second part - a simple pulley. Here we will concentrate on creating a section view, a detail view, and a quick look at drawing title blocks and customization tools.

The Pulley

We're going to use this part in the next lesson (on assembly). We will make it now to see how to create a drawing with a section view, title block and border. Most importantly, we will look at a more orderly way of getting the dimensions onto the drawing instead of showing them all at once as we did for the bracket. As mentioned previously, when parts get even moderately complicated that strategy will take more work than necessary.

First, let's get on with creating the pulley model.

Creating the Pulley

The pulley we are going to create looks like Figure 26. The main interest in this part is the cross sectional shape. The key dimensions of this shape are illustrated in Figure 27.

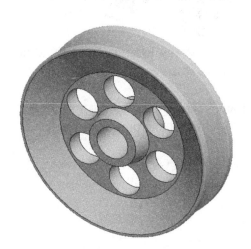

Figure 26 The pulley

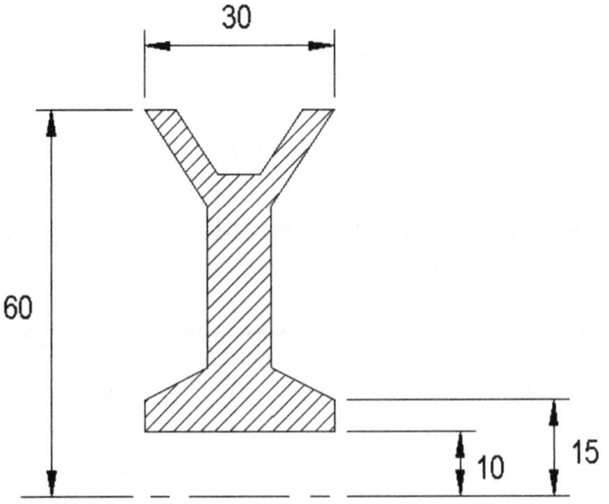

Figure 27 Pulley cross section (dimensions in millimeters)

We could create the base feature as a revolved protrusion using the shape in Figure 27. However, this single feature would require a fairly complicated sketch. Instead, we'll create the pulley using three revolved features then add the holes and rounds.

Start by creating a new part called ***pulley*** using the ***mmns_part_solid*** template. In the appropriate parameter fields, enter something like *[Tutorial pulley #1]* for the *Description* and your initials for *Modeled_by* . You can also enter (or modify) these values using ***Tools > Parameters*** in the pull-down menu.

Create a circular disk (both sided protrusion off **FRONT**) aligned with the origin. Look ahead to Figure 35 to see

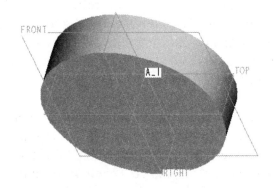

Figure 28 Base feature of pulley

why we want this orientation. The disk has a diameter of *120* and a thickness of *30*. The disk should look like Figure 28.

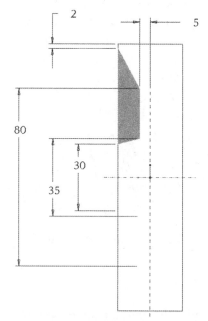

Figure 29 Sketch for revolved cut

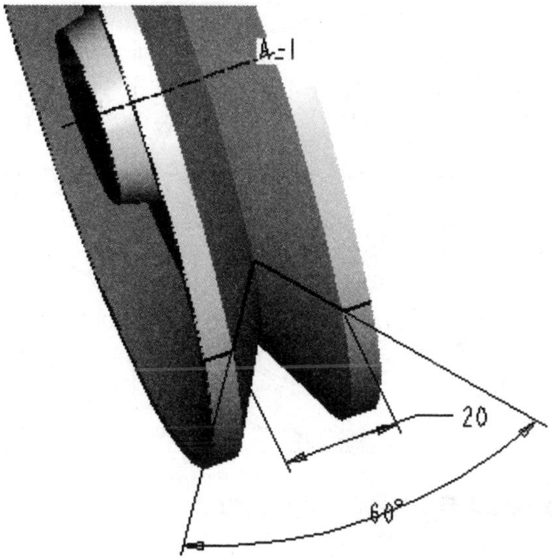

Figure 30 Revolved cut to make pulley groove

Now, create a 360 degree revolved cut on the front side of the disk. The sketching plane is **RIGHT**. The dimensions are shown in Figure 29. The revolved cut can be mirrored through **FRONT** by (with the feature highlighted) selecting the *Mirror* command, selecting the FRONT datum plane, then middle click.

Create the pulley groove around the outer circumference as another revolved cut. Just make a symmetrical 60° V-shaped groove as shown in Figure 30. The vertex at the bottom of the V aligns with **FRONT**.

Add a round at the bottom of the groove with a radius of *3*.

Add the central hole for the pulley axle. This can be created as a *double-sided, coaxial* hole off **FRONT** with a diameter of *20*. The depth is *Through All* in both directions. See Figure 31.

Now we'll create the pattern of holes arranged around the pulley. We start by creating the pattern leader. Again, use **FRONT** as the placement plane and go *Through All* in both directions. Create the hole using the *radial* option (*28.5* from pulley axis). Measure the

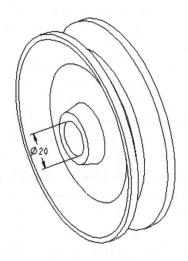

Figure 31 Central hole added to pulley

angle *30* from **TOP**. This is the angle that we will increment to make the pattern. See Figure 32.

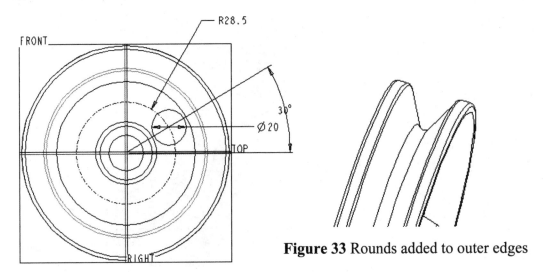

Figure 33 Rounds added to outer edges

Figure 32 Hole Pattern leader

Create the pattern using the first hole as the leader. Increment the angular dimension by *60* and make a total of *6* holes.

As a final touch, add some **rounds** (radius *1*) to the outer edges as shown in Figure 25. All four edges can be included in the same feature - don't create four separate rounds!

That completes the creation of the pulley. Before we go on to the drawing, don't forget to save the part.

Creating the Drawing

① Selecting a Formatted Sheet

For this drawing, we will use a pre-formatted sheet with a title block. Start a new drawing with

> *File > New > Drawing > [pulley]*

You can leave the default template box checked. In the **New Drawing** window that opens up, select *Empty with format.* In the **Format** area, select *Browse.* This takes you to the directory on your system that contains drawing formats. We are looking for a file called **a.frm**. The default location is (for Windows systems with a "generic" Pro/E installation) **<proewildfire_loadpoint>/formats/a.frm**. If you can't find it, either consult your system administrator, or carry on without the format by canceling the command. In the **New Drawing** window, select *OK*.

Assuming you were able to load the format, the drawing window will open with an ANSI standard title block and border already drawn on the A-sized sheet as shown in Figure 34.

The drawing ribbon opens showing that we have one drawing sheet.

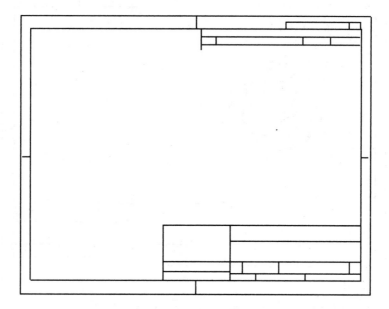

Figure 34 Formatted drawing sheet (A size)

② Creating the Primary View

Since the **Layout** group is open by default when we enter a new drawing, use the RMB pop-up menu and select the command

Insert General View

Click to the left of center of the sheet. In the **Drawing View** dialog, select **View Type** and set the orientation to **FRONT**, then *Apply*. You may have to change the sheet scale (indicated at the bottom of the graphics window) to *0.5*. Close the **Drawing View** dialog window. Your screen should now look like Figure 35. If the view is shaded, don't worry - we will take care of that later.

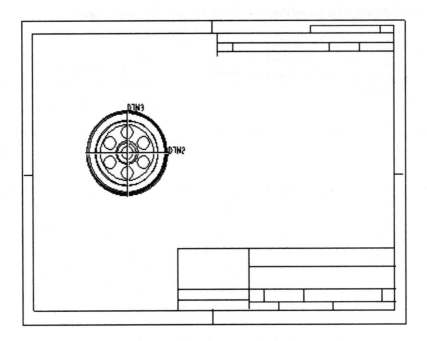

Figure 35 Primary view placed and oriented

③ Add a Full Section View

We will create a full section to the right of the primary view. The section can be created either in the model (using the *View Manager*) or in the drawing. Either way, the section definition will be stored with the model (another reason to keep the model and drawing files together!). The preferred way is probably to create the section definition in the model, which is what we will do in Lesson #10. For now, since the drawing is open, we will do it here.

To create a section in the drawing, we have to specify the type of view, the location of the view, where the section is to be taken, and on what view to indicate the section cutting plane and view arrows. Turn datum plane display on since we will use a datum to define the section plane. Select the primary view (note the red border) and in the RMB pop-up, select

> *Insert Projection View*

Drag the mouse to the right (yellow border shows where the view will be) and place the view.

Now we have to modify some properties of the view and specify where we want the section taken. With the new view selected (red border), select *Properties* in the RMB pop-up. In the **Drawing View** window (Figure 36), under **Categories** select *Sections*. Select the button beside **2D cross section** then click the green "+" sign button. The default to create a new section is a *Planar* section using a single datum plane. In the XSEC CREATE menu, select *Done*.

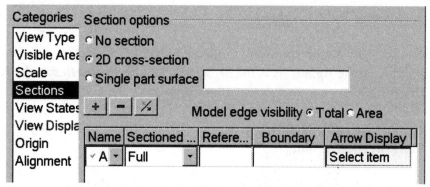

Figure 36 Drawing View dialog for creating section views

Read the message prompt and enter the single character "A" so that our section will be identified on the drawing as *Section A-A*. The **SETUP PLANE** menu opens so that we can specify the cutting plane for the section. We want to use a vertical plane through the pulley. If a datum plane doesn't exist for this, you could create a make datum. In our case, **RIGHT** will do just fine. Select it in the front view or model tree, then *Apply*.

In the **Drawing View** window, slide the horizontal tab all the way to the right to expose the **Arrow Display** collector (see Figure 36). Click in the blank space and read the message window. We want the section arrows to appear on the front view, so click somewhere on the front view, then *Apply*. The arrows appear showing the direction of view onto the section. *Close* the **Drawing View** window. We are finished with the datum planes, so you can turn them off now. Your drawing should look like Figure 37.

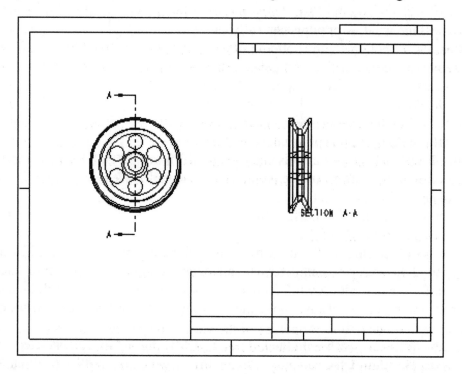

Figure 37 Section view placed

④ **Modify the Section View Display**

Section views generally do not show any hidden edges. Let's turn them off. Double-click on the section view at the right (this is the same as selecting **Properties** in the RMB pop-up). In the **Drawing View** window, select **View Display** in the **Categories** list. Then set

> *Display style (No Hidden)*
> *Tangent edges (None)*

then select **Apply > Close**. For the FRONT view, set the view display to

> *Display style (Hidden)*
> *Tangent edges (None)*

⑤ **Adding a Detail View**

We'll add a broken out detail view of the pulley groove. This will be useful for dimensioning and showing the rounds. We'll also draw this at twice the scale of the drawing. With neither current view selected, in **Layout(Model Views)** select

> *Detailed*

Read the message window prompts carefully as you do this. Pick a point near the bottom of the pulley groove in the section view (you can zoom in to help locate this). A large red X appears. We now want to indicate the area around the pick point to be included within the detailed view. As you click with the left mouse button, a spline curve will be drawn. See Figure 38. Make sure this encloses the groove (four or five points should be enough). When you have fully enclosed the area to be drawn, click with the middle mouse button.

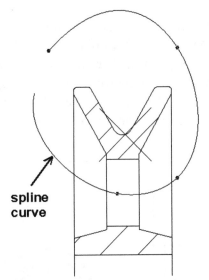

spline curve

Figure 38 Defining boundary of detailed view

A note appears ("See Detail A") on the drawing and the region is surrounded by a circle roughly around the area you identified. The message prompt now asks you to select a center point for the new view on the drawing. Pick a point where there will be enough space for the view (we can always move the view later if this point doesn't work out).

With the new detailed view highlighted, open the RMB pop-up menu and select **Properties**. In the **View Type** category, change the view name to "**B**". Check out the various boundary types. Don't forget you must **Apply** the settings before going to a different category. Now select **Scale** category, enter **1.0**. You should now have a scaled-up detailed view something like Figure 39. You can move the views around by unlocking them and dragging them wherever you want. The notes can be moved by simply dragging them to the desired location (the **Annotate** tab in the ribbon must be selected).

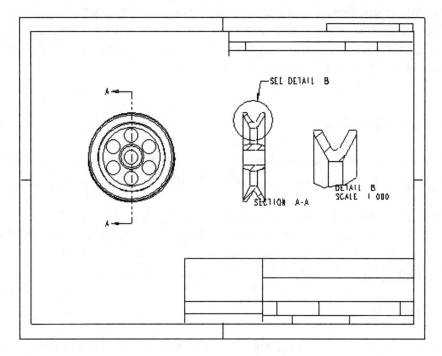

Figure 39 Detail view of section added

⑥ Adding Dimension Details

Instead of getting Wildfire to show us all the dimensions at once as we did for the previous drawing, we will be a little more selective since this part has quite a few dimensions. This will give us more control about initial placement of dimensions, which means fewer changes later (hopefully!). We are going to deal with individual features in the model tree. Select the **Annotate** tab in the ribbon.

In the model tree, select the base feature (the extruded disk) and in the RMB pop-up menu, select *Show Model Annotations*. The dimensions for only the selected feature appear in dark red and are listed in the **Annotations** dialog window (for this feature, look for the diameter and thickness). Check both of these and then select *OK*. You can easily manage the cosmetic changes for these. Look ahead to Figure 40 for some drawing layout ideas.

Right click on the next feature listed in the model tree and then *Show Model Annotations* in the RMB pop-up. You will want to show all of these except the dimension for the angle of the revolve (360°). Clean these up using the methods we saw previously (including *Cleanup Dimensions* in the RMB pop-up menu if things get really messy!). Continue moving down the model tree, picking one feature at a time and showing the dimensions. For the hole pattern, dimension the pattern leader and change (using *Edit > Properties*) the diameter dimension text as shown in Figure 40.

You may find that picking features out of the model tree (if you know exactly what they are in the drawing) is the easiest way to manage the creation of the drawing. In a complex model, it really helps if the features are all named *and* you have thought about how you want to lay out the dimensions before you start! Following standard drawing practice, Pro/E will place each necessary dimension only once (this will be important in a minute or two!), so if you want a dimension in a particular view you must either first create it there, or use *Move Item to View* (in the RMB menu) later.

⑦ Improving the Esthetics

If you haven't already, use the drag handles and the right mouse button to modify/move the dimension details as required to get a better layout.

Let's change the crosshatch pattern in the section and detailed views. Since the section is closely related to the view definition, select the **Layout** tab (if you stay in the **Annotate** tab, you cannot pick the section hatch). Then select only the hatch in the section view so that it is highlighted in red. The in the RMB pop-up menu select

> *Properties*

You can now change hatch spacing, angle, pattern, and so on. The *Retrieve* command lets you choose from standard hatching patterns for different materials (aluminum, iron, copper, steel, and so on). To change the spacing and angle, select

> *Spacing | Hatch > Overall | Half* (click twice)
> *Angle | Hatch > Overall | 30 > Done*

Note that the hatching changes in the detail view as well.

Next, we'll add all the centerlines for circular features. These may already be visible (with labels), however if you turn off datum axis display they will disappear, indicating that they are not yet placed on the drawing. Select the **Annotate** tab. In the model tree, select the base feature and in the RMB pop-up select the *Show Model Annotations*. Because all the dimensions for this feature are already being shown the dialog window automatically picks the tab on the furthest right to show datums. Two axes are indicated - check them both, then *Apply*. Obviously, we could have done this previously when we were showing dimensions.

When you get to the pattern of holes, select all the hole features in the model tree, then in the RMB pop-up, select *Show Model Annotations*. Pick the tab at the far right. A large number of axes will show in the collector window. You will have to be careful about which ones you want to appear on the drawing. For example, there are a number of axes for holes that are either in front of or behind the section plane in the right view. These should probably not be shown. If you accidentally create one of these, no problem - it can be selected and deleted individually later. When all the boxes you want are checked, select *Apply* to confirm, and *OK* to accept.

⑧ Changing Drawing Options

It is likely that the centerlines on the hole pattern look slightly different from Figure 40. The display of these centerlines is controlled by a drawing option. Other options include text height, arrowhead size and style, tolerance display, and many more. To see the options, in the pull-down menus at the top-right select

File > Drawing Options

This brings up a long list of options. They are sorted **By Category** (see the setting at the top right of the window). Default values/settings are indicated with an asterisk "*". This information was read from a default file on your system when you created the drawing. Any values you change here will affect only the current drawing (unless you can change and over-write the system file) and are stored with it.

Browse down this list to get a feel for what you can do in terms of drawing customization.

About 2/3 of the way down the list (or sort the list alphabetically), look for the option

radial_pattern_axis_circle

and in the Value list at the bottom set it to *Yes*. Then select *Add/Change > Apply > Close > Redraw*. The centerline layout should now be circular and radial as in Figure 40.

There is some further discussion of the drawing option file in the *Advanced Tutorial*.

⑨ Adding Notes with Parameters

Finally, add some text to the title block. You can, of course, use notes to create simple text within the title box. You may want some notes to change if the model changes. You can do this with parameters. In **Annotate(Insert)** select *Note* then:

No Leader | Enter | Horizontal | Standard | Default | Make Note

Do you remember entering a value for the parameter *DESCRIPTION* when creating the part using the template? The text was something like "Tutorial pulley #1". Pick a point in the appropriate cell in the title block (see Figure 40). Then type in the following text in the prompt area (without the square brackets):

[&description]

Press enter (twice) when you are finished. The value of the part parameter will appear at the insertion point - this is what the "&" symbol does when used with parameters. You can move the note later to center it in the box. Put a note for the *MODELED_BY* parameter in another box in the title block using the text string

[Modeled by &modeled_by]

Notice that when you select the insertion point, all the dimensions in view are changed to their symbolic form. Try entering a note in the title block with the following text (observe the dimension symbol on your drawing for the diameter of the central hole in the pulley):

[Pulley shaft ⌀ &d15]

For the diameter symbol, use the symbol palette at the right. When you accept this, what happens to the dimension on the drawing? Why does this happen? Select ***Done/Return***.

Can you change the value of the dimension in the note we just created? In any case, it is not good practice to put part dimensions in the title block, so highlight this note and delete it. What happens to the hole dimension? (Hint: Look in the **Annotations** list for the appropriate view in the drawing tree.) Create that dimension again.

Can you enter the note to display the drawing scale? Take a guess for the name of the built-in parameter, and don't forget the "&" symbol.

Add some other notes to fill in the title block. Your company or school will likely have some custom formats that will have title blocks that will automatically be filled with part and drawing parameter information. These formats will typically be set up to work with your installation's part templates.

Your final drawing should look something like Figure 40. Here is a test of your drawing-reading abilities: what is the missing dimension in Figure 40?

⑩ Creating Dimensions

As mentioned earlier, the dimensions placed by Pro/E are the ones used explicitly to construct the model. From time to time, you may have to add some dimensions manually. You can do this using the dimensioning tools available in the **Annotate(Insert)** group. The main dimensioning tools here are

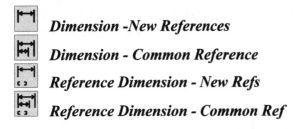

Dimension -New References

Dimension - Common Reference

Reference Dimension - New Refs

Reference Dimension - Common Ref

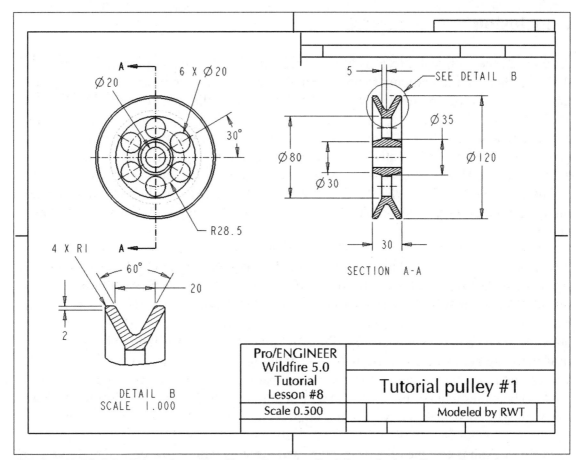

Figure 40 Finished drawing of pulley. Can you find the missing dimension?

These tools are fairly self-explanatory (follow the message prompts) and will be easy to pick up by anyone who has done 2D CAD. The main thing to remember however is that dimensions you create cannot be used to drive the geometry - they are strictly lines on the drawing. These are called "*driven*" dimensions whose value cannot be modified in the drawing (but will change if the geometry of the part changes).

The **Annotate** groups also contains a number of other tools for completing the drawing: surface finish, symbols, geometric tolerances, jogs and breaks, changing the arrow style, managing text styles and format, and so on. You will need to do a lot of exploring to cover this all!

If you want, make a hard copy of the pulley drawing. If you have zoomed in or out on the drawing, make sure that the plot setup is set to *Full Plot* before creating the plot file.

Don't forget to save your drawing.

Conclusion

As you can see, although Pro/E handles most of the work in creating the geometry of the drawing, there is a fair amount to be done manually regarding the esthetics of the drawing. It is for this reason that you need to be quite familiar with drawing practices and standards. Wildfire gives you a lot of tools for manipulating the drawing - we have only scratched the surface here. There is actually an entire volume of Pro/E documentation (several hundred pages) devoted expressly to creating drawings! All this information is available in the Help Center on-line. Some additional drawing tools and techniques are discussed in the *Pro/ENGINEER Advanced Tutorial* from SDC, including multisheet and multimodel drawings, tables, BOM (Bill of Materials), drawing tools, custom templates and more.

The most important lesson here is that the engineering drawing is a by-product of the 3D solid model. We don't so much "make a drawing" as much as just "show the existing model". We observed how bidirectional associativity works in Pro/ENGINEER. It is this capability that gives Pro/E and all its related modules so much power. If several people are working on a design, any changes done by, for example, the person doing the part modeling, are automatically reflected in the drawings managed by the drafting office. As you can imagine, this means that in a large company, model and file management (and control) becomes a big issue. Pro/E contains a number of other drawing utilities to make that management easier, but we will not go into them here.

A second lesson is that the dimensions that will automatically show up in the drawing are those used (for example, in Sketcher) to create the features of the model. Therefore, when creating features, you must think ahead to what information you want to show in the final drawing (and how). This involves your identification and understanding of the design intent of the features in the part. A part kludged together from disorganized features will be very difficult to present in an acceptable drawing.

We will return to creation of drawings for assemblies in Lesson 10. There we will see some more tools and techniques to expand on the ones covered here.

In the next lesson, we will see how to create an assembly using the L-bracket and pulley you created in this lesson. We will also have to create a few small parts (washers, shaft, base plate).

Questions for Review

1.   When creating a new drawing, how do you specify which part is going to be drawn?
2.   Is it possible to create a 2D drawing without a part? What advantages/disadvantages might this have?
3.   The first view added to the drawing is called the _____?

4. How do you set the orientation of a view? Consider both the first view and subsequent views.
5. How do the mouse buttons function for dynamic view control in a drawing?
6. What is the meaning of the following toolbar icons?

a)   b)   c)   d)   e)

7. What is the easiest way to move a view on the drawing sheet?
8. Is it possible to delete a view once it has been created? What about the primary view?
9. How do you show the axis of a revolved features? Can you find an alternate way?
10. How can you edit the text contained in a note?
11. How do you change a section hatch pattern to a standard material?
12. When you select **Show Model Annotation**, in what color do dimension details first appear?
13. Explain the functioning of the three mouse buttons as used to modify dimension cosmetics.
14. How do you select a drawing template? What does it create for you automatically?
15. Describe two methods to move a dimension from one view to another. When might you want to do this?
16. How do you create a text note (for example, to put in a title block)?
17. Can you move or delete views that were created with a drawing template?
18. What happens if you change the value of a dimension in the drawing?
19. What is the difference between shown and created dimensions?
20. Is it possible to add new features, or redefine existing features when you are in drawing mode?
21. How can you produce hard copy of a drawing?
22. When you want to create a section view, at what point in the command sequence for adding the view do you designate it to be a section view?
23. What four items of information are required in order for Pro/E to generate a section view?
24. How can you turn off hidden lines in a section view?
25. What boundary options are available for creating a detail view?
26. What information appears in the drawing tree? What does that depend on?
27. How can you change the spacing and angle of a hatch pattern?
28. How is the design intent reflected in a drawing, and how does this relate back to the part?
29. Do you think it would be possible to have a completely automatic system for creating a fully dimensioned drawing?
30. What symbol is used in a note to tell Pro/E to display the value of a parameter?
31. What other parameters (other than the three we used) are built into the system?
32. How are drawing options set?
33. What is the difference between a *template* and a *format*?

Exercises

Here are some parts to practice producing detailed engineering drawings. You may have created the models for the first two at the end of a previous lesson. Do these again, keeping in mind what you want to show on the drawing - you will probably make the model differently this time!

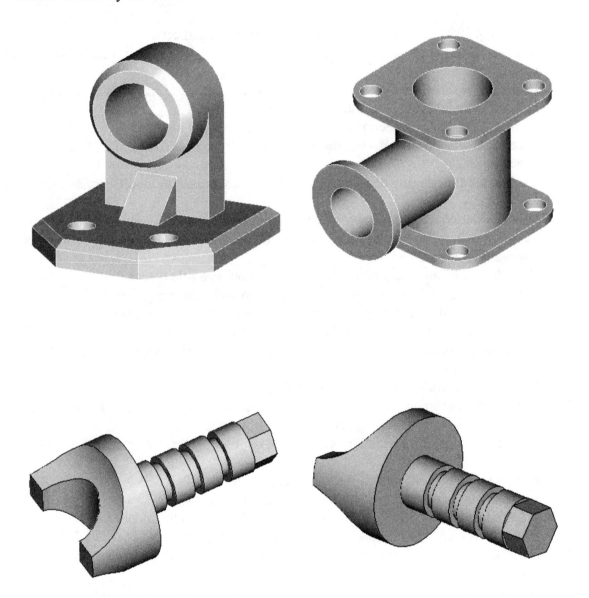

Project

Here is a cut-away view of the final major part of the project. Some dimensions will have to be inferred - use a reasonable estimate. It is not necessary that you reproduce this geometry exactly, but use it to explore the feature creation tools. Some geometry modification may be necessary later when the entire project is assembled. Some careful planning for this part will pay off in reduced modeling time. There are a couple more figures showing this part on the next page.

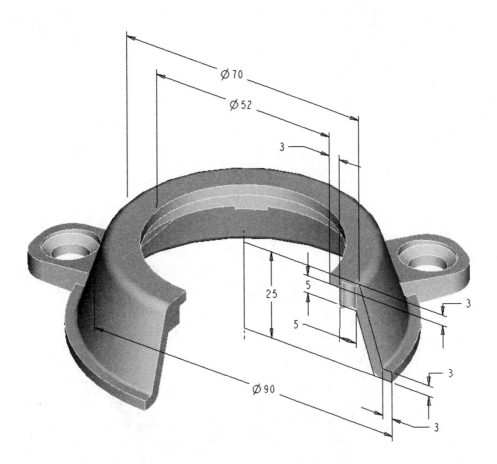

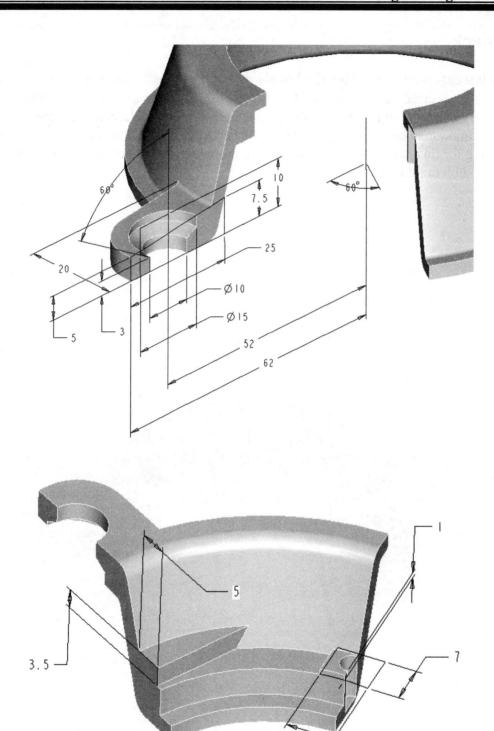

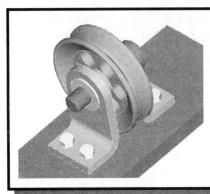

Lesson 9

Assembly Fundamentals

Synopsis

Introduction to assembly mode; assembly constraints; subassemblies; screen layout and assembly options; copying components in assemblies; assigning appearances.

Overview of this Lesson

In this and the next lesson, we are going to look at how you can use Pro/E to create and modify an assembly of parts. You have already created two of the parts involved: the pulley and the support bracket (see Lesson #8). In this lesson, we must first create a number of other simple parts needed for the assembly exercise - a couple of these will involve a new sketcher trick. Then we will use Pro/E to combine the component parts into an assembly. The finished assembly is shown in Figure 1. An exploded view of the components is shown in Figure 2.

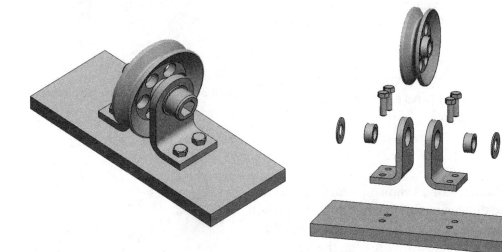

Figure 1 Final assembly containing 13 parts (some repeated)

Figure 2 Exploded view of final assembly

We will intentionally create some of the parts with dimensions different from those required in the final assembly so that in the next lesson we can go over some of the part/assembly modification commands.

The lesson is organized as follows:

1. Creating the Components
2. Discussion of Assembly Constraints
3. Assembly Design Issues
4. Assembling the Components
   ‣ Creating a Sub-Assembly
   ‣ Creating the Main Assembly
5. Assigning Appearances

As usual, there are Questions for Review and an exercise at the end of the lesson.

Creating the Assembly Components

IMPORTANT: Make sure all your parts have units set to millimeters.

The Pulley

As mentioned above, you should have created the pulley in Lesson #8. One thing we forgot to do then was add a keyway to the central hub of the pulley. Do that now: the keyway is **5mm** wide and about **3mm** deep. Create the keyway as a **both sides cut** off **FRONT**. Put the keyway at the 3:00 o'clock position when viewed from the front. (symmetric about **TOP**). The keyway should look like Figure 3.

Figure 3 Pulley with keyway added

You can leave the pulley in session when you move on to the next part. As a safety precaution, you should save it now.

The Axle

Create a part called **axle** as shown in the figure at the right. Use the dimensions shown in Figure 5 (we will change some of these later when we are in assembly mode). See the hint below for creating the hexagonal slot in the head.

Figure 4 The pulley axle

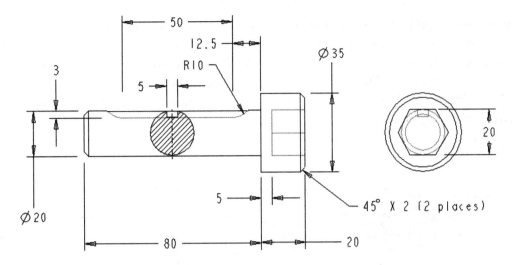

Figure 5 Dimensions for the axle

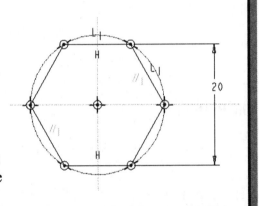

Helpful Hint
To make a hexagonal sketch a bit easier (if
you don't want to use the sketcher palette
tool), first create a circle, highlight it (in red),
then right click and select *Construction*. You
can now sketch the six sides of the hexagon
with vertices on the circle (observe the snaps
that happen with Intent Manager). Add a
dimension for the width across the flats. Then
use the sketcher constraints to eliminate all the
other dimensions.

The Base Plate

Create a part called **bplate**
according to the dimensions
shown. The plate thickness
is *20* mm. Note the two
planes of symmetry. How
can you exploit this?

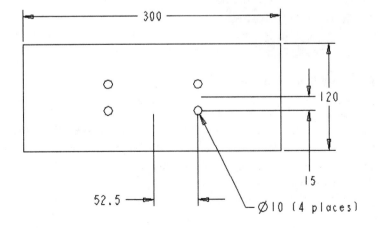

Figure 6 Base plate dimensions

The Bolts

We will need several bolts in the final assembly. These will all come from the same part file **bolt** containing only a single bolt. Note that the threads have not been included for simplicity here. If you wanted to include the thread, you could use a helical cut or what is called a *cosmetic thread*. The dimensions of the bolt are shown in Figure 8. See the hint above for creating the hexagonal sketch for the head. The beveled edge on the head is created with a revolved cut.

Figure 7 The bolt

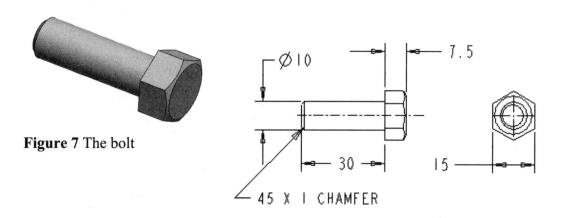

Figure 8 Bolt dimensions

The Bushings

We will need a couple of these too - call the part **bushing**. It is a simple protrusion.

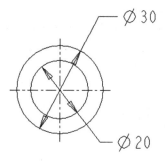

Figure 9 The bushing

Figure 10 Bushing dimensions

The Washers

Our last component part is the washer. It has the dimensions shown in the figure at the right. The easiest way to make this is to do a *Save A Copy* of the bushing part (giving a new name **washer**), *File > Open* the new part, then double-click on the protrusion and edit the dimensions. You may want to change the DESCRIPTION parameter as well:

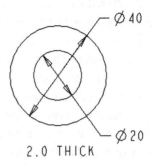

Tools > Parameters

Click on the **Value** entry for the parameter DESCRIPTION and enter a new string.

Figure 11 Washer dimensions

When you start assembling these components later in this lesson, make sure they are all in your start-up directory. And (just another reminder!) all these parts should be in millimeters.

Assembly Constraints

Creating an assembly is actually a lot of fun and not too difficult. Your main challenge will be display management as the screen gets more cluttered with objects. Creating an assembly involves telling Wildfire how the various components fit together. To do this, we specify *assembly constraints*. A component that is fully constrained in the assembly is called *placed* or *assembled*. It is possible to leave a component not fully constrained, in which case it is called *packaged*. Wildfire will be able to tell you whether a new component is packaged or assembled [1].

The geometric relation between any two parts has six degrees of freedom: 3 translational and 3 rotational. In order to completely define the position of one part relative to another, we must constrain (provide conditions for) all these degrees of freedom. Once we give Pro/E enough information it will be able to tell us when the part is fully constrained and we can assemble the part. We proceed through the assembly process by adding another part, and so on. Setting up the assembly constraints leads to a hierarchical structure of the assembly (an "assembly tree", but still called the model tree). Within this structure, different components are related by parent/child relations formed by specifying the constraints.

---

[1] To further complicate things, components in a moveable assembly (a *mechanism*) are joined together by *connections*. This is a special type of constraint that allows motion along specific degrees of freedom. We will not be discussing mechanisms here. For some basic tutorials on mechanisms, go to the Help Center and look for **Mechanism Design and Mechanism Dynamics** in **Functional Areas > Simulation**.

Packaged components will be easy to identify with a special symbol in the model tree. We normally avoid leaving components in this condition. Components that have at least one constraint to a packaged component are automatically considered as packaged only (even if they are fully constrained to the packaged component).

There are a number of constraint types that we can specify. In this lesson, we will use six of them. The rest should be pretty easy to figure out on your own. The individual constraints are used with the surfaces, axes, datum planes, and datum points of the components involved in the assembly. The constraints usually must be used in combinations in order to fully constrain all 6 degrees of freedom. Here are the main constraint types that we will discuss:

DEFAULT

Component is placed so that the default position in the component matches the default position in the assembly. Think of this as aligning the default datum planes of the component and assembly. This is most useful for the first component brought into the assembly and reinforces the requirement for advance planning when creating the component.

MATE COINCIDENT (or just MATE for short)

Two planar surfaces or datums become coplanar and face in opposite directions. When using datums, you must specify which side is involved. This constrains 3 degrees of freedom (one translation and two rotations). Can you think what they are? There are still 3 unconstrained degrees of freedom between the components (what are they?).

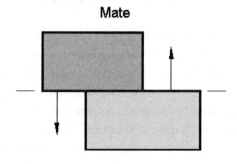

Figure 12 The *MATE* constraint

MATE OFFSET

Two planar surfaces or datums are made parallel, with a specified offset distance, and face in opposite directions. The offset dimension can be negative, and can be used in assembly relations to automatically change the distance between the surfaces. What degrees of freedom does this constraint fix? Which ones are still free?

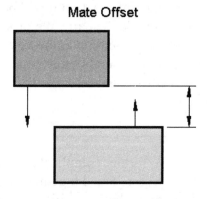

Figure 13 The *MATE OFFSET* constraint

ALIGN COINCIDENT (or just ALIGN for short)

This can be applied to planar surfaces datums, revolved surfaces and axes. Planar surfaces become coplanar and face in the same direction. How many degrees of freedom does this constrain? When aligning datum planes, you will have to specify which side is to be aligned.

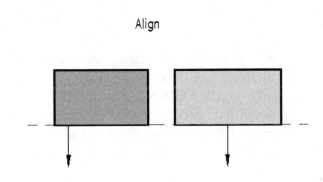

Figure 14 The *ALIGN* constraint with planar surfaces

When **Align** is used on revolved surfaces or axes, they become coaxial. How many degrees of freedom are constrained? Also, note that there are still two possible positions (obtained by reversing the direction of one of the axes) - you can force one or the other with the **Orient** constraint described below.

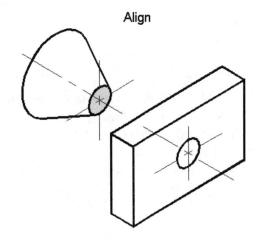

Figure 15 *ALIGN* used with surfaces of revolution aligns the axes

ALIGN OFFSET

This can be used only with planar surfaces: they become parallel with a specified offset and face the same direction.

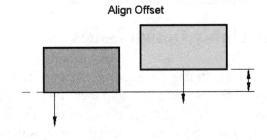

Figure 16 *ALIGN OFFSET* (used with planar surfaces only)

ALIGN ORIENT

Two planar surfaces or datums are made parallel and face the same direction (similar to **Align Offset** except without the specified offset distance). How many degrees of freedom does this constrain?

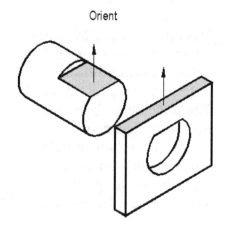

Figure 17 The *ALIGN ORIENT* constraint

INSERT

This constraint can only be used with two surfaces of revolution in order to make them coaxial. How many degrees of freedom does this constrain?

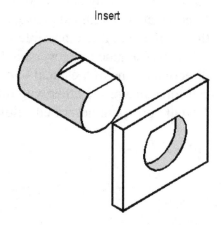

Figure 18 The *INSERT* constraint used with cylindrical surfaces

Assembly Design Issues

Before beginning an assembly (or even before you create the parts), you should think about how you will be using these constraints to construct the assembly. As we saw in Lesson #1, the logical structure of the assembly is reflected in the model tree. Like designing the features of a part, the chosen assembly constraints and references should reflect the design intent. It is possible to create an assembly that fits together, but if the chosen constraints and references do not match the design intent, changes that may be required later could become very difficult. Pro/E does provide tools for dealing with this (the 3 R's also work in assemblies on the assembly references of components), but you should really try to think it through and do it right the first time! Obviously, it takes a lot of practice to do this. The "I-should-have-done-it-*that*-way!" realization is common among new (and experienced!) users.

This is a good time to mention that when you are placing a component into an assembly, it does not matter what order you use to define the placement constraints for the component, since they are applied simultaneously. Pro/E will tell you when you have constrained the component sufficiently for it to be assembled. The order you use can be chosen strictly for convenience.

Do not confuse constraint selection order with the order that components are brought into the assembly. Like the base feature in a part, the choice of the first component in the assembly is important. It would not make sense, for example, to start the assembly of a car with a bolt that holds on the roof rack!

It is possible to create assembly features (like datum planes and axes) that will exist only in the assembly. This would allow you, for example, to use an assembly parameter like an angle or linear dimension between datums, to control the assembly geometry. In this way, if you used the assembly feature as a constraint reference for a number of component parts, you could change the position of all parts simultaneously in the assembly by modifying that parameter. We saw a couple of examples of this in Lesson #1.

Assemblies can also contain solid features (primarily holes and cuts) and it is possible to set the affect of these features on individual components. For example, a cut can be set up to remove material only from selected components. Furthermore, holes through components in an assembly can be set so that they are visible when the part is loaded by itself, or not.

In the context of this lesson, an assembly consists of a number of components that are rigidly constrained to each other - no moving parts! There are additional functions and software modules in Pro/E that allow you to create assemblies of moving parts, that is, mechanisms. This extension lets you create different types of joints and connections (pin, slider, ball, cam, and so on) between components, and drivers to control the degrees of freedom. You can then analyze the motion of components and even create animations of the moving system.

Finally, you should note that Wildfire will happily let you assemble two components that interfere with each other (have partially overlapping solid volumes). Although the parts are "solids", Pro/E does not prevent you from assembling them with interference. Sometimes, in fact, this is the desired result (as in a shrink fit, or designing built-in snaps and catches in plastic parts). More usually, interference happens when dimensional values are not correct (or finalized) in a design. Wildfire has a simple tool that will tell you if any components are interfering (and by how much). It is usually a simple matter to correct the dimensions to remove interference once the assembly is put together.

Assembling the Components

Before you begin, make sure that the parts **lbrack.prt** and **pulley.prt** that you made in Lesson #8 are available in the working directory along with the parts you made earlier in this lesson.

Creating a Subassembly

We will start by assembling the L-bracket, a bushing, and a washer into a subassembly. This will save us some time, since two copies of this subassembly must be inserted into the final assembly. Once created, a subassembly is treated exactly the same way (in regards to subsequent placement constraints) as a single part.

From the **FILE** menu, select

> *New > Assembly | Design > [support]*

Turn off the **Use default template** option and select *OK*. In the **New File Options** window, observe the default assembly template for your system. Since all our parts our in millimeters, we might as well be consistent so choose the ***mmns_asm_design*** template. Enter values for the parameters DESCRIPTION and MODELED_BY and select *OK*. The template has default datums (notice the names) and the usual predefined views. Unless you have a really good reason not to, you should always use a template or at least create the default datums. The advantage of the template is the saved views plus it gives us more freedom in defining the orientation of the first component we define in the assembly[2].

In the pull-down menu, select

> *Insert > Component > Assemble*

or pick the *Add Component* button in the right toolbar. Either way, select the part **lbrack.prt** and then *Open*.

The part appears in the graphics window, either in yellow shaded form or yellow hidden line depending on your display setting. At the top of the screen is the assembly *Add Component* dashboard. This contains virtually all the options required for constraining components brought into an assembly. We will be discussing these options throughout this lesson.

On the left side of the dashboard, see Figure 19, the first three icons on the lower row are grayed out - they have no use in the current context or with the current part. The first

---

[2] Without assembly datums to constrain to, the first component brought into the assembly can only be placed in its default orientation. It is not a good idea to limit your options this way.

pull-down list contains a number of options for creating connections in mechanisms. Have a look at those options, but leave the final setting at the default, *User Defined* . The next list contains the constraints discussed earlier in this lesson, plus some additional ones. The default setting is *Automatic*. This is where you will usually leave this option. With this setting, all you have to do is supply (pick on) the component and assembly references and Wildfire will figure out what kind of constraint you (probably) want. For example, if you pick two planar solid surfaces, it will assume you want a *Mate Offset*; two datums are assumed to be an *Align Offset*; two axes are assumed to be an *Align Coincident*. These assumptions are modified based on any existing constraints, that is, Wildfire will not assume anything that is inconsistent with existing constraints. Just to the right of the constraint type options list is the **Offset Type** selector. Check these out (options are *Coincident*, *Orient*, and *Offset*). If an offset is specified, its value will appear in the text field beside the selector. Finally, note that the current constraint status is indicated: so far, we have specified no constraints.

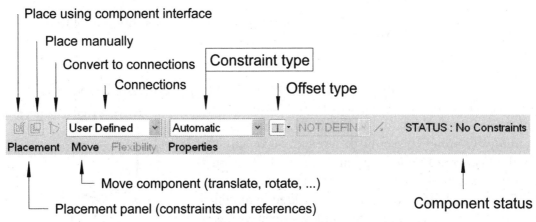

Figure 19 The **Add Component** dashboard (left side)

For this support subassembly, we can afford to place the bracket in the same default position in the assembly as it is in the part. Therefore, in the **Constraint type** list, select *Default*. The bracket will move over so that its datum planes align with the assembly datums. Note that the status is now listed as **Fully Constrained**. Accept the component placement with the green check on the right end of the dashboard, or simply middle click.

Open the model tree. The default will just show the name of the assembly (**support.asm**) and the component (**lbrack.prt**). Select the **Settings** tab, then *Tree Filters*. Select the Display options *Features*, and *Placement Folder*. Apply the new settings. The model tree will appear as in Figure 20. This shows the assembly datums and individual component features. Open up the tree for the bracket component. The placement settings are listed. Find the setting that indicates the default placement.

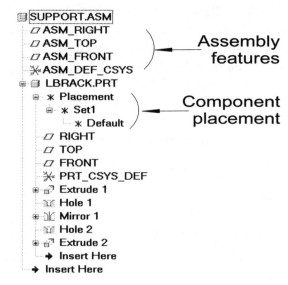

You can turn off the datum planes and coordinate systems if you like. Now we'll add the bushing. Select the *Add Component* button again, find the component **bushing.prt**, and *Open.*

The bushing will appear somewhere beside the bracket and the **Add Component** dashboard (Figure 19) will open up. Here are some new functions available on the dashboard.

Figure 20 The assembly model tree

There are two main display modes when you are doing assembly. These modes are set by the two buttons at the right side of the dashboard, see Figure 21. The default is *Assembly Window*. To see the difference, make sure that only the *Separate Window* option is selected. This puts the current assembly in one graphics window (title: *SUPPORT*), and the component being added in another (title: *BUSHING*). Having both windows open makes it easy to locate references and gives us independent viewing control over the zoom/spin/pan in the two windows. This is useful, for example, when dealing with a small component in a very large assembly. In the separate window the normal Close button (the red X in the top right corner) does nothing - to close it you must turn on the *Assembly Window* button and deselect the

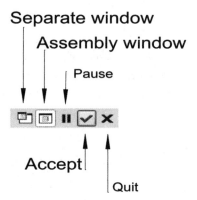

Figure 21 The **Add Component** dashboard (right side)

Separate Window button in the dashboard. We will see that there are a number of useful controls available to manipulate the new component, so you will probably not need the separate window very often. We will do all our assemblies tasks in the same window. The *Pause* button on the dashboard allows you to temporarily pause the assembly operation so that you can do other things with the model (for example, create a necessary datum). Once you are ready to restart doing the assembly, look for the *Resume* button at the same location on the dashboard.

Let's continue with assembling the bushing. **Read the following few paragraphs before proceeding:**

Constraining the component involves three steps:

1. Select the constraint type.
    In the **Constraints** list of the **Add Component** dashboard, you can select the desired constraint. Selecting *Automatic* (the default) allows Pro/E to determine the type of constraint you probably want based on the type of entities you choose. For example, picking two axes basically means you want to do an *Align* (since *Mate* makes little sense with axes). You can, of course, override this constraint.
2. Select the appropriate constraint reference in the component.
3. Select the matching reference for the constraint in the assembly. This can be assembly datums or any other component geometry.

As you add constraints, the position of the component in the assembly will adjust according to the specified constraint. Keep your eye on the **Status** area. You will be told when you have provided enough constraints for the new component to be fixed in the assembly. You have to be a bit careful here, since it will sometimes be possible to include the component at what appears to be the correct position without it being entirely constrained. The dashboard will let you exit without fully constraining the component; as mentioned earlier this is called "packaging" the component. Unless you really want to do this, make sure the **Fully Constrained** status appears before leaving the dashboard[3].

Also, remember that the order of creating the constraints does not matter, nor does the order of picking references on the component or assembly (that is, steps 2 and 3 can be done in either order).

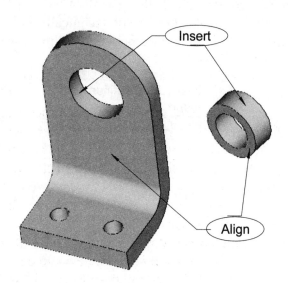

For the bushing, we want to set the constraints shown in Figure 22. The *Insert* constraint makes the cylindrical outer surface of the bushing line up with the surface of the hole[4]; the *Align* constraint keeps the face of the bushing even with the surface of the bracket. Before proceeding with applying these constraints, resize/reorient/move the bracket and bushing displays so that you will be able to easily pick on the appropriate entities.

Figure 22 Constraints for the bushing

---

[3] In older releases of Pro/E, it was not possible to overconstrain a component, that is, continue to add constraints after the status became fully constrained. That is now possible (as long as the constraints are consistent).

[4] As mentioned before, *Insert* actually causes the axes to align. The two surfaces we select for *Insert* do not have to be physically in contact with each other.

Now we'll proceed with the assembly. Make sure the following is selected in the dashboard:

Constraint Type (Automatic)

and pick on the outer surface of the bushing. It highlights in red/orange depending on your display. A small label "**Automatic**" appears with a leader pointing at the bushing surface. Now pick on the inner surface of the large hole in the bracket. The bushing moves over to line up with the hole, the label changes to "**Insert**", and the component status is "Partially constrained". The bushing can still slide along, and rotate around, its axis (hold down the CTRL and ALT keys and drag the component with the various mouse buttons).

Now pick on the flat face of the bushing. Again the "**Automatic**" label appears. Then pick on the flat surface of the bracket. The status message will inform you that the component is fully constrained and the constraint type has been selected as an "**Align**" (with an offset), with some offset dimension picked automatically. On the dashboard, change the **Offset Type** (see Figure 23) to *Coincident*. The bushing will move so that the two reference surfaces line up (see Figure 24). The status now indicates that the bushing is fully constrained. Is that actually true? The answer is no (!), since with just these two constraints the bushing is still technically free to rotate around its axis. Pro/E has determined, with an assumption, that this degree of freedom doesn't matter for this part.

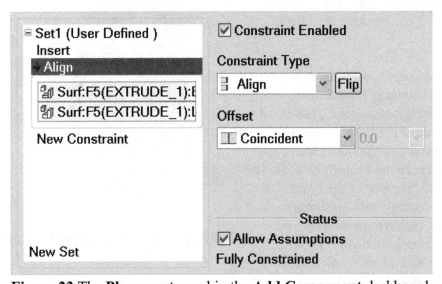

Figure 23 The **Placement** panel in the **Add Component** dashboard

Open the **Placement** slide-up panel on the dashboard. See Figure 23. In the pane on the left, our existing constraints (Insert and Align) are listed. As you select each of these, the associated references are listed and highlighted on the model, and the constraint details are given in the panel area on the right. At the bottom right, in the Status area, the option **Allow Assumptions** is checked by default. This will often be the case for axisymmetric parts constrained the same way as the bushing. Deselect that now. Wildfire tells you that, indeed, the bushing is not fully constrained. What would be required to complete the constraints? (Hint: turn the datums back on.) Don't add this constraint now, since the assumption isn't going to hurt us. Turn the **Allow Assumptions** box back on.

The bushing should be even with one side of the
bracket and protrude slightly from the other (since it is
a different thickness than the bracket). See Figure 24.

If you make a mistake in specifying the type or
references of a placement constraint, you can select it
in the **Placement** panel. For example, click on the
Align entry. The associated references on the
component and assembly are shown in pink or orange.
These are easiest to see in wireframe or hidden line
display. Then, either *Delete* the constraint (use the
RMB pop-up), select a new type, or pick new
component and/or assembly references. Try doing that
now, by picking different vertical (parallel) surfaces on
the bracket. What happens if you pick on one of the
side surfaces of the bracket?

Figure 24 Bushing assembled to
the L-bracket

If you are experimenting with different constraints, it is possible to disable individual
constraints by unchecking the box at the top of the panel.

When you want to create a new constraint, select the ***New Constraint*** entry, specify the
type you want (or ***Automatic***), and pick on the desired component and assembly
references. This button is automatically selected unless you have interrupted the normal
flow of assembly steps.

If you are happy with the bushing
placement, accept it with the middle
mouse button.

Next we will place a washer on the
outside of the bushing. Select the *Add
Component* button and pick the
washer.prt, then *Open*.

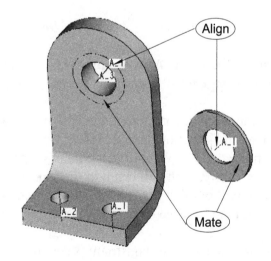

We will create the placement
constraints shown in Figure 25. These
constraints are *Align* (washer and
bushing axes) and *Mate* (washer and
bushing faces). Both of these are
Coincident by default. Leave the
constraint type in the dashboard set to
Automatic and observe the constraint
labels on the model as we go through this.

Figure 25 Placement constraints for the washer

First - the axes. Pick the washer axis. For the assembly reference, how can you make sure you are picking the axis of the bushing and not the hole in the bracket since these coincide in the assembly window? Right click on the bushing/hole axes - one of them will highlight. Now hold down the RMB and select *Pick From List*. This opens a window that lists both axes at the pick point. Select the axis for the bushing (you might have to scroll right in the list to confirm this), and then *OK*.

For the next constraint, just pick on the flat surface of the washer, then on the end surface of the bushing. Set the offset type to *Coincident*. If you select the wrong surface, you may have to *Flip* the constraint (see the button beside the offset type). You may have to go into the constraint list to change the constraint to *Mate*, with the offset type set to *Coincident*.

The status is now indicated as **Fully Constrained** (we will leave **Allow Assumptions** turned on). Accept the placement with the middle mouse button when you are satisfied.

We are finished creating this subassembly, so select

> *File > Save > OK*

Now we will move on to creating the main assembly, with the bracket/bushing/washer sub-assembly treated as a single component.

Creating the Main Assembly

Leave the subassembly window open, and create a new assembly called **less9** using an assembly template as follows

> *File > New > Assembly | Design >[less9]*

Deselect the **Use default template** option and select *OK*. Pick the assembly template *mmns_asm_design*. Enter data for the parameters and then *OK*.

Bring in the first component, the base plate, using the *Add Component* button in the right toolbar and selecting the part *bplate.prt*. We need to constrain this component to the assembly datums. We will experiment with that a bit, showing three ways of doing it. For this assembly, each will result in the same position/orientation of the part in the assembly. For other assemblies, two of these variations will allow more freedom in determining how the component is placed.

The first (and easiest) constraint is set up, as we did for the bracket in the subassembly, by changing the constraint type to *Default*. Do not do this now so that we can check out some other methods for constraining the first component. If you have created the default constraint, open the **Placement** panel, select the constraint, and delete it using the RMB pop-up menu.

To see a second method of constraining the plate, select *New Constraint* and set the constraint type to *Coord Sys*. Pick on the coordinate systems in the component and the assembly. This aligns the XYZ axes of the two coordinate systems. Pretty easy! The coordinate systems in either the component or assembly do not have to be at the origin of the default datum planes and can be oriented in any way in the model. Delete this constraint so that we can see a third option - hold the cursor over the **Coord Sys** label in the graphics window, and select *Delete* in the RMB pop-up menu.

Confirm that the constraint type has automatically reset to **Automatic**. Pick any one of the datums in the component then pick on the corresponding datum in the assembly (component **RIGHT** and assembly **ASM_RIGHT**, for example). Wildfire automatically sets up an *Align Coincident* constraint. Do this for each pair of datums (**FRONT** and **ASM_FRONT**, **TOP** and **ASM_TOP**). No other mouse clicks are required. After selecting the three pairs of datums, the component should be fully constrained. We could, of course, have created any correspondence with the three datums, as long as they were consistent, to reorient the base plate however we like.

You can accept the component placement by clicking the middle mouse button. We don't need the datum planes or coordinate systems any more, so you can turn off their display. Leave the axes turned on.

Now bring in the subassembly. We add this just as if it was a single component. Select the *Add Component* button and pick the *support.asm* sub-assembly that is currently in session. We will set up the placement constraints for the subassembly shown in the Figure 26. Other constraint systems would also assemble the subassembly here, but the ones shown in Figure 26 are closer to the physically meaningful design intent.

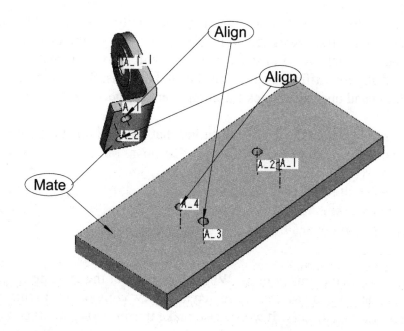

Figure 26 Placement constraints for the subassembly

First, pick the lower surface of the bracket and the upper surface of the base plate. The default constraint for two solid surfaces is ***Mate Coincident***. That is fine here. Then select the axis of one of the bolt holes in the bracket with the axis of the appropriate hole in the base plate. The default constraint here is ***Align*** (check the **Placement** panel). You will see the support shown something like Figure 27 (this will depend on which holes you chose to align, and on how you oriented your parts when you created them). If **Allow Assumptions** is turned on, you will get the message that the component is fully constrained.

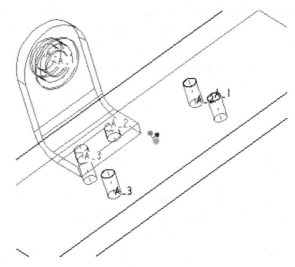

Figure 27 First MATE and ALIGN constraints applied to subassembly

Hmmm... not exactly what we want. Turn off the **Allow Assumptions** option in the **Placement** panel. The bracket is not actually fully constrained yet, since it can still rotate around the hole.   Select *New Constraint* in the **Placement** panel and pick the other bolt hole axis in the bracket and the appropriate axis on the base. This will appear as ***Align Oriented***. This is not coincident to allow for the possibility that the distances between the two axes on the bracket and base plate are not exactly the same. If that was the case, the position would be set so that the misaligned axes would be in the same plane as the first hole. The sub-assembly is now fully constrained without any assumptions. Accept the placement with a middle click.

We'll now bring in another copy of the support subassembly and attach it to the base plate so that it faces the first one as shown in Figure 31. This would be easy to do with the *Copy* command (which we will use later), but we will use the normal procedure so that we will use a slightly different screen display and options. Select the ***Add Component*** button and once again pick the component ***support.asm***[5].

For the first constraint, select the axes of the holes that will end up at the front of the plate.

---

[5] A good question at this point is: Why not just mirror the existing support? When you mirror a component in an assembly, you create a new component. In this case, it would make a new sub-assembly. It would also make mirror copies of all components in the sub-assembly. This is actually a valuable tool to know if that is really what you want. In this case we don't - we want the same component used twice. This will keep the necessary number of components and files to a minimum, and will result in the appropriate entries in the assembly Bill of Materials.

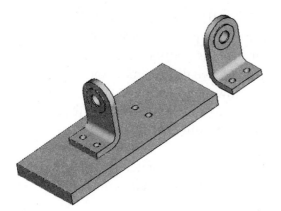

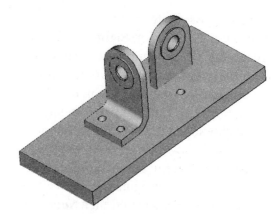

Figure 28 Subassembly brought into session

Figure 29 First hole axes aligned - support buried in base plate!

Notice that in Figure 29 there is overlap (interference) of the bracket and base plate. After you get to this stage, observe the effect of the different view options (wireframe, hidden line, no hidden, shaded) as you spin the assembly. The displays may not be what you expect and will even change with your view orientation if you spin the model. You should be able to recognize these view effects as symptoms that you have interfering components[6].

When you reach the configuration shown in Figure 29, hold down the CTRL and ALT keys simultaneously while you pick on the new support (middle mouse button produces rotate, right mouse button produces translate). This lets you reposition the support manually while maintaining the existing constraints. Drag it above the base plate where you can easily pick (LMB as usual) its lower surface. Then pick on the top surface of the base plate. The *Mate* constraint will occur automatically. Set this to *Coincident*. See Figure 30.

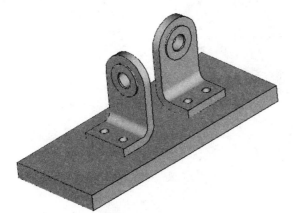

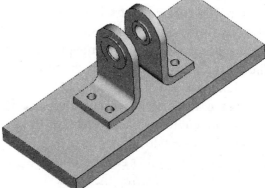

Figure 30 Surfaces mated. Fully constrained with assumptions. No overlap.

Figure 31 Second bolt axis aligned with other hole on base plate

---

[6] Wildfire has other much more sophisticated tools for detecting interference.

You can now rotate the bracket (using CTRL+ALT+MMB) around the first hole axis to position it as shown in Figure 31. The existing mate and align constraints are honored. Again, the status may be showing as fully constrained if assumptions are being allowed. If you turn the assumptions option off, it is possible to leave the assembly dashboard with the bracket looking like it is in the correct position. However, recall that since it is not fully constrained, it is called "packaged" only. This could have undesirable effects later, so we should make sure the bracket is aligned exactly and fully constrained.

Finally, pick on the second hole axes on the bracket and the base plate. This should get you to the final configuration shown in Figure 31 with the bracket fully constrained. Accept the placement and then *Save* the assembly.

Helpful Hint

When you first bring a component into the *Assembly Window*, holding down the CTRL and ALT keys while you pick on the component being assembled lets you drag it around the assembly using the right mouse button. This is much like a pan operation. The left mouse button also translates but sometimes also allows spinning of the part (rather unpredictably). Using CTRL+ALT+middle mouse button lets you spin the component being assembled independently of the assembly itself.

Now we'll assemble the axle using the constraints shown in Figure 32. Before we do the assembly, let's review our constraints. The *Mate* constraint is between the bottom of the axle head and the outer face of the washer. The *Insert* constraint could be with any of the inner surfaces of the bushings or washers on either support. The design intent will be best served if you pick a surface of a bushing. In either case, this constraint will allow the component to be placed, but it will still be able to rotate around its own axis. We'll add another constraint to prevent this by *Orient*ing the lower surface in the keyway and the upper surface of the base plate.

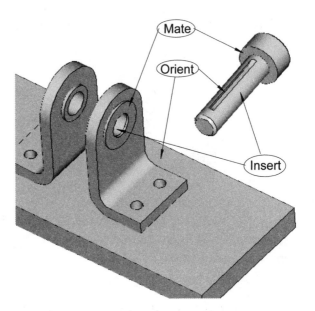

Figure 32 Placement constraints for axle

Bring in the axle. The axle will appear somewhere, perhaps similar to Figure 33. To control the display while placing the axle, a useful tool is available to rearrange components on the screen. Select the *Move* tab in the dashboard. This slide-up panel gives access to several Motion Type options (***Translate, Orient, Rotate***, and ***Adjust***). Leave the default setting and motion reference as

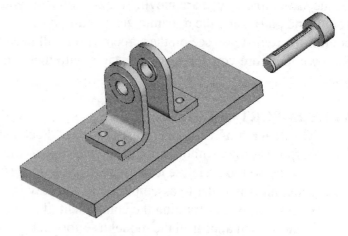

Figure 33 Axle selected for assembly

Translate | View Plane

Read the message in the command window. Left click on the axle and drag it to a position similar to the one shown in Figure 34. Left click again to drop it. By selecting different motion references, we have more precise control over how the component will translate. For example, we can translate normal to a selected surface, or parallel to a selected edge. This is a little different from using the CTRL+ALT+mouse buttons.

Now, for **Motion Type** select the ***Rotate*** option and the **Motion Reference** button, then select the axis of the axle (you may have to set the selection filter to **Axis**), and spin the axle by dragging with the left mouse button. You should be able to spin it a full 360°. See Figure 35. Rotate it again and drop it in the initial position with the keyway approximately on the top of the axle.

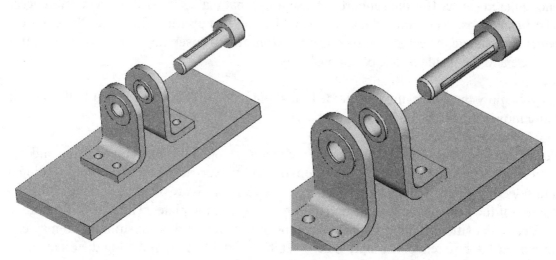

Figure 34 Axle after translating from initial placement position

Figure 35 Axle after rotating around its axis

At the same time as you are moving the component, you can control your view (spin, zoom, and pan) using the dynamic view controls as usual. This gives you considerable control over what you see on the screen. You will need to experiment with these controls for a while before you will be comfortable with them and find which ones work best for you.

VERY IMPORTANT NOTE:

The *Move* command (previously called a "Package Move") is used for cosmetic purposes only. Although it may be possible to move a new component into the correct position relative to other parts, you must still specify the geometric constraints in order to assemble it. If you leave the **Add Component** dashboard without fully constraining the component, it is called "packaged." A special notation will appear in the model tree for such a component. **A new component that is constrained (partly or fully) to a previously packaged component will itself be considered packaged only.**

Helpful Hint

At some point, you will probably accidentally leave the **Add Component** dashboard with an inadvertent middle mouse click. When that happens, just select the component in the graphics window or model tree, open the RMB pop-up menu, and select *Edit Definition*. This brings you back to the dashboard.

When your display shows you a convenient view of the axle and the assembly together, set up the assembly constraints indicated above. We are going to apply the constraints in the order: *Insert*, *Align Orient*, *Mate*. As mentioned earlier, the order of creating these constraints doesn't matter to the final placement. You will find some sequences easier to implement than others. For example, try to avoid the "buried" phenomenon we encountered earlier (for the support subassembly) that makes it hard to select references. The *Insert* constraint should not be any trouble. Set that up first. Go to the **Placement** panel and change the constraint type from **Automatic** to **Insert**. Now pick on the shaft of the axle and the inside of one of the bushings.

As you apply the constraints, recall the hint about using CTRL+ALT. You will find that these moves are restricted because of the existing constraints at the time.

For the second constraint (orientation of the keyway), open the **Placement** panel and in the **Constraint Type** list, start a **New Constraint** by over-riding the *Automatic* setting and selecting *Align*. Change to **Offset** type to *Oriented*. Now pick the surface at the bottom of the keyway on the axle and the top surface of the plate. The axle will rotate to the desired position. If the axle was rotated prior to defining this constraint, you may end up with some different constraints. These can be over-ridden by selecting different entries in the pull-down lists.

Finally, pick on the two surfaces for the *Mate* constraint. We have saved this one for last so that the surfaces are clearly visible and easy to pick out. Change the offset type to

Coincident.

The final position of the axle should be as
shown in Figure 37. Notice the position of
the keyway.

If everything is satisfactory, accept the
placement Otherwise, click on a constraint
listed in the table, select either the constraint
type, component reference, or assembly
reference, and make the appropriate
corrections.

Now is a good time to save the assembly.

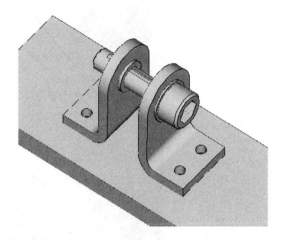

Figure 36 Final placement of axle

We can now bring in the pulley and attach it
using the constraints shown in Figure 37. Use the *Add Component* button and select the
pulley.prt (it should be in session). You might like to experiment with *Separate* and
Assembly window displays, and possibly use shaded views to help identify surfaces.
This is useful when the assembly starts to get crowded with visible and hidden edges,
datum planes and axes, and so on.

Helpful Hint

When your assembly starts to contain a lot of components that you don't
immediately need, you can either *Suppress* them or *Hide* them using the RMB pop-
up menu. The least dangerous of these is *Hide*, since suppressing a component may
accidentally suppress an assembly reference and then child components will also
disappear (usually the ones you need!).

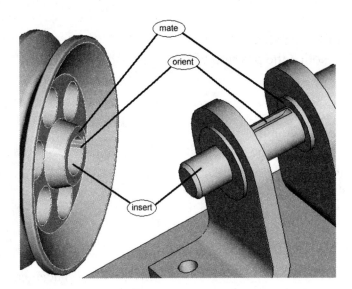

Figure 37 Placement constraints for the pulley

Once again, the pulley could be placed with just the *Insert* and *Mate* constraints and allowing assumptions. But, we want to make sure the keyway lines up with the axle. The *Align Orient* constraint can be used with a side surface of the keyway on the pulley and axle. It is probably best to set this constraint up first, otherwise it will be difficult to see the appropriate surfaces hidden within the model. Conversely, the previous constraints (Insert and Mate) can be disabled in the Placement panel, and the pulley moved out in the open (with

Figure 38 Final position of pulley

CTRL+ALT+RMB) to expose the surfaces. When the align constraint is set up, the previous constraints can be re-enabled. When the pulley is assembled, it should look like Figure 38.

Sometimes, when you pick an axis or surface alignment, Pro/E decides to place the component 180° from where you want it. In that case, select the constraint and try the *Flip* button. You might have to disable other constraints temporarily while you do this, then enable them again.

Finally, bring in the four bolts to attach the brackets to the base plate. We'll bring in the first one and then use the *Copy* command to place the rest. There are a number of advanced assembly commands that would allow you to create a pattern of bolts that would match a pattern of bolt holes. This would allow the assembly to automatically adjust, for example, if the pattern of bolt holes in the base plate was changed (including changing the number of bolts in the assembly). To place a single bolt, the placement constraints are shown in Figure 39. You can *Allow Assumptions* for the bolt placement.

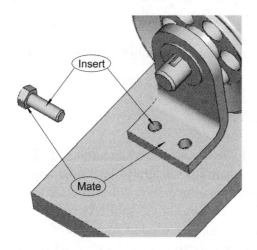

Figure 39 Placement constraints for bolts

Figure 40 Completed assembly

Using *Copy* with Components

Select the bolt in the graphics window, then the *Copy* command in the top toolbar. We have *Paste* and *Paste Special* commands at our disposal that work in a similar manner as for features. Try the *Paste* command first. This opens the **Add Component** dashboard. Open the **Placement** panel - this is not strictly necessary, but lets you keep track of proceedings. All we need to specify are the two assembly references (since the references on the bolt are already known[7]). Notice the labels in the graphics window. The *Insert* constraint is highlighted. All you need to do is pick the corresponding hole surface in the bracket for the copied bolt. Now the *Mate* constraint is highlighted (and the corresponding surface on the bolt is highlighted). Pick on the top surface of the bracket. Presto! The bolt is copied to the new location. Middle click to accept the placement.

Try this again. Since the bolt is still on the clipboard, just select *Paste* again to put the copy at the third location. Add the third bolt. You should be able to place a bolt at a new location with just four mouse clicks (*Paste* command, pick insert surface on bracket, pick mate surface on bracket, middle click).

Add the fourth bolt, and check out how the *Paste Special* command works. The final assembly is shown in Figure 40.

---

[7] The set of references on a component are called its "interface." The interface can be stored with the part. When the part is used again, the component references are already known and all that is required is to specify the matching references in the assembly.

You should continue to experiment with Preselection, Filter Settings, the Move commands, and display modes. Most users prefer the **Assembly Window** mode of operation for specifying constraints, however the **Separate Window** is very useful if you are having trouble picking references in a part, or if you are assembling a very small part to a very large assembly. Some advanced techniques for creating and managing assemblies (repeating and replacing components, component interfaces, and more) are discussed in the *Advanced Tutorial* from SDC.

Save the assembly. Open the model tree and explore the information presented there.

Assigning Appearances to Components

When a component or assembly is displayed in shaded mode, or when a rendered image is created, its appearance is determined by several settings we apply. The most important of the appearance settings is color. Other aspects of an appearance definition are texture, transparency, reflection, shadows, and so on. Appearances can be applied to entire objects or individual surfaces. Defined appearances can be stored in files. A default appearance definition file (*appearance.dmt*) is loaded at program start-up. Once an appearance has been assigned to a component, its definition is contained with the component file. This means if the component is sent to another system the component's appearance will be taken with it.

In the following, we will deal only with color.

IMPORTANT: Make sure that colors are turned on (***Tools > Environment***).

We will assign appearances in two steps: first we define (or choose) the colors we are going to use, then we apply the colors to the desired components. The extent to which you can do this will depend on the specifics of your Pro/E installation and your hardware.

Select the small down-arrow beside the

Appearance Gallery button  in the top toolbar. The appearance gallery opens as shown in Figure 41. This contains three areas. The one at the top (**My Appearances**) contains appearances loaded when you started up Wildfire for this session. This is often called the *color pallette*, but as was mentioned above each appearance contains much more than just color. By default, these

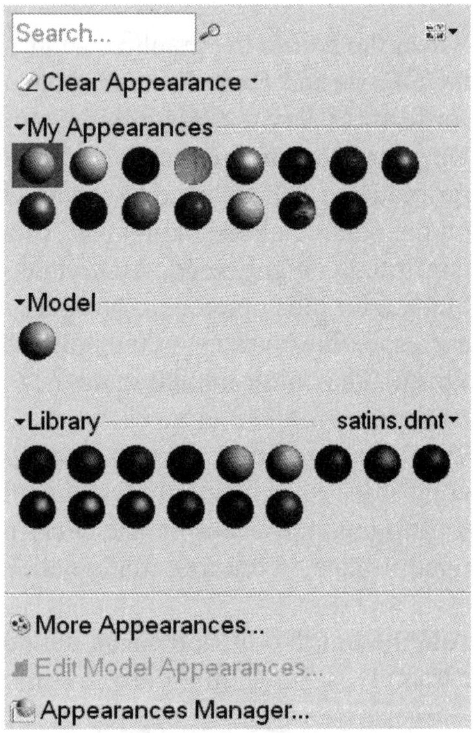

Figure 41 The **Appearance Gallery**

appearances are stored in a file called *appearance.dmt* in the directory *<loadpoint>/graphic-library/appearances*. If that file is missing, only one color - white

- is defined. Each appearance will have a name (use the small button at the top right to control display settings in this menu - including showing the appearance names). The name of the default appearance in Figure 41 is **ref_color1**. If you have loaded another assembly that has defined appearances, they will be displayed here.

The middle pane on the menu shows appearances assigned in the current model. The lower pane shows appearances stored in the system library. A pull-down list in the Library area lets you choose from among the many system libraries for metals, plastics, and appearances for advanced rendering. Some of these are for the PhotoRender engine, and some are for PhotoLux - these are two systems for producing high-quality rendered images of your models.

To assign an appearance to a component, just select it from any of the areas on the menu. The **Appearance Gallery** will disappear and you can then select a component to assign the chosen appearance. When you are finished, select *OK* or middle click. The currently selected appearance then appears in the upper toolbar. To assign it to additional components, just click the button, then select the component and middle click. If you get carried away, the Gallery has a *Clear Appearance* button that allows you to unassign some or all of the appearances (you must open the pull-down list to select what you want to clear). Watch the message area for warnings that may appear (for example some types of appearances cannot be assigned at the assembly level - those involving textures, for example).

Let's define some more colors. At the bottom of the **Appearance Gallery**, select *More Appearances*. This opens the **Appearance Editor** window (Figure 42). In the **Basic** tab, appearances are first organized by **Class** (**Generic**, **Metal**, **Plastic**, **Paint**, and so on). For each class there are a number of sliders that control such effects as the lighting on the model (ambient light, shine, and highlight intensity), edge color, transparency, reflectivity, and more. Leave the **Class** set to **Generic** and click the color patch button just above the top slider at the right. This opens a new window called the **Color Editor**.

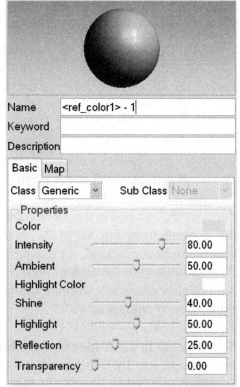

Figure 42 The **Appearance Editor**

The **Color Editor** contains three different ways to select a color. You can expand or collapse these three areas by clicking on the blue bars. The default method is to select values of red-green-blue (RGB) (ranging from 0 to 255) in the new color. You move the sliders until you get the right mix of RGB for the new color, or enter integer values in the range 0 - 255 in the boxes on the right. As you use the sliders to change the value of any color component, the new color is shown at the top of the **Color Editor**, and on the shaded ball back in the **Appearance Editor**. Another method of setting color is to use the **Color Wheel**. This shows a disk containing all the available colors. The current color setting is shown by a small cursor. You can click within the color wheel to pick the new color - this automatically sets RGB values for you. Note that there is also an HSV (hue - saturation - value) method of selecting color. If you select this method with the color wheel open, you can see the effect of the three HSV sliders. The **Hue** slider moves the cursor in circles on the color wheel. The **Saturation** slider moves the cursor radially on the color wheel. The **Value** slider sets the range between black and the color on the color wheel.

Once you have selected a color in the **Color Editor**, select *Close*. The new color will show up in the palette at the top of the **Appearance Editor** window where you can type in a name for the new appearance. When you close the Editor, you can then assign the new color/appearance to the model.

To experiment with this some more, in the pull-down menus, select

Tools > Appearances Manager

This opens a combined window showing the **Gallery** and **Appearance Editor** at the same time. With the mouse in the **My Appearances** area, hold down the RMB and select *New*. This creates a new entry in the gallery, names it "<ref_color1>" and uses the current settings. You can launch the **Color Editor** by selecting the color swatch. Before you do that, select *New* several times. This gives you a number of copies of the currently selected color. You can pick each one individually and redefine its RGB definition, rename it (make sure you hit the *Enter* key after renaming), and so on.

Define the appearance colors in the table shown at the right (these are the "primary" colors) or make up your own color mix. Color selection is a matter of personal preference. However, in general, lighter colors work better than darker ones, and saturated colors (as given) are also a bit "harsh." You might modify each of the colors in the table by increasing the other color components from 0 to, say, 128. Appearance names might correspond, for example, with different materials (steel, aluminum, plastic, ...) You might experiment with the lighting and transparency options as well.

Color	RGB Composition		
	Red	Green	Blue
Red	255	0	0
Green	0	255	0
Blue	0	0	255
Yellow	255	255	0
Cyan	0	255	255
Magenta	255	0	255

The *Map* tab in the **Appearances Manager** allows you to create advanced settings using bump maps, texture files, and decals. These are used with the advanced photo-rendering functions to produce life-like images.

When you have created the colors, *Close* the Color Editor. Back in the **Appearances Manager** window, you can use

File > Save As

to save your newly created appearances. Remember that if you want this loaded automatically, it's file must be called *appearance.dmt* and be located in the directory *<loadpoint>/graphic-library/appearances*[8]. You can use *File > Open* in the **Appearances Manager** window to read in previously saved appearance files and either overwrite or append colors in a stored file into the current session. There may be a system restriction on the total number of colors you can define - see your system administrator for details.

To apply color to the axle, select a color in the palette, pick on the axle then middle click. Pretty simple.

Choose different colors and assign them to the pulley, the base plate, and the four bolts.

When the total assembly is active, we can't individually color the components in the subassembly **support.asm** - if we tried that now, they would all end up the same color since this is treated as a single component in the current assembly. We will have to have the subassembly in its own window. If it currently isn't in your session (if it is you can do this by *Window > support.asm*), bring it in with

File > Open > support.asm

or if it is already loaded, just click on the window containing the subassembly and activate it.

Once you have set all the colors, save the **support** subassembly, and change back to the overall assembly window. If you previously colored the support in the main assembly, you will have to *Clear* that color. Appearances assigned at the highest level in the assembly tree take precedence. In this regard, you should note that colors are preferably defined and assigned at the individual part level. These colors are carried with the part into the assembly where they will stay unless over-ridden. For multiple occurrences of a part (like the bolts), it is easier to assign colors at part level, where you only have to do it once!

See how the display changes for wireframe, hidden line, and shaded displays. In wireframe display the edges of each part are shown in the assigned color. This might be awkward if you want to do any editing of the part, since line color is so important in representing information like highlighted edges, constraint surfaces, parent/child relations, and the like. To turn off the color display, select

Tools > Environment > Colors | OK

All edges will now be shown in the default colors. Turn colors back on again. You may

---

[8] There is a configuration option which allows you to set a search path for multiple *dmt* files. See *pro_colormap_path* in the on-line help.

find yourself toggling the color display state often enough that you might like to add a toolbar button to do that. See the Appendix on customizing the toolbars.

You will probably want to come back later to play with the options for rendering of the model. The entry point for this exploration is, in the top pull-down menus

> ### *View > Model Setup*

You can have fun playing with the *Scene Editor*, the rendering *Room* (walls, ceiling, and floor that can have superimposed images), *Lights* (and shadows) of various kinds, and special effects like fog and perspective. In conjunction with the appearance definitions, it is possible to create photo-realistic images in very high resolution.

We are finished with the first lesson on assemblies. Don't forget to save your assembly - we'll need it in the next lesson. An important thing to note is that when you save the assembly, any component that has been changed will also be saved automatically.

You will also note that the keyway in the axle extends beyond one of the support bushings. Also, the base plate is quite large. In the next lesson we will see how to modify an assembly and its component parts. This will involve creating assembly features (ie. specific to the assembly), as well as making changes to the parts themselves. It is also possible to create new parts while you are in assembly mode (we'll make the key this way, to make sure it fits in the assembly). We'll also find out how to get an exploded view of the assembly, and set up an assembly drawing.

Questions for Review

1. If several identical parts are required in an assembly, do you need a separate part file for each one?
2. What are the main assembly constraints?
3. What is a "packaged" component? How does this restrict what you can do?
4. What degrees of freedom are constrained by each of the main assembly constraints? Draw a sketch and illustrate the constrained and unconstrained degrees of freedom.
5. What entities can be used when specifying assembly constraints?
6. What is the difference between applying assembly constraints to individual components versus a subassembly?
7. What is the difference between *Separate Window* and *Assembly Window*? Where are these options located?
8. How do you select the constraint types?
9. Can you do the assembly operations with a shaded view?
10. If you are in the process of constraining a component and you make a mistake, how can you a) delete, or b) edit a constraint.
11. What does *Move* do, how is it different from using CTRL+ALT and the mouse buttons, and how is it related to applying assembly constraints?
12. Does it matter what order you create assembly constraints? When you are picking references does it matter if you select component references first?
13. Find out how many colors you can define on your local system.
14. How can you specify the colors of individual components in a subassembly?
15. How do you turn off color display in wireframe mode?
16. Which icons disappear from the right toolbar when you open or create an assembly?
17. What aspects of the display are controlled by "appearances"?
18. What (and where) is the default appearance file? What does it do? How can you modify it?
19. How do you change the color of an object?
20. Which takes precedence - an appearance assigned at the part level or at the assembly level?
22. What are the special mouse button functions when assembling a component?
23. What is meant by a *connection* in an assembly?
24. What are the advantages and disadvantages of creating an assembly with and without using an assembly template?
25. What is contained in your system's default assembly template?

Project

Start assembling the vise with this subassembly. Think about an assembly strategy and which constraints you are going to use before you start actually doing anything. Look ahead to the finished product to see how you will be able to constrain this subassembly into the vise.

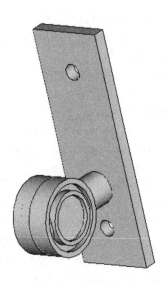

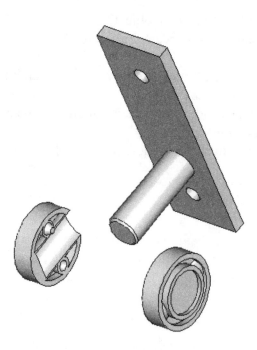

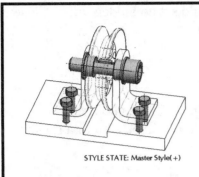

Lesson 10

Assembly Operations

STYLE STATE: Master Style(+)

Synopsis

Examining the assembly database. Declaring active components. Modifying parts in an assembly. Creating parts in assembly mode. Assembly features. Exploded views and display styles. Creating sections. Assembly drawings.

Overview of this Lesson

In this lesson, we will continue to work with the pulley assembly we created in Lesson #9. We start by using some Pro/E utilities to get information about the assembly (model tree, assembly references, assembly sequence). We will then see how to add features to the assembly, modify the parts by changing dimensions and adding features, and create a new part to fit with existing parts in the assembly. We will see how to get an exploded view, and modify it, and how to set up section views and a drawing of the assembly. This seems like a lot, but there's actually not much involved with each topic. Here are the sections of this lesson:

1. Assembly Information
2. Assembly Features
3. Assembly and Part Modifications
4. Part Creation in Assembly Mode
5. Exploding the Assembly
6. Modifying the Component Display
7. Creating sections
8. Assembly Drawings

To get started, make sure all the part and assembly files you created in Lesson #9 are in your working directory. Then start Pro/E and load the assembly:

File > Open > less9.asm

or open your working directory in the Browser and double click on ***less9.asm***. Shut off

all the datums (planes, axes, coordinate systems), colors, and set no hidden lines. Close
the model tree.

Assembly Information

In this section we will look at some commands to dig out information about the
assembly. We saw some of this way back in Lesson #1, so this will be a bit of a review.
Start with

Info > Feature List > Top Level | Apply

The Browser opens with a list very similar to the feature list of a single part. For an
assembly, the list identifies all assembly features (like the assembly datums) and
components, their numbers and ID's, the name, type (feature or component), and
regeneration status of everything in the assembly. Clicking on a listed component will
highlight it in the graphics window. In the small **Feature List** window at the top right,
select *Subassembly* and pick on the L-bracket in the graphics window, then *Apply*. This
lists the components in the subassembly containing the bracket. Finally, select *Part* and
click on the same bracket, then *Apply*. This lists individual part features. You can see that
we can easily dig down quite deeply into the model structure. *Close* the Browser window
and the **Feature List** window and *Repaint* to clear any color highlights.

To see how the assembly was put together (the regeneration sequence):

Tools > Model Player

Select the rewind button to go to the beginning of the model. Proceed through the
regeneration sequence with the step forward button. As you step forward, find out what
information is available using the *Show Dims* and *Feat Info* buttons. The former may not
work as you expect. Show Dims does not show feature dimensions within parts (imagine
what a mess this would make of the screen). Rather, it shows assembly dimensions, such
as would be used in an offset constraint or a component pattern increment. Continue in
the model player until you have reached the last component. Then select *Finish*.

If you want to find out more information
about how the assembly was put together,
in particular the placement constraints:

Info > Component

Pick on the axle. The **Component
Constraints** window will open as shown
at the right. This gives you a list of the
placement constraints used to position the
axle in the assembly. Place the cursor over
one of the lines in the table - a pop-up will
describe the constraint (and remind you of

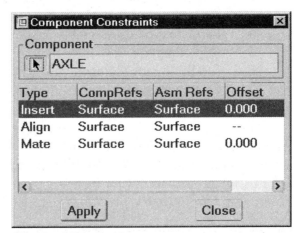

Figure 1 Displaying component constraints

the importance of selecting useful part names!). If you click on the line, the reference surfaces will highlight in purple and blue on the model (this will be easier to see if you turn colors and shading off). *Repaint* the screen, select the arrow button under **Component**, and pick on another component, like one of the bolts to see similar information. *Close* the window.

Another way of looking at the logical structure of the assembly is, of course, with the model tree. Open that now in the Navigator. Click on the small + sign in front of the *support.asm* entries. Note how the individual components are organized in levels. We used two subassemblies - their component parts are on a lower level of the tree. Using the *Settings* button and *Tree Columns* command, add the following columns to the model tree: *Feat #*, *Feat Type*, *Status*. Reformat the column widths as in Figure 2.

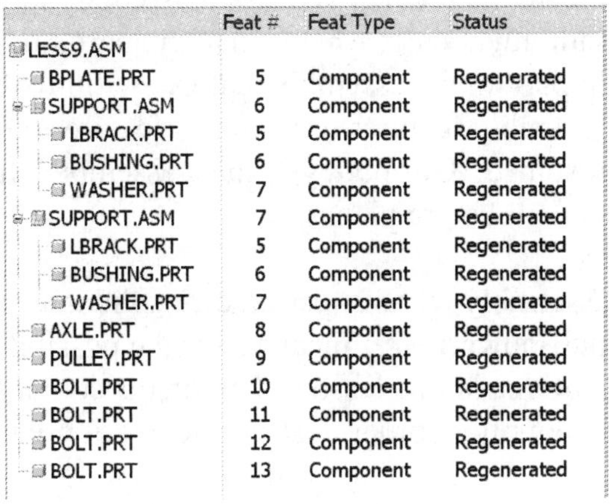

	Feat #	Feat Type	Status
LESS9.ASM			
BPLATE.PRT	5	Component	Regenerated
SUPPORT.ASM	6	Component	Regenerated
LBRACK.PRT	5	Component	Regenerated
BUSHING.PRT	6	Component	Regenerated
WASHER.PRT	7	Component	Regenerated
SUPPORT.ASM	7	Component	Regenerated
LBRACK.PRT	5	Component	Regenerated
BUSHING.PRT	6	Component	Regenerated
WASHER.PRT	7	Component	Regenerated
AXLE.PRT	8	Component	Regenerated
PULLEY.PRT	9	Component	Regenerated
BOLT.PRT	10	Component	Regenerated
BOLT.PRT	11	Component	Regenerated
BOLT.PRT	12	Component	Regenerated
BOLT.PRT	13	Component	Regenerated

Figure 2 The assembly model tree

Select

Settings > Tree Filters

and check the box beside **Placement Folder**, then *Apply*. Expand the entries for each component as shown in Figure 3. These are the assembly constraints used for each component. Clicking on a listed constraint in the model tree will cause the references involved to highlight on the model. This is a pretty simple and useful way to explore the assembly database and model structure.

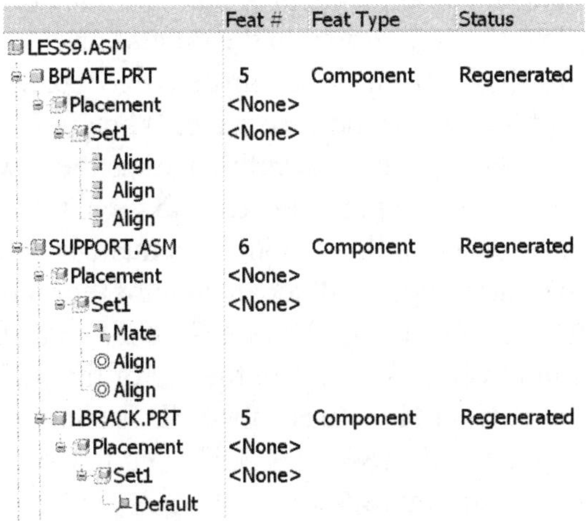

Select *Tree Filters* again and check the box beside **Features**, then *Apply*. Now select one of the + signs in front of a part. The model tree shows all the features in the part. Click on any of these features and it will be highlighted

	Feat #	Feat Type	Status
LESS9.ASM			
BPLATE.PRT	5	Component	Regenerated
Placement	<None>		
Set1	<None>		
Align			
Align			
Align			
SUPPORT.ASM	6	Component	Regenerated
Placement	<None>		
Set1	<None>		
Mate			
Align			
Align			
LBRACK.PRT	5	Component	Regenerated
Placement	<None>		
Set1	<None>		
Default			

Figure 3 Model tree with **Placement Folders** open to show constraints

on the assembly model. If you right-click on any feature, a small pop-up menu will appear with a number of the utility commands we have seen before (*Delete, Suppress, Rename, Edit*, and so on). For the top level assembly (*less9.asm*), right click and select *Info > Model*. Notice that this data has automatically been written to a file (*less9.inf*) - see the message window. The Browser controls can be used to save or print this model information. This is useful for model documentation (in particular, noting the path to each component file). Close the Navigator and Browser windows.

Assembly Features

Creating Assembly Features

An assembly feature is one that is created and resides in the assembly. You can only create them when you are in assembly mode, and they will generally *not* be available to individual parts when you are in part mode unless you explicitly allow it. Like features in part mode, assembly features will involve parent/child relations (either with other assembly features or with part features) and can be edited, patterned, suppressed and resumed. Our pulley-bracket assembly already contains several assembly features - the default datum planes.

Assembly features can also be solid feature types (extrudes, sweeps, holes, ...). Open the pull-down *Insert* menu to see the possibilities. We will create a couple of assembly features in this lesson. The first is composed of a longitudinal cut through the entire assembly in order to show the interior detail[1].

In the right toolbar, select the *Extrude* tool. This opens the extrude dashboard that we have seen many times before, with one addition - the **Intersect** slide-up panel - that we will get to in a minute or two. Select *Placement > Define*. For the sketching plane, pick the right face of the base plate (assuming you in the default orientation). For the **Bottom** sketching reference, pick the bottom face of the base plate. When you are in Sketcher, select your references as the lower surface of the plate (or **ASM_TOP**), the outer edge of the pulley (zoom in to make sure you get the outer edge, and not an edge of the round), and the vertical datum **ASM_FRONT**. Sketch a single vertical line from the top of the pulley to the bottom of the base plate. This should be aligned with **ASM_FRONT**. Your sketch should look like Figure 4.

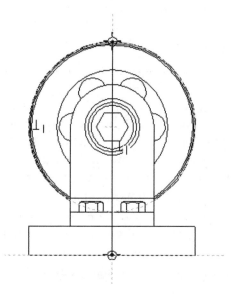

Figure 4 Sketch of first assembly feature (a vertical edge to create a one-sided cut)

Leave Sketcher and make sure the material removal side is on the left of this sketched line (on the front side of the model), and select the depth as *Through All*. Open the **Intersect** panel. This shows which components in the assembly will be intersected by the cut. Notice that *Automatic Update* is checked (on) by default. We can remove components from the list by deselecting this option, then using the RMB pop-up menu to *Remove* selected components so they won't be cut by the feature. Don't do that now - leave *Automatic Update* checked.

---

[1] A more elegant way of displaying a section is available in the View Manager. We will see this later in this lesson.

Open the other slide-up panels to see their
contents - they are the same as the part
mode extrude feature.

The *Preview* button on the dashboard does
not work the same way as it did in part
mode, so we are finished with the
dashboard for now. *Accept* the cut feature.
Turn the part colors back on (in the
Environment window), and shade the
display. The assembly should look like
Figure 5. (Why are two bolts left hanging
out in space?) Note that the keyway in the
axle is too long - extending into the
bushings in both directions. We will fix
this a little later.

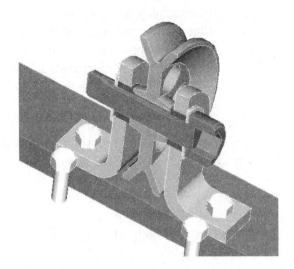

Figure 5 Cut complete - shaded view

We are going to come back to the creation of features in a little while, after a slight
diversion into display management functions. Meanwhile, select the final extrude feature
in the model tree (the assembly cut) and use the RMB pop-up to suppress it.

Assembly Display Management

Pro/E can handle assemblies containing hundreds (even thousands) of components. When
you are working on such an assembly, you may want to temporarily remove some
components from the model for two reasons. First, it will remove some of the screen
clutter, allowing you a better view of the things of current importance. If you are
creating an assembly of a car, for example, and you are working on the rear suspension,
you might want to get rid of all body panels that are blocking your view. Second,
removing some (or many) components will improve the performance of your system
(faster graphics performance, faster model regeneration, less memory required). In the
car example, while working on the rear suspension, you could get rid of the engine and
steering components. Pro/E has special tools to handle very large assemblies which we
won't have time to look at now (Hint: look up *Simplified Reps* in the on-line help). We
will look at some simpler ways, that you have already seen, to find out how they can be
used to solve this problem.

Since we want to do some modifications on the keyway in the axle, we would like to
remove some of the other components from the screen that are blocking our view of this
feature. We have two options to do this: *Suppress* and *Hide*. The differences between
these are as follows:

> *Suppress* - takes the component (and all the references it provides) out of the
>   assembly sequence. This removes it from the model (temporarily) and can
>   speed up regeneration. Any children it has will be suppressed by default or
>   will require some special handling. The component can be brought back into

the assembly by *Resume*.

Hide - keeps the component in the assembly sequence but makes it invisible. It can continue to provide assembly references (so we don't have to worry about its children), and is regenerated with the rest of model when required. The component is made visible again by *Unhide*.

Let's suppress all components in the assembly except the axle and the pulley. This is not strictly necessary to do the modification to the keyway, but it will remove the visual clutter from the screen. Since line color will be important here, turn the colors off.

In the model tree, select the first SUPPORT sub-assembly (the one on the left in the model). Using the RMB pop-up, select *Suppress*. The sub-assembly will highlight in red and the two bolts (which reference a surface of the L-bracket) will highlight in green. Pro/E wants to know if it should suppress the bolts too. Select *OK*. Observe the entries in the model tree, in particular the small black rectangles beside the component name.

Now select the second sub-assembly - the one on the right in the model. Use the RMB and select *Suppress* as before. This component has four children: two bolts, the axle, and the pulley. Since we want to keep the axle and pulley to work on, we will have to handle them in a special way. In the **Suppress** window, select *Options*. This opens the **Children Handling** window that lists the four children (Figure 6). As you select components in this window, they will

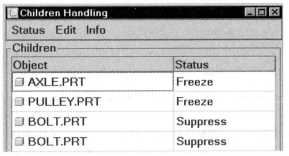

Figure 6 Handling the children of a suppressed component

highlight in green on the model. Leave the two bolts as **Suppress**, but change the axle and pulley components to *Freeze* (click on the cell in the **Status** column and open the pull-down list or select the component and use the **Status** pull-down menu at the top). Freeze will lock the component in its current location - we can't modify its assembly position because some of its references will be missing. When the correct status has been set, select *OK*. You should now see the axle and pulley all by themselves floating above the base plate. Check the model tree display - there is a special symbol for frozen components.

Notice the keyway extending past the edge of the pulley hub on both sides. In the next section, we will modify the dimension of the keyway and add some other assembly features.

Before we do that, let's see how *Hide* works. To get all the components back into the assembly, select

Edit > Resume > Resume All

Everything should now regenerate (including the assembly cut - suppress it again).

Our second option for removing screen clutter is hiding components. Select one of the L-brackets either in the graphics window or in the model tree (expand the subassembly), and then pick *Hide* from the RMB pop-up menu. It's that easy! Notice that the Hide status applies to the L-brackets in both sub-assemblies. Also, since the component is still regenerated, we don't have to worry about losing references for its children (bushing, washer, bolts). Hiding will work well as long as the assembly is not too complex (since we are still paying for the overhead of regeneration). Hide all the components except the axle and pulley, as in Figure 7. Observe how hidden components are indicated in the model tree.

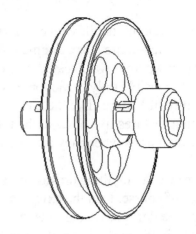

Figure 7 Assembly with hidden components

Assembly and Part Modifications

Active Components and Visibility

Pro/E gives you considerable flexibility in making changes in the assembly that involve components or features. The most common modification is to change one or more dimensions of feature(s) in a part, for example, to remove an interference. However, modifications can also include creating new features or components. Some changes will affect only the assembly, some will affect only sub-assemblies, while others will be felt all the way down to part level. Anything done at the part level (like modifying dimensions) is automatically visible in any higher level subassemblies or the top level assembly. We will see that the converse is not necessarily true. So, when you are working in the assembly, you have to be careful about what exactly you are modifying or creating:

- ‣ part features and dimensions
- ‣ subassembly features and dimensions
- ‣ assembly features and dimensions

There are two principal factors that determine the effect of what is done in the assembly. These factors involve consideration of the *Active Component* and the *Visibility Level*.

The active component is the one which is the current focus of operations. If an individual part is the active component, the next created feature will be added to the part (at the part's insert location). If a subassembly is active, the next component that is brought in (or feature that is created) will be added to the subassembly (at its insert location). By default, the top level assembly is the active component when the assembly is first created or loaded. Thus, in what we have done so far, each new component or feature was added at the bottom of the model tree as the assembly was put together. We will see in a few minutes how we can change the active component.

The concept of visibility level refers to features created in a multi-level assembly. By default, the feature (for example the long cut in our assembly) is visible only at or above the level where it was created. So, if you open the pulley by itself, it does not show the cut - it is visible only in the top level assembly. We will see later how to change the visibility of features like the cut so that they are visible in the part itself. This is handy for creating features like holes at the top level in the assembly and have them visible in individual parts when they are opened alone.

Before we do anything drastic, let's take care of the keyway dimensions in the axle. We could, of course, load the axle in a separate window and make the dimension changes there. We don't have to do that because, even in assembly mode, changes to dimensions defined in the part will be made **in the part**. Thus, these will show up if you bring up the part in **Part** or **Drawing** modes. Let's see how that works.

Changing Part Dimensions

We need to shorten the keyway on the axle, and we want to make this a permanent change in the part (ie. reflected in the part file). First, we need to pick the cut feature that created the keyway so that its dimensions are visible. You can use Preselection Highlighting (it may help if the **Selection Filter** is set to *Features*) to locate this. Double-clicking on the feature should make its dimensions visible in yellow. Alternatively, you can find the feature in the model tree, and use the RMB to pick the *Edit* command. The dimensions will show up something like Figure 8. If you need to move them to make them clearer, select an individual dimension and pick *Properties* in the RMB menu. In the **Dimension Properties** window, select *Move* or *Move Text*. Then click on the screen where you want the dimension placed. Select *OK* and pick the next dimension. You can also change the *Nominal Value* of the dimension while you are doing this.

Change the following dimensions (click on the old value and enter the new value):

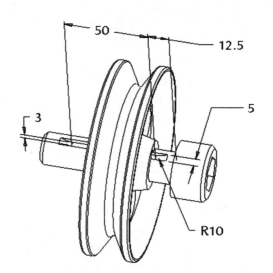

- ▸ length of keyway (between the centers of the curved ends) was 50, new value = *18*
- ▸ distance from shoulder of the axle was 12.5, new value = *20*
- ▸ radius of rounded end was R10, new value = *R5* (both ends)

Now select the *Regenerate* button in the top toolbar. Spin the axle/pulley to verify that the keyway does not extend beyond the end of the pulley hub. To get another view of the new keyway, select

Figure 8 Original dimensions of keyway

View > Visibility > Unhide All

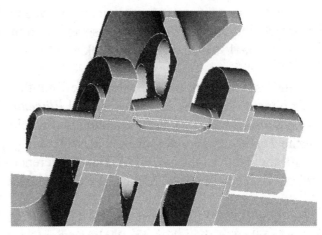

This will bring all the components back into view. Now, resume the assembly cut. If you shade the display, it should look like Figure 9.

To see what has happened to the *axle* part file, we will bring it in by itself. Click on the axle in the model tree to select it, then right click and select *Open* in the pop-up menu. The complete axle should show up in a new window. And, voilà, the keyway has changed. If

Figure 9 Axle keyway with new dimensions

we also had a drawing of this part and brought it up in **Drawing** mode, we would find that it has also been updated. Close the part window by selecting the X at the top right or using *Window > Close*.

Activate the assembly window with *Window > Activate* or use **CTRL-A**.

While we are dealing with part modifications, change the dimensions of the base plate. Use the selection filter to pick the base plate protrusion. Then use the RMB and pick *Edit*. Change the following dimensions:

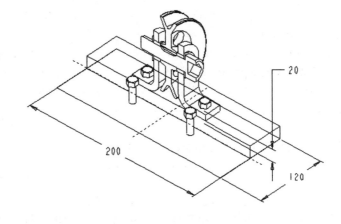

- ▸ overall length was 300, new value = *200*
- ▸ half-length was 150, new value = *100* (if necessary)

Figure 10 Base Plate dimensions

The new base plate dimensions are shown in Figure 10.

Select *Regenerate*. Since these changes were made to the part, they will also be reflected in the original part file. Before we continue, suppress the assembly cut. You can select it in the graphics window by picking on any of the cut surfaces.

Adding another Assembly Feature

We are going to add a U-shaped cut to the base plate in between the L-brackets. We want to do this in the assembly so that the width of this new cut will be determined by the placement of the two L-brackets. We can't open the base plate part and create this cut there since it requires references that are defined in the assembly. So, we must create the cut in assembly mode. We still have several options to deal with, each will result in a different model structure. We will look at three variations.

For our first variation, we'll create the new cut the same way we created the other assembly cut. Select the *Extrude* tool and *Placement > Define* (or use the RMB and *Define Internal Sketch*). For the sketch plane, select the long front face of the base plate. For the *Top* sketching reference plane, select the upper surface of the base plate. To control the width of the cut, add sketcher references by selecting the inside vertical surfaces of the L-brackets. Make a sketch as shown in Figure 11. Accept the sketch.

Back in the extrude dashboard, for the depth, select *Through All*. The *Remove Material* button is selected automatically. Make sure the removal direction is inside the U. Open the **Intersect** slide-up panel and deselect **Automatic Update**. Select (using CTRL) all the listed components except the base plate, then use the RMB and pick *Remove*. Notice the **Display** column for the intersected models indicates our top level assembly. Also, the pull-down list for the **Set Display Level** is set to *Top Level*. Accept the feature. The assembly should now show the cut in the base plate as shown in Figure 12.

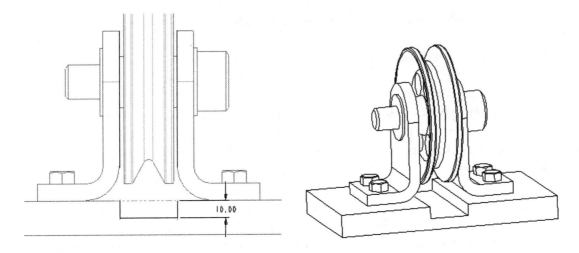

Figure 11 Sketch of second assembly feature

Figure 12 Completed cut in base plate

Go to the model tree and make sure that

Settings > Tree Filters

has checks beside all display objects. You should see that a second extrude feature has been added to the assembly at the bottom of the tree. It was placed here because, by default, the top level assembly is the active component. The previous feature listed is the big cut we made before, and is currently suppressed as indicated by the small black square. Expand the base plate listing in the model tree. You will see that both assembly cuts are also listed there (one is suppressed).

Now ***Open*** the base plate in its own window. You should find that the dimensions have changed (since we did that at the part level), but the new U-shaped cut does not appear in the part or model tree. Recall that the second factor which determines the extent of a modification is the visibility of the new feature. By default, our U-shaped cut was visible only in the top level assembly. Let's see how to change that. Select the ***Window*** command in the pull-down menus and switch back to the assembly window.

Changing Feature Visibility

In the assembly, we need to redefine the new cut so that it is visible at the part level. Select the cut in the model tree and in the RMB menu, pick ***Edit Definition***. In the extrude dashboard, open the **Intersect** slide-up panel. Remove the listed component. In the pull-down list near the bottom of the panel, change the **Default Display Level** setting from ***Top Level*** to ***Part Level***. Now pick the base plate. ***Accept*** the feature in the assembly. It should look the same as before. However, open the window containing just the base plate. There is the cut! It is now visible in the part, and in any drawings of the part. Check out the model tree of the part and the feature information for the cut - this tells you where it was made ("*Feature was created in assembly LESS9.*").

Creating a feature in the assembly and controlling its visibility can be very useful. For example, the assembly feature might represent a custom design modification of a standard part. You may not want this modification to be reflected in the part model or its drawings (which could be used in other assemblies as well), so you would set the visibility to the top level assembly. Conversely if you want the feature to show up in the part model, set the visibility to the part. Creating the feature in the assembly also means that you can selectively affect many components in the assembly. For example, if you want to create a bolt hole through several parts, you can do that in the assembly and the holes will always line up perfectly. To make sure the hole shows up in each part, set its visibility to part level and pick all the parts where you want the hole to appear[2].

Select the cut in the base plate's model tree and ***Delete*** it. If you do this in the base plate part, it will disappear from the model tree there, but still exist in the assembly model tree. Return to the assembly, select the cut, then ***Edit Definition***. If you check the ***Intersect*** panel, you will see that there are no intersected parts listed. This shows you can remove a part from the visibility list of an assembly feature by deleting it within the part. Now ***Delete*** the cut in the assembly. There is a third option we should consider for creating the U-shaped cut.

Changing the Active Component

Suppose we want to create the U-shaped cut in the base plate part (that is, not as an assembly feature and without intersecting any other components in the assembly). That is, we want to add the cut to the base plate itself and not have it in the assembly at all, although it will certainly be visible there. However, we can't create it in the part window because we need the references provided by the L-brackets in the assembly. We have to

---

[2] How would you dimension the location of these holes in each part drawing?

make it in the assembly, but we want it added to the part. Since the top level assembly is the current active component, any cut we create will appear in the top level assembly model tree. The solution to this dilemma is to change the active component to the base plate.

Select the base plate in the model tree (or in the graphics window), and use the RMB to pick *Activate*. You may be asked to confirm this (if you changed the active component by accident and without knowing, you could create quite a mess of the model!). Several changes will occur on the screen. First, in the graphics window, a label ACTIVE PART : BPLATE will appear. A more subtle change in the model tree is a small green diamond that appears on the lower right corner of the active component's icon. Third, the non-active components have become translucent. They aren't automatically hidden because it is likely that we want to use references from them. Finally, you will note that some of the toolbar icons have changed - it doesn't make sense to have assembly-related icons in view when a part is active. This final screen change does not occur if you have set a subassembly as active.

Now, select the *Extrude* tool and create the U-shaped cut exactly as we did before. Use the L-bracket surfaces for the width references. Make a *Through All* cut. Notice that the **Intersect** slide-up panel does not exist, since we are creating this feature in the part. Also, unlike creating the extrusion in the assembly where the default was a cut, at part level the default is a protrusion. Make sure you change this into a cut, and it is a good idea to use a closed sketch. Accept the feature.

Open the base plate window. Our cut is visible. Select the cut and use RMB to open the *Info > Feature* window in the Browser. This will tell you that the feature was created in the assembly. What is the implication of this? To see that, you will need to save the current assembly (this will automatically save the base plate) and then erase the assembly (and all components) from the session. Notice that when you returned to the assembly window from the base plate window, the active component had reverted to the top level assembly. Now, with nothing else in session, open the base plate by itself and call up the *Info* window for the cut. Try to use *Edit Definition* and *Placement > Edit*. Because the rest of the assembly is not in session, there are a number of missing references ("external references"). These can be a major cause of problems in complicated assemblies if file management and model organization are not well thought out. If you get into any trouble here, back out of the feature without making any changes (select *No* and *Cancel* as required).

Bring the complete assembly back into the session by opening it, and the problems with editing the U-shaped cut disappear.

What would happen to this cut if we suppressed either L-bracket? What if we used *Hide*?

To see more implications of what we have done, open the base plate in a window by itself and change the location of the holes. Referring back to Figure 6 in Lesson 9, change the dimension 52.5 to *65*. This should move the brackets apart and widen the cut. Assuming that you created the other holes by mirroring, that's all you should need to do.

Now *Regenerate* the part. The cut does not change (yet!). Go to the assembly window and select *Regenerate* there. The cut widens as the two brackets follow the holes in the base plate[3]. Still in the assembly, change the dimension back to *52.5* and *Regenerate*. Can you explain the sequence of events that occurs resulting in the new display (follow the sequence of parent/child relations from the position of the first hole to the width of the cut)?

Part Creation in Assembly Mode

When you are working with an assembly, you may want to create a new part that must exactly match up with other parts in the assembly. You could, of course, do this by creating parts separately (as we have done up to now) and very carefully keeping track of all your individual part dimensions and making sure they all agree. You might even use relations to drive part dimensions by referencing dimensions in other part files. Here, we will find out how to create a new part using the assembly geometry as a guide and a constraint, much like the assembly features (the cuts) we created earlier.

We are going to create the key for the axle/pulley. To simplify the environment, suppress (or hide) all the other components and assembly features except the axle and pulley (if you use *Suppress*, remember to *Freeze* these children). Turn on the datum planes and hidden lines. You might like to hide the assembly datums for the support subassembly. To create the new part, select the *Create Component* button in the right toolbar. In the window that opens, select the options *Type(Part)* and *Subtype(Solid)*. Observe the other subtype options. As you put your cursor on these, a tool-tip pop-up will give you more details. The most useful of these (after *Solid*) is probably *Mirror*. This option lets you create a new part which is a mirror copy of a single existing part. In the **Name** area, enter a new part name "key" then *OK*.

In the **Creation Options** window, check out the options for the creation method. Again, a tool-tip will provide more information. These options basically give you different starting conditions for the new component you are creating such as default features and constrained location within the assembly. Select the **Create Features** option, then *OK*. Our key will consist of a single protrusion based entirely on assembly references so this will give us the least cluttered part model.

Now the graphics window indicates that the active part is KEY. In the model tree, a new part *key.prt* has been added to the assembly and is the active component (notice the green diamond). (NOTE: in the top toolbar and *File* pull-down menu, the *Save* and *Save A Copy* buttons are grayed out when the top-level assembly is not active.) The right toolbar contains the regular part-level feature creation tools. Select the *Extrude* tool, then *Placement* > *Define*. For the sketch plane, select **ASM_RIGHT**. For the *Top* reference plane, select **ASM_TOP**. It is probably better to use assembly datums for these

---

[3] The need to *Regenerate* a model twice in order for modifications to propagate through the model does occur from time to time.

references, since they are less likely to change or be suppressed. Select *Sketch*, then in Sketcher, zoom in on the central hub of the pulley.

We will use the existing edges of the keyway in the axle and pulley to create the sketch for the key. Close the **References** window. If you get a message about missing references, you can ignore it. Selecting existing edges will create references automatically. Select the

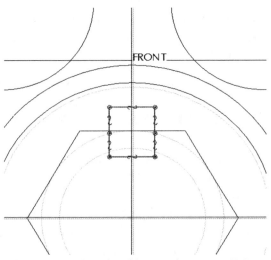

Use Edge

button. In the **Type** window, use the *Single* setting and click on the edges of the keyway in the axle and pulley (these are hidden); then *Close* the **Type** window. Be sure to select them all (six picks), to create a rectangular, closed section as shown in Figure 13. Note

Figure 13 Sketch of key using *Use Edge*

the symbol on the sketched lines that indicates they are using an existing edge.

We didn't have to provide any dimensioning information for sketcher - it automatically reads the dimensions from the previous parts. This means that if we change the keyway dimensions in the pulley, the key will automatically change shape. Note that we have not explicitly connected the width of the keyway in the pulley to the width in the axle. You might think about how you could do this. If we didn't do this, what would happen if you increased the keyway width in the axle but not the pulley? How could you avoid this potential problem? (Hint: Recall our discussion of assembly features.)

Accept the sketch. For the depth of the key protrusion, select *Symmetric*, and enter a value of *18*. Accept the feature.

Check out the model tree - you should see that a feature has been added to the *key.prt*. Make the top-level assembly active (select it and use the RMB menu). Resume the longitudinal cut to see inside the assembly (select the cut in the model tree, use the RMB and pick *Resume*). You can also select

View > Visibility
Unhide All

and shade the display. You can now see our rectangular key. See Figure 14. Why hasn't the key been cut along with all the other parts?

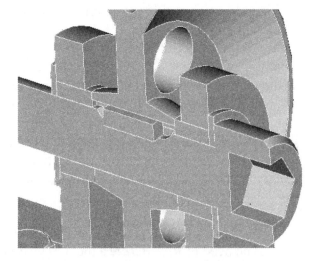

Figure 14 New *key.prt* in assembly

Now is a good time to save everything. You will find that the new part file **key.prt** is automatically saved for you - when you select *Save* in assembly mode, every object that has changed since the last save is also saved. Open the key into its own window; the only dimension shown on the part (with *Edit*) is the length. All the other dimensions are determined by the edges used in the assembly, and therefore can't be modified within part mode. What do you think would happen the next time you start Pro/E if you try to open the key part by itself?

Helpful Hint

If you are going to create parts in assembly mode, try to arrange as many *size and shape* dimensions as possible to be contained within the part. Use other assembly features only for *locational* references (like alignments, or dimensions to locate the new part). The fewer external references you have, (generally) the better.

If you load a part containing assembly references, these can sometimes be hard to track down. Let's see what we can dig out for the key. Select the extrude in the key part model tree, then

>   *Info > Reference Viewer*

The **Reference Viewer** opens. Notice the parents are identified by feature name and location. These include both assembly features (like ASM_RIGHT) and features in other components. Close the **Reference Viewer** window.

With the first feature in the key part created, you can continue to add new features to the key either in its own part window, or in the assembly window. Remember that by making the key the active component, the next feature(s) you create would automatically be added to the key.

Exploding the Assembly

A useful way of illustrating assemblies is with exploded views. Creating these is very easy. Return to the assembly window. First, suppress the longitudinal cut and unhide all the components (*View > Visibility > Unhide All*). Getting an exploded view is a snap. In the pull-down menu at the top select

>   *View > Explode > Explode View*

All the parts will be translated by some default distance. You should see something like Figure 15.

The assembly has been exploded in directions, and by distances, determined by Pro/E. For a better view arrangement, we can change the explosion positions as follows. Select

EXPLD STATE: DEFAULT

View > Explode
Edit Position

This opens the **Explode** dashboard (Figure 16). We modify the exploded position of each component by specifying a motion type (*Translate, Rotate*, or in the *View Plane*) and a

Figure 15 Default exploded view

motion direction reference (solid or datum plane, edge, axis, or coordinate system). Once the motion reference is defined, we select one or more components and drag them in the chosen direction. You might like to turn off the axis datum tags (with *View > Display Settings > Datum Display*).

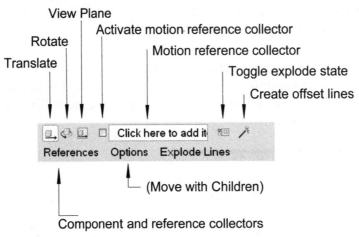

Figure 16 The **Explode Position** dashboard

Let's try this out. Make sure the **Translate** direction button is selected in the dashboard. Then click in the motion reference collector to activate it, then select the top surface of the base plate. It will highlight in orange. By default, this will result in explode directions normal and parallel to this plane. Now click on the pulley. A temporary direction triad will appear at your pick point, with the X-axis normal to the base plate surface. If you picked an edge for the direction reference instead, the X-axis would be parallel to that edge. If you mouse-over one of the three orthogonal directions (X, Y, or Z), that direction indicator will show as a bold dark red line. This will indicate the drag direction. Go ahead and drag the pulley with the LMB. Look ahead to Figure 17 for its final resting place. The dynamic view controls on the MMB are still available, so you can reposition the model orientation however you like[4]. If you click on another component, the XYZ direction triad will switch to it, and you can then drag it around.

Open the **References** panel. You should see the currently movable component listed there. Select it and in the RMB pop-up select **_Remove_**. Now hold down the CTRL key and click on all four bolts. The move triad will appear on only one of them, and all four bolts will be dragged the same direction and distance.

Remove everything from the **Components to Move** area with **_Remove All_** in the RMB menu. Open the **Options** panel. Check the box **Move with Children**. Now select one of the L-brackets and drag it sideways. You should also see the bushing and washer move with the bracket. Similarly, if you select and drag the axle, the pulley should move with it. If you select the *support.asm* entry in the model tree, the entire subassembly and its children (bolts, too!) will move.

Sometimes you don't want to explode all the components. Clear the box for **Components to Move**. Select (with CTRL) one L-bracket, bushing, and washer on one side. Now select the **_Explode State_** toggle in the dashboard. The three components move to their unexploded position[5]. Selecting the toggle again will explode them.

You can probably pretty accurately guess how the **_Rotate_** and **_View Plane_** motion direction options work. Give them a try.

See if you can position all the components as shown in Figure 17. When you are finished, middle click to accept the final explode positions. These will become the new default explode positions for this session. However, we will have to do something further to ensure that our

Figure 17 Modified explode distances

explode positions are stored permanently in the assembly.

---

[4] One thing you cannot do is select a view in the **_Named View List_**. These saved views contain explode status and position data. So if you selected the FRONT view, for example, you would get the unexploded FRONT view. This is actually a handy way of defining and saving different exploded view configurations and view directions.

[5] You can add a column in the model tree that indicates the explode state of all the components in the assembly. Check it out!

To save the current explode positions as the default, select

> *View > View Manager*

or pick the *View Manager* button 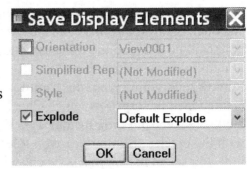 in the top toolbar.

In the view manager window (see Figure 20), pick the **Explode** tab. The default explode state is listed. Select that and in the RMB pop-up select *Save*. This opens the **Save Display Elements** window (Figure 18). Make sure the Explode box is checked and select *OK*. You are asked to confirm that you want to update the default explode state. This will reset the default explode positions to the ones we set up in the previous section - exactly what we want. Select *Update Default* then *Close* the View Manager window.

Figure 18 Saving the explode state

Before we continue to the next section, unexplode the assembly:

> *View > Explode*
> *Unexplode View*

If you do a lot of work in assembly mode, you will probably find it useful to add the Explode command button to the top toolbar. It will allow you to quickly toggle between exploded and unexploded views.

> **NOTE: Because we have saved the explode positions with the current assembly file, there is no need to create another assembly file (for example using *Save A Copy*) containing the exploded assembly.**

Component Display Style

Display styles provide another tool for dealing with the display of very complex assemblies with many components. So far, we have seen the *Suppress* and *Hide* commands to deal with the problem of screen clutter. In addition, the display toolbar buttons control all related entities on the screen in the same way: datums are either on or off, components are either shaded, wireframe, hidden line, and so on. Here is an easy and very flexible way of setting the display of individual components in a complicated assembly. Before we start, expand the *support.asm* components in the model tree. We are going to set the display appearance of each component individually. Turn *Shading* on and colors off.

Modifying Component Display Styles

Select the two L-brackets (using CTRL). Then in the pull-down menu, select

View > Display Style > Hidden Line

The two components now appear in hidden line instead of shaded. This allows us to see "through" the brackets without taking them right out of the model (or making them transparent, which requires an appearance definition and the use of color). The graphics window also contains the notation for the STYLE STATE : Master Style(+). We'll find out what this means in a moment.

Now select the base plate and pulley and pick

View > Display Style
No Hidden

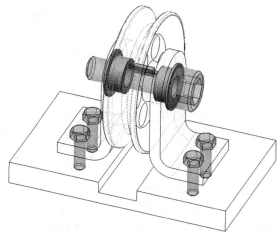

Finally, pick the axle and the four bolts (with CTRL) and select

View > Display Style
Transparent

The screen should look like Figure 19. Now, use the toolbar buttons at the top (***Shaded***, ***Hidden Line***, etc) to change the

Figure 19 Display style

display state. These buttons now affect only the parts we have not included in the style definition (bushings, washers, and key).

We would like to set up the model so that we can get to this display style easily whenever we want. This is accomplished with the *View Manager*.

Select *View Manager* button in the top toolbar. Pick the *Style* tab. You will see the style **Master Style(+)**. The "+" sign indicates that the master style has been modified. Select this and in the RMB pop-up, select *Save*. This opens the **Save Display Element** window in which you can typeover the default name (*Style0001*) of the new style with something like "*mystyle*". Select *OK* in the **Save Display Element** window. You should now be back in the **View Manager** window as shown in Figure 20.

Figure 20 The **View Manager** window

If you want to change back to the original Master Style display state, just double click it in the **View**

Manager window (or select it and choose **Set Active** in the RMB pop-up). You can easily move back and forth between these (or any) defined display styles.

If you want to change any settings for a display style, try this: highlight our newly created **Mystyle** in the **View Manager** pane, and select **Redefine** in the View Manager **Edit** pull-down menu. This brings up the EDIT window (Figure 21) which allows you to edit the display. If you select the **Show** tab, you can select a desired display state, then pick on components in the model tree or the graphics window. This also temporarily changes the contents of the model tree to show the display state of all components as defined in the selected style. In addition to the four states we have seen so far (wireframe, no hidden, hidden, and shaded) we can also **Blank** a component. This is essentially the same as hiding it. With the **Blank** tab selected, pick the key in the model tree, then **OK**. It will not disappear until you press the **Update Model** button 👓 .

The buttons at the top of the EDIT window are **Undo**, **Reset** (to remove a style setting from a component), **Show Selected** (Navigator will show only those components that have a defined style), **Show Info** (about selected components), and **Rules** (for automatically determining a display state).

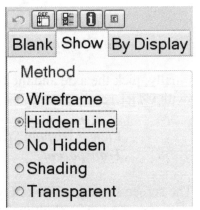

Accept the current style definitions using **Accept** (green ✔) in the EDIT window. This returns you to the **View Manager**. At the bottom of this window, select **Properties**. This brings up a display (Figure 22) of all the components in the assembly that have a style defined. There are buttons across the top that correspond to each possible style. Select a component and pick on the desired style to make a change. Which button corresponds to **Blanking** the component?

Figure 21 Editing display styles

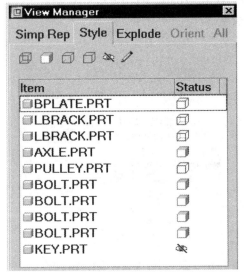

Figure 22 The View Manager Properties pane

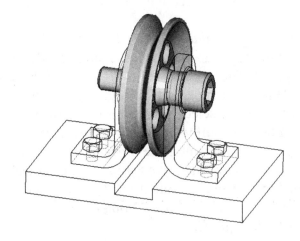

Figure 23 Component display state #2

Try out the various *Properties* options to set up another display style as shown in Figure 23.

To return to the normal display state, select the *List* button in the **View Manager.** The small "+" sign that appears indicates the style definition has changed. If you want to keep these changes, in the RMB pop-up select *Save.* In the **Save Display Elements** dialog window, change the style name to something new, like *Mystyle2.* Once the style is saved, the "+" sign disappears.

Modifying the Explode State

Pick the **Explode** tab in the View Manager window and select the listed style "Default". In the RMB pop-up, select *Explode,* then (again in the RMB pop-up) *Copy.* This creates a new explode state - call it something like "*myexplode*". In the **View Manager** window, double click on it to make it active (with the small red arrow). Now pick

> *Edit > Toggle Explode Status*

A small menu appears at the right and another column is shown in the model tree. Expand the model tree entries for the two support sub-assemblies. In each sub-assembly, pick on the three components (LBRACK, BUSHING, WASHER) either in the model tree or the graphics window. This will toggle their status to *Unexploded.* In the small **Explode Status** window at the right, select *Done.* The model now appears as in Figure 24; note the location of the bushing and washer components in the bracket.

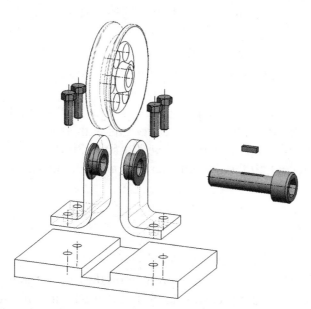

Figure 24 Explode state with modified explode status of some components

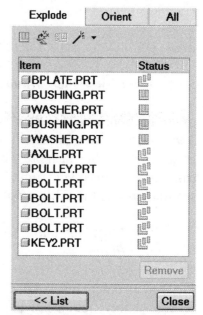

Figure 25 Setting explode properties in the View Manager window

With the Explode tab still selected, at the bottom of the **View Manager** window, select

Properties. In this window (see Figure 25), you can toggle the explode status of components in the assembly, edit their explode position, and add or modify the explode offset lines using the buttons just below the tab at the top. Return to the previous **View Manager** window using *List*.

We will not explore it here, but the *All* tab in the view manager window allows you to set up combinations of view states, including component display style and explode status, among other options. You might like to experiment with these functions. An advantage of these view state definitions is that they will be available easily to other users, and in the creation of drawing views of the assembly. Close the **View Manager** window and save the assembly. Return the model to the unexploded master style (not *mystyle*) using the **View Manager**, and set a shaded view display.

Sections

Cross-sections, or just sections, are very common in assembly drawings (which we will get to next). Although sections can be created in drawing mode (as we did with the pulley in Lesson #8), it is often handy to have them available when you are working in assembly mode. This can allow you to check for fit and/or interference between components, measure clearances, and just generally help understand how an assembly fits together. Sections are very easy to create. You can define multiple sections in the same model, of different types and at different locations, and display as many of them at the same time as you like.

In the pull-down menus, select

> *View > View Manager*

or use the appropriate toolbar button. In the View Manager window (Figure 20) select the *Xsec* tab, then *New*. A default section name is presented. Typeover this with a new section name - "A" then press enter. This now opens some of the old-style Pro/E cascading menus on the right. We will accept all the defaults here for a single planar section through the entire model:

> *Model | Planar | Single | Done*
> *Plane*

Pick on the datum plane **ASM_FRONT**. (Note: make sure you pick on the one in the top level assembly, not the bracket subassembly - this is easiest to do in the model tree if you have the **Features** filter turned on). The section displays in yellow. If you leave the **View Manager** window, the section will disappear. It is defined but not currently visible. To make it permanently visible, re-enter the view manager, select the section **A** and in the RMB pop-up, turn on the *Visibility* option. The section will now stay visible until you turn visibility off.

Note the different hatching in the different components. It is possible to change the properties of the hatching so that each component is hatched in a different color, different hatch style angle and spacing, and so on. Select the section "A" and in the RMB menu, select *Redefine > Hatching* to access these tools. The *Pick/Next/Previous* options at the top of the menu will help you select the desired hatch. The most common modifications to make are the hatch spacing and angle, and to retrieve a defined hatch pattern (steel, aluminum, glass, etc.). When you have set up your own hatching scheme, select *Done > Done/Return* to get back to the **View Manager**.

Select the newly created section A and in the RMB pop-up select *Set Active*. This creates a clipped state for the model exactly as if you had created a cut along the section plane. There is a toggle (select the *Display* button) to decide which side of the section plane to remove, and you can turn off the visibility of the hatching independently of the clipping state. To remove the clipping, select *No Cross Section*, then in the RMB select *Set Active*.

You might like to experiment with some of the other sectioning options. For example, you can have multiple sections defined simultaneously, each with a unique name. These can be displayed independently. With the desired visibility set up, exit the **View Manager**.

An important thing to remember is that assembly sections can only be created on the top level assembly datums (or make datums created in the assembly). These sections will be available in drawing mode - we will make use of our section "A" in a few minutes.

Save the assembly. Section definitions, including clipping and hatching settings, are saved with the assembly.

Assembly Drawings

Our last task is to create a drawing of the entire assembly. We will not do any dimensioning here, just lay out the views and provide some leader notes. Turn off the display of all datums (planes, axes, points, Csys). Then select

> *File > New > Drawing > [less9asm]*

Deselect the **Use default template** option, and use an empty A-sized drawing sheet. The drawing ribbon appears at the top of the screen[6]. Select (in the RMB pop-up)

> *Insert General View* (or select the *Model Views(General)* button)

---

[6] If you haven't done Lesson #8 on creation of drawings, you should probably go back and do that now. A lot of the drawing ribbon functions will not be discussed here, only some of the ones relevant to assemblies.

In the **Select Combined State** window, select *No Combined State > OK*.

Pick a view center point on the left side of the sheet (look ahead to Figure 26 for the placement, although you can always move the view later). For the view orientation, in the **View Type** category select RIGHT, then *Apply > Close*. The default display style (shaded, hidden, etc.) of the view is controlled by the buttons in the top toolbar (use *Repaint* after changing settings). Modify the scale of the drawing to **0.5** by double-clicking on the scale legend at the bottom of the drawing and entering the new value.

Now we'll add a section view that uses the section "A" that we defined previously. Select the primary view we just created, then in the RMB pop-up select

>   *Insert Projection View*

Make the center point of the view to the right of the main view. Now we have to set up the section. With the new view highlighted (red border), in the RMB pop-up, select *Properties*. In the **Drawing View** window, select the **Sections** category, then *2D cross-section*. Press the *Add* button ("+"). Our previously created section "A" appears in the list. Move the list slider to the far right and click in the collector under **Arrow Display**. Now pick on the primary view. Select *Apply*. The section view appears with the sectioning arrows on the first view.

Before you finish with the section view, change the View Display panel to

>   *Display style (No Hidden)*
>   *Tangent edges (None)*

Apply the new settings, then *Close* the Drawing View window. Notice that by explicitly assigning a display style to the view, it becomes unaffected by the top toolbar buttons.

Let's add one more view - the exploded assembly. You may have to unlock and move the two existing views down a bit to fit this one in. Then select (in the ribbon)

>   *Model Views (General)*

or just use the RMB pop-up and select *Insert General View*. This time, for the presentation select *DEFAULT ALL > OK*. Place the view near the top of the sheet. In the **Drawing View** window for this new view set (or check - some were determined by the presentation option) the following:

>   **View Type** - orientation set to Default orientation
>   **Scale** - set a Custom scale of 0.25 (don't forget to *Apply* it)
>   **View State** - select *Explode components in view* and in the pull-down list
>   pick the named state ("myexplode") we created previously
>   **View Display** - set to *No Hidden* and turn off the tangent edges

With all settings complete, select *Close*.

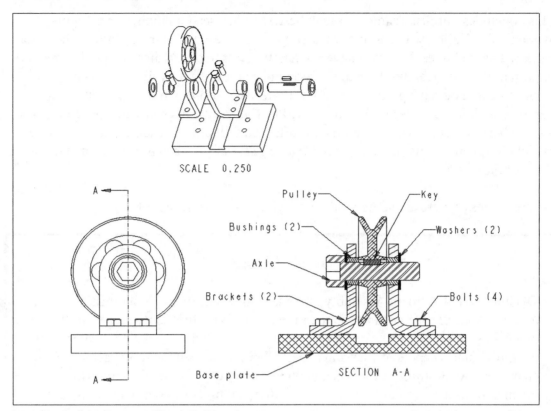

Figure 26 Final assembly drawing

We're almost finished. You should probably modify the hatching in the section view (pick the hatch, then in the RMB menu select *Properties* and play with the spacing, angle, and hatch pattern). You can set the hatch pattern for each component separately. Any hatch properties set in the assembly will be carried over to the drawing. This includes standard patterns for common materials (iron, steel, aluminum, and so on), hatch spacing and angle, color. When you are finished setting the hatch for a component, select *Next* or *Pick* to move on to the next one. As you would expect, the hatch styles of the components are independent of each other. Finally, select the **Annotate** tab in the drawing ribbon and add some leader notes. Your final drawing might look something like Figure 26. This is a keeper!

There is lots more you can do with assembly drawings. For example, you will typically use multi-sheet drawings for an assembly. The first couple of sheets would show the entire assembly, possibly with exploded views and sections, and a Bill of Materials (BOM). Subsequent sheets would show individual components. All these sheets can be contained within a single drawing file. And, of course, all drawings are associative to the original solid models. If the assembly represents a mechanism, you can create multiple positions of the system and store them as "snapshots". Each snapshot can be placed on the drawing. These topics are discussed in the *Advanced Tutorial*.

This concludes our discussion of assemblies. We have seen a number of the tools available for dealing with assemblies, assembly features, and some utilities to help you work with assemblies. What we have not had time for here is a discussion of some very important ideas concerning how to use assemblies most effectively in a design environment. You have probably heard of terms like "top-down design, bottom up implementation". Because of associativity, Pro/E is very powerful when used in this way. As you become more experienced with Pro/E, you will discover ideas about "skeleton models", "layouts", and others. The *Advanced Tutorial* presents more information on some of these topics.

Before we leave, here are some final points you should know about:

Helpful Hints

❶Using *Save A Copy* in Assembly mode is somewhat tricky. You must remember that the assembly file does not contain the parts themselves, only references to other files. In previous releases, Pro/E would automatically make duplicates of all the individual component files and append their names with an underscore "_" character. As of Pro/E 2001, when making a copy of the assembly file, you are given options about what to do with the individual part files (copy them, rename them, etc.). **Do not use *Save A Copy* in Assembly mode unless you really know what you are doing!** That is, practice this some time with a simple assembly (like the bracket subassembly we made here) when you have enough time to experiment and with parts/assemblies that you can afford to lose or damage. Don't try this the night before the big project is due.

❷ If you want to change the name of an assembly (or part) file, use the *File > Rename* function in Pro/E. For assemblies, you must do it while the assembly is in session so that the new name can be registered in the assembly. If a part is used in an assembly, renaming the part file will automatically update the assembly if it is also in session (even if it isn't being displayed). **If you copy, move, or rename files outside Pro/E, you can expect trouble!** One of the most common error messages you will get when retrieving assemblies is "Component not found" because the component's name or location has been changed without the assembly knowing about it.

In the next, and final, lesson in this book, we will return to the creation of features, with an introduction to sweeps and blends. These are among the more complicated features available in Pro/E, even in their simplest forms. However, they can produce a very wide variety of geometric shapes, and should be in your basic modeling "toolkit."

Questions for Review

1.   How can you find out the order that components are brought into an assembly?
2.   How can you determine the assembly constraints used for a particular component?
3.   What happens if you left click on a component in the model tree? Right click?
4.   In the assembly model tree, is it possible to find out what individual features were used to create an individual component?
5.   What is an *assembly* feature?
6.   Can assembly features refer to individual part features, or only to other assembly features?
7.   What kind of features can be created as assembly features?
8.   What are the differences between using the default and the empty assembly template?
9.   Can you modify individual dimensions of a part while in assembly mode? Is this a permanent modification (that is, is the part geometry changed if you load it alone)?
10. In assembly mode, how can you add a feature to a part so that it becomes a permanent feature in the part? What advantages would this have? What is the alternative?
11. If you change a feature dimension on an assembly drawing, what happens to the part containing that feature a) by itself, and b) in an assembly?
12. Describe two ways that you get a cut-away view of an assembly. What are the advantages of each method?
13. How do you explode an assembly?
14. What does ***Automatic Update*** do when creating a cut through an assembly?
15. How can you explode some components and not others?
16. Draw a graphical representation of the model tree for the pulley assembly, and trace all the parent/child relations in the assembly.
17. What is contained in an assembly template?
18. There are a couple of ways you can set up the display so that some of the assembly components are transparent. What are they and what are their advantages and disadvantages?
19. If you want a section view in an assembly drawing, does the assembly model require a cut feature along the sectioning plane?
20. What does the command ***Activate*** do?
21. How do you set up a display style? What options are available? Where is the style stored?
22. Can you combine display styles and explode states in random combinations?
23. Can a model have more than one section at a time? Can you display more than one at a time?
24. How is the active component indicated in the model tree?
25. Assembly sections can only be defined using _____.
26. Under what circumstances would you set the visibility of an assembly feature to Top Level? What about setting it to Part level?
27. What is the difference between ***Suppress*** and ***Hide***?
28. What happens if a sub-assembly is the active component when you select the ***Create Component*** tool?
29. Can you drag and drop the insertion point in the assembly model tree?

30. Can you reorder components in the assembly tree using drag and drop?
31. How can you change the assembly references of a component?
32. Can you select a Hidden component for a feature operation (like *Edit* or *Suppress*)?
33. Is a section created using a clipping state in View Manager visible at part level?
34. Suppose an assembly feature is visible in a part. What happens if you delete it (a) in the part, and (b) in the assembly?
35. What is the difference between intersection and visibility in regard to assembly features?
36. How do you change the intersection settings and visibility settings for an assembly feature?

Project

Complete the vise assembly using the parts you made at the end of each lesson. There is one more part to make - the ring shown below. It fits underneath as shown in the second figure. Create this part in assembly mode, using the existing features for dimensional references. A cutaway and exploded view are shown on the next page.

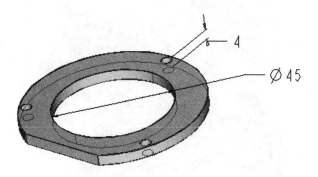

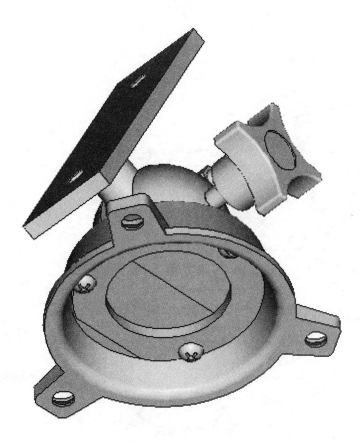

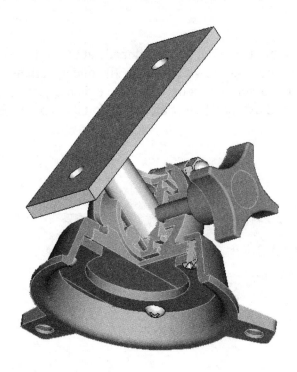

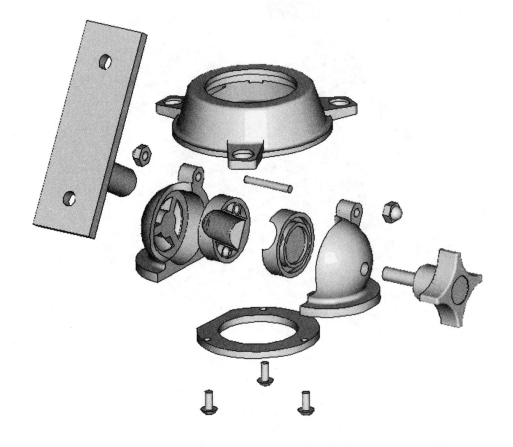

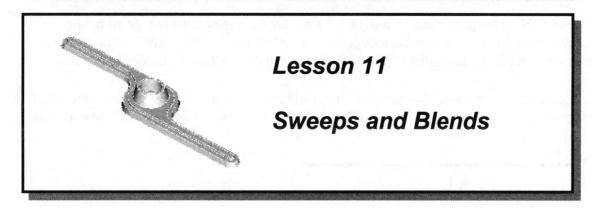

Lesson 11

Sweeps and Blends

Synopsis

Simple sweeps and blends; sketched holes; the *Shell* command.

Overview of this Lesson

So far in these lessons, we have, surprisingly, only used two types of sketched features (extrudes and revolves) to create most of our geometry. There are actually six more types of sketched features and this lesson will introduce you to the simpler versions of two of them. These can both be used to either add or remove material (protrusions and cuts) and can pack a lot of geometry into a single feature. Even these simple versions are quite complicated, which is why they have been left until last! The two features are:

Sweeps - a feature that sweeps an open or closed section along a specified trajectory (like an extrude that follows a curved path)

Blends - a feature that allows smooth transitions between specified cross sections (like an extrude or revolve with a varying cross section)

Sweeps and blends are advanced modeling features with many options. We will have a look at simple versions of these to create four different parts. These are totally independent of each other, so you can jump ahead to any one of these:

1. Sweeps
   ‣ Closed Section
   ‣ Open Section
2. Blends
   ‣ Parallel Blend
   ‣ Rotational Blend

So far in the Wildfire release of Pro/E, only the first of these four feature variations uses the new dashboard-based interface. The other three use the old, cascading-menu style. Presumably, these will be updated to the dashboard interface in a future release. For this reason, we will not go into much detail with these features here, other than to point out the required geometric references and elements. Advanced sweeps created using the *Variable Section Sweep* tool in the right toolbar are discussed in the *Advanced Tutorial* from SDC. This tool does not currently allow some of the options presented below (sweeping an open section to produce a solid). Also, the default feature created by the tool is a surface, although a toggle will convert legal (ie. closed) surfaces into solids.

Along the way we will also create what is called a *sketched hole*, and discover the **Shell** command. As usual, there are some Questions for Review and Exercises at the end of the lesson.

Sweeps

There are a number of different sweep geometries available in Pro/E. We will look at just two of them for creating solids: sweeping a *closed* section along an *open* trajectory, and sweeping an *open* section along a *closed* trajectory[1]. Even for simple solids, other combinations exist and can produce a wide range of geometries, as illustrated in the figures below. Another combination not shown (open trajectory, open section) can produce only surfaces. A sweep can be used to create a protrusion or cut. In the following, we will just create solid protrusions.

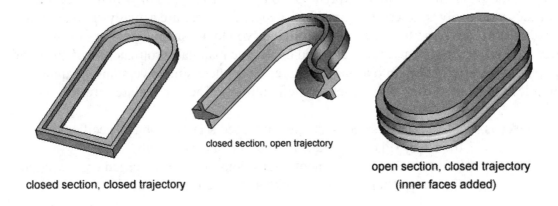

closed section, open trajectory

closed section, closed trajectory

open section, closed trajectory
(inner faces added)

Closed Section, Open Trajectory - The S-Bracket

The first part we are going to create is shown in Figure 1. The part consists of two features: the solid protrusion block at the left, and the S-shaped sweep coming off to the right.

Figure 1 The S-bracket

---

[1] *Helical sweeps* are covered in the *Advanced Tutorial* from SDC.

Start a new part called **s_brack** using the default template. First create an extrusion using **TOP** as the sketching plane and **RIGHT** as the **Right** reference. The extusion is **one-sided**, with a **blind** depth of **60**. The right edge of the sketch **aligns** with **RIGHT** and the sketch is symmetric about **FRONT**. The sketch for this protrusion is shown in Figure 2.

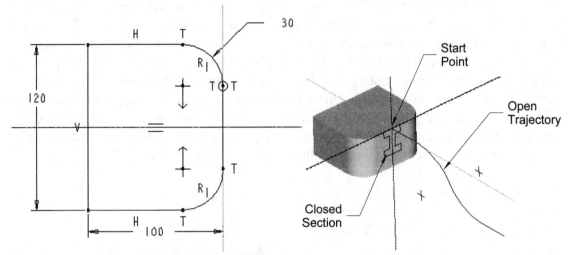

Figure 2 Sketch of the S-bracket base feature

Figure 3 Elements of a simple sweep

Now we will create the sweep. The elements of a simple sweep feature are shown in Figure 3. The major elements are the *trajectory* and the *section*. The trajectory is the path followed by the section as it is swept. In this case, the trajectory is *open* and the section is *closed*. For simple sweeps, the section stays perpendicular to the trajectory. The trajectory can be either an existing edge or datum curve, or it can be sketched as we will do here. The cross section of this sweep is like an I-beam. It is created on a sketching plane located at the *start point* of the trajectory. The section sketch does not have to lie on the trajectory at the start point, that is, it can be offset.

Defining the sweep is done in two steps: creating or selecting the *sweep trajectory*, then creating the *cross section*. The geometry of these is shown in Figures 4 and 6. We have a couple of options for the procedure we follow to define the trajectory. For either option, the trajectory is a sketched curve. The difference is whether we create the curve first and then launch the sweep command, or launch the sweep first and then select or create the curve. For our first sweep, we'll create the curve first.

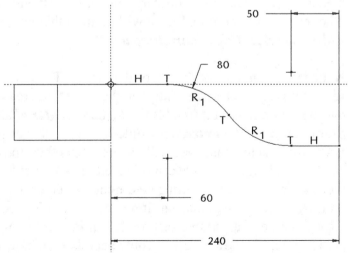

Figure 4 Sketch of datum curve (trajectory)

Select the *Sketch Tool*. Pick the **FRONT** datum as the sketching plane. The default **Right** reference is the **RIGHT** datum. When you get into sketcher, select the top of the block as a reference (and you can remove the TOP datum plane reference). Create the sketch shown in Figure 4.

Now we will create the sweep. The sweep creation tools are located in two places in the Wildfire interface. One tool (*Variable Section Sweep*) is in the right toolbar. This tool uses the new dashboard interface and gives you access to options for making advanced sweeps. We will be using this tool in our first sweep using all the defaults to keep things simple. The current implementation of this sweep tool in Wildfire does not cover all possible sweep geometries. Many additional options are available using commands in the pull-down menus that follow the old cascading-menu style of operation. We will see this in the next part we make. One presumes that all the sweep tools and commands are to be consolidated in the dashboard interface in a future release of Pro/E.

With the datum curve highlighted in red (as the last feature created), select the *Variable Section Sweep* button ![icon] in the right toolbar.

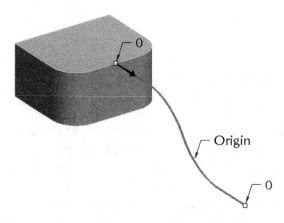

The sweep dashboard opens and the sketched curve becomes highlighted with a heavy red line (with a label *Origin*). At each end of the trajectory are two square handles and parameters (currently set to 0) which we will discuss later. At one end of this trajectory, there is a yellow arrow pointing along the trajectory. This defines the *start point* of the trajectory. Position the

Figure 5 The sweep trajectory

cursor on each of these elements and hold down the RMB to see the options in the pop-up menus. We want to have the start point at the left end as shown in Figure 5. If it is at the other end, just left click on it - it will jump to the other end. Or, you can hold down the RMB and select *Flip Chain Direction*.

Notice the dashboard at the top of the screen. The default is to create a swept surface (the second button). Select the button on the far left to create a swept solid. This changes the dashboard options a bit (it adds the *Remove Material* and *Thin Feature* options, for example). Open the *References* slide-up panel. The origin trajectory (our sketched curve) is listed in the top pane. We will leave all the other options in this panel alone. In the *Options* slide-up panel, we can select either a *Variable Section* or a *Constant Section*. As their name applies, this setting determines whether the feature will allow the swept section to change size/shape as it moves along the sweep trajectory. A constant section is a special case of a variable section. It requires less computation, so use it when appropriate, like now! We will come back later to explore the *Merge Ends* option.

Now, we move on to the second step - creating the cross section. Select the *Sketcher* button in the dashboard (third from the left) or select *Sketch* in the RMB pop-up menu. The view reorients so that you are facing onto the right face of the block. The screen should show you a yellow cross hair that automatically defines your sketch references. This is centered on the *start point* of the trajectory with the sweep coming toward you. You might like to rotate the view a bit to see the orientation of the sketch that is determined automatically by Pro/E. Use the Sketcher tools (or select the shape in the Sketcher palette. Hint: use a scale of 10) to create the cross section shown in Figure 6. The constraint display has been turned off in the figure - can you figure out what constraints are active?

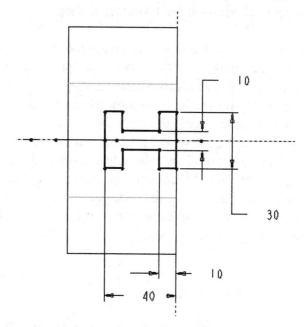

Figure 6 Sketch of sweep cross section

When the section sketch is complete, you can select *Accept* in the Sketcher menu. The sweep will preview. If everything is satisfactory, you can *Accept* the sweep. The part should now look like Figure 7.

If you double-click on the sweep, you will see all the dimensions for the swept section. To change the dimensions of the trajectory, select the sketched curve in the model tree and select *Edit* in the RMB menu. Not all combinations of dimensions are guaranteed to work, however. For example, if you increase the height of the

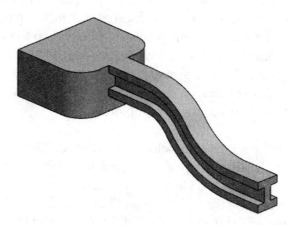

Figure 7 Completed sweep

section from 40 to 60, then 80, then 100, the feature will eventually not regenerate. Try to figure out why. (A hint is given at the end of this section!)

Finally, notice the model structure in the model tree. The sketched curve and swept protrusion are separate features, with the sweep being a child of the curve. If you aren't going to use the curve for anything else, you might want to *Hide* it in the model tree so that it doesn't appear on the screen (as in Figure 7). This would also prevent you from accidentally picking it as a reference for another feature. Let's see how. In preparation for the next version of a sweep, suppress the swept protrusion, keeping the curve in the tree.

Alternate Method for Creating Sweep

Previously, we launched the sweep tool with the curve pre-selected (highlighted in red). This time, make sure the curve is not pre-selected (it should just be showing in blue), then select the *Variable Section Sweep* tool. The sweep dashboard opens. Follow the prompts in the message window. Since it was not pre-selected, the first thing to do is to select a curve or chain to form the origin trajectory. Pick on the blue sketched curve. Make sure the start point is at the left end (click on it if necessary), select the *Solid* button in the dashboard. This gets us to the same place we were before, with the trajectory highlighted in bold red, with the start point at the correct end. We won't proceed any farther than this, since the procedure is the same as before. Don't bother creating the section; instead, *Cancel* the current feature with the red X in the dashboard. *Resume* the previously created sweep.

Extending the Trajectory

You will recall that at each end of the origin trajectory there was a "0" parameter. What are those for?

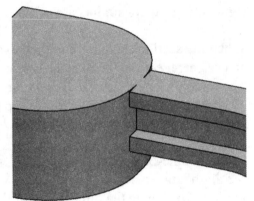

To see a potential problem with the current sweep definition, *Edit* the block and change the radius of the rounded corners to **55**. *Regenerate* the part and zoom in on the junction of the sweep to the block. You will see small cracks on either side (Figure 8). The sweep is obviously not meeting up with the block on the rounded surfaces. There are three ways to fix this problem.

In the model tree, select the sweep and then (in the RMB pop-up) *Edit Definition*. This opens the dashboard and shows the preview of the sweep, including the trajectory and the parameters. Pick the one at the block end of the sweep and change

Figure 8 "Cracks" formed at junction of sweep and block

it to **10**. The sweep extends tangent to the existing trajectory by the new value. See Figure 9.

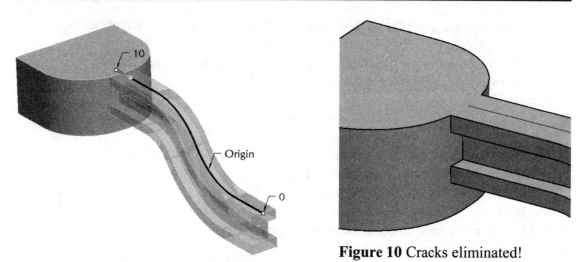

Figure 9 Extending the trajectory

Figure 10 Cracks eliminated!

The change in the trajectory "buries" the end of the sweep in the block. If you accept the feature, the cracks will be eliminated (Figure 10).

As an alternative to extending the trajectory by a specified amount, try this. Select the sweep and *Edit Definition*. Pick the square marker at the start point and select *Extend To...* in the RMB menu. Pick on the vertical face on the opposite side of the block. This will extend the trajectory all the way across the block (and removes the parameter value). Accept the sweep, then double click on the sweep to see where the section sketch has been moved.

To return the origin trajectory to its original shape, use *Edit Definition* again. Use the RMB pop-up when selecting the square marker at the start point and select *Trim At...*. Carefully pick the short straight section of the edge between the two rounds (at the original sweep start location). The sweep origin trajectory is now defined the same as it was before.

A third method to deal with the cracks is as follows. Open the *Options* slide-up panel. Select *Constant Section* and check *Merge Ends* (notice the contents of the pop-up tool tip - exactly what we are looking for). Accept the feature. This is perhaps the cleanest way to deal with the junction of sweeps and solids.

Save the part for future experimentation. For example, find out how large a crack can be filled in with the *Merge Ends* option.

Before we leave this sweep, you should note the following:

- It is not strictly necessary for the cross section to lie exactly on or touch the trajectory. If the section is offset from the trajectory at the start point, then the sweep will be offset.
- You have to be careful that during the sweep, the cross section doesn't pass through itself - this can occur when the radius of a trajectory corner is very small (relative to

the section size), and the section is on the inside of the curve. Remember in a default sweep, the section remains normal to the trajectory.

- You can sweep a closed section around either an open or closed trajectory.
- The trajectory can also be formed as a three-dimensional spline.
- The trajectory does not have to be a sketched curve - any chain of edges will do (depending on the type of sweep). Try selecting the edge chain around the top surface of the block. This includes both tangent and square corners.
- The trajectory need not be formed of tangent edges. If there are corners in the trajectory, for some sweeps Pro/E will produce mitered corners in the solid, as shown at the right.

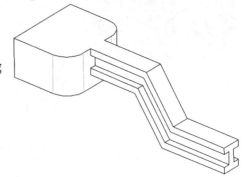

Figure 11 Mitered corners

Let's move on to the next type of sweep. Close the **s_brack** window and erase it from session.

Open Section, Closed Trajectory - The Lawn Sprinkler

This version of the sweep command will be used to create the part shown in Figure 12. This part has only three features: the sweep used to create the base with two arms, a revolved protrusion to create the hub, and a sketched counter-bored hole down the central axis of the hub. A detailed view of the arm cross section is shown in Figure 13. The stepped contour is the same all around the base of the sprinkler - this is what we will create as a sweep. The options to do this type of sweep have not yet been ported to the Wildfire dashboard interface, so we will have to use some of the old-style cascading menus.

Figure 12 The Lawn Sprinkler

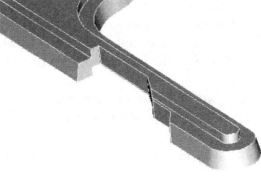

Figure 13 Close-up of lawn sprinkler cross section

Start a new part called **sprinkler** using the default template. The first feature we will create is the base with the extending arms, using a sweep. As before, we do this in two steps: first the sweep trajectory (Figure 14), then the swept section (Figure 15). The trajectory is a closed curve while the section is open. For the section we only need to create an open curve showing the stepped edge detail. We will use a special command to fill in the surfaces between the open swept edges at the top and bottom of our sketch. The trajectory curve will be created as part of the sweep itself rather than using a separate curve (which would also be possible). Starting in the top pull-down menus, select:

Insert > Sweep > Protrusion[2]

The **Elements** window is now open on the right showing that we are currently creating the Trajectory definition. This window is the old equivalent to Wildfire's dashboard interface. In this window we can keep track of the sweep elements (trajectory and section) as they are being defined. To do that, we make picks in a series of cascading menus below the Elements window (usually accepting defaults). As you go through here, keep an eye on the message window at the top for prompts. First, select

Sketch Traj

With *Plane* highlighted (notice that we could create a make datum here), select **TOP** as the sketching plane (select *Okay* to accept the view direction downwards), and then the **RIGHT** datum as the **Right** reference plane (again we could use a make datum for this). This should bring you into Sketcher where you can create the curve shown in Figure 14. This trajectory is for the outer edge on the bottom surface of the part. The swept section will be inside and above this trajectory. Unless you are very good with Sketcher, don't try to sketch this all at once. Sketcher allows you to cycle through the draw - constrain - dimension - modify - draw sequence as often as you wish. Build the sketch up in stages. For example, start with a central circle, add one arm, trim away the circle, add the other arm, trim the circle, and so on. Notice how few dimensions are actually required to define the sketch. Try to create these as strong dimensions and constraints as soon as possible while you are sketching.

---

[2] Notice that only *Protrusion* and *Thin Protrusion* commands are available at this time for making solids. Normally, *Cuts* and *Thin Cuts* are also available - they aren't at this time since there is nothing to remove material from. Notice that the old-style Pro/E menus differentiated between protrusions and cuts at quite a high level, instead of making this a simple toggle on the dashboard as in newer versions.

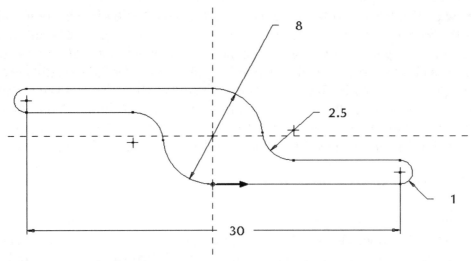

Figure 14 Lawn sprinkler sweep trajectory (Sketcher constraint display turned off)

Notice the location of the start point (with the arrow). To change the start point, select the desired vertex and then pick **Start Point** in the RMB menu. When the curve is created, select **Accept**.

We now move on to create the cross section of the sweep. We only have to sketch the stepped edge detail with an open curve. We will tell Pro/E to fill in the top and bottom surfaces of the part from the free ends of the sketch. If you don't do this, the feature will fail unless it has a closed section.

If it isn't already selected, pick **Attributes** in the **Elements** window, then click the **Define** button. Then select ("*Add Inner Faces*")

Add Inn Fcs | Done

You will be taken into Sketcher to create the sweep section. Again, you are presented with an edge view of the trajectory, with the yellow cross hairs to show where you will create the section (its sketching plane). You might have to spin the view a little to get a better idea about the orientation of the part. Sketch the open line shown in Figure 15. Compare this sketch to the cutaway view of the sprinkler back in Figure 13. You can see where the inner faces will be added, and why this only works for closed trajectories.

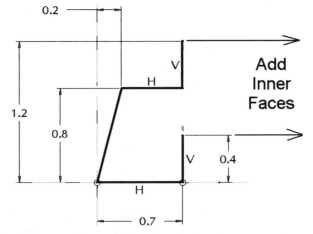

Figure 15 Lawn sprinkler sweep section

The purpose of the cross hair is to show you the relative position of your sketch and the trajectory. As stated above, the cross section does not necessarily have to touch the trajectory. The free ends of the cross section will be closed in by the inner faces of the sweep. When the sketch is finished, select **Accept**. You can ignore the WARNING in the message area about the open ends. Finally, in the **Elements** window you can **Preview** the feature. Select **OK** if it is satisfactory. The part should look like Figure 16. If something is not quite right, select one of the elements (Trajectory, Attributes, or Section) then the Define button to go back and check that everything was done correctly.

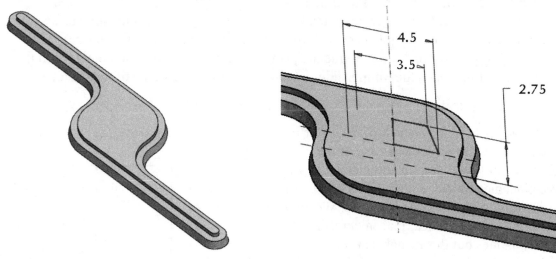

Figure 16 Completed sweep

Figure 17 Dimensions of hub

Open the model tree. This sweep is entirely contained (trajectory plus section) within a single feature. Notice the feature icon shape - it is different from the previous sweeps. If you want to change dimensions of either the trajectory or the section, you have to select the feature with a double click in the graphics window, open the RMB pop-up menu, and select **Show Sketch Dimensions**.

Add the hub as a revolved protrusion, sketched on FRONT and using the dimensions in Figure 17. Note that the height of the hub is measured from the TOP datum.

Creating a Sketched Hole

Finally, create a counter-bored hole on the axis of the hub. This time, instead of a straight or standard hole, we will specify a cross sectional shape for the hole, including the counterbore. This is called a *sketched hole.* This type of hole is essentially a revolved cut that is automatically revolved through 360 degrees. We provide the cross sectional shape of the hole using Sketcher. The placement references are the same as a straight hole. Normally, users will use either a *Coaxial* placement or define a placement point. Sketched holes are handy (especially if the sketch is stored in a library) if you frequently make hole shapes with non-standard cutting shapes, like combinations of tapered, stepped, counterbored, and/or countersunk geometries. If you are only going to do this once, you might be better off just making a revolved cut.

Select the *Hole* tool in the right toolbar. The **Hole** dashboard opens. Select the *Use Sketch* button. The dashboard changes to offer two additional options - reading an existing sketch profile (say for a specially shaped cutting tool that you use frequently), or creating a new one. Select the latter with the *Activate Sketcher* button ▦ . In the Sketcher window that opens up, create the sketch shown in Figure 18. You must create the centerline and you must also close the sketch down the centerline. When you accept the sketch, you're back in the hole dashboard. Select the axis of the hub for the primary reference. The **Coaxial** placement type is then automatic. The previewed hole will appear as a cylinder. Open the **Placement** slide-up panel to see this. Observe the Placement pane, and then hold down the CTRL key while you select the top surface of the hub. The shape of the hole is now shown (easier to see in hidden line mode). If necessary, pick the *Flip* button beside the primary reference so that the hole goes in the proper direction. Open the **Shape** slide-up panel - it shows the shape of the sketched hole.

The placement plane is the top surface of the hub. Pro/E will take the top edge of the sketched hole and align it automatically with the placement plane, with the axis of the hole coinciding with the axis of the hub. We also could have used a linear placement using the datum planes but this means that if the hub moved, the hole would not go with it.

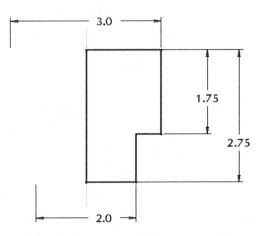

Notice that such options as *Through All* are not available. That is why the dimension scheme for the hub was chosen (it would be easy to set up a relation between the depth of the hole and the height of the hub above the lower surface of the sprinkler).

Figure 18 Sketched hole profile

Accept the hole feature. That completes our lawn sprinkler part. Save it now.

So, that's the end of sweeps! As you can see, these are quite complicated features, packing a lot of geometric information into a single feature. You might like to go back and edit any of the dimensions of the sweeps to see what happens. You can modify either the trajectory, or the section, or both! Be aware that arbitrary modifications might make the sweep illegal, so save your part before you try anything drastic. If you are using the dashboard interface, it is very easy and convenient to experiment with different options since you always have a preview of the feature on the screen - if the sweep is illegal, it will not preview.

Close the sprinkler part and remove it from the session.

Blends

A blend is like an extrusion with a changing cross section. Some systems call these "lofts." The different cross sections are specified using a number of sketches. To create the blend, the distance between cross sections is then specified. This can be either a linear distance (forming a *parallel blend*) or an angular distance (forming a *rotational blend*), or a combination of these (a *general blend*). You can maybe imagine what a *swept blend* would involve. In the following, we will look at the first two of these. A blend can be used to create a protrusion or a cut. Some restrictions apply:

♦ At least two sections are required.
♦ Each section must be created separately and constrained to either the existing geometry, a previous blend section, or a local sketched coordinate system.
♦ Each section must have the same number of vertices; normally this means the same number of line (or arc) segments. This rule can be overridden using a *blend* vertex (see the on-line help for information on this).
♦ Each section has a starting point (one vertex on the sketch) - these must be defined to align all the sections properly or else the resulting geometry will be twisted.
♦ For a rotational blend, the section planes can be no more than 120 degrees apart.
♦ For a rotational blend, a coordinate system is needed in the sketch of each section, whose Y-axis will be the axis of rotation of the blend. This is created at the same time as you make the section sketch.

The sections of the blend can be connected either with *straight* (ie. ruled) surfaces (see Figure 19)[3], or with *smooth* surfaces. In the following, we will create two parts that illustrate the basic features of blends.

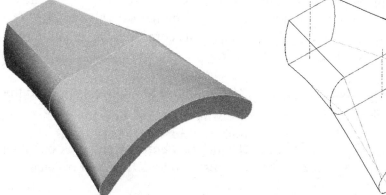

Figure 19 A straight, parallel blend

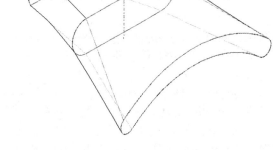

Figure 20 Straight, parallel blend; wireframe showing sections

---

[3] Note that this does not mean *flat* surfaces. A ruled surface is one where from every point along the curve defining one section there exists a straight line or edge to a matching point on the adjacent section.

The blend creation tools have also not been updated to the new Wildfire interface. Instead, they use the old cascading-menu style. Presumably, this update will be done in a future release. The essential elements will be the same.

Parallel Blend

This is the simplest form of a blend. We will create the part shown in Figures 19 and 20. This blend has three sections as seen in Figure 20.

As usual, there are a number of ways of setting up this feature - in this case, how the sections are defined. These can all be created within the blend feature definition, but the Sketcher operations can become quite complicated (primarily due to screen clutter). On the guiding principle that "simpler is better," we will create three separate sketched curves, then in the blend feature use these curves simply to define edges in the section sketches (with the *Use Edge* tool). The sketched curves will be created on a couple of permanent datum planes, but make datums would do just as well. Finally, we will drive the geometry with a couple of parameters to locate the datum planes and length of the blend.

Start up a new part called **blend1** using the default template. The first thing to do is to create a couple of parameters that will drive the geometry. In the top pull-down menus, select

> *Tools > Parameters*

Click the small green "+" sign and add two real number parameters "*L1*" and "*L2*", each with a value of 400.0, then select *OK*.

We will now create a couple of datum planes. Select the *Datum Plane* tool. Click on the FRONT datum. The default is an **Offset** datum. Where the offset distance is indicated (in the dialog window or in the graphics window), change the numerical value to "*L1*". You will be asked if you want to add a relation; select *Yes*. This completes the creation of our first datum plane, DTM1. Select *OK* or middle click.

Create a second datum plane, offset by distance "*L2*" from DTM1. Once again, add the feature relation when prompted.

If you open the *Tools > Relations* window, select *Look In(Feature)*, and pick on either new datum plane, you can find a listing of the relations used to define their offsets.

Now we will create our three sketched curves that will define the blend sections. Select the *Sketch Tool* and select FRONT as the sketching plane. The default RIGHT reference is fine. The first sketch is shown in Figure 21. The sketch is symmetrical about RIGHT and the lower edge is along TOP. Notice that the sketch has four vertices. This is important, since each section in the blend must have the same number of vertices.

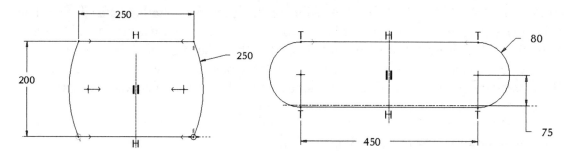

Figure 21 First sketch for blend (on FRONT)

Figure 22 Second sketch for blend (on DTM1)

The second sketch (Figure 22) is created on the second datum plane DTM1. It is also symmetric about RIGHT, and contains four vertices. Note the lower edge is not on TOP.

Finally, create the third section sketch on DTM2. This sketch is shown in Figure 23. Again, it has on four vertices. When complete, your model should look like Figure 24.

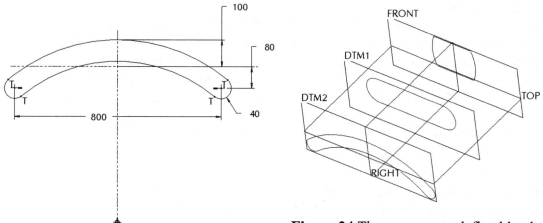

Figure 23 Third sketch for blend (on DTM2)

Figure 24 Three curves to define blend sections

To create the blend, start in the pull-down menus:

>   *Insert > Blend > Protrusion*
>   *Parallel | Regular Sec | Sketch Sec | Done*
>   *Straight | Done*

Follow the prompts in the message window. We will select defaults as much as possible. The first element to be defined is the sketch of the blend sections. All the sections are sketched on the same sketching plane in the blend. Select **FRONT** as the sketching plane (creation direction coming forward), and **RIGHT** as the *Right* reference plane. The sketcher references (TOP and RIGHT) are chosen for you automatically.

Each section of the blend is sketched separately (although eventually all sections appear in the same sketch). This includes dimensioning, aligning, regenerating, and so on. When each section is completed, we will move on to the next section with a special command. Do NOT select *Accept* in Sketcher until all sections have been defined. For a parallel blend, when we move on to the next section, the previous section will remain displayed on the screen in gray. The new sections can use the old ones for constraint references, or they can be defined with respect to other part features.

You should now be in Sketcher looking at the FRONT datum plane. The three sketched curves are visible. The first blend section is created by selecting the *Use Edge* tool in Sketcher and picking on the four edges that make up the first sketch (the one we created on FRONT) or use the *Loop* option. See Figure 25. Note the round dot and arrow on one of the four vertices (on the figure, it is in the upper left corner). This is called the *start point* and shows the direction that

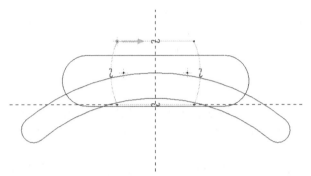

Figure 25 Selecting edges for the first blend section

vertices will be traversed in the section. Since this section has four vertices, each section we use in the blend must also have four, corresponding to each other in number and in sequence (clockwise here) starting from the start point. If you make an error with the start point on any of the sections, the blend will become twisted. If your sketch's start point is not in the position shown, left click on the desired vertex, then hold down the RMB and select *Start Point* from the pop-up menu. You may have to repeat this to get the direction correct.

When you have the sketch defined, **DO NOT** select *Accept* since this indicates that *all* the blend sections have been created[4]. Instead, hold down the RMB and in the pop-up menu select

Toggle Section

This will take you to the next section. The previous section is grayed out, and

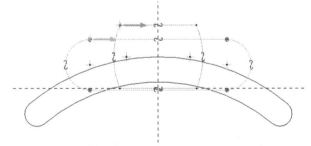

Figure 26 Selecting edges for the second blend section

Sketcher is now used to create the second section. Once again, select the *Use Edge* command in Sketcher and pick the edges of the sketch on the middle datum plane. Once again, the start point should be on the left end of the upper vertical edge. The sketch is shown in Figure 26.

---

[4] If you try to leave Sketcher with only one section defined, you will get an error message. After the second section, if you accidentally leave Sketcher too early, in the Elements window select **Section** in the elements list, then click the *Define* button and select *Sketch*.

When that one is regenerated
successfully, toggle to the third section
(select *Toggle Section* in the RMB pop-
up menu). The final sketch is shown in
Figure 27. Make sure all your start
points are located correctly. (Use the
right mouse button to get the pop-up
menu.)

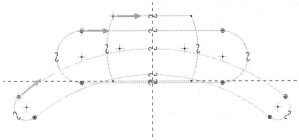

Figure 27 Completed blend sketch showing all
three sections (note the start points)

If you need to go back to a previous
section, use the RMB pop-up menu to
select *Toggle Section*. You can then cycle through each of the sections to make
corrections using Sketcher.

The active sketch is shown in yellow. When the third section is complete, select *Accept*
to leave Sketcher.

Now we define the distance, or depth,
between each blend section. See the
message window. Eventually, we will use
the parameters L1 and L2 for this. For now,
enter the numerical values (both are *400*)
when prompted for these distances. This
should complete the specification of the
blend. *Preview* the part, and select *OK*
when you are satisfied with the part. The
feature should now look like Figure 19
(remember this is a straight, parallel blend
for now). Open the model tree and note the
icon that indicates this is a blend feature.

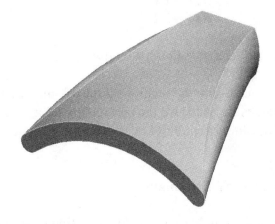

Figure 28 Completed blend

Select the protrusion in the model tree, then
in the RMB pop-up, select *Edit Definition*. This opens the elements window that we saw
before. Select

> *Attributes > Define*

and change the *Straight* attribute to *Smooth*. This produces the final shape shown in
Figure 28. These are no longer ruled surfaces.

You might like to try to *Edit* the dimensions of the cross sections. These are driven by the
three sketched curves. Selecting these and using the *Edit* command in the RMB pop-up
will let you change blend dimensions. To change the distance between the blend sections,
just double click on the feature itself.

Let's set up some relations that use the two parameters to set the distance between blend sections. In the pull-down menu, select

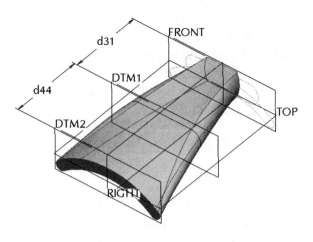

Figure 29 Blend distances

Tools > Relations

In the *Look In* pull-down list, select

Feature

and pick on the blend feature. The two offset dimensions between the sections will be shown symbolically (**d31** and **d44** in Figure 29).

Enter the two relations (your symbols may be different)

> **d31 = L1**
> **d44 = L2**

in the relations dialog window.

To make sure the relations are working, open the **Parameters** window and enter new values (try **600**) for the parameters **L1** and **L2**. *Regenerate* the model. You might like to trace the parent/child relations for this model, starting with the default datums.

The *Shell* Command

Just for fun, here is a feature creation command we haven't mentioned before. Pre-select the blend feature (edges highlighted in red) and in the right toolbar, pick the *Shell* tool
⬚ . This defaults to hollowing out the highlighted object (shelling it) using a default thickness for the remaining shell wall (see the dashboard). The interior edges are shown in preview yellow. A flip button allows you to create the shell on the inside or outside of the model.

In addition to shelling the model, we want to remove the two end surfaces. Open the **References** slide-up panel. This contains two panes. Click in the **Removed Surfaces** pane and pick on the front and back surfaces (using CTRL) as shown in Figure 30. These will highlight in red as they are picked. Change the shell thickness to *5*. *Preview* the feature. The designated surfaces have been removed. The other pane in the **References** panel allows us to set different thicknesses for different regions of the shell. Accept the shell feature. The part looks like Figure 31. Open the model tree and observe the icon used to indicate the shell.

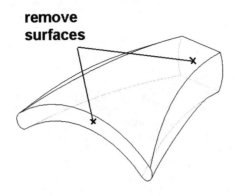

Figure 30 Surfaces to be removed during Shell creation

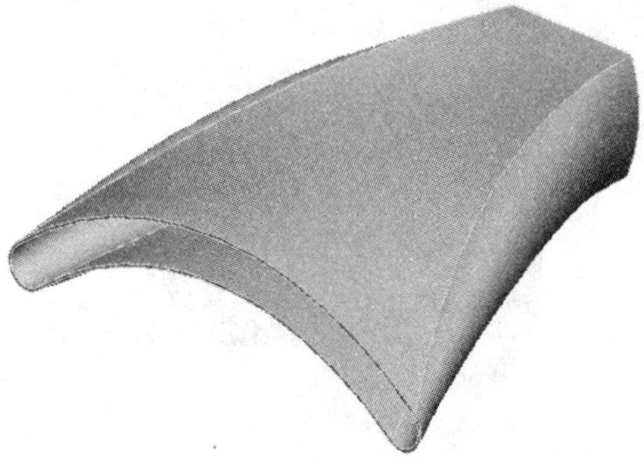

Figure 31 The *Shell*ed part

The ***Shell*** command can handle quite complicated geometry, but is not foolproof. You may find that the command will fail sometimes if the geometry is too complicated. Normally, the shell command is used fairly early in the model before this situation can develop.

Let's move on to our last new feature in this lesson. Save the current part (for later experimentation) and remove it from session.

Rotational Blend

A rotational blend is set up by specifying the cross sectional shape on a number of sketching planes that have been rotated around a common axis. The usual restrictions apply as to the number of vertices in each section and the start point. Consecutive sections can be no more than 120 degrees apart.

Rotational blends are another feature that has not migrated to the new interface style. Maybe next time...!

We are going to make the part shown in Figures 32 and 33. Note that the surfaces on the blend are smooth, except for the two end surfaces.

Figure 32 Smooth rotational blend - front isometric

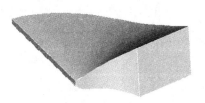

Figure 33 Smooth rotational blend - rear isometric

If we select straight surfaces, we will get the shape shown in Figure 34. This shows a little better where the four sections of this blend are going to be created. Because these sections are on different planes, we will find that, unlike the parallel blend, you will define each sketch by itself in its own sketch window. Also unlike the parallel blend, you move from one section to the next using *Accept* in the Sketcher toolbar instead of *Toggle Section* as we did before. What ties the sections together is a coordinate system that we create in each section sketch.

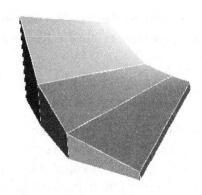

Figure 34 Straight rotational blend

Start a new part called **blend2** using the default template. You can delete the default coordinate system. Then start the blend creation:

> *Insert > Blend > Protrusion*
> *Rotational | Regular Sec | Sketch Sec | Done*
> *Straight | Open | Done*

Now we are ready to start sketching the various blend sections.

Select **FRONT** as the first sketching plane (the view direction is okay), and **RIGHT** as the *Right* reference plane. We are going to create four cross sections, with a separation of 30 degrees between each section. Therefore, the total angle of rotation of the blend will be 90 degrees. Each section must include a coordinate system in the sketch (discussed below). The rotation will occur around the Y-axis of this system.

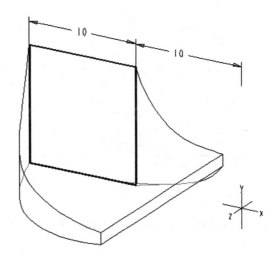

The first section is a square sketched directly on **FRONT**. The lower edge is along **TOP**. The dimensions of the section (and its position on the final blend), are shown in Figure 35.

Figure 35 Rotational blend - section 1

Draw and dimension the sketch. Before you toggle to the next section, you must create a coordinate system in the sketch. This is done using the *Reference Coordinate System* tool in the right toolbar of Sketcher that looks like ![icon]. This is on the *Create Point* flyout. Do not confuse this with the *Datum Coordinate System* tool. Or, use the *Sketch >Coordinate System* command in the top pull-down menu. Place the sketched coordinate system to coincide with the origin of the datum planes (where the existing references cross). Notice the direction of the Y-axis.

Take note of the start point of the sketch and correct it if necessary (we want the top left corner). Since we are moving on to a different sketch plane for the next section, select *Accept.* You will be asked for the "y-axis rotation angle" to the next section. Enter *30*.

A new sketcher window opens up. In this window, you need to sketch the second section and supply a sketch coordinate system as before. Pro/E will automatically align this system with the one in the first section. The blend "rotation" is around the Y-axis of the system. Dimension the sketch to the coordinate system and make sure the start point is on the correct vertex (top left corner). The second section has the dimensions shown in Figure 36.

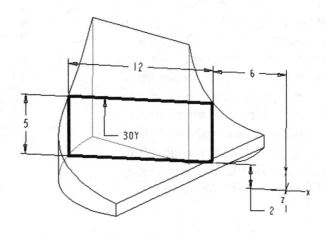

Figure 36 Rotational blend - section 2

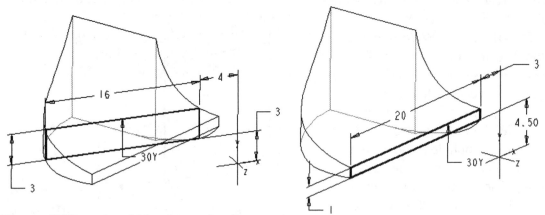

Figure 37 Rotational blend - section 3

Figure 38 Rotational blend - section 4

When you select *Accept*, proceed on to the next (third) section. The rotation angle is again 30 degrees. The third and fourth section dimensions are shown in Figures 37 and 38 above.

When the fourth section is complete and you are asked to continue to the next section, type in *n*. The message window should indicate that all elements are complete, and you can *Preview* the part.

If your start points aren't correct on any section (the blend will be twisted or may even fail), highlight **Section** in the Elements window, then click on *Define*. Follow the message window instructions. Eventually you will get to the Sketcher menu. Select the desired vertex and use the right mouse pop-up menu to set the start point.

Back in the Elements window, select the **Attributes** element, then *Define* to change the **Straight** attribute to **Smooth**, and *Preview* the part. Select *OK* when you are satisfied. Try to *Edit* dimensions in the blend by double-clicking on it in the graphics window. The feature appears as shown at the right. Note the alignment of the coordinate systems embedded in each section sketch and the dimension values for the angles between sections. Try setting all the angle increments to 60° - this should give you a total 180° rotation for the blend.

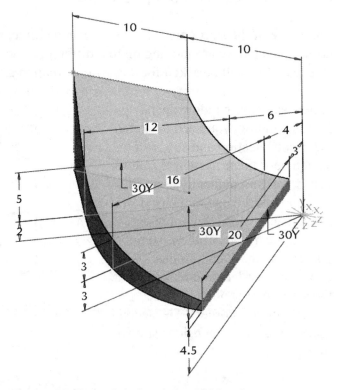

Figure 39 Completed rotational blend

That completes our limited presentation of blends. As you can see, blends contain a lot of geometric information and are therefore a bit more difficult to set up. However, they offer considerable flexibility and can create very complex shapes not attainable with the simpler features. There are advanced features (swept blends and helical blends, for example) that offer even more complexity/flexibility. Consult the on-line help for information about these.

Just for fun, let's try a variation of the *Shell* command on this rotational blend using a small "negative" shell thickness. Pre-select the two end surfaces (using CTRL), then pick the *Shell* tool. Enter a thickness of **0.25** and then pick the *Flip* button in the dashboard. Accept the feature. This creates the shell by adding material to the outside of the model, then removing everything from the original surface inward. This is like making a mold or negative image of the part. This will not always work (for example if the part has a very complicated geometry), and is not really the best way to make molds for parts anyway.

Save the part and close it.

This concludes our study of blends. It will be interesting to see how these are handled if/when they become incorporated into the new interface style.

Conclusion

Well, we have reached the end of this series of Pro/ENGINEER lessons. We have gone over the fundamentals of creating basic parts, assemblies, and drawings. Much of the material has been presented only once. It is likely that you will have to repeat some of these lessons to get a better grasp on Pro/E, and it is certain that you will need much more practice to be proficient. In some instances, we have only scratched the surface of Pro/E functionality and it is up to you to explore deeper into the commands and options. The more you know and are comfortable with, the easier it will be to perform modeling tasks with Pro/E. You may find that you will also begin to develop a different way of thinking about part design. As your modeling tasks get more complex, the need to plan ahead will become more important.

You should also remember that what we have covered is only the first step in the integrated task of design and manufacturing. From here, you can head off in a number of directions: engineering analysis using Finite Element Modeling, mechanism kinematics and dynamics, manufacturing analysis, mold design, sheet metal operations, piping layout, and much more. Good luck on your journey and have fun!

Questions for Review

1.   Draw a 3D sketch of an example of each of the following sweeps:
      ▸   closed section, open trajectory
      ▸   closed section, closed trajectory
      ▸   open section, open trajectory
      ▸   open section, closed trajectory
      What additional information will be required to create each (or any!) of these features?

2.   How many of the vertices of the swept section have to align with or be on the sweep trajectory?

3.   What problem may arise if the swept section is "large" and the sweep trajectory has a "small" radius arc in it?

4.   What happens if the sweep trajectory has discontinuities (kinks) in it rather than being composed of smooth "tangential" transitions?

5.   What is the difference in the model between creating the trajectory curve sketch first and then launching the sweep tool, or doing these in the reverse order?

6.   When first entering the Sketcher window to define the section for a sweep, it is often difficult to understand the orientation of the view. How can you determine the location and orientation of the section with respect to the trajectory?

7.   Find out what happens if you put the start point in the middle of an open trajectory.

8.   In the exercises above, the swept section was normal to the trajectory. Is it possible to create a sweep where the section is oriented at an angle to the trajectory?

9.   What does the parameter at each end of the origin trajectory? What is an alternative, and what does it do?

10.   Can you change the geometry of the trajectory independently of the geometry of the section?

11.   What is meant by "inner faces" of a sweep?

12.   Can a closed section have any inner faces?

13.   Can you have multiple non-overlapping closed sections in a single sketch for a sweep?

14.   Can a sweep trajectory intersect itself (like a figure-8)?

15.   What are the essential common characteristics of all sections in a parallel blend?

16.   When creating a blend, what is meant by the "start point" of the sketch?

17.   What is meant by a ruled surface?

18.   In a straight, parallel blend must the sections all be centered on a common axis or point?

19.   Are all parallel blends symmetrical?

20.   In a parallel blend, do the sections have to overlap in the sketch?

21.   What are the essential common characteristics of all sections in a revolved blend?

22.   How can you change the dimensions of a section in a sweep or blend?

23.   What happens if you try to delete one of the sections in a blend?

Exercises

Here are some parts to try out using the commands in this lesson.

This page left blank.

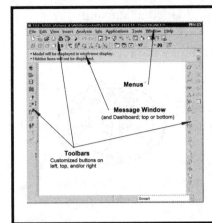

Appendix

Interface Customization Tools

Synopsis

Configuration settings; customizing the screen toolbars and menus.

Overview

This appendix introduces some tools for customizing your Pro/E working environment. The major customization tool is the configuration file (default: *config.pro*). We'll also look at ways for managing and creating your own custom toolbars.

Configuration Files (*config.pro*)

Launch Pro/E, or if it is already up erase everything currently in session and set your working directory to your normal start-up directory.

By now, you should be familiar with the commands for environment settings that are available in

> *Tools > Environment*

These aspects of the Wildfire working environment (and much more!) can also be controlled using settings stored in configuration files (*config* files for short). Wildfire has several hundred individual configuration settings. All settings have default values that will be used if not specifically set in a *config* file.

The most important *config* file is a special file called *config.pro* that is automatically read when you start up a new session. You can also read in (and/or change) additional configuration settings at any time during a session. For example, you may want to have one group of settings for one project you are working on, and another group for a different project that you switch to during a single session. In this tutorial, we will deal only with the use of the single configuration file, *config.pro*, loaded at start-up.

Several copies of *config.pro* might exist on your system, and they are read in the following order when Pro/E is launched:

♦   *config.sup* - this is a protected system file which is read by all users but is not usually available for modification by users. Your system administrator has control of this file.
♦   Wildfire loadpoint - this is read by all users and would usually contain common settings determined by the system administrator such as search paths, formats, libraries, and so on. This file cannot normally be altered by individual users.
♦   user home directory - unique for each user (Unix)
♦   startup directory - the working directory when Wildfire starts up[1]. This is highlighted in the Navigator on start-up.

Settings made in the first copy (*config.sup*) cannot be overridden by users. This is handy for making configuration settings to be applied universally across all users at a Pro/E installation site (search paths for part libraries, for instance). An individual user can modify entries in the last two copies of *config.pro* to suit their own requirements. If the same entry appears more than once, the last entry encountered in the start-up sequence is the one the system will use. After start-up, additional configuration settings can be read in at any time. These might be used to create a configuration unique to a special project, or perhaps a special type of modeling (sheetmetal, for example). Be aware that when a new configuration file is read in, some options may not take effect until Pro/E is restarted. This is discussed more a bit later.

Settings in *config.pro* are arranged in a table. Each row is composed of two entries in the following form:

config_option_name   config_option_value

Option values can be composed either of text, single numbers, or series of numbers. A listing and description of many *config* options is contained in the on-line help. Select the following (starting in the pull-down menus):

Help > Help Center

Then pick the link under **Books** in the Navigator pane on the left:

Pro/ENGINEER Wildfire 5.0 Configuration Options

This opens a 166 page document listing all the available options in alphabetical order. It also contains some information on changes in the options from previous versions. The document contains a short description of the options. There is a search function (see the

---

[1] In Windows, right click on the Pro/E icon on the desktop (if it exists), select **Properties > ShortCut** and examine the **Start In** text entry field.

toolbar at the top) for finding keywords either in the option name or description. For example, a search for "font" returns 41 entries. Although this makes finding the options much easier, you are encouraged to explore the on-line help - you might find just the setting you need to make your life easier! For instance, in the left Navigator pane select the following:

> *Pro/ENGINEER Functional Areas*
> *> Fundamentals*
> *> Pro.ENGINEER Fundamentals*
> *> Configuring Pro/ENGINEER*

The entries below this contain slightly longer explanations of many, but by no means all, the available options. Your system may have a standard configuration file available for you to use as a basis for your own work. As you gain experience, you will undoubtedly want to create your own version of this file.

Close the Help window.

The Configuration File Editor

You can access your current configuration file using

> *Tools > Options*

This brings up the **Options** window. If your system has options set already, these will appear in the window. If not, the central area of the window will be blank, as in Figure 1. We'll discuss the operation of this dialog window from the top down.

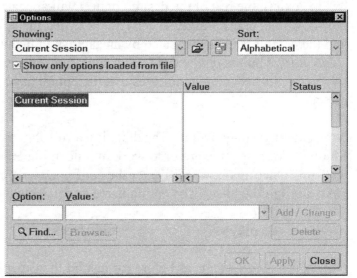

The **Showing** pull-down list at the top will let you choose from a number of configuration groups (Current Session, your start-up config.pro, or elsewhere). Select *Current Session*.

Figure 1 The Options window for setting and editing the configuration file

Deselect the check box just below the **Showing** pull-down box. After a couple of seconds, a complete list of all the Pro/E configuration options will appear. The first column shows its name, and the second column shows its current value. A value with an asterisk indicates a default value.

Note that you can resize the column widths by dragging on the vertical column separator bars at the top of the display area. At the very far right is a long (scrollable) one-line description of each option.

Browse down through the list. There are a lot of options here (over 750!). Note that the options are arranged alphabetically. This is because of the setting in the **Sort** pull-down menu in the top-right corner. Change this to *By Category*. This rearranges the list of options to group them by function. For example, check out the settings available in the **Environment** and **Sketcher** groups. The list of options is a bit overwhelming. Fortunately, there are a couple of tools to help you find the option name you're looking for. Let's see how they work.

Check the box beside "Show only options loaded from file" and select *Sort(Alphabetical)*. Note that the options listed here are only those that are different from the default settings.

Adding Settings to *config.pro*

Assuming you have a blank *config.pro*, let's create a couple of useful settings. At the bottom of the **Options** window are two text boxes for entering option names and values. If you know the name of the option, you can just type it in to the first box. For new users, a useful setting is the following. In the text box below **Option**, enter the option name *prompt_on_exit*. As you type this in, notice that Pro/E anticipates the rest of the text box based on the letters you have typed in. After typing enough characters (up to the "x" in "exit"), the rest of the desired option will appear; just hit the **Enter** key. In the pull-down list under **Value**, select *Yes*. Note that the option name is not case sensitive and the default value is indicated by an asterisk in the pull-down list. Now select the *Add/Change* button on the right. The entry now appears in the data area. A bright green star in the **Status** column indicates that the option has been defined but has not yet taken effect.

Now enter a display option. The default part display mode in the graphics window is **Shaded**. Many people prefer to work in hidden line mode - let's make it the default on start-up. Once again, we will enter the configuration option name and pick the value from a drop-down list. The option name and value we want are

>   **display**   **hiddenvis**

Now select *Add/Change* as before (or just hit the Enter key after typing the "h"). Add the following option to control how tangent edges should be displayed

>   **tangent_edge_display   dimmed**

Another common setting is the location of the Pro/E trail file. As you recall, the trail file contains a record of every command and mouse click during a Pro/E session. The default location for this is the start-up directory. Theoretically, trail files can be used to recover from disastrous crashes, but this is a tricky operation. Most people just delete them. It is handy, therefore, to collect trail files in a single directory, where they can be easily removed later. There is an option for setting the location of this directory. Suppose we don't know the configuration option's specific name. Here is where a search function will come in handy.

At the bottom of the **Options** window, click the ***Find*** button. This brings up the **Find Option** window (Figure 2). Type in the keyword ***trail*** and select

Look in(ALL_CATEGORY) > Find Now

Several possibilities come up. The option we want is listed as **trail_dir** - scroll the description to the right to confirm this. Select this option and then pick the ***Browse*** button at the bottom to identify a suitable location on your system for the value. Perhaps something like *c:\temp*. Then select ***Add/Change***. The new entry appears in the **Options** window. In the **Find Option** window, select ***Close***.

For some options, the value is numeric (eg setting a default tolerance, number of digits, or the color of entities on the screen). In these cases, you can enter the relevant number (or numbers separated by either spaces or commas). For example, under **Option**, enter the name **system_hidden_color**. Then under **Value**, enter the numbers **60 60 60** (separated by spaces). These give the values of red,

Figure 2 Finding options for *config.pro*

green, and blue (out of 100). Equal values yield gray; this setting will brighten the hidden lines a bit from the default value. Select ***Add/Change*** or just hit ***Enter***.

We have now specified five options. To have them take effect, select the ***Apply*** button at the bottom. The green stars change to small green circles in the Status column.

For practice, enter the options shown in Figure 3. The order that the configuration options are declared does not matter. Feel free to add new settings to your file (for search paths, libraries, default editors, default decimal places, import/export settings, and so on).

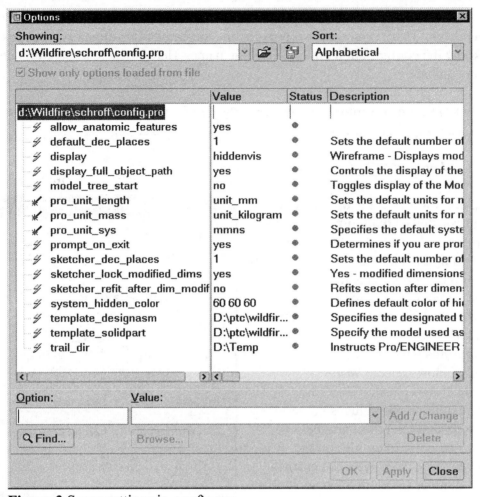

Figure 3 Some settings in *config.pro*

Notice the icons in the first column beside the option names. These mean the following:

    ⚡ (lightning) - option takes effect immediately

    ✶ (wand) - option will take effect for the next object created

    ▣ (screen) - option will take effect the next time Pro/E is started

If you are using a *config* file from a previous version of Pro/E you may see a "stop sign" (actually a red circle with a line through it), which means that the option is no longer used.

Try to add an illegal option name. For example, in Release 2000i there was an option **sketcher_readme_alert**. Type that in to the **Option** field. When you try to set a value for this, it will not be accepted (the ***Add/Change*** button stays gray). Pro/E only recognizes valid option names! Thus, if you mistype or enter an invalid name, this is indicated by not being able to enter a value for it.

Saving Your *config.pro* Settings

To store the settings we have just created, select the *Save A Copy* button 🖫 at the top of the **Preferences** window. At the bottom of the new window, type in the desired name for the file - in this case *config.pro* and select *OK*.

Loading a Configuration File

To load a new configuration file, select the *Open File* button beside the **Showing** list. Select the desired file and then *Open*. Note that these settings will be read in but not activated immediately (note the green star). Select the *Apply* button and observe the green star.

Deleting Configuration Options

With the configuration file name visible in the Showing field at the top, highlight one of the options and select *Delete*. Selecting *Apply* automatically saves the new settings. *Close* the window.

Now select *Close* in the **Options** window.

Checking Your Configuration Options

Because some settings will not activate until Wildfire is restarted, many users will exit after making changes to their *config.pro* file and then restart, just to make sure the settings are doing what they are supposed to. Do that now. This is not quite so critical since the window shows you with the lightning/wand/screen icons whether an option is active. However be aware of where Wildfire will look for the *config.pro* file on start-up, as discussed above. If you have saved *config.pro* in another working directory than the one you normally start in, then move it before startup. On the other hand, if you have settings that you only want active when you are in a certain directory, keep a copy of *config.pro* there and load it once Wildfire has started and you have changed to the desired directory. To keep things simple, and until you have plenty of experience with changing the configuration settings, it is usually better to have only one copy of *config.pro* in your startup directory.

Note that it is probably easier to make some changes to the environment for a single session using *Tools > Environment*. Also, as is often the case when learning to use new computer tools, don't try anything too adventurous with *config.pro* in the middle of a critical part or assembly creation session - you never know when an unanticipated effect might clobber your work!

Customizing the Interface

In addition to the environment settings, there are several ways of customizing the Pro/E interface: using *config.pro*, toolbars, menus, and mapkeys. An example of a customized interface is shown in the figure below. When you modify the interface layout, your changes will be saved in a *config.win* file in a directory of your choice (usually the current working directory). It is possible and permissible to have several different *config.win* files in different directories, each with a different customization of the screen to suit the work you may be doing on files in that directory.

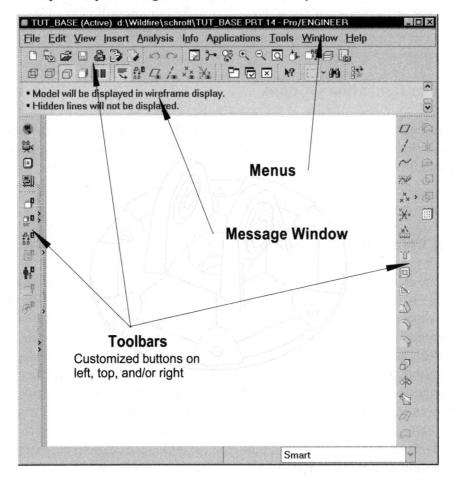

Figure 4 A (somewhat cluttered) customized screen layout

In this section, we will introduce methods to customize the toolbars and menus.

Toolbars

With the cursor on the top toolbar, click the right mouse button. This brings up a menu like the one shown in Figure 5. This shows the toolbar groups currently displayed (see check marks); the groups can be toggled to include/exclude them from the display. Each group contains a set of functionally-related shortcut buttons.